**Symbol of
Orgonomic Functionalism
Embracing the Earth**

Pulse of the Planet

Heretic's No

***Emotions, Protocells, Ether-Drift and Cosmic Life Energy:
with New Research Supporting Wilhelm Reich***

Research Report and Journal of the
Orgone Biophysical Research Laboratory, Inc.
Serial Version: ISSN: 1041-6773   Book Version: ISBN 0-9621855-8-2

Editor: James DeMeo, Ph.D.

Contents:

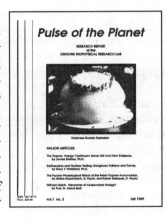
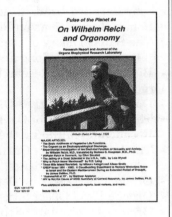
Pulse of the Planet #5   Edited by James DeMeo
Heretic's Notebook: Emotions, Protocells, Ether-Drift and Cosmic Life Energy :
with New Research Supporting Wilhelm Reich
Serial Version: ISSN: 1041-6773   Book Version: ISBN: 0-9621855-8-2

DISTRIBUTION TO BOOKSELLERS
Natural Energy Works, PO Box 1148, Ashland, Oregon 97520 USA
Tel/Fax: 541-552-0118 demeo@mind.net http://www.natural-energy-works.com

Editor's Note: Advancing the Discoveries of Wilhelm Reich

About 30 years ago, I became intrigued with the writings of the late Dr. Wilhelm Reich on the controversial subjects of *biological energy* and his thesis that blocked emotions and sexual repression led to mental illness, neurosis and violence. I met and studied with some of the scientists who had worked with Reich, experienced the *orgone therapy* Reich had developed, undertook my first experimental evaluations, and eventually became the first student at a mainstream American university to earn a Ph.D. for scientifically testing Reich's ideas.

For those who don't know, Reich was one of the youngest and most energetic members of Sigmund Freud's inner circle — while his name today has been politically erased from the "official history" of psychoanalysis, in the late 1920s he was factually one of the primary workers and leaders within the *International Psychoanalytic Association (IPA)*. However, he was ultimately centrifuged out of that organization for his social reform and anti-Nazi work, which had upset some of the IPA's more conservative elements. Where psychoanalysis has remained static and unproductive, Reich's *sex-economic* theory by contrast has blossomed into a productive and powerful theory for explaining human behavior among cultures around the world, from ancient to modern times.

Historians have since documented the general capitulation of German psychoanalysis to the Nazis, but not so Wilhelm Reich, an Austrian-Ukrainian of Jewish heritage. Freud's early work strongly suggested emotions and sexuality were expressions of a tangible energetic "something", but it was Reich who provided the clearest evidence that the Freudian *libido* was a *real energy*, discharged during emotional expression and sexual orgasm. Parental or social punishments against the youthful expression of emotion, or of sexual love, led to internalized repression — obedient young people learned to hold back their feelings and sexual desires, but this was accomplished only by literally tightening one's muscles, binding the energy down within the body and creating a powerful conflict of internal bioenergetic tension. If repression became chronic, the consequent chronic internal tension formed a neuromuscular *armoring* (much like the metal armor of a Medieval knight) by which the individual protectively walled themself off from their own forbidden inner feelings, and the punishing outer world of painful experiences. Reich developed

therapeutic methods to help people give up their emotional armor; but he also approached the problem from the social and political side of things, working to pass laws against child abuse, to protect children against adult seduction but also to legalize their own romantic relationships (as with the teenagers Romeo and Juliett), to end compulsive marriages, give women equal rights and pay, and to make divorce and contraceptives more freely available. For this, he was attacked by the Nazis, whose ranks were in fact composed of various anti-sexual "moral majoritarian" religious extremists, misogynists and pedophiles.

By the mid-1930s, Reich had been kicked out of the IPA, his books attacked and burned by the Nazis and German Communist Party. He fled to Denmark, and later to Scandinavia; while there, he undertook some of the first bioelectrical experiments on the subject of human sexuality and emotional expression. Reich's bioelectrical experiments proved that human emotion, sexual excitation and orgastic discharge were *measurable phenomena*. It was a breakthrough discovery in the field of human sexuality and psychology — but the first of a series of discoveries that would increasingly put him at odds with the prevailing academic/scientific *status quo* of his time, and of the present time as well. Science of the 1930s was intolerant of open discussion of "orgasm", and Reich's books uncompromisingly focused upon such issues: *The Function of the Orgasm*, *The Sexual Revolution*, *People in Trouble*, and *The Mass Psychology of Fascism* are breakthrough classics hardly mentioned even today, but nevertheless a light-year ahead of reductionist biochemical-genetic behavior science and "biological psychiatry".

Reich's later microscopical experiments with ameba would produce other breakthroughs in the biological sciences, in his discovery of the specific process of *bionous decay of tissues* into small life-particles (termed "apoptosis" by modern biology), which lay at the *basis of cancer cell formation*. Reich's findings on cancer are directly observable, and not just some speculative theory — his observations on precancerous cellular processes significantly predated those of George Papanicolaou (of "Pap-test" fame), and Reich believed his scientific priority had in fact been stolen. To this, we can add that today, his pioneering work on *bions* and *biogenesis* has nearly been forgotten, though his experiments continue to yield life-like protocellular and cellular forms, just as he described them in the 1930s. Classical microbiology of today, with its acknowledgment of primitive microbes

* An earlier version of this article was printed in the *Lithiagraph,* Ashland Oregon, V.14(6):1, 9, July 1998.

within extremely hostile super-hot or frozen environments (ie., *extremophiles, Archaea,* etc.), appears dramatically closer to Reich's descriptions than to the static and sterile world of classical microbiology of his day. Science journals today regularly publish photographs of protocellular forms strikingly similar to those of Reich, created in laboratories using protocols similar to his pioneering methods — though Reich is never mentioned.

Unlike conventional medicine, Reich's discovery also revealed *the role of emotional-sexual energy in the psychosomatic process.* What at first appeared to be only "bioelectricity" was later clarified by Reich as a much more powerful bioenergetic force — a form of *life-energy* at work within living organisms, expressing itself as emotion and sexual excitation, but also directly observable in the microscope as a bluish-glowing field around living blood cells and other microbes. This bluish-glowing energy, which he eventually called *orgone energy* (to preserve its relationship with living processes), was later observed as a subtle *blue-glowing energy-field* (or aura) around organisms, trees and even mountain ranges. The blue orgone also exists in a free form within the atmosphere and in lakes and the oceans — Reich wrote about an "envelope" of blue-glowing energy surrounding the Earth long before the first satellite photos confirmed it.

Orgone energy in the atmosphere is a physical phenomenon similar to the older ideas of "vital force" and "cosmic ether" combined, but far more dynamic and tangible in nature. It behaves lawfully, fills all space, expands and contracts in pulsatory rhythm, and interacts differently with different material substances: every kind of matter appears to attract the orgone, but the energy is bound to, or discharged from matter at different speeds. Water strongly attracts the orgone, or life-energy, giving rise to the phenomenon of *living water* (described classically as "activated" or "structured" water) which is fundamental to life processes, and to the Earth's weather as well. Orgone has also been demonstrated in high vacuum proving it *fills all space* much as a *cosmic dynamic ether.* Reich's experiments in these directions led to even more controversy: New methods for treating chronic diseases such as cancer, and for ending drought and greening deserts were developed and tested, with positive results. New theoretical approaches were also opened for possible detoxification of nuclear waste, and for turning of motors powered by the background sea of cosmic energy — a new source of pollution-free energy, which some day might propel humankind to the stars. Fantastic? Surely! But founded upon new experimental tests and observations in the best tradition of the natural sciences.

During the course of Reich's investigations, he developed a special metal-lined enclosure which attracted a high charge of orgone energy inside itself, directly from the atmosphere: *the orgone energy accumulator.*

The orgone accumulator was proven to charge seeds and increase garden plant growth, speed the healing of burns and cuts, boost the overall vitality and immune-strength of organisms, and there are a number of physical experiments which demonstrate anomalous phenomena inside the accumulator. Reich observed that certain kinds of low-energy contractive illness, such as cancer, would often symptomatically yield with careful application of the orgone accumulator. After he moved to the USA, he treated people experimentally with his combined emotional/orgone-energetic approach. By the 1950s, following a malicious press smear-campaign (concocted by his old enemies from the Stalinist left), he was subjected to a grinding "investigation" by US Food and Drug Administration, which was at that time (1955) engaged in an all-out war against natural healing methods (the repression of natural healing methods has always been a major agenda of organized medicine, the pharmaceutical industry and the FDA). The FDA obtained a court injunction which ordered the *banning and burning* of Reich's books — any book containing the forbidden word "orgone" was ordered destroyed, even his classics on human sexuality which only mentioned orgone energy in the preface. The FDA factually burned Reich's books and journals on several occasions (most recently in 1962), while Reich was given a 2-year jail sentence for a misdemeanor technicality, dying in prison in 1957. The FDA's attack against Reich constituted a major *fraud upon the courts and the American people,* and the Reich legal case continues to overshadow the better-known Scopes Monkey Trial in constitutional significance, in that *American courts, including the Supreme Court, authorized the burning of scholarly books and the jailing of scientists for maintaining unorthodox viewpoints.*

In this #5 issue of *Pulse of the Planet* — the first one to be organized and published since 1993 — we present a collection of essays and experimental research papers which flesh out various aspects of Reich's sex-economic and orgone-biophysical findings, building upon work previously published. The topics range as wide as Reich's own research, from babies and emotions, through the subjects of bions and biogenesis, the orgone energy accumulator and cloudbuster, to the questions of "free energy" and UFO phenomenon. This issue also supplies new evidence in support of the ether-drift experiments of Dayton Miller, whose work was prematurely dismissed by the physics establishment.

The science of *orgonomy* — focusing upon orgone energy functions in nature — surely will constitute the core foundation of a new life-affirming and technologically-fruitful science for the 21st Century. The reader should not be disappointed.

James DeMeo, Ph.D.
Greensprings, Oregon

Orgonomic First Aid for Mothers and Infants*

by Eva Reich, M.D.

Introduction:

It is my distinct pleasure and honor to introduce to you, Eva Reich, our first conference speaker, which is quite appropriate, for she is the daughter of the founder of Orgonomy, Wilhelm Reich. She reconnected with her father in the United States some years after he settled here and worked diligently and frequently and brilliantly with him while he was alive. Subsequently, after his death, she has dedicated her life to teaching her father's work especially in the area of infants and children. She describes her activity, her purposes or goals, as "humanizing humanity". That's her term. She has traveled all over the world, lecturing, giving workshops, lending her heart and soul to the betterment of mankind. I call her a missionary.

Dr. Eva Reich:

First of all, thank you for inviting me because we haven't seen much of each other for the last twelve years since I was in Brooklyn studying obstetrics at Down State Medical Center, King's County Hospital, in 1973 and 74.

I'd like to say that Gentle Bio-Energetics is my name, for lack of anything better, for what I've been trying to transmit to just ordinary people. It's not therapy but a sort of crisis intervention at the time the things are actually happening so you don't have to, 30 years later, go back and primal what happened to you when you were separated from your mother after birth, but you can actually be with your mother after birth. That is a struggle because, as you know, there is a lot of power politics in official medicine that is controlling the system, that controls what happens to mothers and babies.

Now this support that we can give as peers, as equals, not as therapist/patient, to each other during the various stages of the child bearing years is very easily taught once you have a few basic ideas. The ideas rest clearly on (Wilhelm) Reich's vision that all human babies are born pretty alive, very feeling, loving, with a good field, usually very open, very sensitive, and that something happens to human beings that squelches them. He wrote about this process of the squelching of

* Transcript of a lecture given by Dr. Eva Reich at Wagner College, Staten Island, New York, at a 1986 conference sponsored by the *American College of Orgonomy*. Transcribed by Richard Overly and Ann Cannon, and reprinted with permission.

life in his book, *The Murder of Christ*. Basically, it has to do with the history of childhood and with how, not only the birth process, but the whole matter of reproduction and women and children have been treated by mankind, which is human kind.

I'm not a feminist, but I am beginning to be aware of language that expresses the male bias in history. Lloyd DeMause has really done a great service to humanity in bringing together the field of history and the field of psychology, showing how little was recorded about what really went on with how we treated babies and little children. When he looked into this matter from a historical point of view he found very little material. It just wasn't on the books because women weren't writing books. Lloyd DeMause has established a whole field of science called Psycho-History. He rests his case about the cruelty that was inflicted on young life upon a psychoanalytic viewpoint.

We have emerged from this psychoanalytic viewpoint into a functional, orgonomic viewpoint which means we are looking at the living processes from a bioenergetic viewpoint. This hasn't come into medicine yet, in general. So I am transmitting this viewpoint to ordinary mothers, children, parents, fathers, etc. In simplest terms, I've sort of boiled the whole thing down to a nugget.

The prevention of armoring is very important and we should study how babies actually do armor. I'll get to that later because very little was known about that, about how it actually happens. There are lots of records from the Orgonomic Infant Research Center that Wilhelm Reich founded, I think it was '49 and maybe it went on until about '53. But all these files are in the trust fund and will be locked up there until 2007, so we can't wait for those. But the idea has survived. I think there was a kind of...flaw isn't the word...there was a bias built into Reich's formulation of the purposes of his research center. He looked for "perfect" mothers so he could start with good new life that was pretty OK. That's a value judgment that really doesn't exist in the real world. Every woman is where she is and that's where she's at. I have simply not paid any attention [to psychiatric orgonomic labels]. I have taken each person, as a full spirit, because I accept them as they are because I am a follower of Jesus. Here they are and they can always get better from that place. And this frees me from a lot of constraints. It has really opened the way for me.

So we are actually studying what really happens

between babies and mothers. I have a very positive viewpoint. Wilhelm Reich was a very positive thinker. He thought the core functions of the organism, that which you were as a baby, were really good. You're born good and all this evil, all this violence is something you develop in reaction to what is happening to you in the world. This is not a viewpoint shared by the Catholic church, by the way, who believes in original sin. In some ways, the people who are looking for "perfect" mothers put a burden on the whole process. So I just did without that concept.

I believe in peer support groups, and they are springing up pretty world wide, but not always with an orgonomic basis. My most successful support groups right now are in Vienna and in Munich. I just want to tell you that the new work is what is happening in the advice stations for natural birth, where women volunteer in countries where there isn't much volunteerism, where there is a space to meet, and women meet and deal with these crisis problems in a very good way. Therefore, maybe we'll need less therapy in the future.

Reich mourned, after he became a psychiatrist, the fact that there was much more neurosis created by the world than there would ever be therapists. And if you read "Science '86," there are now 160,000 therapists and 30% of the American population is in counseling. So the need is there, which is a change from when Reich came onto the world scene [in the 1920s], at which time, the mask was prevalent. We now see that we live in an irrational world and that we'd better change something. We've become aware that what we need to change is our human character structure. That dawning awareness is entering the world and so we are a part of that process. I feel terribly optimistic about that approach. It is bearing great fruits.

My approach is very gentle and loving. When I read Dr. Elsworth Baker's memorial volume and about his sore thumb when they were pressing on the muscles, I said, "Ah, this is not where I came in." I came in with little premature babies about 1950-51 after I'd had a year of therapy myself with Dr. Baker. I went into a premature nursery at Harlem hospital, and there I discovered that you have to deal very, very delicately with these tiny beings which sometimes weighed just a pound or more. That's where they were surviving then, and now they are surviving even younger and smaller. But you can't treat them with a strong thumb that hurts afterwards. So I got driven by this life experience into what I call Butterfly Touch Therapy. The best simile that I could give is that when you touch the wings of a butterfly you don't want to come away with its scales on your fingers; you want to be so light that when you release that butterfly your hands are without the scales. So, the butterfly touch is a very delicate touch. (See the end of the speech for detailed information on Butterfly Touch Massage and other tools mentioned.)

And secondly, every baby is a very delicate system and so the therapy is very brief. It might be 5 minutes a day. I was walking around this premature nursery where pre-term infants were dying of dependent pneumonia because they were just lying there [immobile] in total autism with closed eyes. I began to stimulate their chests, stroking the rib cage, sort of tickling between the ribs a little bit. This gentle touch, applied five minutes (maybe three minutes a day) to each baby, kept them alive. They didn't die if I did that. They didn't get these pneumonias and this was an a-ha! for me. So I developed, during my Harlem pediatrics experience, a lot of applications of orgone therapy based simply on common sense and what I experienced myself. That differs from any kind of strong Bio-Energetics done to grown-ups.

Later on, I discovered that grown-ups contain the little baby in their structure, and even the most rock hard man will respond to this butterfly touch. So this has been an answer. What do you do with these set structures? You start from the gentle end and sometimes that is what they need. They need rebirthing. They need to go back into their baby feelings.

Also, economically this doesn't cost much. We're spending billions for war and death and very little for this positive aspect to nurture new life. If I do nothing else at this conference than to ask officially, publicly for a reversal of priorities from death to life, then I've done something towards this purpose. If we just took what one little tank costs and started some studies, I think we'd do better. We need to reverse the priorities and begin to see that these early beginnings are very important.

Now Reich was a pessimist about it. He said, "If the early twig is bent it will never be OK [straight] again. If the protoplasm doesn't sparkle (famous quotation) you are lost forever," and that doomed attitude has crept in. I don't have it. I see such changes happening, sometimes in one minute, in a baby that's so touched or treated. I know we can reverse the whole process at any point.

OK, now to apply this tender concern, this peer support kind of bioenergetics, and Gentle Bio-Energetics: during pregnancy, during the first phase of the childbearing year, many women become very vulnerable. They cry easily; they're very delicate [emotional]. You know that. It's known, but nobody's understood it. To me, it makes common sense that the energy system, the dynamics of repression, of how you get through life by hardening yourself, the armoring becomes unequilibrated, shall we say, unbalanced, by the addition of the new [fetal] energy system, this warm, growing, living system. Every women feels her uterus warm if she is alive and aware. This baby is added and many women bloom during pregnancy from this added energy level. Some don't have enough structured defenses and things spill over. Therefore, the emotional work with women is very delicate, very brief, and it doesn't take much to get to what they are really feeling.

Baby Massage is a valuable tool for expansion in a person who is contracted. And what I am trying to say is that we work just to the point where the block is. It comes from Radix basically...you stimulate...they breathe...they charge up with some energy. Ahhh...breathing through into the pelvis, and then something rises, something happens, an emotion comes...tears, anger, stoppage. They hold the emotion and at the point of stoppage, (that's the idea of Reich in Character Analysis) from that point, in the pregnancy work, we don't push on. We just leave it there saying, "Yes, that's enough for you. Good. OK. Lets deal with what just came up." Or "Let's go through it again to see if we can help you to cry it out." I might cycle through it again. We try to understand the need of this woman for this block. She always has a good reason why she stops at this point. If she opens too much she is too vulnerable. Women do collapse from this openness, and it is called postpartum psychosis. I know after I gave birth I felt like my bottom had no support. I was just raw and open and everything was too much for me. I wanted just to be alone with my baby somewhere.

It's like in physics. If we look at this system too hard scientifically we disturb the system. My solution of how to teach this stuff is to have maybe two or three people there, your husband, a friend, other children, whatever, and then have the other people watching in a way so that you are not totally aware of this gang of people staring. So when we do this work we're going to have to find new research methods. I want to say that the things that come up are not often deep emotions. Sometimes they're the surface layers, the attitudes, the fears, the aloneness, the chaos of our lives.

When Reich wrote his books marriage was structured, society was rigid. Now we have chaos. Families are collapsing; women are very often alone in their parenting; everything is crumbling around us. Also, women have the problem of juggling time; they're doing jobs at once. So we're getting these concerns.

It depends where you go in the world what problems the pregnant woman is going to present to you. In some places, it is still maternal exhaustion, hunger, or not enough resources in the family. In Ecuador, they have no family planning to speak of and every woman on the street is pregnant and has an organ-pipe row of children, one in the arms, one in the belly, and three tagging behind. The average number of children, if there is no birth control, is at least 7 per woman. That's the average. So women get exhausted. And 100 years ago many of them died before the husbands were through; husbands had several wives each of whom had many children.

Here, we are swinging over into the opposite. Women are working. "How am I going to juggle career and baby?" And I think single parenting, chaos, and divorce are the major issues now, which they were not at Reich's time. At his time, sexual repression was the issue. But if you go to Austria, in the rural areas, sexual repression and slavery of the young to the old, the tyranny of the old and fascism in families still, in the sense of domination by a patriarchal father, is the issue. So wherever you go in the world the problems are a little different, and maybe the United States is the most ahead in this process of disintegration of the former forms.

OK, so maternal exhaustion...I find that exhaustion and fatigue [of young mothers] is the big thing. We can deal with the fear of pregnancy by sending the women to good natural childbirth education classes. And there is wonderful work at *International Childbirth Education Association (ICEA), NAPSAC,* and the *Midwives of America.* You can get the information. You no longer need to go into birth ignorantly. You can see films of how babies really slide out. I recommend birth in the squatting position (see film by the Brazilian obstetrician Claudio Paciornik). The priorities need to be turned around. These are the things we need to assist, study, and support.

When we do this kind of work with a pregnant woman we need to include persons significant to her, whoever they may be. Somebody was telling me about a lesbian couple who decided to have a child; then that is the significant other person. I am not judgmental about who that mother chooses as her important person. Maybe it's her mother. This changes the men and this is one of the most interesting things I am watching, especially in South America. Until recently, men weren't allowed in on the birth process. Now we include them, and they are beginning to teach democracy in the family.

Yes, the men are becoming involved. Interestingly enough, I am finding that some men, and this is amazing when you read Freud and all about penis envy, when we do include them, begin to show uterus envy, pregnancy envy. Yes, I am beginning to see that. Men are getting honest enough to say, "I wish I could be doing this." La Leche League has some males lactating from stimulation...things like that. What I find so great, in terms of how this approach can change the world, is that macho men become what I call human. This is at work as a process in South America right now.

So we have the people who believe in education in order to make a better birth experience and beginning for the world. And they say, "Relax, relax, relax," and they have millions of classes that teach relaxation. Yes, and that's helpful. I've gone to places in Ecuador at the main public hospital in Quito. Nobody had heard [the lesson about relaxation there yet]. Everybody is like this, "Grrr!!", lying flat. In Venezuela, also, flat on the back "Ooohhh!!", like this on a bed during labor. And that is not good for the labor. But that isn't the question we need to ask. We need to ask what it is that's tensing up the woman? That's where I've thrown the spotlight in this work.

I got into this at Harlem hospital years ago in the 1950s when I use to have fun as a pediatric resident. I would go into the obstetric wards and there were these Haitian women, women from Harlem, and some of the Caribbean women, singing along [during their labor]. And the louder they sang the faster the birth went, "Oh Lordy, Lordy, Hallelujah!" And they would give birth. And it helped. So vocalizing, having an open throat helps the birth process to go through. And we have to realize that what is called the orgasm reflex needs to be open, that birth is ahhh...an opening process from above downward. And if the woman is at all tight because she has sexual guilt and fear, or she was hit for touching herself genitally, etc., then she will clamp onto her pelvic floor and retract her pelvis, and that will hold the birth back. So, I was going around, as a resident, telling these woman, "OK, ahh, ahhh, sing! sing lying on your side. Ahh, ahhh, get your pelvis forward into a C-curve." And low and behold! Pop! Pop! Pop! The babies were coming [right away]. This is a true story.

The insight was that anything that makes retraction of the pelvis is not good for the birth process. Anything that helps the pelvis [the sacrum and coccyx] to come forward, as it would in the orgasm reflex, helps the birth process. Therefore, high heels are out. And in France you see pregnant woman going top heavy on very high heels which is wrong because it gives them an artificial lordosis and holds up the birth. So, by all means, low heels. This is just common sense. But this is orgonomic thinking, yes?

Now another thing that will help women, and that hasn't been said enough, except by some of the alternative [birth rebels] and not officially, is to abreact [act out] the main worries before the infant arrives. Now that is an important point because the women get too busy after the baby is there to have time for their own feelings. That's why we need to clear their problems and conflicts before, and certainly we need to help them with their own memory cassettes about their own birth. And with this I do not have much experience, but there are several ways. And one of them is wet rebirthing, which was done by the THETA Institute in San Francisco, and I don't like the so called rebirth hyperventilation otherwise. They had a pool, a sensory deprivation tank. Women who were pregnant were going in with a snorkel and just hanging there, having rebirthing experiences, getting through and clearing their own memory cassettes. Bad personal experiences with their own [past] birth is, I think, now one of the most common obstacles to a good, easy birth [in the present].

By the way, from an obstetrical point of view, the question arises, "Where in the world are the births easy?". On the islands of the Caribbean, I found one hour births even with the first baby. I have quite a bit of evidence that if you have a good birth memory then it's easier for you. So it is worthwhile for women to find out from their own mothers, "How was mine?" because that is going to influence unconsciously how I hold myself. And if there's an abyss of fear, and this fear is a darkness

in the eyes which we can detect before the birth, then we need to deal with it. Bring it out. Bring it up. Ahhh! The hee-bee-jee-bees! And out it will come. Now there are many techniques [to bring up this material from the memory cassette, e.g. Frank Lake's Psychodrama Rebirth]. I don't want to go into too much detail, but this kind of assistance we can render.

Now I want to say one sad word: the volunteerism that was supporting these birth associations is petering out because there need to be two jobs to feed a family. Women don't have as much time anymore as we had a little while ago, 10 years ago, due to inflation. Now there are other means we can use to support these women. For instance, the problem in Austria and Germany is isolation. In a city setting there, people are not as friendly as in America, starting to talk to strangers. So each one is sitting alone in her little house or apartment and she is going bananas. Wait until she has a baby. Then she will really be lonely. So that is where the self-help groups help too. They supply a meeting place.

Also, we can use some Bach Flower Remedies which are homeopathic remedies for the soul. We have some for utter terror (Rock Rose). We have some for "I can't endure anymore" (Sweet Chestnut). And, in the birth process itself, if the woman is saying, "I can't anymore", you give her some Rescue Remedy which has five things in it and she can go a little longer. I'll go back to that later when I talk about the accumulator.

So the sharing of these experiences, the consciousness raising groups that the women's libbers have introduced can be applied in this field, and they work like magic. Women are telling each other what [birth and having babies] is like. Women are discussing their problems and it's confidential. We don't go gossiping about it. When I have a group I usually say, "This is not for gossip. This is personal stuff, and it will not go beyond me."

One other thing that the self-help groups can do is to fill the practical needs. It's sometimes as simple as "Who is going to baby-sit my baby when I'm going to the dentist or while I go shopping?" or "Who is going to do the housework?" They need assistance. In the old days, when we had extended families, that was easy. Now, these are the surface things that any self-help [barter] group can provide.

Then we have societal problems that come up: "My husband lost his job." "My boyfriend walked out when I got pregnant." That is one of the most common ones right now. Men can be sexual partners, but the moment a bit of responsibility enters they flee, and it's because of their own primal experiences. This pattern of the primally-needy male that can't be adult, supporting the woman during the pregnancy, is a major one that I am running into. The men are stuck on their own unfulfilled baby needs...some of them. I am not generalizing about men, but many men desert at this point; they simply are no help.

Sometimes there are acute illnesses in the family; somebody is dying. In retrospect, I go back into the cases of unsettled babies, those that scream a lot, and I find Ah Ha! another child died during this pregnancy, or Ah Ha! somebody was critically ill, a cancer patient who is petering out while the woman is pregnant, etc., or the woman had to flee. She was in war time; she was fleeing and giving birth, while the bombs were dropping.

In my work, these traumas come up and we try to heal them. And yet, we can prevent them by giving more support to women in these situations, right? One system is the buddy, daily telephone check-up with somebody who is a friend of yours outside of the group. Another is the gestalt dialogue, where you talk to a pillow and take both sides and express what you are really feeling in this psychodrama, gestalt way. Very healing.

We share body feelings in the group: "Yes, my sexuality is increasing; I'm like a hot oven." "What are the positions that are OK during intercourse [when pregnant]?" (on the side with a gentle wash first); "I have no interest," or, more commonly, "I am too exhausted." There is a lot of practical advice that needs to be given.

In each group of, let's say, a hundred women who are being prepared for birth with these childbirth courses, there will be maybe up to five who are really prepsychotic, who have had severe symptoms. If you are a childbirth educator you ought to learn how to pick them out so that they get special attention. They ought to be referred to orgonomists or therapists who know a little bit more about it. And this I think would prevent some of the post partum psychosis. I've talked to a lot of childbirth educators and I think learning to pick these women out involves recognizing their extreme tension, extreme perfectionism and idealism. The room has to be perfect; the bed has to be made. But when you have a baby you get too busy and this cracks up the perfectionist women, who are really compulsive. They are running away from their own inner turmoil by becoming perfectionists.

We can do a modified therapy. We do this with the highly pregnant woman semi-sitting because if she is flat the uterus presses on the big blood vessels. We do brief sessions. (I saw one bioenergetic practice session at a public hospital near Paris and they were two hours at it, lying flat on their backs. And they were exhausted going, "Ahhh! ahhh! ahhh!" You know, working their breathing and pushing these women to a point of exhaustion. This I think is wrong. It would be better to tell women, "Sleep before the birth. Have rest.") The aim of this modified therapy is to assist the woman to breath through from the mouth to the toes, and this we can teach quite rapidly using the ideas of psychophonics. (In the speech Eva Reich modeled the technique. Here is presented a verbal description by the editors combined with her words.)

The technique combines an "ahhh" sound with the breath and is a very gentle process. The idea is not to push either the breath or the sound. Don't provoke, and above all, don't hurt. The goal is to find where the breath or the sound gets stuck and then to learn to open so the breath flows through the whole body. Usually, it gets stuck at the diaphragm; sometimes in the throat. Emotions, sensations, or memories may occur at the stuck place.

The woman gently places her hands over the upper part of the chest breathing naturally and making an "ahhh" sound with each exhalation. Tell her: "Hear the ahhh sound, following, not forcing, your breath. Breathe down into your voice, continuing to make the sound every time you exhale. Feel it, ahhhhh——(deep and long) Follow the breath and sound. Feel the sensations, the vibrations. Feel where it gets stuck, where the vibration stops, where you can't go on. Continue to breathe with the sound, where it gets stuck, until it opens. As the ahhh sound moves deeper [lower down] into the body, keep moving the hands down the body, staying with the sensations each time until the vibration of the sound is felt. (As you assist the woman you may lightly place your hands over hers and can model the breathing and sound).

In this way, try to teach or guide, in one session, how to get the breath to go all the way from the head through the toes in a wave-like movement. The body will naturally move into a C-curve with the pelvis rocking forward on the exhalation as the breath moves down to the toes and the woman will feel it all through her body. This is mechanical but it helps. Accept what comes and later teach everybody Baby Butterfly Massage to prevent some of the problems.

Certainly we are going to try to get some heat into the pelvis. And we look for cold zones. The woman may have a very hot forehead and then below her ocular level it's cold. And you can really feel a strong barrier right here, and then the nose, and from there on, is cold. She's schizoid and she has a split or a division in her energy streaming. What we try to do is to get the energy to stream through. I am now using Polarity Therapy to help that. We want her to expand her energy field. Contracted women are very common, especially in cities. They move inward a little bit, like a snail into a house for safety, from this extremely loud world. So they draw their field in; they are cool and they don't radiate.

Normally a pregnant woman's energy expands. I was in a motel bed with my pregnant daughter, who was taking her state boards in nursing five days before the birth [happened], and I couldn't stay in the bed with her. She was just so hot that I had to get on the floor because of the high energy level. It was intolerable to me.

To expand without fear is the aim. I would like to say, also, that we can do some rebonding during pregnancy. I'll give you one quick case history of the kind of problem that comes my way. When I do these open clinics anybody can come with their problem. This was in Australia. A lady came to me whose husband had a vasectomy because they already had four children. The vasectomy was badly done, or somebody didn't tell them to wait three months afterwards and check the sperm again. Anyway, she had a conception, and it was definitely an unwanted conception. So this uterus had a failure to thrive. It was cold with low life energy. She felt no connection with that baby. We were heading for disaster, for a relationship of lifelong disturbance from an unwanted conception. So I did some breathing with her, and we got into her dislike of the situation, her anger about the doctor who had done the vasectomy, and we released some feelings. And then, always after the release of some feeling, I do a gestalt dialogue with the material that comes. Then we deal with the material: "Why are you angry?" (Sometimes I don't even talk while the anger is coming out.) "Put your hands on this uterus. There's a person in there? Can you talk to the baby?"

Since Frans Veldman did his Haptonomy lectures in America, people are aware that you can talk to the baby. This is a person in there. By the way, I've just read a very good book from Austria, where a mother writes about talking with the fetus. She talked to her baby: "Look I really didn't want you. Why did you come? This is going to be a catastrophe." And then I said, "OK, now, what does the baby have to say?" Remember, she has already released some feelings and she is rather open. And the baby says, "Love me". She burst out crying and the uterus got hot. Her energy flooded right through and she expanded. And she had a relationship with that fetus. From that moment on, it went OK. So you can work on a reversal, on a rebonding with a fetus already in the uterus. I have many, many case histories, but that is a very dramatic one, a real breakthrough, and the payoff was the hot uterus. The heat goes through; it becomes alive.

After a polarity session, post Cesarean, with a lady I had not seen before, she reported, "Ah, now my pelvis is hot." We had never seen each other before, but we accomplished this aim in a single one and a half hour session. Many such mothers regain the orgasm reflex after polarity and write to thank me. So, contrary to the Orgonomic Therapy teachings that you go very carefully and the last to open is the pelvis, I really aim, in one session, to get the woman as far as we can, without pushing it, to feel through, to get connection with the uterus, to feel right on through her toes. I want to say that this has greatly influenced my work with other patients so that I do this in *all* adult sessions, too. In each session, I try to go through with a wave of feeling right to the toes, which includes the genitals.

Now we have to look at each woman's specific armor mechanism. That is, we look for how she tightens up when she gets to this "enough point" of "I don't want anymore." And each person has their own way of doing that. She'll stop her breathing; she'll suddenly detach and go away with the eyes; she'll lock up, get cool inside, and draw into herself. Whatever she does, I say, "Listen, dear, you're doing this now all under the stress of my working with you on this, but I think you'll do it during labor when labor gets tough. So let's try and dissolve some of this tendency. But it has a good reason in your life, and we've got to find out where that comes from, if we can, because these tension attitudes are going to appear again during labor."

And then I teach the Baby Massage, which I have discovered is a modified vegetotherapy. It connects the whole body and loosens the muscles. I teach that to the husbands. And the husbands [if they choose] are there during the birth. They're the birth attendants; they're the monitors. (Bradley first brought the husband into the delivery room to help.) And now the husband learns Baby Massage and can say, "OK, breathe through," as he reminds her that labor is getting tough. He does a little bit of loosening, "OK, ahhh...keep your jaw open. Breathe through. Let your voice come through. Stay with me with your eyes. Keep your pelvis forward. OK, I'll rub you down, stroke you through." You know. He can help. He can shake those abductors, keep them soft. "OK, keep them open," and so on. I think that's beautiful. There's a film, "Marty and ... (?)" It's done in a hospital in New York City. It's about a black couple, and he is just helping the woman through the hard part of the birth with eye contact. It's a beautiful film and it works. OK, so this is what we aim for. And the husbands are very helpful.

I also use the accumulator (orgone blanket) to charge up. Now, I find the accumulator helps the best during birth because we can heal local wounds like episiotomy wounds which, by the way, are not necessary. (With an episiotomy we convert a natural process into a surgical process.) And we can maintain the ladies' energy level. I have several reports, one from Australia (Margaret Trudgeon) and one from Ecuador (Maria Alarcon) that we can recharge women who are tiring during a long birth, not only with Rescue Remedy but, with the accumulator [blanket], to the point of "lumination" [expansion of the field]. Good! Now they can go on a while. Also, the bath helps. But I wanted you to know that, for strength during labor, the accumulator is a helpful thing. And I think it bears investigating.

Now, during birth, our support should be very non-interventive and quiet. We should be there for the woman; we do not leave her alone [unless she wants solitude]. And preferably the person should know something about Bio-Energetics. Michel Odent says that obstetrics is based mostly on the pathologies. He had his Cesarean rate down to 5% in a hospital in Pithiviers, France. And Cesarean sections? What are they up to now in America? 25% at least. In Brazil, they are up to 90% with the upper class. It is catastrophic. It is a mechanical world. So to get back to natural birth we need a good obstetrician standing by, and he should have the attitude of respecting the natural instincts, the natural law in the woman.

And Michel Odent is the master, so read his book, "Birth Reborn". Odent found something interesting, that if the woman is not disturbed and she stays in her pleasure state with the birth, a dreamy state, that she produces endorphins out of her own hypothalamus, and these make a pleasurable state. Otherwise, as Grantly Dick-Read discovered, the moment you stress her and disturb her, she goes into what we would call a bioenergetic contraction, the endorphin production stops [adrenaline is released], and a vicious cycle of pain, fear, and tension is set up.

Therefore, we need to study the interventions that doctors make in the birth process. I have a cousin in Australia, Lisa Muhlen, who did a study, not from hospital records, but she went to students of a health college, who each interviewed five women who had each just had a baby and checked what was done to them. She found almost 99% intervention. Nobody got by without something being done. An induction, a drug forced separation, whatever you want, it was there, even when the hospitals called it "natural birth".

The doctors got very upset about this study because it didn't use their resources. It went beyond them to the ordinary people, and it showed that you can almost not escape [interventions]. So we need a person at the birth who will defend a woman because she is so busy with the process of birth that she can't defend herself. We need a birth assistant and a monitor, somebody who works with the woman and somebody who says to the doctors, "Wait. She doesn't want anesthesia. She doesn't want the drug; she is doing fine. She is grunting because it is hard work."

Some do have pain and those should be relieved. The best relief is a vertical birth in a pool, a large bath, or under a hot shower. All obstetrical stations should have those. They are now building hospitals without these facilities. I am hurt because we know now that instead of using drugs we can relax the woman. She just floats [in water]. It's the buoyancy. She gets dreamy [and may not want to get out of the tub for the birth] and the babies slide out. We don't have to intervene. I am very impressed by that way. All we do is lift the baby to the surface [immediately, into the air]. So the water birth has been a tremendous help.

Now during birth, keep the pelvis forward. And keep the positive thinking. I've been accused of having too many instruments and of bringing negative thinking into the birth situation because I was scared. All doctors are taught to be scared about birth. So that's where midwives come in. And I've been impressed by the midwives; they can be so gentle working with the woman. You don't even know they're there and they do so much better than the male obstetricians. All doctors should learn about natural birth before they learn about pathological births.

In countries where Cesarean rates are so high, I teach women self-examination. They take a sterile glove; they learn how to go into the vagina and feel whether there is progress or not, whether the cervix is opening or not. She can just feel it, sitting on a toilet seat or squatting down. To defend women from unnecessary Cesarean births I am teaching self-help.

Wilhelm Reich had a diagram (see Figures 1 and 2) showing that during pregnancy the little baby is an energy system *inside the mother's energy system*. After birth, this little baby's system needs to be *next to the mother* [within arms reach]. This is a very fundamental point. It simply cannot yet maintain itself outside of a human field. I don't know whether Reich ever wrote this, but he showed this little diagram: here's the mother with her core (which is her belly), periphery, and field, and here is the baby with its core, periphery, and its field (Fig.1).

So after birth, the natural law has it that this little baby is no longer is inside but now is in the field of the mother, within arms length, and it needs that field (Fig.2), because that is what keeps the baby's field

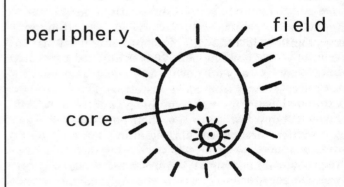

Figure 1. Energetic Field of Baby in Womb of Pregnant Mother

Figure 2. Field of Mother with Newborn Baby

expanded.

You take away the mother's field and the baby's field collapses. The result may be "iatrogenic hypothermia" (coolness caused by separation from the mother). No heater will do the same as the mother's energy field, but this requires the mother to be in a state of expansion. That means we need to feed them after birth. We shouldn't starve them. No big meals, but we should give them juices to maintain the blood sugar. Give them fruit and so on. There's an awful lot of obstetrical detail here that I am not going to go into, but our main aim is: to keep the field expanded on both sides, mother and baby should not get separated.

To separate the mother and baby, right after birth, I always call a crime against humanity, and that's what is done since all South American hospitals copy the United States, the great mechanical genius. In the public hospitals, they are ripping those babies away at the moment they come out, not even showing them to the mothers sometimes and it's horrendous. It's like a bad joke imitation of the kind of obstetrics practiced in this country on the majority. It's a mechanical way. It has gotten a little better since we explained some things there. But literally, at the Pavilion Concepcion in Caracas, about four years ago, on one side there was a huge table, 100 births a day, tables with women screaming, lying flat, tense with no privacy, no attendant, episiotomies, blood flowing, forceps being used just to learn how...and, on the side, babies stacked like cord wood. They literally fell down and got lost. Terrible. So we need to go away from mass obstetrics. The American College of Obstetrics and Gynecology, I don't know if it is still so, but a few years ago, their policy was to close the smaller birth hospitals, planning for only 5000 births and over per year. They want big factories, and then they will need high risk nurseries. Well, with our kind of obstetrics, we don't need the high risk nurseries. Occasionally, we send a baby [to intensive care], but rarely. The morbidity, the mortality is much better with the natural way.

The baby should stay in the mother's field, or we should repair the ruptured bond as soon as possible. This is where *Gentle Bio-Energetics* comes in. For instance, let's say a mother went into shock and had to be given IV's or something, perhaps she had some bleeding. They rushed the baby off to the nursery, but maybe she recuperates in twelve hours, and she is ready to have her baby again. Well, then we need the Baby Massage. We need something to help her to regain the ability to just hold her baby which would have happened in the first hour because naturally a mother massages.

Ashley Montagu has described this natural massage every animal, every mammal does very well. Yet women can lose the ability to touch. Also, there are women who were told, "Don't touch," in countries where it is not OK to touch the body. There are countries where we're not allowed to touch yet. We're changing that, but women sometimes don't know how to touch. I've been working on this for 10 years, saying that we're reversing the pendulum and that it's all right to touch your baby. It's exactly what it needs. Now don't touch it *all* the time. When it sleeps you may want to put it down. Have the symbiosis which is a symbiosis of the fields, and also have the release.

So there is the process of normalizing after the birth shock. There Bio-Energetics comes in. I learned about all this as a pediatric resident resuscitating newborns that weren't breathing well, because they had too many drugs. And I learned that if you put them into a C-curve, put the organism into the position of the C-curve (the orgasm reflex, so called) then the breathing reflex goes through as you stimulate the diaphragm and intercostal spaces between the ribs.

And I found certain places where babies reacted. For instance, they would have a tremendous cleft that was like a white pressure ring around the level of the eyes. And this you sometimes still see in grown-ups, but you can release it in 5 minutes on a baby by doing Baby Massage, by stroking it, and working to get the energy flowing through. They may have become stuck in an inspiratory attitude [with a high chest], and many babies stay there and become adults who go around like this. I found some people, during birth primals, who looked like bulldogs, who really were pushing during the birth and not getting out. Churchill, I think, had birth trauma. And there in this position all the energy is going up [into the upper body], and it is all blocked because of the birth experience.

So you get all sorts of body attitudes. Above all, you get schizoid dissociation, mostly due to the birth anesthesia which knocks the little soul out of the body in that baby. I once did a study in Harlem. I walked around and counted 100 babies, 12 hours after birth. 30% were just sleeping, you couldn't rouse them to suck, because they were still burning off their anesthetics. (As we have now learned, babies don't have the excretory organs for such big doses. Much more is known about this now.) The other 70%, "Wah! wah!" They were red and screaming with nobody soothing them or touching them. And in those days, they starved babies for twelve hours after birth, which is totally against the natural law where the baby can go to the breast and suckle all the time. So the rebonding, in such a situation, is enhanced by Baby Massage.

And for resuscitation, we can also use foot-reflexology. Recently, in one of these water births, with a very heavy woman, the baby's head got stuck. The baby, blue as a plum, slid out and wasn't really breathing. We had a little leeway so we left the cord connected. The baby was still on this double system, getting oxygen through the cord for quite a few minutes. I began some foot-reflexology and that baby just started to breathe. No slapping, no holding upside down, not even suctioning of the mucus because, in a vertical birth, the mucus comes anyway. Leboyer says we should put the babies in a water bath, but we can use our means. I think the use of a sterile accumulator blanket, in this situation, really should be explored, but there we run into the hospital rules which forbid such exploration. But we can keep both mother and baby warm by covering them with a warm blanket. They need rest, sleep, and feeding after the birth.

I have studied placenta feeding, for which I have been attacked hugely, but it is a natural biological problem and I am having very good success. The placenta is eaten in little bits, like a grape, cut by the husband. When the placenta is chewed, within two minutes after the first chew, the uterus contracts into a rough firm cannonball-like thing. This tremendous contraction seems to be due to peptides that are in the placenta. Nature recycles. The mother is getting all sorts of substances, such as gamma globulins, that we extract from the placenta. It's really a nutrient package, which can't be purified because these are delicate enzymes. The uterus retracts below the pubic bone in three days instead of ten. This could be studied but that is not Bio-Energetics. It's just the natural law about birth.

When it's a Cesarean we can have the father bond, and we now know that holding is important. Portage, having the baby on the body, is important because it stays in a human field. After the baby is out, we should treat mother and baby as a dyad; even the sick dyad needs to be treated together. This is a major bone of contention between me and medicine. They'll let you do a birth room thing but, if anything goes wrong, they whisk you to another part of the hospital where you are treated like a machine. We need to assert the human right to stay together even if one of the two is dying.

Parenting problems is the area where Bio-Energetics comes in the most. As with post partum, everybody is so exhausted, it was such a big event that they don't go to groups. So you can only help with this individually by visiting them in the home. There is a tremendous need, instead of bombs, tankers, and super missiles, for half-way places for mothers and babies in a bit of trouble. We have it in Holland and in Australia [Adelaide, S.A., a motel-like place] where the mother can go for 4 to 6 weeks for adaptation problems. If she doesn't feel ready to go home all alone, if she has depression, if the baby is a little cranky and screams, if she is just too exhausted, she has a place to be. This does not exist yet in America as far as I know. This is a wonderful service where she will get fed; it's clean and she can be visited twenty-four hours a day by her loved ones. Her husband can sleep in the room with her if he wants.

It is a very necessary service because the problem in modern civilization is who is the extra hand that is going to come in there? The thing that peer groups can supply is a network of women that come to help each other. The midwife comes to visit for a while but she is too busy.

The husband has to go back to work. Then it gets tough. In South America, even the middle class has servants but not in America. We need someone with the extra hands for the mother. And we don't need nannies, who come in and take over the baby and control it like the royal family has in Britain. That was the habit of the upper classes. The mother says what she wants. The person has no opinions about the treatment of the baby. She simply is the extra hands to do the housework, the shopping, the cooking, the cleaning, the diapers, etc. These are the needs.

The depressions very often start at this point and this is very prevalent in Europe. We can treat them with Bach Remedies and peer support and by keeping husbands home even longer than one week. How long is the paternity leave here? (laughter!) Maybe none. We need to include the father.

Then when there is enough rest, and there is an energy field, when there is this peaceful surround, when they're not on the streets without shelter, we get peaceful babies successfully breast fed. This was the big revelation to me when I was a country doctor doing country home births. Here were babies that didn't cry. I was used to these batteries of raging, screaming meemies and these babies rarely [only occasionally] cried. When things go wrong, we get the unsettled babies, and the screaming starts, and it doesn't stop. A vicious circle begins.

I would like, and I invite anybody, to do a research study of these unsettled babies. Sometimes, there are certain extra difficult situations, and we can pick them up from the mother's character disturbances, her armor, or the individual situation. But, usually, it starts due to something obstetrical or pediatric, some intervention, and then the babies start to scream and they can't be soothed. How many people had such a baby? People suffer and it goes on sometimes for months. How many months for you? (to class participant) Several months. Two or three months is an adaptation period to the world, which one can call the "fourth trimester" of the child bearing year.

I've done some unique work with unsettled babies and this is where I'd really like to go with my research. First of all, we can prevent this by all these good things we do before and during birth. But once we get an unsettled baby, and they're everywhere, the families are driven crazy. They don't sleep; they get irritable; everybody is irritable. The baby gets tenser and tenser. The mother gets tenser and tenser. And it just doesn't work. This is my experience. And there exists not so much general anxiety in the mothers that nurse once the breast feeding is established. I've run into the screaming baby as the big post partum problem in the women who do not nurse. [1996 comment: Now in Berlin and Munich, Germany, there exists *Schrei-Ambulanz*, screaming baby outpatient clinics.]

Nobody knows what to do. Pediatricians tranquilize. All they know is tranquilizing or sometimes re-hospitalizing. *Baby Butterfly Massage* is an alternative to drugs that dissolves the problem. We can work with the mother's problem, dissolve her armor, and heal her bad experience (usually it's a bad birth experience). She can talk to the obstetrician in a kind of psychodrama (gestalt dialogue). She can let out her grief that it went differently; it went to Cesarean; it wasn't natural birth (that is the most common disappointment right now). People have big expectations and really something else happens. We can deal with that and then the mother calms down.

We can use *Bach Remedies* to soothe her upset state, her sense of disappointed sadness (Gentian, etc,), her sense of "I can't take anymore!" (Sweet Chestnut). I use a whole series of remedies. I give the baby Rock Rose for the terrors; Star of Bethlehem for shock. There is a lot we can do with Bach Remedies. We work on all fronts bioenergetically.

In Australia in 1976 and 1977 through a radio offer to help unsettled babies, I saw a series of fifteen screaming babies (six in Perth and nine in Melbourne) everyday for up to a week. I just said that I was doing free work and they could come. I gave them each an hour and a half. There was half an hour for the baby to show the Baby Butterfly Massage and to see how the baby was armored; there was one hour for the mother. And then there was follow up. Within one week, all of the babies had stopped screaming. We *can* do something that will make a difference and this is what we need to study. [The *Child Birth Education Association* of Melbourne provided the space, telephone service, and support. The availability of this free clinic was announced via public radio.]

If you look at psychiatric patients you often get the history of a difficult birth...this baby was difficult. How many of you are psychiatrists? Do look into the story of the birth. I would say, in general, that few of them can say, "I had a good, natural, slip-out birth. I was breast fed all I wanted, etc." They will give you a history of difficulty in that phase. So we can prevent some of those later difficulties and even prevent psychosis, yes, with these means. We are aiming for a peaceful baby whose needs are fulfilled. And then the happy parenting reinforces itself and it gets easier. (I need students in this. I am really ready to teach it. I have students all over the world, but I don't have any in America yet because of the prevailing mechanistic viewpoint.)

Then there are other problems. I want to speak of the stunning experience I had in Japan, two years ago [1984], that really upset me. I was a great believer that good beginnings prevent armoring and that we're OK if we just have a good beginning. Let's just teach all the mothers of the world these things...etc. In Japan, I found, in general, beautiful, soft, loved children with as much body contact as they want, family bed, breast feeding infinitely long (in the outskirts, maybe not in Tokyo anymore) and really the signs of glowing, rosy, beautiful children. And then, descends the school system. It takes the child from the parents and it armors them, consciously [at age six!].

Recently, I heard from somebody in Bulgaria that the same thing is done behind the iron curtain. I think we'll win this battle, this struggle, even behind the iron curtain, if we bring our ideas about armoring there. I'm hoping to do that and that's one reason I want to be in Vienna so much because it is very near; it's right in there. What I say in Vienna penetrates. What I say in West Berlin penetrates that wall. {1996 comment: The wall melted in 1989.]

So I am hoping that we can get human transformation, and I want you to know some good things are happening in Russia. It's beginning. There's a midwife from Finland, by the name of Lena Valvane, who actually has been invited to Leningrad [St. Petersburg]. She is teaching birth people. I've taught her something; she's bringing these things to others. I don't think that I'm too safe going there but she is doing it. There is sort of an open hole in that curtain. We are humanizing even there. We're saying, "Hey, it is not necessary for the red army chorus to stand like this and sing out of a high chest. It is not necessary to retreat into yourself because the housing shortage is so great that the only place to go is inside." I see a world where, instead of war and missiles, we solve our problems with human transformation which starts at birth, and that is what this is all about. Thank you very much.

For information or training for the tools mentioned here contact: Richard C. Overly, *Gentle Bio-Energetics Foundation*, 29 Lovers Loop Rd., Asheville, NC, USA, 28803 Phone: 828-298-5454 Email: rcoverly@earthlink.net http://www.gentlebio-energetics.com
Butterfly Touch Massage - book $15, audio tape $10, both together $20 (also available on our web site as e-course); *Gentle Bio-Energetics: Theory for Everyone, vol. 1* and *Gentle Bio-Energetics Tools for Everyone, vol. 2* - $30 each. Add $5 shipping and handling in US for small orders. Contact above for quantity orders. The Gentle BioEnergetics Foundation is a non profit organization with the purpose of making available the theory and practice of Eva Reich's Gentle Bio-Energetics with kindness and compassion to enhance the quality of life for people of all ages.

Update on *Saharasia*: Ambiguities and Uncertainties about *"War Before Civilization"**

by James DeMeo, Ph.D.**

Introduction and Background

In 1992, I was invited to Vienna, Austria, to give lectures on my research, and while there visited the *Natural History Museum*, which at the time had a large collection of East European artifacts organized chronologically. The display cabinets lined a pathway, which allowed one to see recovered artifacts and scenes reconstructing daily life, starting with the most ancient down to modern times. I made my way through the earliest collections of primitive stone tools, through Neanderthal times, and into the epoch of early *Homo sapiens*. Simple villages were shown in the reconstructed scenes, along with agriculture and animal domestication, some early types of pottery, fabrics and copper implements formed into decorative shapes. Settlements slowly grew in size, naturalistic artwork developed along with what I call "mother-dolls" (clay figures of women, what some have interpreted — wrongly I believe — as a "mother-goddess"). Artifacts of simple clay, stone, ceramic, copper, and even woven fabrics appeared, along with simple, yet elegant architecture, and the technology associated with agriculture, animal herding and hunting progressively improved in sophistication. All in all, it basically recorded an ordinary, though certainly vital and exciting existence of hunting, farming, dancing, and peaceful human relationships.

When the collection arrived at the middle of the fourth millennium BC (c.3500 BCE, or Before the Current Era) a broad white stripe, interrupting the path, had been painted on the walls and floor of the Museum gallery, bearing bold dark letters "CIVILIZATION BEGINS". Upon walking over that line, the display very dramatically included all kinds of war-weapons, battle axes, shields and helmets. Artifacts related to horse-riding warriors appeared, as did crowns, coins and tombs for kings and other big-man leaders. Fortifications, palaces and temples then appeared, with all the evidence for war-making, despotic, and murderous *Homo normalis*, as discussed in Wilhelm Reich's monumental clinical discovery of human armoring,[1] the biophysical source of neurotic behavior and impulses towards sa-

dism and brutality, and the wellspring for virtually every authoritarian social structure which exists, or which has ever existed.

This example from the Museum depicts "civilization" in a manner quite unflattering as compared to the usual definitions, and implies that warfare and social violence is a relatively recent invention by our species, of only around 6000 years duration. It also implies that we have become so accustomed to warfare and violence as the "norm" that we have difficulty even conceptualizing there might be, or might have been in our most ancient past, another mode of social existence free of the horrors of warfare and all but the most uncommon examples of interpersonal violence. This point of view, however unrecognized or unpopular, has much evidence to support it.

In the decade before my visit to Vienna, from around 1980 through 1986, I undertook one of the most systematic global cross-cultural investigations on human behavior and the origins of violence that has ever been undertaken, as an effort to evaluate and test these ideas. My dissertation on the subject, presented to the Geography Department of the University of Kansas, created a controversy, but was accepted and eventually published as *Saharasia: The 4000 BCE Origins of Child Abuse, Sex-Repression, Warfare and Social Violence In the Deserts of the Old World*,[2] with various summary articles published in journals.[3]

This work demonstrated a previously-unknown global geographical pattern in the archaeological-historical literature, and in several large and widely-used anthropological data bases. The newly discovered geographical pattern demonstrated a strong spatial correlation between the world's most harsh *patriarchal-authoritarian* modes of social structure (synonymous with Wilhelm Reich's definition of *highly armored* character structures) to the most harsh global desert regions — in North Africa, the Middle East, and Central Asia — to which I gave the term *Saharasia*. Areas most distant from Saharasia, in Oceania and the New World, showed the softest and most fluid and flexible democratic and egalitarian social structures (synonymous with Reich's lightly armored, or unarmored character structures). Figures 1 and 2 reproduce my World Behavior Map, and the correlated Dryness Ratio Map identifying the world's harshest contemporary desert regions. Table 1 presents the dichotomous social-cultural factors which were mapped in the original study.[2,3]

* Presented at the *International Psychohistorical Assoc.* 24th Annual Convention, 6-8 June 2001, New York.
** Director, Orgone Biophysical Research Lab, Greensprings, PO Box 1148, Ashland, Oregon 97520 USA. Tel/Fax: 541-552-0118   demeo@mind.net

Table 1: DICHOTOMOUS BEHAVIORS, ATTITUDES & SOCIAL INSTITUTIONS

Part of a cross-cultural analysis of 400 and 1170 different cultures, organized according to a matrix of 63 cultural variables identical or similar to the ones below, with the finding of a 95% positive correlation between the variables. This demonstrated the dichotomy below captured the essential framework of human behavior, of how people and cultures actually functioned. (Detailed in Chapters 1 and 3 of *Saharasia*[2])

	Armored Patrist	*Unarmored Matrist*
Infants & Children:	Less indulgence	More indulgence
	Less physical affection	More physical affection
	Infants traumatized	Infants not traumatized
	Painful initiations	Absence of pain in initiations
	Dominated by family	Children's democracies
	Sex-segregated houses or military	Mixed sex children's houses or age villages
Sexuality:	Restrictive, anxious attitude	Permissive, pleasurable attitude
	Genital mutilations	Absence of genital mutilations
	Female virginity taboo	No female virginity taboo
	Vaginal intercourse taboos	No intercourse taboos
	Adolescent lovemaking severely censured	Adolescent lovemaking freely permitted
	Homosexual tendency plus severe taboo	Absence of homosexual tendency or strong taboo
	Incest tendency plus severe taboo	Absence of incest tendency or strong incest taboo
	Concubinage/prostitution may flourish	Absence of concubinage or prostitution
Women:	Limits on freedom	More freedom
	Inferior status	Equal status
	Vaginal blood taboos (hymenal, menstrual & childbirth blood)	No vaginal blood taboos
	Cannot choose own mate	Can choose own mate
	Cannot divorce at will	Can divorce at will
	Males control fertility	Females control fertility
	Reproductive functions denigrated	Reproductive functions celebrated
Culture, Family, Social Structure	Patrilineal descent	Matrilineal descent
	Patrilocal marital household	Matrilocal marital household
	Compulsive lifelong monogamy	Noncompulsive monogamy
	Often polygamous	Rarely polygamous
	Authoritarian	Democratic
	Hierarchical	Egalitarian
	Political/economic centralism	Work-democratic
	Military specialists or caste	No full time military
	Violent, sadistic	Nonviolent, absence of sadism
Religion:	Male/father oriented	Female/mother oriented
	Asceticism, avoidance of pleasure, pain-seeking	Pleasure welcomed and institutionalized
	Inhibition, fear of nature	Spontaneity, nature worshiped
	Full-time religious specialists	No full-time religious specialists
	Male shamans/healers	Male or female shamans/healers
	Strict behavior codes	Absence of strict codes

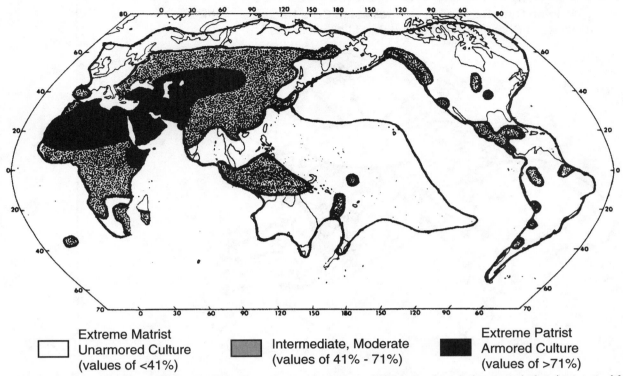

Figure 1: The World Behavior Map (Detailed in Chapters 3, 4 and 5 of *Saharasia*[2])

For the period roughly between 1840 and 1960, as reconstructed from aboriginal cultural data.

☐ Extreme Matrist Unarmored Culture (values of <41%)

▨ Intermediate, Moderate (values of 41% - 71%)

■ Extreme Patrist Armored Culture (values of >71%)

The Percent-Patrist values were composed from an index of 15 different cultural characteristics (extracted from a longer list of 63 similar factors already showing a high degree of correlation). Regions with a high degree of patrism are defined by the presence of: Female Premarital Sex Taboo, Segregation of Adolescent Boys, Male Genital Mutilations, High Bride Price, Polygamous Family Organization, Patrilocal Marital Residence, Patrilineal Descent (without Cognatic Kin Groups), Patrilineal Land Inheritance, Patrilineal Movable Property Inheritance, High God, Class Stratification, Caste Stratification, and Slavery. Regions possessing few of these traits were defined as predominantly matrist in character, while intermediate regions possessed a mix of both matrist and patrist traits.

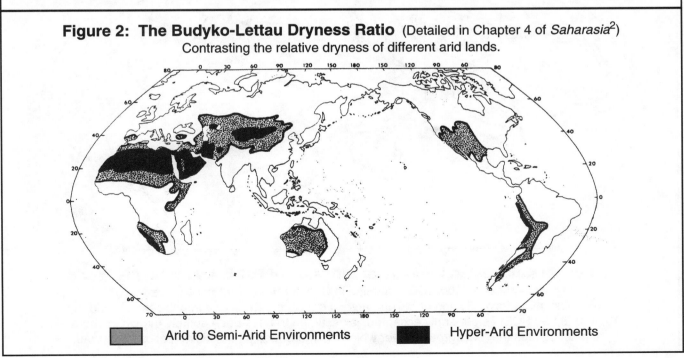

Figure 2: The Budyko-Lettau Dryness Ratio (Detailed in Chapter 4 of *Saharasia*[2])

Contrasting the relative dryness of different arid lands.

▨ Arid to Semi-Arid Environments   ■ Hyper-Arid Environments

Figure 3: Generalized Paths of Diffusion of Armored Human Culture (Patrism) in the Old World, *after* c.4000 BCE.
1. Arabian Core Region 2. Central Asian Core Region
(Detailed in Chapters 4 and 5, and Part III of *Saharasia*[2])

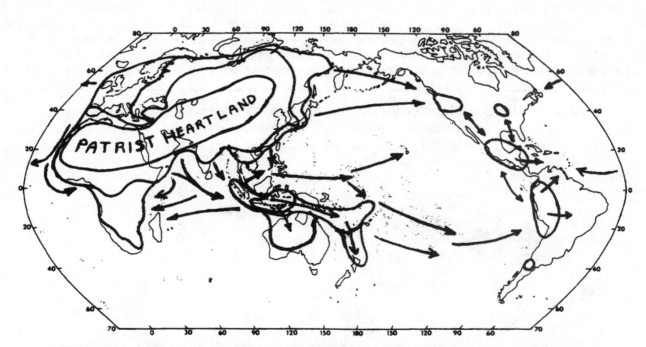

Figure 4: Suggested Patterns of Diffusion of Patrism Around the World
Starting after c.4000 BCE. (Detailed in Chapter 5 and Part III of *Saharasia*[2])
The earliest migratory diffusion of culture, across the Bering Strait and into the New World from
c.18,000 - 8,000 BCE, as generally accepted, is assumed to have been entirely matrist in character,
and constitutes the "background" over which the more recent patristic migrations occurred.

Additionally, I developed a new archaeological-historical data base, which when mapped showed a very strong correlation between the first drying-up of Saharasia around 4000-3500 BCE, to the general origins of human social violence — the earliest regions to dry up within Saharasia, notably in Arabia and Central Asia and their immediate peripheries, showed some of the earliest clear and unambiguous signs of social violence apparent in the archaeological record. Figures 3 and 4 present the maps as derived from the archaeological and historical materials.[2,3]

In *Saharasia*, I made the following argument: Human violence and warfare were the products of social institutions which inflicted great pain and trauma upon infants and children, as well as intensive repressive sex-frustration within the adult world, giving rise to sadistic impulses which were then channeled back into those same social institutions. Painful trauma and sex-repression experienced by children within such armored-patristic societies was adapted to and psychologically defended, and hence repetitively inflicted upon each new generation as "tradition" by the older generations. Drought and famine, extremely traumatic and deadly by themselves, were the triggers which drove previously peaceful unarmored-matristic human social groups towards increasingly disturbed and violent-sadistic behaviors, whereupon new social institutions appeared to guarantee their persistence, even under moist environmental conditions of food abundance.[1,2]

At the time when I undertook the basic research for *Saharasia*, a review of available archaeological materials demonstrated only a few regions in the Middle East, ranging from Anatolia into the Levant, and as far south as Jericho, possessed "fleeting glimpses" of violence prior to my marker date of c.4000 BCE. These unclear traces of violence appeared to begin around 5000 BCE, but were also timed to sub-phases of drought, aridity and land-abandonment, suggesting a similar drought-desert causation for the genesis of violence as was presented and argued for the post-4000 BCE event. The drying up of Saharasia after c.4000 BCE was, I argued, *the most significant climatological change which occurred on planet Earth following the end of the last Ice Age* (which ended around 10-8,000 BCE). In any case, at the time, according to the knowledge at hand, it appeared that neither drought nor violent episodes starting at the earlier date of c.5000 BCE were widespread, continuous, or persistent in the archaeological record. Only after c.4000-3500 BCE did drought and violence grip entire regions across the whole of Saharasia, a situation which I argued has lasted over 6,000 years, to be expressed in the more recent anthropological data as seen in the World Behavior Map. Archaeology, history and anthropology all presented mutually agreeable and reinforcing patterns on the world maps.

The exacting details of my Saharasia discovery with full citations has already been peer-reviewed and published.[2,3] Aside from these introductory notes, I shall assume the reader has a general familiarity with the earlier findings and underlying theory.

New Evidence For Ancient Violence

By 1999, I was alerted to new archaeological findings and books which *claimed* evidence for ancient human violence dating to well before c.4000 BCE. The book *War Before Civilization*[4] by Lawrence Keeley, is perhaps the most representative and widely-quoted example of this new genre of books, which basically argue for the innate, genetic or human evolutionary causation of war and violence, in opposition to the environmental-social-emotional causation argued in my *Saharasia*. Keeley's book laid down two basic arguments.

Argument One: *Intertribal warfare of an extreme and ruthless quality, as well as social-familial violence, existed among so-called "primitive" cultures long before the arrival of European colonials.* To this argument, I give a qualified agreement. In *Saharasia,* I cited some of the same evidence noted by Keeley, such as the butchery and despotism present among the New World Aztec, Inca, and Maya culture, long before the arrival of Columbus, Cortez or Pizarro. Likewise, the despotic nature and savagery of some African and Asian cultures were detailed in *Saharasia*, well back into history and prior to any contacts with the oftentimes equally despotic and savage Europeans. The findings on this point, in both my *Saharasia* and Keeley's *War Before Civilization* defeated many widespread myths about the supposed "peaceful" nature of "primitive man", "living in harmony with nature" — certainly, there are many well-documented cases of violence and organized warfare among isolated "primitive" tribal groups. This was never in question. However, unlike my *Saharasia*, Keeley presented these examples in such a manner as to mischaracterize *all* primitive cultures as carrying the seeds of violence. And so I do object to making any kind of widespread and global extrapolation of these signs of violence among *some* aboriginal cultures as "proof" of an *assumed* but unproven ubiquitous violence among all cultures, in all regions, at all times. Also, the authors taking this line of argument almost always fail to take a genuine cross-cultural approach, and rarely openly address the various *peaceful aboriginal societies* as documented in various anthropological studies from the late 1800s and early 1900s, as detailed in my *Saharasia*. As a consequence, this first argument of Keeley did not undermine or challenge my work in any manner. In fact, some of the archaeological evidence cited by Keeley and others for violence among ancient peoples of the New World — and which *I did not cite or know about until after completion of Saharasia* — were located almost precisely in those regions where my World Behavior Map predicted such evidence might be found. More on this last point is given below. With confidence, I can therefore report, archaeological evidence on the question of "primitive violence" in more recent times, but prior to the epoch of European colonialism, provides excellent additional supporting evidence for Saharasian theory.

Argument Two: *Archaeological evidence for warfare and massacres exist in some very old archaeological sites, as early as 12,000 BCE, well before my c.4000 BCE marker date.* Keeley and other authors on the subject specifically mention ancient fortifications and graveyards filled with victims of violent deaths, well before c.4000 BCE. These archaeological reports superficially appear to provide a serious challenge to Saharasian theory, mainly because of the early dates. However, a close look at the original citations from the archaeologists who did the field work, and from those who are intimately familiar with the details, resolves the question in favor of the environmental-social-emotional causation implicit in Saharasian theory.

To better understand the context and specific details of these new archaeological findings gathered by Keeley and others for violence and warfare prior to c.4000 BCE, I shall explicitly address the major points of evidence.

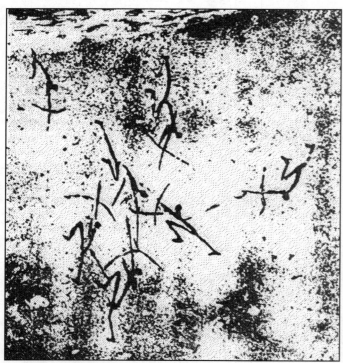

Spanish Archers, rock art from Morella la Villa, Castellon, dated to "late Neolithic" (c.3000 BCE?)[5] Hunters in a ceremonial dance, or warriors in a battle? None of the figures appear injured or dead, and archaeology of the region does not support the idea of warfare at this early period. Similar rock art in Australia, claimed as evidence of violence, is even more abstract and ambiguous.[7]

Spanish and Australian Rock Art: Dancing or Fighting?

Keeley and others have often cited an article "The Beginnings of Warfare" by Trevor Watkins[5] to support the idea of a very ancient violent humanity. But Watkins does not provide such support. Watkins says: *"The origins of warfare are hidden in the mists of human prehistory, but by 1200 BC there was a long tradition of armies, campaigns, pitched battles and siege warfare".*[5] It is quite a leap from "prehistory" to 1200 BC, and the latter date would surely be in good agreement with the chronology for first-origins of violence published in *Saharasia.* Watkins also stated, after a long discussion of human hunting skills and tools:

"The difficulty lies in recognizing whether a heavy arrowhead or a large spearhead, superbly and skillfully chipped from flint, was used for the hunt or as a weapon in fighting among humans. Only in one or two rare examples of later rock-art from south-east Spain are there pictorial references to the use of bows and arrows in conflicts between groups of people. Even then one is entitled to ask if what we are shown is a skirmish between rival bands or serious, organized warfare."[5]

I would amplify this qualification to seriously question if the rock art depicts a battle at all, as it can equally be interpreted as a scene of hunters engaged in a ceremonial dance of some sort, possibly in preparation for a hunt. Without some other evidence of violence in this same region, such as fortifications or skeletons with imbedded arrowheads, the Spanish rock art can only be viewed ambiguously.

Even so, if we give the benefit of the doubt to those who argue the Spanish rock art are battle scenes, it still would appear to be in agreement with the chronologies for first-origins of violence as given in *Saharasia.* There is only one undated rock-art reproduction in Watkins' article, from Morella la Villa, Castellon; a wider selection of similar rock art of the period is found in the work by Beltran, *Rock Art of the Spanish Levant,*[6] and it does contain a few scenes which are more supportive of the argument for group violence — as with the claimed "battle scene" at the Les Dogues site — but even here, the art may only record a village dance anticipating or celebrating a hunt. Whether violent, or not, it is reasonable to assume nearly all of this Spanish rock art is "late hunter-gatherer" period, approximating the "late Neolithic" identified in *Saharasia,* which would date the artwork no earlier than c.3000 BCE, well into the epoch of intense desertification which gripped North Africa.

Rock art depicting highly stylized and abstracted humans has been found in northern Australia,[7] dated as far back as c.8000 BCE, but the Australian images are even more ambiguous. Rock art which is so intensively stylized and abstract, such that even the simple form of a human being is difficult to make out from the drawings, where a specialist is required to point out what is a head or arm or torso, cannot be easily held up to conclude much of anything — especially when a simple line bisecting such a drawing is then interpreted as a "spear". To my knowledge the Australian scenes have not been matched to evidence of violence in skeletal remains in the region at those early dates. Below, some discussion will be given to the issue of confirmed interpersonal violence among ancient Australians in more southerly regions, also at very early dates — but significantly, only in relationship to a period of intense aridity and probable episodic famine.

Jericho, Catal Huyuk and Anatolia: Occasional and Discontinuous Violence in a Region of Early Drought and Desertification

Two of the earliest cities, Jericho and Catal Huyuk, are often misrepresented as having been subject to episodes of warfare during their earliest occupation layers, which have been dated to c.8350 BCE and c.6500 BCE respectively. Both had early enclosure walls which have sometimes been argued as evidence for fortifications — but without other evidence to support the existence of warfare, this interpretation is not warranted: the walls could just as easily have been for corralling and protecting domestic animals from roaming lions, hyenas or other large deadly or nuisance predators which are known to have inhabited those regions.

As discussed in *Saharasia,* the earliest evidence for social violence appears in Catal Huyuk and other Anatolian sites only temporarily, during a period of drought and attendant social decline, at around c.5200 BCE.[8] Drought and violence spread across Anatolia, Syria and the Levant *as a dominant and unrelenting social character only after c.5000-4300 BCE*, and Catal Huyuk was only finally destroyed after c.4800 BCE. This is close to the time of the world's first documented fortress, at Mersin, which was destroyed around 4300 BCE.[9]

The successive settlements and abandonments of Jericho were also timed to episodes of drought and land-abandonment across the wider territory, and there are walls and towers apparent at the site very early in its history. However, the earliest walls could have been for containing or protecting domesticated animals from predators, or possibly to protect against water and mud flows during heavy rains. The large circular tower of Jericho is one widely-noted bit of archaeology which is claimed to be "proof" of warfare, given its obvious similarities to towers found on genuine defensive fortifications elsewhere at later dates. However, a tower by itself does not warfare make. It could just as easily have been a lookout for predatory animals, or for long distance signaling.[10,11]

Jericho did eventually develop clearly defensive fortification walls, towers, and tombs for possible "kings", constituting some of the earliest evidence anywhere for possible conflict and social stratification.[11] However, like Catal Huyuk, Jericho's architecture does not prove itself to be the product of a social response to violent conditions, at least not until much later in the archaeological sequence, during periods of relatively harsh environmental conditions. Only then does the architecture take on a fortress-like quality, and unambiguously serve the purpose of protection against human attacks. Roper provided support for this viewpoint, stating that no signs of violence could be found at early Jericho, aside from the ambiguous walls and tower.[9]

Archaeologist Bar-Yosef made an extensive evaluation of early Jericho and came to basically the same conclusions,[12] additionally finding *an absence of evidence for warfare in the entire Near East region between 12,000 - 6,000 BCE*. While hunting technology was well developed, evidence for warfare could not be found.

Ancient ruin of Jericho (above top) and its Neolithic tower (bottom). Construction features such as towers and enclosure walls are not, by themself, evidence of warfare or social violence. Large walls can be impounds for domesticated cattle, or protections against water and mud flows during rainy periods, while observation towers have many civil purposes. (from Kenyon[11])

In *Saharasia* I acknowledge the early evidence at Jericho and surrounding regions, stating:

"[Early] Jericho was deserted by c.7500 BCE... [leaving] no traces of violence at the site...[and this was] connected with the increasing aridity of the area. ...the evidence at Jericho appears to reflect the unique geography of the city at a time when temporary local or regional desiccation was occurring... Only fleeting visions of military conflict, fortifications, social stratification or cranial deformation occur in the Near East before c.5000 BCE, appearing here and there at isolated sites, and without any clear pattern or widespread distribution.... It is only after c.4000 BCE when desiccation became more widespread and intense that these initial traces of disturbed human behavior begin to blossom in clear, unambiguous and often organized institutional forms." [10]

Watkins also mentioned a clay sling-shot found at Catal Huyuk, and clustered buildings with rooftop entries and other factors which he interpreted as evidence for violence and warfare — but as discussed in *Saharasia*, James Mellaart, the man who excavated Catal Huyuk, viewed the same evidence firsthand and came to nearly opposite conclusions.[13]

It will be useful to review one of the original tables from *Saharasia* (Table 2, below), giving general dates for the onset of desert conditions, and the onset of first-evidence for patrism and violence. The Middle East, Anatolia, Iran, and Soviet Central Asia show their earliest signs of climatic degradation towards aridity at c.5000 BCE. Jericho was affected by these oscillatory environmental pressures much earlier, perhaps as a chronic feature of its unique geography, close to the Dead Sea and Jordan Valley.[10,11] The arguments presented in *Saharasia* therefore anticipate some discontinuous and episodic signs of social turmoil and conflict starting at those same dates, but without persisting or widespread effects.

European Causewayed Encampments

Keeley also argued a whole series of causewayed encampments which existed across Western and Central Europe were unambiguous "fortifications", mixing up the dates of *first habitation* with the appearance of *first violence* without careful reference. In short, he *extrapolated the violence backward in time,* without evidence for doing so. The archaeologists who excavated these encampments were not convinced the earliest habitations had any clear war-defensive functions. They were composed of concentric rings of shallow earth hills and trenches posing no significant obstacle to climb — with only about one meter distance between hilltops and trench-bottoms — which were also repeatedly broken with wide openings or "causeways" to facilitate the free passage of people in and out of those encampments, from the periphery all the way into the core. They appeared more in the manner of an unusual village architecture with mounds for privacy screens or trenches for animal corrals, allowing for separate family encampments. They appear to have served the functions of a central place for trading and seasonal gatherings, and in some cases as cemeteries. Later in the archaeological sequences, many of these encampments were raided by warriors using bows and arrows, and the battle-axe. Only then were the encampments transformed into closed defensive fortifications which rapidly were destroyed and/or abandoned.

While Keeley variously mentioned dates of "5000 BC" or "4000 BC" for the appearance of violence at these sites, my own review of his cited references could not confirm such early dates. As best as I have been able to determine, from various reports published in many

---

Table 2: Summary of Dates for Ecological and Cultural Change:
(From Chapter 8 of Saharasia[2], page 365)

Location	Onset of Desiccation	Onset of Major Patrist Phase
North Africa (West)	c.3000 BCE	c.2600-500 BCE
North Africa (East)	c.3000 BCE	c.3100 BCE
Arabia	c.4000 BCE	c.4000-3500 BCE
Levant/Mesopotamia	c.5000-2500 BCE*	c.3500-2500 BCE
Anatolia	c.5000-2000 BCE*	c.4000-3500 BCE
Iran	c.5000-2000 BCE*	c.4000-3000 BCE
Soviet Cent. Asia	c.5000-3500 BCE*	c.4000-3500 BCE
West China	c.3000-2000 BCE	c.2000 BCE
Indus Valley	c.2000 BCE	c.2000 BCE

* Oscillatory and regionally-isolated climate changes,
with the most intense aridity occurring after c.4000 BCE

different languages, the earliest violence is documented at those encampments farthest to the east, as in Bavaria (c.3200 BC) followed by later conflicts in France and Denmark (c.2800 BC), followed lastly by conflicts in England (c.2600 BCE) — if true, this would be excellent *confirmation for Saharasia*, suggesting the arrival of violent invaders from Anatolia or Central Asia, moving on a Westerly migration route. Details on a few of these specific sites will be given momentarily.

The primary source for the "causewayed encampments" is: *Enclosures and Defences in the Neolithic of Western Europe*, edited by Colin Burgess, et al.[14] The various contributing authors, all of whom were field archaeologists who excavated these sites, pointed to the general dates given above for the first onset of violent conditions. Evans has given a general overview of the causewayed enclosures:

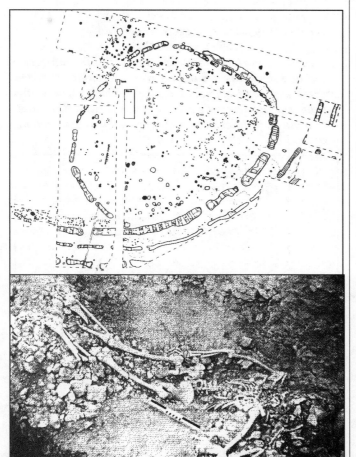

Hambledon Hill Stepleton Enclosure, Dorset, England (Top) the earliest such enclosure in the British isles, dating to c.3500 BCE. Bottom: Skeleton of a man, shot in the back with an arrow, with child, preserved under a collapsed and burned wall dating to c.2680 BCE, the earliest evidence for social violence in the UK. (from Mercer [17])

"Few monument forms have undergone such frequent radical re-assessment in their interpretation. Even now, after twenty-one examples have been excavated, they still stubbornly frustrate neat categorisation, and we are left with the impression of the blind men encountering the elephant... Unlike other major 'ritual' sites of the third and second millennia bc, the status of causewayed enclosures as 'monuments' has been somewhat ambiguous; their morphology would link them superficially with both henges and hillforts, yet their segmented ditches have led to doubts about their defensive capability..." [15]

In speaking about "The Neolithic Höhensiedlungen (high settlements) of Central Germany", Starling states:

"It is suggested that these sites were the communal foci of groups who used them for a variety of symbolic and practical activities, rather than centres of political and territorial control." [16]

We can review the archaeology at a few of these sites:

<u>Hambledon Hill, Dorset England</u> is considered to be the oldest causewayed enclosure in England dating to around 3500 BCE. It was located close to a river system connecting to the sea, suggestive of an optimal location for trading of regional agricultural and other goods by boat. Archaeologist Mercer stated:

"About sixty [enclosures] are now known to exist within the southern half of England, and they range in size from about 1 - 60 hectares and in location from seasonally waterlogged valley bottom sites to sites set on hilltop and promontory positions... from single ditched enclosures to sites with up to five concentric rings of ditches with...a wide range of function. As a class of site, however, they are united by one idiosyncratic constructional feature - the ditches consistently appear to be 'causewayed' or interrupted at frequent and irregular intervals, in a manner that suggests that they were not conceived by their builders as barriers in their own right but simply as a linear quarry for the construction of an internal bank or rampart." [17]

The Hambledon site was progressively transformed into a fortification, its ditches containing macabre evidence of corpse disposal, with human skulls set upright along periphery.[17] Also, many bones of young children were found in one section, giving the overall impression of slaughter and mayhem. The site was finally destroyed by fire during an attack by archers, with an arrowhead in one skeleton of a man carrying a child, found under a collapsed building wall. There is no question, this site showed violent events taking place.

But at what dates? Carbon material found in trenches, which contained a vertical mixture of materials from different settlement periods, were dated by radiocarbon at 2610 BC, 2730 BC and 2890 BC, with errors of +/-150 years. Other radiocarbon dates were recorded at 2530 BC, 2650 BC and 2720 BC, with errors of +/- 130 years.[17] This is a rough average of 2686 BC, which suggests

Hambledon Hill experienced perhaps *a thousands years of peaceful habitation before the unambiguous appearance of warfare.*

Crickley Hill, Glouchester England was first occupied in the "early Neolithic". The archaeologist Dixon reported the earliest occupation had a series of mounds organized into rings, with shallow trenches and causeways leading into the interior. No artifacts of any kind were found in those earliest phases. At the final enclosure (phase 1d) there were larger ditches with fenced roads leading into the interior. Dixon reports:

"The fate of this final enclosure was clearly shown by the thick spread of flint arrowheads, over 400 of which choked the eastern entrance passageways and fanned out along the roadways into the interior. The enclosure had quite obvious been defended against archery attack..."[18]

After this attack, there was erected

"... a 70m long track leading up to a circular platform inside the enclosure, totally flat and clear of structures except at edges... we may consider it to have been the settlement's shrine" (p.84) and *"Like the Danish examples, the Crickley shrine was burnt down."*[18]

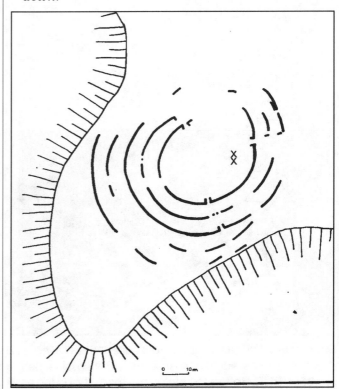

Crickley Hill, England (Top). Wide "causeways" allow free movement from the periphery to the core of the settlement. Constructed in the early Neolithic (c.3000 BCE?), it was attacked and eventually destroyed between c.2000-1000 BCE. Bottom: Distribution of arrowheads from an assault dated after c.2000 BCE. (from Andersen[18])

DISTRIBUTION OF LEAF ARROWHEADS

Causewayed Enclosure, Schalkenberg, Quenstedt, Germany, dated to c.3300 BCE. Sites in Bavaria have C14 dates of burning and abandonment ranging between c.3000 - 2000 BCE. (from Starling[16])

Clearly, this is evidence of warfare and violence — but at what date? Dixon says:

"The date of the end of the ritual phase 1e is still uncertain, though radiocarbon dates may eventually provide a guide. It occurred before the building of the hillfort, the latter perhaps early in the first millennium BC"[18]

This is the only mention of a date in the entire excavation report, but clearly demonstrates a very long period of peaceful conditions, from the "early Neolithic" (c.3000 BCE?) until the appearance of violence sometime after c.2000 BCE, with its final destruction after c.1000 BCE.[18]

A large number of similar causewayed enclosures are found scattered across continental Europe, as far east as Germany, all with generally similar architectures and probable social functions. As best as I can determine, all show peaceful conditions at their earliest dates of construction, with violence appearing only later on, in keeping with the generalized dates given in Saharasia for the onset of violence in Europe.

Keeley, in his book, simply identified the approximate dates when these causewayed encampments were firstly constructed, and without clarifications left the reader with the clear impression those were the dates when violence first occurred. However, the dates for the onset of violence were in fact as I have given them above in these representative examples.

It should also be mentioned, that the Spanish rock-art depicting an apparent archery battle, mentioned above and identified with the "late Neolithic" or "late hunter-gatherer" period, may be chronologically connected to the same appearance of violence in the above causewayed encampments. Again, this is all support for the chronology and geography of violence as given in Saharasia.

Talheim, Schletz and Ofnet Cave, Germany: Massacres or Skull Burial Customs?

A collection of 50 human skeletons with evidence of trauma injuries was found at the Schletz site, dating to c.4000 BCE by radiocarbon determination. Another collection of 34 skeletons but with contradictory dates (of c.5500 to 4000 BCE depending upon dating method) was excavated at Talheim.[20,21,22] It appears likely, these people were in fact massacred, as determined from many trauma blows, and the haphazard manner in which the bodies were heaped into a shallow ditch. The dates suggest they may be connected with the social disruptions which led to the destruction of the causewayed encampments across Germany and the rest of Europe. The ambiguity in dating on these sites appears as a consequence of different dates being estimated by different researchers, and by different results being obtained from different radiocarbon laboratories. This problem also appears to affect the Ofnet site, as discussed below.

The Ofnet Cave in Bavaria is one of the most widely-cited "proofs" of early evidence for social violence. Claims have been made the site is proof of a single massacre, with the possible taking of heads as trophies of war.[4,21,23] From reading such accounts one would never know

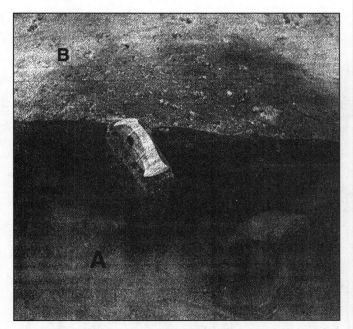

Battle-Axe at Causewayed Enclosure Camp in Sarup, Funen, Denmark. The lower part of the excavation (labeled A) is dated to c.3500 BCE, suggesting a more recent date for the upper strata (B) containing the battle-axe. (from Andersen[19])

Massacre at Talheim, Germany, dated between c.5500-4000 BCE. (from Bahn[20])

there were dissenting voices on the subject. The original excavation was undertaken in 1912 by Schmidt,[24] with all subsequent discussions on the finds focusing upon the remains of the skulls themselves. Grahame Clark described the site as follows:

"A more specialized form of collective burial is implied by nests of skulls found in caves and rockshelters in south Germany, notably at Ofnet and Kaufertsberg near Nördlingen and at Hohlestein, Lonetal, near Ulm. Signs of cutting on the upper neck vertebrae suggest that the skulls had been detached from their trunks shortly after death. Their numbers, one nest at Ofnet comprising twenty-seven and another six skulls suggest that they relate to social groups comprising in all probability a number of hunting bands. Again their condition, those in the middle showing signs of having been pushed together and those on the periphery relatively intact and undisturbed, argues that, as in the later chamber tombs, they had been buried over a period of time." [25]

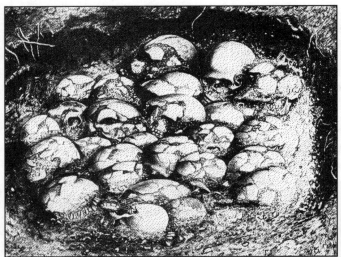

Ofnet Skull Nest, Germany, misrepresented as a group massacre, actually appears as a site for sequential skull burials which included grave offerings. (from Schmidt[24])

Neolithic Skull Burials from Jericho, evidence of a burial custom, not massacres. (from Clarke[25])

The Ofnet skulls — composed of four male, seven female, and 15 children — were coated with red ochre, and accompanied by personal ornaments and microliths. No mention of a violent massacre was made by Clark.[25] A more recent study of the skeletal materials by Jörg Orschiedt of the Archaeological Institute at the University of Hamburg confirms not only the *sequential* burial of the crania, but also refutes the theory of violence for all except a small sample of the skulls.

"A reexamination of the skulls from the Ofnet cave in southwest Germany showed that these and similar deposits should be understood as the expression of a special burial custom rather than head hunting practices from the late mesolithic. ... the reduction of group sizes in the late mesolithic as well as the demographic structure makes it unlikely that this deposit was a single event. The site was used several times as a burial place. As grave goods perforated canines of red deer and shells, probably necklaces, were placed on or around the heads. Red ochre was found around the heads and in the filling of the pits. The reexamination of the traumatic lesions on the Ofnet skulls showed that at least only six individuals had died from fatal blows. These heads were deposited on the northwestern rim of the larger skull pit and could possible represent a single event. The injuries were caused by a blunt, axe-shaped object. Most of the injuries are located in the occipital area. The only exception are two male individuals with several traumatic lesions which occur also on the parietal and frontal areas." [26,27]

Skulls on display in Hallstatt, Austria, in an old church.

These descriptions considerably tame down the descriptions of "massacre at Ofnet" from 32 individuals to a maximum of six.

The concept of skull-burial as a funeral custom, it must be noted, has a long history extending to sites beyond only Ofnet. Skull burials were found in Jericho, unrelated to any kind of violent death.[11,25] The city of Hallstatt, Austria, still has a display of hundreds of decorated skulls in a small church (now a museum) which the author visited most recently, evidencing a burial custom which ended only in the 1960s.

And what of the date for the Ofnet cave? Several radiocarbon dates of c.11,000 BCE were obtained in the 1980s, but these are today rejected in favor of newer dates of around 5500 BCE, obtained with newer methods said to be more accurate.[26,27] Assuming the six crania mentioned by Orschiedt were factually the consequence of deaths by violence, the date of c.5500 BCE would still place them too early to be explained by any invasion of warrior groups out of Central Asia, being abandoned around 4000 BCE under the pressures of desertification. We might postulate some kind of migratory invasion from Anatolia, bringing social violence into Europe from that region at c.5500 BCE, but to my knowledge there is no evidence supporting this, and no other sites as early as Ofnet which support the idea. However, a great deal hinges on the issue of chronology.

If Talheim and Schletz are interpreted at the younger end of their chronologies, that is closer to c.4000 BCE, then they would fall into the general dates for the arrival of Central Asian, battle-axe and Kurgan peoples, who devastated the causewayed enclosures and wreaked havoc across Europe — discussed in *Saharasia*. This would leave only the Ofnet site as a riddle, falling outside the bounds of Saharasian chronology for the first-origins of violence in Europe. We might ask, why the original radiocarbon dates of 11,000 BCE have been rejected in favor of newer ones at c.5500 BCE? Given the problems which afflict radiometric dating methods, rendering them imprecise and sometimes questionable, might the c.5500 BCE date also be too old?[§] If we assume these sites occurred at the older end of their proposed chronologies, at c.5500 BCE, then they would not yet be explainable within the context of Saharasian

theory.

The geographical placement of the Ofnet site, in relative close proximity to the Talheim and Schletz sites, nevertheless suggests a regional clustering of deadly events which, irrespective of chronology, are highly anomalistic and isolated in character, occurring as they do against a larger background of peaceful conditions across the wider geography of Europe for the greater part of prehistory. Only punctuated examples of violence seem to have occurred.

Ambiguous Evidence for Early Violence in China

Keeley also mentions skeletal remains in China for "very early violence", but again, the original archaeological report in question tends to undermine this interpretation, and confirm *Saharasia*. Underhill has written on the subject of warfare in Neolithic China,[28] and was cited by Keeley for his "early China violence" assertion. Underhill did discuss the finding of a skeleton of a man with an arrowhead in his thigh, dated to around c.5000 BCE, and found buried in a *Yangshao* archaeological strata, which is generally acknowledged to hold no clear or unambiguous evidence for warfare or violence. This single skeleton is the only recorded case of a Yangshao skeleton with an imbedded projectile point, to my knowledge, and the site where it was found holds *no other evidence for war or violence*. Taken together, the evidence suggests a hunting accident. This idea was also considered by the field archaeologists and written into their report, but was not mentioned by Keeley.

Underhill also presented a chart for "defensive structures" in Neolithic China, and specifically identified two in the Yangshao period (before c.2500 BCE). However, both were marked as having a "debatable defensive function" — both were mere ditches surrounding habitations, or segments of ditches "possibly" joined by palisade-style fences. These are not conclusive by any means, and are at best ambiguous evidence for warfare and violence. One must ask, if these people had permanent settlements and domesticated animals, where did they keep them if not inside such an enclosed compound?

Later evidence for warfare in China is unambiguous. In discussing the subsequent *Longshan* culture, Underhill describes "...*evidence for a degree of violence not present during the pre-Longshan period.*"[28] These include grave evidence for mass executions, amputations, scalping, hacking of the limbs, and battle deaths, along with various weaponry (including jade battle-axes) not found in earlier times. Also present during the Longshan were child-sacrifice under or near foundations of buildings. Underhill also gives a chart identifying weapons found in various archaeological sites, such as axes, knives, spearheads, and arrowheads.[28] The earliest of this evidence is dated to c.2700-2100 BCE, and comes from Anyang, home of the earliest totalitar-

---

§ The "correction" of the original radiocarbon dates for the Ofnet skulls from 11,000 BCE down to 5500 BCE, is suggestive of problems in the basic assumptions and methodology of radiometric dating. If today the dates are revised to a younger age by more than 5000 years, then tomorrow it would not be surprising to see the same skulls re-dated once again, perhaps closer to the period of Kurgan invasions into Europe (c.3500 BCE)? If so, then virtually *all* of the unambiguous evidence for violence across Europe would appear as the product of a single major social transformation consequent to the drying-up of Saharasia.[2,3] See the Appended "Note of Caution About Radiometric Dating Methods", on p.42-44.

ian Chinese society (Shang Dynasty), which was formed by invaders from the western, desertified regions of Central Asia.

All of these findings are in good agreement with what has already been written in *Saharasia*,[2] on p.345-348. The transition time from generally peaceful conditions to intensive warfare in China of c.2500 BCE given by Underhill, is in approximate agreement with my own figures for the first-time arrival of violence in Western China.

Jebel Sahaba, Egypt: Unambiguous Evidence for Social Violence and Warfare/Murder During an Early Period of Intensive Aridity

The ancient cemetery at Jebel Sahaba, on the desert highland plateau overlooking the Nile River Valley in Egypt, contains over 50 persons who were victims of a massacre, shot up with projectile points and showing other signs of violent death. The violence is unquestionable, and in Saharasia I had relied upon the chronological discussion by Michael Hoffman in his *Egypt Before the Pharaohs*,[29] which in keeping with other signs of violence in the region I had gathered, allowed placing Jebel Sahaba at c.4500 BCE.

Fred Wendorf's *Prehistory of Nubia*[30] presented the original field archaeological reports, which ambiguously placed the site between 12,000 BCE all the way down to 5000 or even 4500 BCE, based upon similarities between the flint projectile points imbedded in the skeletons to Qadan-era stone tools found at nearby

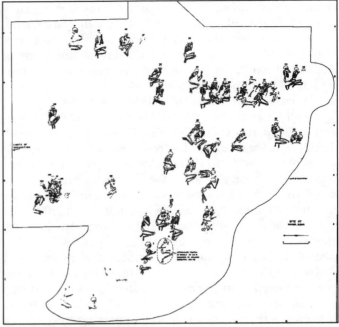

Jebel Sahaba Cemetery, unambiguous evidence of social violence and murder or warfare on the village level, during an epoch of intense aridity. (reproduced courtesy of Fred Wendorf, from the *Prehistory of Nubia*)[30]

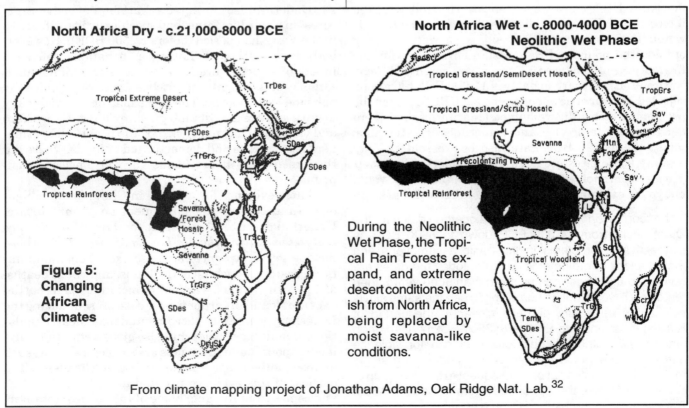

North Africa Dry - c.21,000-8000 BCE

Figure 5: Changing African Climates

North Africa Wet - c.8000-4000 BCE Neolithic Wet Phase

During the Neolithic Wet Phase, the Tropical Rain Forests expand, and extreme desert conditions vanish from North Africa, being replaced by moist savanna-like conditions.

From climate mapping project of Jonathan Adams, Oak Ridge Nat. Lab.[32]

Figure 6: Histogram of North African Basin Wet Phase C-14 Dates. The period between c.8000-3000 BCE (or c.10,000-5000 BP) had the greatest frequency of high or intermediate lake levels. The data suggests, the period before 8000 BCE (or 10,000 BP) was as dry or drier than conditions of today. Locations of the lakes are indicated on the map. (After Nicholson, in *Saharasia*,[2] p.221)

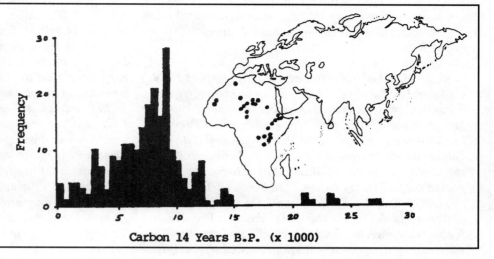

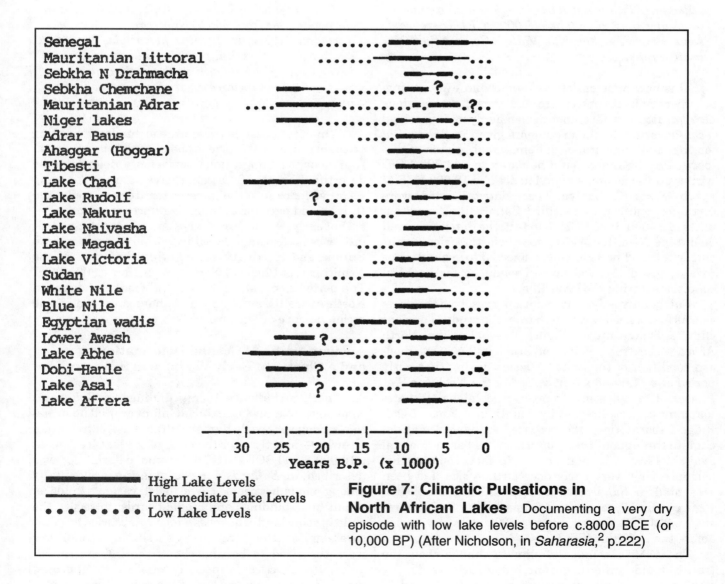

| High Lake Levels |
| Intermediate Lake Levels |
| Low Lake Levels |

Figure 7: Climatic Pulsations in North African Lakes Documenting a very dry episode with low lake levels before c.8000 BCE (or 10,000 BP) (After Nicholson, in *Saharasia*,[2] p.222)

sites. Wendorf originally openly expressed concerns about the ambiguous dates, but only in more recent years have radiocarbon evaluations been undertaken of the skeletons themselves. He discussed the newer findings, as follows:

"The Jebel Sahaba skeletons have only one post 1968 C14 date of 13,700 bp [11,700 BCE] on collagen from a human femur. It is discussed in the Conclusions to our book on Wadi Kubbaniya (1989) SMU Press. I wish we had more dates, but this agrees well with the Gadan artifacts imbedded in the skeletons. In 1968 the Gadan was not well dated, but subsequent work places that industry between 14,000 and 12,000 bp [12,000-10,000 BCE]. This was not the oldest evidence of violence in the Nile Valley. The Wadi Kubbaniya skeleton had a healed parry fracture, a partially healed wound with point imbedded in right humorous, and two points in the lower abdomen that killed him. This is dated by geology and the artifacts at greater than 20,000 bp [18,000 BCE]. There was some violence in the Nile Valley. Competition for limited resources?" [31]

This new information was somewhat eye-opening, as superficially it appeared to challenge the conclusions of *Saharasia* — in fact, upon deeper analysis, it provided a *confirmation* for the arguments given in *Saharasia*, for the environmental-social-emotional origins of violence. Jebel Sahaba could be dated to c.11,700 BCE, with yet other evidences for violence at c.18,000 BCE at nearby Wadi Kubbaniya. These dates, I noted, were certainly before my identified Saharasian transition dates of c.4000-3500 BCE — in fact, the dates were well before the Neolithic Wet Phase of North Africa, occurring at a time I had not even subjected to evaluation or review, given the widespread evidence for peaceful conditions during that Wet Phase.

Further investigation eventually resolved the question as follows: New research from the study of ancient climates is presented in Figure 5, revealing that North Africa was extremely dry and arid, similar to the modern condition of the Sahara Desert during that early period of c.21,000-8000 BCE, *before* the Neolithic Wet Phase. The maps are from a larger global climate-mapping project directed by Jonathan Adams of Oak Ridge Laboratories, who prepared sequential maps of climate throughout the Quaternary, as based upon all available scientific evidence. [32] In fact, some of this evidence for a very early dry North Africa had been presented in *Saharasia*, though without discussion. Figures 6 and 7, reproduced from Chapter 8 of Saharasia, [2] p.221-222, depict this pre-8000 BCE dry period before the Neolithic Wet Phase.

These African maps of climate change show the transitions identified in graphs, but not discussed in my *Saharasia* research, regarding a very dry period in

North Africa before c.8000 BCE, and prior to the wet and lush period which lasted from c.8000 BCE until at least c.4000 BCE. After c.4000-3500 BCE, dryness again gripped North Africa, and indeed all of Saharasia.

Taken together, these data demonstrate, *the violence documented at Jebel Sahaba occurred during a very dry period in North African prehistory — a time of desert, low-vegetation and probable famine conditions — the violence did not occur during a time of plentiful food supplies.* As such, the evidence from Jebel Sahaba and Wadi Kubbaniya supports the overall Saharasian discovery through validation of the environmental-social-emotional mechanism.

Another interesting factor which may be related here, is the existence of a few other skeletal remains suggestive of violent deaths in Sicily and southern Italy. Thorpe has reported:

"Two late Paleolithic bodies from about 11,000 BC have been found in Italy with flint points lodged in the bones. One from San Teodoro cave in Sicily, was a woman with a flint point in her pelvis. The other was a child with a flint point in its backbone, found in the Grotta del Fanciulli on the Italian mainland. Whether the points were spear-tips or arrowheads is unclear." [21]

While it is possible these were examples of hunting accidents, it is within the scope of the overall Saharasian theory that migrations from a more violence-prone desertified North Africa could have occurred, to bring social violence into the moister territory of Sicily and Italy — and perhaps even farther north into Europe — at that early period. However, if so, the patristic-violent influences must have certainly withered away in both Europe and North Africa following the onset of the Neolithic Wet Phase in North Africa after c.8000 BCE. The period of moist conditions and food abundance in North Africa does not appear to have any identifiable social violence or warfare.

Ancient Artificial Cranial Deformation and a Cluster of Early Violence in S. Australia

Another challenge to my findings in *Saharasia* came in the claims for artificial infant cranial deformation among very early human cultures in Australia and elsewhere, shortly after the close of the last Ice Age, at c.10,000-8,000 BCE. Artificial cranial deformation was described in *Saharasia* as originating accidentally among nomadic peoples who used various kinds of infant head-bindings and cradle-boards, to secure the child in some kind of harness which was carried by adult caretakers on a long trek. Very harsh desert conditions were theorized to be underlying the infant cranial-deforming practices, especially where they appeared among a higher percentage of the population, eventually to become an admired group-identification feature. Deforming head-bindings were subsequently applied to infants as a "social custom", to continue the identifying marks even after the tribal group had settled down. Artificial cranial deformation therefore appeared as a trait which originally started by accident, but which spread with deliberation with the growth of nomadic lifestyles, and militant nomadism specifically. As discussed in a chapter in *Saharasia,* in Eastern Europe and Central Asia, at least, a deformed head often became a mark of the ruling class. The deformations were then undertaken more purposefully and with extreme measures indicative of a great deal of pain and agony for the infant. Mild forms of infant cranial deformation may therefore be associated with dry desert conditions and nomadic subsistence. More extreme forms as found in high-caste central-state societies surely were life-threatening ordeals for the infant, who also was swaddled tightly as an associated custom. Both of these practices, I argued in *Saharasia*, marked a *severe loss of emotional and nurturing contact between mothers and babies,* with generally low parenting skills combined with a buried anger towards the child (ie, a willingness to inflict painful trauma upon babies for the sake of "cultural tradition").

The existence of this painful practice at such very early archaeological periods superficially appeared to challenge the findings of Saharasia as the source of human armoring and child-abusive practices. However, a close examination revealed this was not the case.

Firstly, the most ancient examples for artificial cranial deformation appear to have little in common, in terms of the severity of the deformations, as compared to the more intensive and deadly practices of more recent historical periods. The examples of artificial cranial deformation given in *Saharasia* demonstrated adult skulls of frightening proportions, with foreheads towering upwards in a highly abnormal manner. The deformations were unmistakable, even to the non-specialist, based upon one's general observational knowledge of what the normal human crania looks like. By comparison, the late Pleistocene examples of artificial cranial deformations from Eurasia and Australia were quite minor, and even difficult to identify by the non-specialist.

The more severe deformations from more recent historical times surely produced a far more extreme infant trauma, with a more extreme disruption of the maternal-infant bond, and with more profound psychosomatic consequences as compared to the prehistoric examples. One can simply look at the skulls side-by-side, to get a sense of the greater amounts of pressure

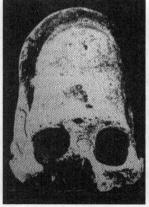

Severe historical examples of Artificial Infant Cranial Deformation from the last several thousand years.
Left to Right: Russia, Peru, Mexico

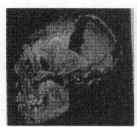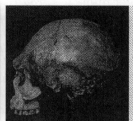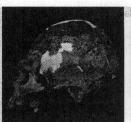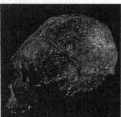

Ancient examples of mild or uncertain Artificial Infant Cranial Deformation,
Late Pleistocene/early Holocene periods.[33]
Left to Right: Shanidar 1 Neanderthal (Europe), Shandingdong Upper Cave 102 (China),
Coobool Creek (Australia), Kow Swamp 5 (Australia), and Cohuna (Australia).
(Reproduced courtesy of Peter Brown,[33,34] from http://www-personal.une.edu.au/~pbrown3/Deform.html)

(using boards, tourniquets, metal bands, etc.) which must have been applied to the historical infant crania, and for longer time periods, to create their crania of more distorted and gigantic proportions. By comparison, the *prehistorical* infant cranial deformations could have been produced by simple cloth bands or flexible straps, for much shorter period. Some of the most ancient examples are today reclassified as "questionable", while others may be the consequence of adult activities, such as use of a forehead strap to carry heavy loads "Kikuyu style". Even so, some of the prehistorical deformations were of apparently sufficient severity as to correlate with episodes of social violence.

A very ancient Neanderthal crania (Shanidar 1, below) from c.53,000-42,000 BCE was once considered an example of artificial cranial deformation, but today this is considered highly questionable. Other skulls have been found in Jericho, Cyprus, Iraq, Lebanon and Syria, dating between 7-4,000 BCE.[31] As mentioned in *Saharasia* (and quoted above), these latter examples appear alongside correlated evidences of drought, land-abandonment and some isolated signs of social violence; a sub-phase of aridity existed, which spread across those same regions, strongly suggesting the genesis of this pain-inflicting ritual to the use of the nomadic backpack cradleboard.

A Chinese crania of early Homo sapiens (Shandingdong Upper Cave 102, below) was acknowledged has having suffered severe postmortem damage, but nevertheless is considered to represent an isolated early case of artificial deformation from adult use of the forehead strap. As such, it would represent a feature created not in infancy, but after the child was able to walk around and carry a heavy load. The location was near Beijing, dated somewhere between 30,000 to 8,000 BCE, a very uncertain time span.[33] In any case, this isolated example of *adolescent-adult* cranial deformation does not suggest infant trauma which might push an entire social group towards violent behavior. And as mentioned previously, no such violence has been found in the early Chinese archaeology.

As presented by archaeologist Peter Brown, the examples of cranial deformation from late-Pleistocene Australia appear better documented, with larger numbers of examples from sites such as Coobool Creek, Kow Swamp, Nacurrie and Cohuna. These sites are all found in SE Australia, dating from c.11,000-7000 BCE, where some additional evidence of tribal violence and conflict is also present:

"...well demarcated, single or multiple depressed fractures [exist] on the frontals or parietals of 59% of the females and 37% of the males. The majority of the fractures were located on the left side of the frontal and left parietal, which is consistent with a blow from a right-handed person, where the combatants are facing each other. In each instance there was

bone regrowth associated with the fracture indicating that the people had survived what was often severe trauma." [34]

The above findings suggest a childrearing mode which tolerated a high degree of infant discomfort and trauma, in association with an adult culture infused with impulsive but generally non-lethal episodes of interpersonal violence. Given its non-lethal character, it is most probable that this violence was confined within existing social groups rather than indicating tribal warfare per se, though tribal conflict of a non-lethal nature cannot be ruled out. The fact that more female skulls showed depressed fractures than male skulls (59% versus 37%) demonstrates a significant social rage directed towards females,[34] who probably were the ones to whom the responsibility of culturally-demanded artificial cranial deformations was entrusted. If so, these Australian skulls may be the earliest evidence to exist showing the relationship between a harsh and pain-inflicting ritual directed at infants, which later produced a social violence directed more often than not towards the maternal figure.

What of the climatic conditions in SE Australia at this early time period, of c.11,000-7000 BCE? According to Adams' climatic reconstruction,[32] the period from c.16,000-10,000 BCE was extremely arid in most of SE and Central Australia, much drier than as seen in the modern times. After 10,000 BCE, conditions changed towards a slightly moister situation in those regions, more characteristic of the modern "outback" steppe or savanna-like climate, inland from the coastal zone. To quote from Brown again:

"Although there is an ethnographic account of cranial deformation from northern Victoria, there is no evidence of the morphological pattern associated with deformation in the several thousand 'recent' crania from Victoria, South Australia and New South Wales in Australian museum collections. There is also no evidence of cranial deformation in the prehistoric samples from Roonka (7000 BP)... the mid-Holocene Barham series... or the Murray Valley group... and dated to 6000-750 years BP. In Australia, artificially deformed crania have only been recovered from Kow Swamp, Nacurrie and Coobool Creek. These sites are in close geographical proximity ... The presence of artificially deformed crania in these three sites, and their absence from mid-Holocene and recent sites in the same area, suggests that they share a common cultural and chronological association." [34]

To summarize: The Australian sites mentioned here are located in the same general region. Extreme desert conditions existed across this region at the time when cranial deformations first appeared and were adopted; this suggests they developed from environmental pressures known to demand an intensive nomadism and use of back-pack cradles or similar apparatus for securely carrying babies around, which also deformed their crania. Social violence of a limited nature also developed around the same time, from the full complex of human responses to aridity and famine as noted in my Saharasia. Cranial deformations later became a social institution, and were purposefully re-created in later generations. Finally, both cranial deformations and social violence gradually disappear from the archaeological record following centuries of somewhat better environmental conditions and food supplies, disappearing entirely after c.7000 BCE.

Post-Saharasian Violence Among Pre-Columbian Tribal Cultures

One of the more controversial assertions made in *Saharasia*, was that the earliest migrants into the Americas were of a uniformly peaceful character, not prone to social violence because they held a more matristic and unarmored form of social organization. They attended to the needs of infants and children, and did not sex-repress their adolescents and adults. This argument was supported by the ethnographical evidence presented in the World Behavior Map, but also by the geographical locations of those cultures in the Americas which were of a more violent characteristic. Violence in the Americas, before Columbus, was found only in certain locations, and was not widely or randomly distributed on the map. The reader is referred back to my *Saharasia*[2,3] for full details on this question. Here, I am mainly interested in the following question: Do the locations of various archaeological sites recently dug up and showing clear evidence for violence among native North American cultural groups, before the arrival of the Europeans, agree with the locations for violence in the Americas as determined by the World Behavior Map? Or not? This question can be directly answered by a locational comparison, as follows.

We can summarize some recent publications documenting either significant and ongoing interpersonal or intergroup social violence, as determined from skeletal remains, or even outright massacres suggestive of merciless and intensive tribal warfare, well before the arrival of Europeans into the Americas. The facts presented in the various papers are not in question. The point of interest for this paper, and for my Saharasian discovery, are the *locations* and *chronology* of the various archaeological sites, which are summarized in the following listing.

Major New World Sites of Violence and Warfare

1. SE Michigan, Riviere aux Vase, c.1000-1300 CE. Collection of several hundred skeletons showing signs of conflict and violence, predominantly against women.[35]

2. Illinois, Norris Farms, pre-Columbian. Substantial intergroup violence.[35]

3. South Dakota, Crow Creek, c.1300 CE. Site of a tribal massacre of around 500 individuals, men, women and children, but with a deficit of reproductive-age females.[20,35]

4. La Plata River Valley, Four Corners, c.900-1300 CE. Substantial non-lethal interpersonal violence, especially against females.[36]

5. Santa Barbara Channel, S. California, c.1490 BCE or earlier to 1804 CE. Collection of 753 remains, demonstrating healed non-lethal cranial vault fractures in 128, or 17%,[37,38] with a similar high percentage of projectile point injuries and deaths. Males were more affected than females, children or the elderly, suggestive of combative roles.[38]

6. Central Southern Mexico, sites at Tetelpan, San Luis Potosi, and Mexico City, c.500 BCE - 1521 CE. Substantial interpersonal and intergroup violence with organized warfare, human sacrifice and possible cannibalism.[39]

7. W. Tennessee Valley, primarily late Archaic, c.2500-500 BCE, possibly earlier. Collection of several hundred skeletons showing signs of violent death and trophy-taking.[40]

8. SE Alaska, British Columbia, NW USA - Pacific NW Coast., c.3000 BCE - 900 AD. Substantial interpersonal violence with non-lethal skeletal injuries ampli-

Crow Creek Massacre, South Dakota, a collection of 500 individuals killed in inter-tribal violence, c.1300 CE, in a region identified on the World Behavior Map as possessing isolated armored patrist groups within a background majority of unarmored peaceful matristic cultures. (from Bahn[20])

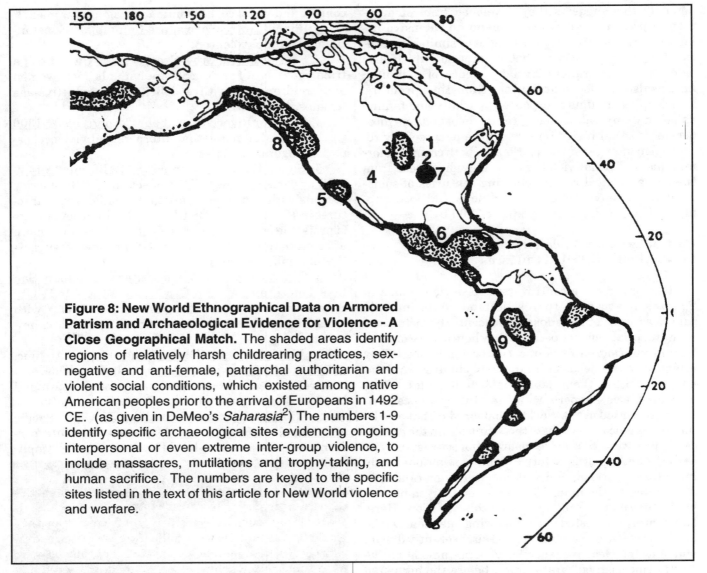

Figure 8: New World Ethnographical Data on Armored Patrism and Archaeological Evidence for Violence - A Close Geographical Match. The shaded areas identify regions of relatively harsh childrearing practices, sex-negative and anti-female, patriarchal authoritarian and violent social conditions, which existed among native American peoples prior to the arrival of Europeans in 1492 CE. (as given in DeMeo's *Saharasia*[2]) The numbers 1-9 identify specific archaeological sites evidencing ongoing interpersonal or even extreme inter-group violence, to include massacres, mutilations and trophy-taking, and human sacrifice. The numbers are keyed to the specific sites listed in the text of this article for New World violence and warfare.

fied eventually into organized warfare, defensive villages, especially after 1500 BCE.[41,42]

9. Peru, Coastal zone, Nasca and Ostra sites, c.3000 -1500 BCE. Ostra Site: Early (c.3000 BCE) ambiguous evidence of stone-weapons which might as easily have been used for other purposes.[43] Later unambiguous Nasca Artwork and mortuary evidence (c.1500 BCE) of warfare and headhunting, including mummified heads in the manner similar to later Jivaro and other head-hunting groups in adjacent regions.[44]

The above list of archaeological sites, when plotted on a map, shows a striking degree of correlation to those areas of the World Behavior Map identified from anthropological sources as containing high degrees of patriarchal authoritarian, violent culture. This suggests, *the social violence identified in those archaeological sites constitutes the historical underpinnings of the later social violence and patrism recorded in the ethnographical data.* Likewise, there is *a general absence of*

identified archaeological evidence for violence in most other regions of the Americas, with a similar absence of armored patrism in the ethnographical data for the unshaded parts of the map. While this could simply reflect a lack of sufficient archaeological data for other parts of the New World, as discussed below there is much evidence in the archaeological record for peaceful conditions in the unmarked areas of the maps.

The above points are additionally in agreement with the pre-Columbian contact theory advocated in *Saharasia,* specifically regarding coastal arrival points of relatively violent invaders from the Old World, some of whom came from pyramid-building regions, and reproduced the same at their new homes in the New World. All are dated to time periods *well after* the 4000-3500 BCE origins of violence in the Old World, and well into the period of massive shipbuilding among the Old World kingly empires, who very likely transmitted violence into the New World according to the patterns given on the World Behavior Map.

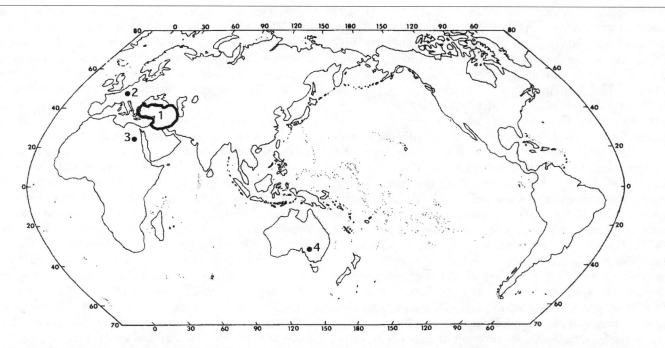

Figure 9: Confirmed Sites of Anomalous Violence in the Pre-Saharasian Period (Before c.4000 BCE)
1. Generalized region of isolated examples of violence and infant cranial deformation, Anatolia and Middle East, c.5000 BCE or possibly a bit earlier. **2.** Massacre sites at Ofnet, Talheim, Schletz, c.5500-4000 BCE. **3.** Massacre site at Jebel Sahaba, c.10,000 BCE. **4.** Region of early Australian infant cranial deformation and familial/intra-Group social violence, c.11,000 - 7,000 BCE. All of these regions, except for item #2 above, were characterized by harsh desert conditions at the time when social violence and warfare appeared. Widespread, massive and persisting social violence and warfare did not appear, however, until after c.4000-3500 BCE, when the larger part of Saharasia began to dry up, as discussed in the book *Saharasia*.[2]

Conclusions

The information contained in the above sections can be organized both temporally and geographically, into four major regional categories of prehistorical violence:

1. As discussed in *Saharasia*, and revisited in this article, there are a scattering of sites across Anatolia and the Middle East which showed "fleeting glimpses" of social violence as early as c.5000 BCE, and possibly even earlier. These are timed with a temporary episode of drought and aridity coincidental to the abandonment of many villages and sites across the region. This early evidence for land-abandonment and probable mass-migrations, with possible social violence appearing here and there, along with a few cases of infant cranial deformation, did not become epidemic, widespread or persistent in character. Drought appeared, followed by scattered and isolated signs of social disturbance. When wetter conditions reappeared in the region, settlements thrived once again under peaceful conditions.

2. A cluster of sites in southern Germany document violent conditions at several sites between c.5500-4000 BCE. These massacre sites, at Talheim, Schletz and Ofnet, may factually fall into the younger end of this range of dates, which would place them well within the time-line of events described in *Saharasia*, when Europe was transformed by invasions from Central Asia. If the older dates eventually prove to be correct, then they would be anomalistic within the framework of Saharasian theory, but might nevertheless eventually prove to have some relationship to the isolated, scattered and non-persisting signs of violence which spread across Anatolia and the Middle East — coincidental to the a sub-phase of aridity and land-abandonment, as described above (in #1). In either case, these massacre sites are not located in a formerly dryland region, and no obvious mechanism related to environmental pressures such as famine and starvation can be invoked to explain the spontaneous genesis of isolated violence. I suggest, these sites can only be understood as the consequence of cultural diffusion of warlike groups out of the neighboring drylands, either from Central Asia at c.4000 BCE, or from Anatolia after c.5500 BCE. Or, we should have to discover some other as yet unknown process whereby human behavior was anomalously driven towards violence within only a small number of tribal groups within the region. The geographical clustering of the German sites does not support the assertion of any widespread or ubiquitous violence, but rather, the opposite, of isolated violence within a larger ocean of peaceful conditions.

3. The violence in the Nile Valley at Jebel Sahaba,

Wadi Kubbiyana and a few other sites at c.12,000 BCE does not fit within the original Saharasian chronology of drought and famine starting at c.4000 or even 5000 BCE, but nevertheless does occur during an earlier period of intense aridity, prior to the Neolithic Wet Phase of North Africa. As such, this very early violence in North Africa confirms the basic drought-famine mechanism for the genesis of violence as given in *Saharasia*. Whatever violence did exist at this very early time, however, was so scattered and isolated in its distribution, that it died out once the Neolithic Wet Phase developed. Once North Africa became wet and lush, supporting grasslands and trees with large herbivores, and numerous large rivers and lakes, evidence for human violence vanishes, only to reappear after c. 3500 BCE, when North Africa dries out again. In this latter case, the violent conditions persist, along with the harsh arid conditions, from c.3500 BCE all the way down into the modern era as a global phenomenon, to be recorded by ethnographers and anthropologists, and documented in *Saharasia* on the World Behavior Map.

4. In SE Australia, we have what appears to be an episode of "Saharasian"-type genesis of small-scale inter-group social violence — to include artificial infant cranial deformation, and generally non-lethal familial and tribal fights directed mostly at women — during an episode of unusually dry and possibly episodic famine conditions. The violence appeared during hyper-arid conditions starting at c.11,000 BCE, but died out and vanished by c.7000 BCE, after wetter conditions returned. This suggests the strong influence of desertification and aridity on social conditions, as detailed in *Saharasia*.

Figure 9 identifies these four locations or regions of confirmed archaeological evidence for anomalous violence in the pre-Saharasian period, before c.4000 BCE.

After c.4000-3500 BCE, when all of Saharasia began declining into an intense and widespread aridity, the process of drought, famine, starvation and land-abandonment intensified, forcing the mass migratory events described in *Saharasia*. Violence then irrupted again, this time as a response to a more widespread and persisting drought-famine situation which forced the abandonment of entire regions. We have detailed here, the arrival of the new famine-affected and violent Central Asian migrants across the region of the European causewayed enclosures. They wreaked havoc among peaceful villages and trading centers, and ushered in the epoch of the battle-axe, Kurgan warrior nomads, fortifications and warrior-kings, and were followed by subsequent waves of new immigrants who carried the seeds of violence in their desert-borne and desert-bred social institutions.

As argued in *Saharasia*, violence became anchored into human character structure, by virtue of the development of new social institutions for justifying and glorifying sadism and butchery, even when directed towards infants and children, and towards the opposite sex. The key for transmission of early famine-related violence outside of the dry regions is found in the development of new social institutions which re-create the violence generation after generation, irrespective of climate. The earliest episodes of human violence, specifically identified in the above four points, did not persist in such a manner, and this may be due to the fact that human social groups at these earlier dates had not yet developed either the size or the organizational complexity by which new social institutions could be readily preserved over the long term. One hypothesis which might explain the findings is, the conditions in Anatolia and the Middle-East generated some elements of social disturbance and violence within a small percentage of cultures, who then migrated into Southern Germany and committed massacres. A similar thing could have occurred in the region of the Nile, leading to the anomalous episode at Jebel Sahaba and Wadi Kubbiyana. At some point, these hypothesized violent cultural groups died off, or were assimilated into other peaceful cultures, or otherwise vanished. Peaceful social conditions then continued once rains and food supplies became abundant once again.

Much of the claims for violence in the archaeological record, described as "prehistoric" in the most general terms, really demands to be more critically reviewed and precisely reported in terms of both dates and locations. Human bones with cut-marks do not automatically constitute "evidence for cannibalism", given the existence of funeral rituals where the bones of the dead are cleaned of their flesh. Hunting accidents — where an occasional projectile point is found in an isolated human skeleton — cannot, by themselves, stand as evidence for widespread social violence and warfare, especially where the injured individual shows signs of bone-healing and sympathetic burial. Abstracted rock-art which claims to depict a person killed with numerous spears, but which requires a specialist to make the interpretation and to point out the details, falls down into the realm of ambiguous speculation at best. If the eye of an ordinary person cannot detect violence in the rock art scenes, it is likely that the violence existed only within the specialist's imagination. And in some cases, it surely is possible that later generations of violent people might have drawn spears on top of older rock-art of human subjects, just as people today add graffiti to "dress up" existing pictures of people — where archaeological digs fail to show violence in skeletons and structures, evidence from rock art can only be suggestive, at best. And, the date for the first-settlement of a location should not be confused with the date for the first clear and unambiguous evidence for violence. A site can be occupied for hundreds or thousands of years before the first clear signs of violence appear.

I have shown here, the violence in early China, in the causewayed enclosures of Europe, in Neolithic Spanish rock art, and in massacres of New World cultures before Columbus, all fit well within the parameters given in *Saharasia*, and these examples provide additional compelling support for the overall Saharasian theory. This is especially so for the Americas, where *most* of the evidence for village-scale massacres fits within those regions identified on the World Behavior Map as clusters of armored patrism. The close geographical associations are, in fact, striking.

What is at issue is: how, where, and under what conditions does human social violence and warfare develop. Is it something that can occur anywhere, under any conditions, something which lurks below the surface of the human character just waiting to spring forth to wreak social havoc? *Or does human violence conflict with and go against our basic biology, requiring only the most severe trauma to bring it forth; either trauma in the womb, in the crib, in the home and family, or the larger trauma of severe drought, land degradation, the disruption of food and water supplies, and the attendant famine and starvation conditions which follow?*

All of these considerations were given focused discussion in *Saharasia*, and so will not be repeated here — but the issue is, to what extent has Saharasia's ancient historical components been challenged by these newer archaeological findings? From the discussion in this paper, I have shown that the larger Saharasian theory is not so easily challenged, due to the specificity of its theoretical construct — since the early violence identified at the c.4000-3500 BCE marker date is connected to the existence of severe drought, desertification, social displacement and famine within human populations, one can expect to find *similar social responses under similar environmental conditions, even if those conditions occur earlier than c.4000 BCE.* But more to the point, archaeology simply does not support the fantasy that ancient humans were just as warlike and bloody as either the historical or contemporary "civilizations". On the contrary, *the farther back one goes in time, the more difficult it is to find clear and unambiguous evidence for human violence, and what does exist is observed to be regionally isolated and anomalous.*

Brian Ferguson, who has extensively reviewed the archaeological record for evidence of human violence, has the following to say on the question, written as a conclusion for the book *Troubled Times: Violence and Warfare in the Past:*[45]

What does this evidence tell us? Paradoxically, by documenting violence and warfare and showing variations over space and time, these chapters highlight their absence in much of human prehistory. And this research is gathered together specifically to demonstrate the existence of violence. Another wide-ranging collection on "paleopathology at the dawn of agriculture" (Cohen & Armelagos, 198)[46] is striking for the relative absence of the sort of evidence pre-sented here. Partly that may be neglect. But where trauma is specifically discussed, in many cases there is little or nothing to suggest any social pattern of violence. (Curiously, much of the evidence of trauma in Cohen and Armelagos comes from sites within the Mississippi drainage...

Other works similarly indicate a late emergence of violence and war. A survey of south Asian sites (Kennedy 1984: 178, 183)[47] finds limited skeletal evidence of trauma. Most of that appears in Harappan contexts, and even there earlier reports of massacres have been seriously questioned. In the Levant from the late Paleolithic well into the Neolithic, indications of violence and war are conspicuously absent from the abundant skeletal and settlement remains (Rathbun 1984; Roper 1974; Smith, Bar Yosef and Sillen 1984).[9,48,49]

A dedicated search for archaeological signs of war in South America (Redmond 1994)[50] produces little that is convincing and early. On the pre-ceramic Peruvian coast, any indication of violent conflict is late and limited to a few locations (Quilter 1989:65, 78, 85),[51] except for the highly problematic findings at Ostra (Topic 1989).[43] On the plains of western Venezuela, evidence of war only appears along with agricultural intensification and the rise of chiefdoms, post 500 AD (Spencer and Redmond 1992: 153).[52]

Europe and the Mesolithic and early Neolithic does produce some indications of personal violence (Meiklejohn et al 1984; Whittle 1985)[53,54] as discussed previously, but these are exceptional. The situation in China is similar: a very few signs of interpersonal violence (two skeletons with imbedded points) gives way to widespread evidence of war — fortifications, specialized weapons and multiple osteological signs — only in the final Neolithic, along with the development of economic inequality, not long before the rise of states (Underhill 1989).[28] A similar change occurred in prehistoric Japan, where evidence of violent death goes from about .002% of approximately 5000 skeletons from pre-agricultural Jomon times, to over 10% of all deaths in the subsequent, agricultural Yayoi epoch (Farris, n.d.).[55] In all these areas, war ultimately becomes entrenched and widespread, leaving unmistakable indicators. Again, it is difficult to understand how war could have been common earlier in each area and remain so invisible. ...

Roper (1969: 448)[56] calls into question some alleged instances of killing in the Paleolithic, but others remain convincing. The Australian rock art noted earlier (Tacon and Chippendale 1994)[7] indicates an early pattern of lethal violence, individual and then collective, but it stands as an exception that highlights the rule: individual killings seem rare and organized killing nearly absent throughout most of our collective past.

...if our ancestors were killing each other..dying after being stabbed, clubbed, or shot, we would see it in their remains. ...

The evident absence of warfare during most of our evolutionary past sinks a boat load of theories."[45]

Fuergeson is not alone in such an assessment. Consider the words also of Richard Gabriel, from *The Culture of War*.[57] Gabriel's statements are all the more illuminating given his basic belief in the roots of violence in our genetic-mental make-up:

"Using the Stone Age cultures of Homo sapiens and Neanderthal as a starting point, we find some remarkable data about the development of war. Man required thirty thousand years to learn how to use fire and another twenty thousand years to invent the fire-hardened, wooden-tipped spear; spear points would come much later. Sixty thousand years later, man invented the bow and arrow with transverse stone points. Ninety thousand years after the beginning of the Homo sapiens Stone Age, man learned to herd wild animals, and four thousand years later he learned to domesticate goats, sheep, cattle, and the dog. At about the same time there is evidence for the beginnings of systematic harvesting of wild grains, but it would take yet another two thousand years for man to learn how to transplant these wild grains to fixed campsites and another two thousand years to learn how to plant domesticated strains of cereal grain. It is only after this development, around 4000 BC, that warfare makes its appearance as a major human social institution. In sum, man has known war for only about 6 percent of the time since the Homo sapiens Stone Age began.

Once warfare had become established, it is difficult to find any other social institution that developed as quickly. In less than a thousand years, man brought forth the sword, sling, dagger, mace, bronze weapons, and large-scale fortifications. The next thousand years saw the emergence of iron weapons, the chariot, large standing professional armies, military academies, general staff structures, military training regimens, the first permanent arms industry, written texts on tactics, military procurement, logistics systems, conscription, and military pay. By 2000 BC, war had become the dominant social institution in almost all major cultures of the Middle East. ...

For the first ninety-five thousand years after the Homo sapiens Stone Age began, there is no evidence at all that man engaged in war on any level, let alone on a level requiring organized group violence. There is little evidence of any killing at all." [57]

These statements, from scholars intimately familiar with archaeological evidence, suggest a strong con-firmation for the basic ideas presented in my *Saharasia*. This being the case, what are we to make of the various books and articles which continue to claim — without solid evidence — a violent and blood-drenched ancient history for our species? There are many books on violence in prehistorical periods which take great care in presenting archaeological evidence,[23,58,59,60,61] but none reviewed by this author was as bold in its unsupported claims and assertions of early violence as was Keeley's, which unfortunately tended to bias everything towards his own basic assumptions of the inevitability of war — that's not uncommon in today's world where "genetic determinism" dominates the sciences, and where the daily newspapers yield up plenty of evidence for the violent interpretation. Keeley and supporters are totally correct about violence among some "primitives" and their citations on warfare among Native American cultures has proven a treasure of additional evidence to support my Saharasian maps for the New World — and for much of the period of written human history, advocates for a deep rootedness of violence in the human species can draw from a wealth of evidence to support their viewpoints. However, this evidence becomes increasingly scarce the farther back into pre-history one digs, and it nearly vanishes entirely prior to c.4000 BCE. At a more basic level, in the assumption of the *innate* nature of violence, its "inevitability" and "genetic evolutionary roots" in our most ancient past, *the evidence simply does not support such a conclusion.*

The original conclusions given in my *Saharasia*,[2,3] first presented and published in the 1980s, are almost totally supported by the more recent archaeological evidence, even as articulated by the most staunch supporters of early-violence theory: *Generally peaceful social conditions existed worldwide, prior to the drying up of Saharasia after c.4000-3500 BCE. During the Saharasian wet period of c.8000-4000 BCE, peaceful social conditions prevailed as a world-wide phenomenon, with only the most isolated and even questionable of exceptions. Where social violence did occur prior to 4000 BCE, it was in almost every case in association with the episodic appearance of harsh drought and famine conditions — only after such conditions became widespread and persistent does human social violence become a sustained and ongoing characteristic of the human animal.* Only *after* enduring the horrific and ongoing trauma consequent to massive drought and famine conditions, do the original peaceful and social human societies succumb and fall to the glory of violent warrior kings and patriarchal blood-lusting gods. Without the desert, without Saharasia, both history and humanity would today be entirely different.

References:

1. Wilhelm Reich, *Character Analysis, Mass Psychology of Fascism, The Sexual Revolution, People in Trouble,* and *The Function of the Orgasm.*

2. James DeMeo, *Saharasia: The 4000 BCE Origins of Child-Abuse, Sex-Repression, Warfare and Social Violence, In the Deserts of the Old World,* Natural Energy Works, Ashland, 1998. (Revised from the dissertation: *On the Origins and Diffusion of Patrism: The Saharasian Connection,* Univ. Kansas, Geography Dept., Lawrence, Kansas, 1986.)

3. James DeMeo, "The Origins and Diffusion of Patrism in Saharasia, c.4000 BCE: Evidence for a Worldwide, Climate-Linked Geographical Pattern in Human Behavior", published in: *Kyoto Review* 23: 19-38, Spring 1990 (Japan) ; *Emotion* 10, 1991 (Germany); *World Futures: The Journal of General Evolution,* 30: 247-271, 1991; and *Pulse of the Planet* 3:3-16, 1991.

4. Lawrence Keeley, *War Before Civilization,* Oxford Univ. Press, NY, 1996.

5. Trevor Watkins, "The Beginnings of Warfare" in *Warfare in the Ancient World,* J. Hackett, Ed., Facts on File, NY 1989, p.15-16.

6. A. Beltran, *Rock Art of the Spanish Levant,* Cambridge Univ. Press, Cambridge, 1980.

7. P. Tacon & C. Chippindale, "Australia's Ancient Warriors: Changing Depictions of Fighting in the Rock Art of Arnhem Land, N.T.", *Cambridge Archaeological J.* 4:211-248, 1994. Also see: Lewis, D.: *Rock Paintings of Arnhem Land, Australia,* BAR Int. Series 415, 1988; Tacon, P.: "The Power of Stone: Symbolic Aspects of Stone and Tool Development in Western Arnhem Land, Australia", *Antiquity* 65:192-207, 1991.

8. DeMeo, Saharasia, 1998, ibid, p.284-295.

9. M.K. Roper, "Evidence of Warfare in the Near East from 10000-4300 BC" in *War: Its Causes and Correlates,* M. Nettleship, et al, Eds., Mouton, The Hague, pp.299-340, 1974.

10. DeMeo, ibid., p.259.

11. K. Kenyon *Digging Up Jericho,* Praeger, NY, 1958, p.127, 134.

12. O. Bar-Yosef, "The Walls of Jericho: An Alternative Interpretation" *Current Anthropology,* 27:157-162, 1986.

13. J. Mellaart, *The Chalcolithic & Early Bronze Ages in the Near East & Anatolia,* Khayats, Lebanon, 1966; J. Mellaart, *The Neolithic of the Near East,* Thames & Hudson, London, 1975.

14. Colin Burgess, et al, Eds., *Enclosures and Defences in the Neolithic of Western Europe, Vol.1 & 2,* BAR International series 403(i) and (ii), 1988.

15. Christopher Evans, "Monuments and Analogy: The Interpretation of Causewayed Enclosures" in Burgess, et al, ibid., p.47.

16. N. J. Starling, "The Neolithic Höhensiedlungen (high settlements) of Central Germany", in Burgess, et al, ibid., p.419, 427.

17. R. J. Mercer "Hambledon Hill, Dorset, England", in Burgess, et al, ibid., p.89, 95-96.

18. P. Dixon, "The Neolithic Settlements on Crickley Hill", in Burgess, et al, ibid., p.75-87.

19. Neils Andersen "The Neolithic Causewayed Enclosures at Sarup, on South-West Funen, Denmark", in Burgess, et al, ibid., p.354.

20. Paul Bahn, *Tombs, Graves and Mummies,* Barnes & Nobel, NY 1996, p.48, 50.

21. Nick Thorpe, "Origins of War: Mesolithic Conflict in Europe", *Archaeology* #52, April 2000. http://www.britarch.ac.uk/ba/ba52/ba52feat.html and "Origins of Violence - Mesolithic conflict in Europe" http://www.hum.au.dk/fark/warfare/thorpe_paper_1.htm

22. M. Stuiver, A. Long & R.S. Kra, eds. "Die Datierung des Massakers von Schletz", *Radiocarbon* 35(1), 1993. http://www.nhm-wien.ac.at/NHM/Prehist/Stadler/LVAS/QAM/14C/Schletz.html

23. David Frayer "Ofnet: Evidence for a Mesolithic Massacre", in Debra Martin & David Frayer, Eds., *Troubled Times: Violence and Warfare in the Past,* Gordon and Breach, 1997, p.181-216.

24. R.R. Schmidt *Die Altsteinzeitlichen Schädelgräber aus der Grossen Ofnet-Höhle und von Kaufertsberg,* J.F. Lehmanns, München, 1913.

25. Grahame Clarke, *Mesolithic Prelude,* University Press Edinburgh, 1980, p.62, 93.

26. Jörg Orschiedt, "Ergebnisse einer neuen Untersuchung der spätmesolithischen Kopfbestattungen aus Süddeutschland", *Urgeschichtliche Materialhefte* 12, 1998, p.147-160. Presented to the Paleoanthropology Society, 2000 Conference, abstract posted to: http://www.paleoanthro.org/abst2000.htm#orschiedt

27. Jörg Orschiedt, "Manipulationen an menschlichen Skelettresten. Taphonomische Prozesse, Sekundärbestattungen oder Kannibalismus?", *Urgeschichtliche Materialhefte* 13, 1999.

28. Anne Underhill, "Warfare During the Chinese Neolithic Period: A Review of the Evidence", in Diana Tkaczuk and Brian Vivian, Eds. *Cultures in Conflict: Current Archaeological Perspectives* , Univ. of Calgary, Canada, 1989, p.221-223, 230-234.

29. Michael Hoffman, *Egypt Before the Pharaohs,* Barnes & Nobel, NY, 1979, p.98.

30. Fred Wendorf, *Prehistory of Nubia, Vol.2,* Southern Methodist Univ. Press, 1968.

31. Fred Wendorf, personal communication, Feb. 2001.

32. Jonathan Adams, *Sudden Climatic Transitions During the Quaternary,* with sequential climate maps http://www.esd.ornl.gov/projects/qen/nerc.html

33. Patricia Lindsell, *Artificial Cranial Deformation* (from a dissertation in progress) 2001. More information is also available from Peter Brown and Patricia Lindsell at: http://www-personal.une.edu.au/~pbrown3/Deform.html Also see: Don Brothwell, "Possible Evidence of a Cultural Practice Affecting Head Growth", *J. Archaeological Sci.* 2:75-77, 1975; K.A.R. Kennedy, "Growth, Nutrition and Pathology in Changing Demographic Settings in South Asia", in Cohen & Armelagos, ibid., pp.169-192, 1984.

34. Peter Brown, *Coobool Creek. A morphological and metrical analysis of the crania, mandibles and dentitions of a prehistoric Australian human population. Terra Australis,* 13. Department of Prehistory, Australian National University, Canberra 1989, p.71, 170. Also see: Brown, P.: "Artificial Cranial Deformation: A Component in the Variation in Pleistocene Australian Aboriginal Crania", *Archaeol Oceania* 16:156-167, 1981.

35. Richard G. Wilkinson, "Violence Against Women: Raiding and Abduction in Prehistoric Michigan", in Debra Martin & David Frayer, Eds., *Troubled Times: Violence and Warfare in the Past*, Gordon and Breach, 1997, p.21-43.

36. Debra Martin, "Violence Against Women in the La Plata River Valley, A.D. 1000-1300, in Martin & Frayer, 1997, ibid., p.45-75.

37. Patricia Lambert, "Patterns of Violence in Prehistoric Hunter-gatherer Societies of Coastal Southern California", in Martin & Frayer, 1997, ibid., p.84, 93-98.

38. Philip Walker, "Wife Beating, Boxing and Broken Noses: Skeletal Evidence for the Cultural Patterning of Violence", in Martin & Frayer, 1997, ibid., p.164

39. Carmen Ma, et al, "Evidence for Human Sacrifice, Bone Modification and Cannibalism in Ancient Mexico", in Martin & Frayer, ibid., p.217-239.

40. Maria Ostendorf-Smith, "Osteological Indications of Warfare in the Archaic period of the Western Tennessee Valley", in Martin & Frayer, 1997, ibid., p.241-265

41. Herbert Maschner, "The Evolution of Northwest Coast Warfare", in Martin & Frayer, 1997, ibid., p.267.

42. Gary Coupland, "Warfare and Social Complexity on the Northwest Coast", in Tkaczuk & Vivian, 1989, pp.205-214.

43. J. Topic, "The Ostra Site: The Earliest Fortified Site in the New World", in Tkaczuk & Vivian, ibid.,1989, p.215-228.

44. Donald Proulx, "Nasca Trophy Heads: Victims of Warfare or Ritual Sacrifice", in Tkaczuk & Vivian, pp.73-85, 1989.

45. Brian Ferguson, "Violence and War in Prehistory", in Martin & Frayer, 1997, p.332-334.

46. N. Cohen & G. Armelagos, Eds., *Paleopathology at the Origins of Agriculture*, Academic Press, Orlando, 1984.

47. K.A.R. Kennedy, "Growth, Nutrition and Pathology in Changing Demographic Settings in South Asia", in Cohen & Armelagos, ibid., pp.169-192, 1984.

48. T. Rathbun, "Skeletal Pathology from the Paleolithic through the Metal Ages in Iran and Iraq", in Cohen & Armelagos, ibid., pp.137-167, 1984.

49. P. Smith, et al., "Archaeological and Skeletal Evidence for Dietary Change during the Late Pleistocene/Early Holocene in the Levant", in Cohen & Armelagos, ibid, pp.101-136, 1984.

50. E. Redmond, *Tribal and Chiefly Warfare in South America,* Memoirs of the Museum of Anthropology, Univ. of Michigan, Ann Arbor, 1994.

51. J. Quilter, *Life and Death at Paloma: Society and Mortuary Practices in a Preceramic Peruvian Village,* Univ. Iowa Press, Iowa City, 1989.

52. C. Spencer & E. Redmond, "Prehispanic Chiefdoms of the Western Venezuelan Llanos", *World Archaeology*, 24:134-157, 1992.

53. C. Meikeljohn, et al, "Socioeconomic Change and Patterns of Pathology and Variation in the Mesolithic and Neolithic of Western Europe", in Cohen & Armelagos, pp.75-100, 1984.

54. A. Whittle, *Neolithic Europe: A Survey*, Cambridge Univ. Press, Cambridge, 1985.

55. W. Farris, *Sacred Texts and Buried Treasures: Essays in the Historical Archaeology of Japan*, undated manuscript, cited in Ferguson, op cit., p.348.

56. M.K. Roper, "A Survey of the Evidence for Intrahuman Killing in the Pleistocene", *Current Anthropology*, 10: 427-459, 1969.

57. Richard Gabriel, *The Culture of War: Invention and Early Development*, Greenwood Press, NY, 1990, p.20-21.

58. Jonathan Haas, *The Anthropology of War,* Cambridge U. Press, NY 1990.

59. Debra Martin & David Frayer, Eds., *Troubled Times: Violence and Warfare in the Past*, Gordon and Breach, 1997.

60. John Hackett, Ed., *Warfare in the Ancient World*, Facts on File, NY 1989.

61. Diana Tkaczuk and Brian Vivian, Eds. *Cultures in Conflict: Current Archaeological Perspectives*, Univ. of Calgary, Canada, 1989.

The following web pages present additional information on James DeMeo's *Saharasia*:
http://www.orgonelab.org/saharasia.htm
http://www.orgonelab.org/xdemeo.htm

Many thanks to the various authors for permissions to use their photos and illustrations. In a few cases, we could not locate the author and so a few items may not be properly credited. In such cases, when so informed, we will be happy to add such credits or to remove the item from subsequent printings.

Postscript:
Other Supports for *Saharasia*

Aside from the question of evidence for warfare in the archaeological record, as covered in detail in the prior section, there have been a number of relevant issues which have come to my attention since the publication of *Saharasia* — sometimes in the nature of a challenge — which have provided added validation. One small item, also, requires a correction. We can briefly review these matters.

The *Mosuo*: Peaceful Unarmored-Matristic Culture of the Southern Chinese Mountains

A new ethnography has recently appeared, by the German scholar Heide Göttner-Abendroth, *Matriarchat in Südchina,*[1] which identifies another matristic culture which has been able to maintain its sex-positive and peaceful ways into the modern era, largely by virtue of their isolated geography. They are, in many respects, similar to the *Trobriand Islanders* of Melanesia, or the *Muria* peoples of India (thoroughly discussed in Chapter 3 of *Saharasia*[2]) who survived into modern times without being overwhelmed by neighboring patriarchal authoritarian cultures, by virtue of their geographic isolation. Among the Mosuo, women and girls enjoy a high status and the *right to have lovers before marriage*, in social institutions that affirm a girls sexuality, rather than crushing it down. Men are likewise sexually and socially free, and the marriages are not written in stone. Inheritance and families are traced matrilineally. This is an almost unbelievable set of social circumstances given the rigid patriarchal authoritarian nature of the larger Chinese culture, where softer matristic qualities were largely extinguished under centuries of totalitarian patriarchal rule by various Dynastic (or Communist) despots. Also of great interest is the tribal oral history of the Mosuo. As reported by Göttner-Abendroth, the Mosuo were forced to migrate from an original homeland in *Mongolia* around 5000 years ago, following invasions by more warlike people who came from more western parts! Their current homeland, centered on Lake Lugu near the upper Jang tse kiang river in Southern Szetschuan province, is composed of moist semi-forested mountains of a moderate climate. Assuming their oral history is correct, it provides additional support for the origins of armored patrism in China, as already given in Chapter 8 of *Saharasia.*[2]

Very Ancient Male Genital Mutilations?

Male genital mutilations were discussed in a section of my *Saharasia*, as an important cross-cultural correlate with severely authoritarian, patristic and violent societies. This fact had always upset people who were supporters of circumcision for either religious or "hygienic" excuses. As given in *Saharasia*, the earliest unambiguous evidence for such mutilations as circumcision comes from an unmistakable bas-relief at the Tomb of Ankhmahor (6th Dynasty c.2300 BCE) at Saqqarah, Egypt (in *Saharasia*[2], p.119) One critic suggested I had been premature in dismissing the idea of male genital mutilations in ancient prehistorical times, suggesting the use of stone knives to perform the mutilation in more recent historical periods is a kind of "evidence" for its existence in Neolithic periods, or earlier. I reject this argument entirely, as it has no demonstrable basis in the archaeological record. Likewise, rock art from prehistorical periods holds no clear or unambiguous evidence on this subject. Nevertheless, I was informed there was evidence of mutilated penis' to be found in the book *Prehistory of Sex* by Timothy Taylor,[3] where depictions of various "phallic batons" were shown. The images were interesting, but hardly proof of anything in the way of mutilations — one of the batons depicted a "double penis" which might be worn by a man for some rather humorous ritual, while others suggested tattooing of the penis, in the manner of decoration seen in various "penis tops" found in Oceania. Since the erect circumcised penis looks nearly identical to the erect uncircumcised penis, such carvings and drawings prove nothing one way or the other, except that early humans took a lighthearted interest in sexuality, fertility and the sexual organs.

Herbs for Fertility Control

An entire chapter in Saharasia was devoted to this question, of contraceptive herbs used by native subsistence-level women to control their fertility. In the last several years, groups of women in the USA and Europe have gathered sufficient information on herbs native to their regions, and have started using the herbs for fertility control, regaining the ancient knowledge as it previously existed among either native North American tribes, or pre-Christian Europe. The herbs being discussed by these women's groups work to bring on a late menstruation, much in the manner of the "morning-after pill", or they can be taken in higher doses to produce a full abortion. The herbs also appear to be much cheaper and easier to use, with less pain and side-effect complications, than the new chemical abortive pill RU-486. This new information on the herbal contraceptives is posted to various internet sites.[4]

Artificial Infant Cranial Deformation in Egypt

One sub-chapter in Saharasia was devoted to the subject of artificial infant cranial deformation around the world, giving citations to published accounts of the practices, with eye-witness quotes about its traumatizing effects upon the infant. For historical cranial deformations, a primary source was E. J. Dingwall's book *Artificial Cranial Deformation*,[5] which presented an argument about the possibility of dramatically severe artificial infant cranial deformations being carried out in Egypt at the time of Akhenaten. Recent conversations with the scholar Jörg Dendl in Berlin, Germany, suggest this line of argument — for *ancient* Egyptian cranial deformations — is based solely upon various statues of Akhenaten, his daughters and wife, and has so far not been confirmed with the presentation of any deformed skull as obtained from a mummy or similar remains. This cautionary note therefore should be added, regarding the potential absence of direct confirming evidence for artificial cranial deformation in ancient Egypt. Milder forms of artificial cranial deformation do appear in North Africa in *more recent times*, and Dingwall published examples of these, to include examples among Coptic Christian groups in Egypt.

References:

1. Heide Göttner-Abendroth, *Matriarchat in Südchina*, Kohlhammer Verlag, Stuttgart, 1998.
2. James DeMeo, *Saharasia*, Natural Energy, 1998.
3. Timothy Taylor, *Prehistory of Sex*, Bantam Books, NY 1996, p.129.
4. See the chapter on "Contraceptive Herbs" in DeMeo, 1998, ibid, and newer information posted at: http://www.orgonelab.org/contracep.htm
5. E. J. Dingwall, *Artificial Cranial Deformation*, J. Bale, Sons & Danielson, Ltd., London, 1931.

APPENDIX:
Open Questions, and a Note of Caution on Radiometric Dating Methods

The following article was written approximately in 1983, as an Appendix to the doctoral-dissertation version of *Saharasia*. At the time, I was advised by my good friend and mentor Prof. Robert Nunley, to *not* include this material in the dissertation, as it might "sink the ship". Saharasia was already properly described as a "marriage of heresies", and this additional material raising critical questions about radiometric dating methods as absolute determinants of the age of an artifact or archaeological deposit, would simply have been "too much". The article is now being published, as during the ensuing years, *the described problems have neither been openly addressed nor resolved by mainstream science, and they remain as relevant open questions regarding the validity of dates given to the few very ancient skeletal remains documenting social violence prior to the widespread aridity which created Saharasia starting around c.4000 BCE.*

The arguments in my *Saharasia* were developed using conventionally-accepted dates, including radiometric dating methods, which, *in most cases*, are merged with available evidence from other dating methods, such as relative stratigraphy and dendrochronology (tree-ring dating). Used in this manner, where radiometric dates considered "too extreme" in the face of other evidence are quietly discarded and ignored, conventional methods can yield up a reasonable set dates with an internally-consistent logical chronology. When used in isolation, however, radiometric methods are fraught with complications and risky unproven assumptions which sometimes throw their results into serious question.

Specifically, I point to the very early dates given to the skeletal remains in southern Germany, at Ofnet, Talheim and Schletz, and at Jebel Sahaba and Wadi Kubbiyanna — these sites clearly show evidence of early isolated social violence (as discussed in the preceding article "Update on *Saharasia*"), but in most cases do not appear to be independently dated by any other means than a few samples subjected to radiometric analysis. In my view, this raises open questions about the dates, and the possibility they might actually be *much younger*, with *the evidence of the violence itself placing them at a much younger period, closer to c.4000 BCE, when violence became epidemic across these same regions.*

While the subject material in the present article deserves, and easily could be supported with additional citations, it is presented in the original form, with minimal editing for clarification.

— James DeMeo, Greensprings, December 2001.

The last two decades (prior to c.1980) have seen the development and application of radiometric techniques for absolute dating. Unfortunately, some very large and important problems of basic assumption exist regarding radiometric dating techniques, problems which appear to be either generally unknown or widely ignored. The basic assumptions which have been challenged include, but are not limited to: A) variations in radioactive decay rate "constants",[1] B) elemental and isotopic stability (transmutation of elements),[2] and C) the absence of assumed uniformitarian conditions in the near-Earth geomagnetic, solar-terrestrial and cosmic-ray environment.[3] These problems may result in built-in random or systematic errors in various radiometric techniques which could be either moderate or extreme for any given artifact.[4]

Radiometric dates are not always published. A set of radiometrically-derived dates may be classified as "questionable" by a researcher simply because the dates obtained do not fit a particular theorist's view on the general time period an artifact is assumed to represent. In one recent North African study, over 25% of the radiocarbon (C^{14}) dates listed were generally rejected because they were considered either too old or too young for the consensus view on the artifacts in question.[5] The authors of that study are to be commended for publishing all their radiometric dates, both accepted and rejected, as public disclosure of such discrepancies is atypical, the usual procedure being to simply file away and forget radiometric dates which do not fit into one's working hypothesis. It would be preferable if date-rejection criteria were developed and adhered to *prior* to radiometric analysis, such that obtained dates would independently either verify or oppose dates determined through other dating methods. These concerns aside, it is notable that many European archaeologists have for years entirely rejected radiocarbon dating given the wide divergence of such dates from previously developed chronologies, and problems exist between Soviet and Western dating systems as well.[6]

Other examples of problems with radiometric dating techniques may be cited. Settlements, grinding stones, and grain kernels (barley and wheat) were discovered at one North African site. The artifacts were dated to c.16,000 BCE by an initial series of radiometric analyses, suggesting a very early period of food production.[7] However, later radiometric analysis of the grain kernels themselves, found in buried hearths and on the floor surfaces of buried structures, yielded dates ranging between c.2800 BCE and CE 1100. Other unpublished radiometric dates on the grain were discarded, the reason given being possible contamination at the analytical laboratory. The field researchers involved stated *"there were no indications of disturbance at the excavation site and apparently no nearby sources from which later organic remains could have been derived"*. However, acting upon the basis of radiometric analysis alone, the same field researchers concluded that the grain was *intrusive*, probably dating from c.2800 BCE. They did not attempt to explain how the youthful grain became positioned at the same stratigraphic layer as the older, "deeply buried" grinding stones. It is apparent the field researchers accepted the older radiocarbon dates at the site, but rejected the younger dates on the grain, as that is what could most easily be incorporated with other evidence identified by their *in situ* field work.[8]

Another study discussed radiometric dates from materials in sediment beds which varied in a paradoxical manner, with materials higher up in the sediments yielding older dates than materials at greater depth, which yielded a younger date. The "inversions" of C^{14} dates sometimes exceed the limits of standard deviation error-bars, strongly suggesting some (or all!) of the dates cannot be correct. Also, materials collected at the same depth layer gave discordant dates, even when collected in concentrated samples, and the straight linear relationship between depth and C^{14} age did not hold true. In this particular study, where C^{14} inversions were discovered, rather than question the validity of the radiometric dating technique, the researchers chose *a-posteriori* to invoke an argument of soil movement, something which their field observations failed to originally suggest.[9]

Other studies have demonstrated significant errors in C^{14} date determinations where inorganic carbonates are involved; radiometric dates can vary widely from age determinations made through other dating methods, and similar dates can be obtained across large regions of different geological age and structure.[10]

It is of significance that the first systematic control studies cross-testing radiocarbon methodology and accuracy were performed in 1975. In these studies, a sample material of known and established age (such as a single layer of tree-ring) was ground up and homogenized, and then sent to different radiocarbon laboratories for evaluation. Or, multiple samples of the same identical-age preparation were sent to the same laboratory. The laboratory technicians, in these control studies, were not informed they were evaluating different samples from the same source material, but instead thought they were testing different unique samples of potentially different ages. The results were revealing: radiocarbon age-determinations varied widely between different analytical laboratories, and within the same lab. The variances were significantly greater than the margins of error, indicating that the true errors in C^{14} dating may approach or exceed four times the stated values.[11]

Given the problems of basic assumption mentioned above, such a "hierarchy of definitiveness" which places radiometric techniques in a superior position to all other forms of reasoned analysis, is unacceptable from a scientific point of view. It has been said that dates estimated through artifact typology, relative stratigraphy, or historical methods alone, without corroborating radiometric analysis, should be viewed with caution. I believe that the reverse is at least equally true, that *materials dated through radiometric techniques alone, without corroborating reference to history, artifact typology or stratigraphy, should be viewed with caution.*

Where dating techniques conflict with each other, no absolute chronology should be strictly formulated; in such a case preference clearly should be given to the field site analysis. Radiometric techniques are not inherently superior, being only one of many dating methods, possessing their own strengths and weaknesses, and their own special problems of basic assumption. Given the uncertainties discussed by the various authors cited in the first reference above, it is seen that the "hard physical science" underlying radiometric dating really does contain a great deal more slop and squish than its proponents have admitted.

References:

1. Dudley, H.C. *The Morality of Nuclear Planning*, Kronos Press, NJ, 1976; Anderson, J.L. & G.W. Spangler: "Radiometric Dating - Is the 'Decay Constant' Constant?", *Pensee*, 4(4):31-3, Fall 1974; "Serial Statistics: Is Radioactive Decay Random?", in *J. Physical Chemistry*, 77:3114-21, 1973; Emery, G.: "Perturbation of Nuclear Decay Rates", in *Annual Review of Nuclear Science*, Annual Reviews, Inc., Palo Alto, CA, 1972.

2. Kervran, C.L.: *Biological Transmutations* Swan House, 1972, and Crosby Lockwood, 1971.

3. Seuss, H.E.: "Secular Variations of the Cosmic-Ray-Produced Carbon 14 in the Atmosphere and their Interpretations", *J. Geophys. Res.*, 70:5937-52, 1965; Seuss, H.E.: "Climatic Changes, Solar Activity, and the Cosmic Ray Production Rate of Natural Radiocarbon", *Meteor. Monogr.*, 8(30):146-50, 1967; Renfrew, C.: "The Tree-Ring Calibration of Radiocarbon: An Archaeological Evaluation", *Proceedings, Prehistorical Society*, 36:280-311, Dec. 1970.

4. A series of papers rasing questions on radiocarbon dating appeared in *Pensee*, Spring-Summer 1973: W.F. Libby: "The Radiocarbon Dating Method"; I. Velikovsky: "The Pitfalls of Radiocarbon Dating"; H.C. Sorensen: "The Ages of Bristlecone Pine"; T. Mowles: "Radiocarbon Dating and Velikovskian Catastrophism"; I.M. Isaacson: "Carbon 14 Dates and Velikovsky's Revision of Ancient History - Samples from Pylos and Gordion"; A.W. Burgstahler & E.W. MacKie: "Ages in Chaos in the Light of C14 Archaeometry".

5. Wendorf, F.: "The Paleolithic of the Lower Nile Valley", in F. Wendorf & A.E. Marks, eds, *Problems in Prehistory: North Africa and the Levant*, SMU Press, Dallas, 1975, p.134-135.

6. Waterbolk, H.: "Thirty Years of Radiocarbon Dating: The Retrospective View of a Groningen Archaeologist", in *14C and Archaeology*, W. Mook & H. Waterbolk, eds., PACT, Proceedings of the 1st International Symposium, 1983, p.17-24; Kohl, P.: "The Namazga Civilization: An Overview", in P.Kohl, ed., *The Bronze Age Civilization of Central Asia, Recent Soviet Discoveries*, M.E.Sharpe, NY, 1981, p.xxvii.

7. Wendorf, F., et al: *Science* 205:1341, 1979; Wendorf, F., et al: *Loaves and Fishes: The Prehistory of Wadi Kubbaniya*, Dept of Anthropology, Southern Methodist U. Dallas, 1980; Wendorf, F., et al: *Science 82*, 3:68, Nov. 1982.

8. Wendorf, F, et al: "New Radiocarbon Dates on the Cereals from Wadi Kubbaniya", *Science*, 225:645-6, 1984.

9. Cohen, D., et al: "Radiocarbon Dates from Gombe Point (Kinshasa, Zaire) and Their Implications", in Mook & Waterbolk, 1983, ibid, p.441-52.

10. Hotzl, H., et al: "Problems Involved in 14C Age Determinations in Carbonates", in *Quaternary Period in Saudi Arabia, Vol. 2*, A. Jado & J. Zotl, eds., Springer Verlag, NY, 1984, p.325,329; cf. Harkness, D.: "The extent of Natural 14-C Deficiency in the Coastal Environment of the United Kingdom", Mook & Waterbolk, 1983, ibid, p.351-64; Riggs, A.: "Major Carbon-14 Deficiency in Modern Snail Shells from Southern Nevada Springs", *Science*, 224:58-61, 6 April 1984.

11. Scott, E., et al: "14-C Dating Reproducibility: Evidence from a Combined Experimental and Statistical Programme", in Mook & Waterbolk, ibid, 1983, p.133-45.

Orgonomic Functionalism

A lecture by Myron Sharaf, Ph.D.
Presented in Berlin, Germany, 22 October 1989*

Editor's Introduction:

This lecture by Myron Sharaf was a highlight of the *Wilhelm Reich Tagung: Beiträge zur Lebensenergieforschung (Wilhelm Reich Conference: Contributions to Life Energy Research)*, a two-day event which featured presentations by different professionals from the USA and Germany. Myron was known for his engaging and personal speaking style, where he would walk among and speak directly to individuals in the audience, without significant lecture notes, oftentimes using volunteer members of the audience in demonstrations, to help make a point. He could quickly bring to life the most slumbering of audiences. His speaking style, as well as the subject material for this particular lecture, were difficult for the German audience, presented as it was in English with no simultaneous translation — this provided some challenges, but also points for humor. The lecture is presented here as it was transcribed from audiotape*, with some minimal editing. For those of us fortunate enough to have known Myron, and heard him speak, this paper provides another opportunity. [Bracketed sentences are from the audience.]

Dr. Myron Sharaf:

I remember Reich once told his students, "Find your own words." Not his words, but your own words. And I did not really understand fully what he meant, because, being quite young at the time, and still today, I don't quite feel that there is another way to say "orgone," or "armored," or "orgone accumulator" than to use his words. But there are other words, not for orgone accumulator or orgone, but for a lot of things. And it's important to find one's own words.

That's how we've become differentiated leaves on a common tree. Otherwise, I'll just go around saying "orgone," "orgastic potency," "Dor" — it gets very boring. Orgonomy can become very boring if it's just repeated as some catholic ritual. It has to be used freshly, as does orgonomic functionalism, to which I will get in a few minutes.

The silence surrounding orgonomy — in its central aspects, not something like body therapy, but its central aspects — is as large as the work itself. And I am

* Many thanks to Linda Ketron for transcribing the original audio lecture tape. Dr. Sharaf was a practicing therapist, author and lecturer residing in Newton, Mass. He passed away in May 1997, and a memoriam is given on p.272.

fascinated why, after Reich's work began 70 years ago, he's been dead for 30 years, people can't blame his personality, or his being in jail anymore, and yet very little happens. You really can count it on your fingers and toes — a little more than that — what goes on seriously. It puzzles me on the one hand; on the other, it's rather clear: Because it's frightening. I know from my own inner experience; it's not easy to keep in touch with these concepts, techniques, and findings.

I'd like to begin talking about the silence. The silence is particularly great, interestingly enough, around my topic — orgonomic functionalism.

I would like to begin with functionalism in the sense of some general distinctions, not as a precise method of thought. The general distinctions are expressed best in Reich's *Ether, God and Devil* — which I heartily recommend you read. The wonderful thing about Reich, it's like great music. If you haven't heard great music in a few months, it sounds like you never heard it before. And when you read Reich after not having read him for awhile, it feels like you haven't read it before. It's one such book. It's one of his absolute best books. And in that book, among other things, he distinguishes between functionalism, mechanism, and mysticism. I will leave aside animism which he also discusses, a primitive way of seeing the world which he found closer to functionalism than either mysticism or mechanism. But it distinguishes right away, or early in the book, the rapidity [sic] of mechanism — that it wants these exact, perfect, absolutely repeatable; it tolerates uncertainties and ambiguities poorly; it compartmentalizes, breaks things down into ever smaller divisions for greater and greater exactness, and in so doing, makes things more complicated. Now, there's a nice saying: *He who knows only his own side of the case, knows little of that.* How many got that? Be honest. If you're in an argument with someone, and you don't understand their side of the argument, you don't understand fully your own. Because it's a dynamic interaction. And I've seen orgonomists and psychoanalysts and everybody else argue as though they win all the points. It's like watching a tennis match in which, you know, one player wins every point. And that's a very boring tennis match and, intellectually, that's a very boring intellectual match.

Mechanism has advantages over orgonomy in its own realm. An electric bulb will turn on and off, absolutely predictably, barring the bulb going dead, or a power shortage, or something mechanical and correctable. You can't get in that accumulator and have a light bulb go on. Figuratively, whether an "orgone-light bulb" goes on – whether orgone-irradiation goes on – depends on the weather, your own inner state, depends on pollution, depends on a number of things. It's not an absolutely predictable device. Reich once said he was aware of this dilemma about ... he had a motor — which everyone wants to know about, but nobody finds out about — they don't find out about what's available, so I don't have much compassion for them not finding out about what's not available. He once said of the motor, which ran at differing speeds depending on the weather, it could slow down to nothing on a very humid day, and he said rather ironically, who would want a motor that functions according to the weather? You want to go somewhere, and you can't go, the weather turned bad. I say that only to show the complexity of these things. On the other hand, a light bulb and most mechanistic inventions cannot charge the energetic core of the organism. And the accumulator, under the right conditions, can. So, the accumulator is like a high roll; a high roll is when you throw dice for a thousand dollar. I mean, you may lose, but if you win, you win a lot. Any questions?

So that is one of the things — the much more fluidity of functionalism, a basic nature, as you would put it, which I think people are coming to these days from various roots, like the study of fractals by Mandelbrot, for one, and chaos theory; there's a lot of phenomena that have to do with basic nature that are very irregular and hard to predict. The study of the weather, or the stock market also depends upon something very unpredictable, or human emotion; and blood pressure which is also highly unpredictable. They're trying to see what kinds of patterns they can find given the irregularities. I don't really know much about it, but sounding as though I do. But I think it's a fascinating theory, one of those theories that connects with orgonomy, but which you have to be careful to see where it connects. And where it doesn't.

I'll just read a little of Reich on that, just to get a flavor of his prose.

"The typical mechanistic physicist thinks according to the principles of machine construction which he essentially has to serve. A machine has to be perfect. Hence, the thinking and acts of the physicist must be perfect. Perfectionism is an essential characteristic of mechanistic thinking. It tolerates no mistakes, uncertainties; shifting situations are unwelcome. The mechanist works on artificial models of nature when he experiments. The mechanistic experiment of the 20th century has lost the essential part of genuine research — the handling and imitation of natural processes which stand to work for all pioneers in natural science."

I think this is very important in terms of the processes of research and, for Reich, it was indispensable to begin in a highly qualitative way. To look at the atmosphere, to look at Dor clouds, to look at the sky — before he started measuring anything. But unlike the mystic who is happy to look forever, he wanted to move to measurement. You know, Reich is hit from the right and the left. The right (science) hits him for not measuring well enough. The left (people of... well, I don't know what exactly to call them, mystic is a little extreme... but new age-type people), they criticize him for measuring at all. That it's all "flow", being "with it", and it's beyond measurement. So, in that sense he's different from both the mechanists in beginning qualitatively and trying to preserve qualitative aspects in his quantitative design. As the whole idea of shifting the thinking about the accumulator, which he originally thought of as rays entering the body, like x-rays, in which case you could put a mouse in a big accumulator, to an energy field interaction between the organism sitting in there and the accumulator. They're like two people who radiate together. And, therefore, he'd have to put a mouse in a small accumulator to have that field interaction. So he shifted his design and his experiment to fit the conditions.

I would like to emphasize because it's often not emphasized how much of a "mechanistic" scientist Reich was, in the sense of wanting proof and wanting to really test it. As he said to students, "Prove me wrong," which is a wonderful statement, a very positivist statement, that a statement only made sense if it could be proven wrong. If you go around saying, you know, some day it's going to rain. It's really hard to prove you wrong; someday it's most likely going to rain and nobody's going to be around here until the end of time to find out if it rains. But if you say it's going to rain within three days, you've got something much better ... within two days, within one day. A more useful prediction. And Reich was interested in predictions and a lot of this work came out of negative findings. Of not getting what he wanted to get. Even though there are other times you read him you feel that anything he wants, he gets, but other times, you read more closely, he didn't get what he wanted.

In the oranur experiment, for example, he thought that orgone energy would diminish the effects of nuclear radiation. To his surprise, a negative finding, the nuclear radiation triggered a big reaction on the part of orgone energy, made orgone energy much more destructive than it had hitherto been. That was a surprise, it was a negative finding. He had many negative findings: His whole sex-political work viewed from one angle was a negative finding. His sex-political work didn't rally the masses, as he thought it would; communism didn't bring sexual affirmation, as he thought it would. And out of that came many, many changes in his thinking and procedures. One of the problems is that he can sound so dogmatic at times that you cannot realize how much he is changing. He can sometimes be like somebody who's madly in love with a woman, who's then disappointed, and then suddenly madly in love with another woman. You say, well, what about the first one?

Essentially, Reich does see the mechanistic scientist as a compulsive character. Things are warded off, feelings warded off. There are very thick boundaries, and that's being studied more and more, the concept of boundaries. People who rigidly distinguish between day and night, self and other, play and work, fantasy and reality, often have quite thick boundaries. People with thin boundaries blur everything. They're likely also to be more creative and more vulnerable to emotional illness, the thin-boundary people. Thick-boundary people do pretty well, just in terms of everyday functioning. Not much life. It's thin-boundary people who tend to be attracted to orgonomy, because orgonomy does put a tremendous emphasis on commonness, not separating. In fact, it also emphasizes separation. But thin-boundary people often want everything to belong to everything else and there's an appeal to them in orgonomy from that viewpoint. They don't want to separate, classify, and categorize, put everything in its pigeonhole; too much so, everything equals everything. But the trouble with the mystical person who often is attracted to orgonomy is that there's a wall between excitation and the perception of the excitation, as in the schizoid, they are spacey, flakey, space cadets. You know what a "space cadet" is. It's a spacey person who goes up into the skies ... that's a joke. A space cadet is somebody who is not grounded in the world, he's up in space. They're often like that, and they're rather difficult people, in terms of orgonomy, because they're attracted but then they always want to mix it with something else and combine everything, with astrology, with this, with that. And it's not disciplined. And it's confusing. The advantage of the mechanist is that he tends to keep away; he doesn't get all excited and then disappoint you. So those are some of the distinctions.

I do think the emphasis on a lawful irregularity, or a lawful fluctuation, is a beautiful idea. I mean if people were at a conference like this and it were mechanistic, they would be here exactly at 9:00, paper one would stop at 9:45, paper two at 10:45, boom, boom, boom, boom. Mystically, which it sometimes is here, papers would go on for several hours, and you'd just feel the "vibes" of when it should stop. Functionalism, as it has been here sometimes, would be neither way, something else, a sort of orderly mess.

I like this: *"The world of orgonomic functionalism is a vigorous, free, and still lawful and harmonious world."* [Reich] It's a beautiful thing to think about, trying to conceptualize something like the wind, you know, which is so vigorous and free, and yet which, I believe, is also lawful and harmonious. *"In it"* — this is in the world of orgonomic functionalism — *"there is no empty space,*

Symbol of Orgonomic Functionalism

See Wilhelm Reich's *Function of the Orgasm* for detailed discussion

which the mechanistic physicist postulates because he cannot feel nature. In it, too, there is no space for spirits and phantoms, which mysticism believes in but is not able to demonstrate. The world of functionalism is then no shadow world as it is for the abstract mathematician but it is a tangible, praktisch [sic] (German for practical), full, pulsating world, perceivable and measurable at the same time." Did you get the English? Would you say yes or no? Who didn't get it? You didn't get it. Okay, I'll try to speak more slowly. [Audience requests to translate or rephrase the book; more difficult to understand quotations than speech; Sharaf translates to high hilarity.]

But that idea of orderliness and freedom — it's a beautiful idea. Casal says it about music, too; he has a wonderful recording where he is talking to students about music, he says, "You can be as free as you like," in his rich, Spanish accent, "but with order. Fantasy as much as you like, but with order." You cannot do just what you please. And Reich is very good on that. You can tell from his work, he was an extremely disciplined person who was not mechanistic. I never knew how he got done what he did, because he seemed, a lot of times, quite relaxed.

I wanted to say a few words now about the more systematic diagram [of orgonomic functionalism]. Someday we may worship at this symbol the way Christians worship at the cross. Without knowing what it means. Back to polarities. In psychoanalysis... the polarity that most interested him was Freud's polarity of impulse and restriction from outer world, or worlds, simply because sometimes the outer world responded positively, but the problem came when the outer world punished or inhibited the original impulse. Then psychoanalysis had inner divisions, like between the impulse or id and self-preservation, and between the libido and death instinct. And then the structural theory between the id and the ego and superego. But I feel Reich really gets going with this in a paper that Bernd Senf cited which is very little known in America ever since the sixties — in the sixties it was better known because it was part of Reich's Marxist arbeit (work)— "Dialectical Materialism and Psychoanalysis." It's just an absolutely brilliant paper; I just read it again.

In the paper, psychoanalysis, as he applies dialectical materialism to it, takes on a much more swinging character, intellectually. Because he sees the impulses as thesis, and the block from the outer world as antithesis — an antithesis which is like a whole series of policemen: First, it's like in the general culture which could be like the national police; then it's local police, the family, which really instill it; and then, it's internal police, namely the parents inside you or me, saying "don't do that." And it doesn't matter if the content shifts. The parents may have said "don't be sexual," but the current value today may be "be sexual." But how they are the same? How are they functionally identical? That's right, it's an order. But, it's even more than that, if you listen carefully to the tone in which people speak to themselves, it's often very punishing. They don't just say, "it'd be nice to be sexual." They say, "I'm bad, I'm no good, I'm armored, I'm dead," in a very hostile, self-hating way. So the message, and the tone, you can almost put it together with the tone of the parent saying, "don't be sexual." The tone is the same. As McLuhan used to say, "The message is the medium." The message changes, but the medium of punishing stays the same.

All that stuff, the police stuff, is seen as antithesis, and the synthesis is what happens to that impulse, the repressed impulse, afterward. And it often reemerges as what? What happens to an impulse that is repressed? [Audience member: It becomes destructive.] It becomes destructive, that's part of it and a good part of it. But also it becomes a symptom very often, a compromise between those two forces, a synthesis, a destructive synthesis, but a synthesis. Say a person whose sexuality has been thwarted, the impulse is repressed, but at the same time it comes out. Part of the energy drive (I'm going to get to that in a minute, the energy) — say in hysterical characters (women or men), the impulse emerges as a flirtatiousness. Coquettishness, sexiness, provocative. Seductive. That contains the defense against sexuality, because the person has no intention of carrying through with this. And the seductiveness is partly aimed at finding out where is the danger, so I can avoid it. But it also expresses some sexual energy, clearly. And it's also destructive because it gets the other person on edge; it's a mixed message. And gets them destructive. That thesis, antithesis, synthesis is very beauti-

fully developed by Reich in that paper, and as well as his love of dialectical materialism — not just as a method of thought, but as a way of viewing history and life. That everything was in movement; he talks about functionalism as a vigorous, moving world, well, so was dialectical materialism.

Psychoanalysis had many static concepts; for example, the oedipus complex was considered always there, always would be there. It was like a fixed point, like a stationary earth or a stationary sun — the oedipus complex was there. And Marx did see it that way, Marx and Engels. There was a matriarchal time, then there was a patriarchal time, then there could be a communist time where the family form would be totally new. It doesn't matter whether he was right or wrong in content, it's the way of looking, of not seeing things as fixed, as being dependent on other conditions, social conditions. And Reich was enormously interested in that because he was interested in the changed individual, somebody who was not neurotic, not armored, not just trying to treat him through therapy but treating him through history — history as therapist — and he saw Marxism a way to get that. Now to me the point where Reich branches out into his own thinking is around, well it's slow, it's around 1930, he talks in dialectical materialism and psychoanalysis about a common source of energy, say for self-love and love of others in libido. He's not now talking thesis, antithesis in this moment; synthesis is a common principle that yields two things: love of self, love of others. Now if that impulse is broken up, say in his example the child masturbates, thinking of its mother (the boy child), the impulse is no longer safe, the child is afraid (I'd like to think of my mother, but I'm afraid to because I'll get punished, or I'd like to masturbate, but I'm afraid to). There are various solutions: he can give up masturbation; he can also give up that unity of tenderness and sexuality and think of his mother and act toward her tenderly and masturbate in some perverse way, you see, or the perverse fantasy. A practice he may continue with women into whore women and saintly women. Well that's all very obvious, the content is obvious, but the method is not so obvious of one thing yielding two. There, disturbed energy can yield a split between tenderness and sexuality.

In *Character Analysis*, he gets it even more clearly when he's looking the energy of the repressing forces. Not the content — the content that says "Don't masturbate" — he knows where that comes from; it comes from the outer world, it's internalized. What gives the internalized content its energy? And there he has a very nice statement in which he says — the basic idea is simple and the puzzle is that it hadn't been discovered before — the energy to deny sexuality comes from sexuality. The impulse starts to go out ... [drawing on board] ... then is blocked, it turns in against itself. Sexual energy is blocking the sexual energy. And that's very clear if you see people who fight sexuality, against adolescent sexuality, for example. You can see clearly that it's a sexual energy driving that fight against sexuality. They can think about it all the time, they can ... get off on it. Just as, say, in a symptom of washing your hands, the energy of that symptom comes from the anal impulse because you're constantly concerned with dirt, if you're washing your hands. The content "Be clean" is something else again. That came from outside. But it often is that way. We're often using the same energy as what we're trying to stop. And we just tie ourselves in ropes. And so I think one of the most important parts of therapy is to teach people to stop trying. Reich often said that, "Stop trying." And Lowen has a very nice phrase here, "Accept defeat." He has exercises around it. And it's contradictory, people think if they accept defeat, they are defeated. It doesn't mean that.

A very nice example of that is found in religion: If you search for God, the more desperately you search, to overcome your disbelief, very often the less you believe. If you cry at 3:00 AM in the morning out of the feeling, "My God, I don't believe." At 4:00 AM, you may believe. So you can't cry in order to believe, because God won't be manipulated and neither will life energy. Is that statement clear? Maybe I'm defeated about English and should just accept it, talk more slowly, then you'll all understand.

What one usually thinks about Reich is that he was extremely loyal to Freud and Marx; he was like somebody who's on a ship that is sinking and he would throw over different parts of the stuff on the ship to keep it afloat. Like he'd throw over the death instinct theory, cultural theories, dictatorship of the proletariat but he always wanted to keep some — which he always did keep — but he kept them at his own cost for awhile. He must talk about dialectical materialism until he came to America, and many psychoanalytic concepts, then he began to get his own thing going: orgone energy, orgonomic functionalism, work democracy. He didn't talk in those terms of a common functioning principle, till quite a bit later (eight, nine years).

And he began to use this symbol more and more. I'll just give a very few examples of it. There are healthy forms of this, say, like orgastic potency, love and work. Now you often call this the common functioning principle, or CFP, with variations.

Orgastic Potency — Love / Work

The older concept of antithesis, doesn't really fit — love and work — they're not really antitheses. But there could also be sicker forms which have more of an orgastic impotence CFP, and one set of variations may be moralism and pornography.

Orgastic Impotence — Moralism / Pornography

These have a quality of fighting each other; moralists often fight pornographers and vice versa. But they're also identical in the common functioning principle because they can shift; moralists can become pornographers, as some of our churchmen have become in America.

[Question from audience: What does the CFP mean?] Common functioning principle. It's the thing that unites; these two are united in that third deeper thing. And this thing should often be close to the other two. Say you want to understand the change in the world today of the East and the West becoming less militaristic — both the East and the West — you say, what's the common functioning principle of that? You can't say orgone energy. It isn't close enough to the phenomenon, nor is orgastic potency. It has to be sensible. There are many things in where he used this, and he always used it, always looked for the opposite in nature, in people. That's not so uncommon — to look for the opposite — if you see somebody super sweet, you think, when is he going to hit me. Right? Are you with me? Or against me? Actually afterwards, I'm going to hear people say, "You know, I didn't understand much of what you said." If you have something to say, say it now. Did you hear about the super sweet person? Did you understand it? I see all these blank faces. Yes. Do you know what "sweet" means? If you see someone very polite, you may look for the opposites, right? It's not natural to be that sweet. So we do look for the opposite. What we look for much less is the common functioning principle of these two phenomena, and we look for it less in phenomena that are less clear-cut than sweet and hostile.

I'm going to go on now to some examples of this that interest me and that I've been thinking about, that Reich didn't write about ... It was a side of Reich I didn't like too much; I mean, he really wanted to own the intellectual world, a part of himself. I remember once I had an idea, I didn't have too many ideas, but I had a pretty good idea. It was very much connected with what his idea was. So when he read it, he looked up sort of annoyed and he said, "Why didn't I think of that." I mean, he'd thought of a million ideas, I'd thought of one, and he wanted to think of it.

I would like to start off ... In the core of the organism, there is only: "yes". In the sense of a full impulse; it may be a destructive one against some kind of real threat, but it basically acts fully. If that impulse is frustrated, it turns into "no" and "yes", like in the hysteric. The sexual impulse is frustrated, it turns into the "no, I won't be deeply sexual/yes, I will be coquettish, provocative, flirtatious, sexy." Now, the question is, these "yes/no's" are a very important part of our lives, we deal with them all the time ... I think, most people do, many people do, I do. And it goes on in the mind as a kind of debate, which Reich talks about, and I'll just quote a few sentences: "I love you but I'm afraid of being punished for it." The polarity is love/fear. Is that clear to everybody? "I hate you because I'm not allowed to love you but I am afraid of gratifying behavior." There's punishment for hate, as well as for love. And one of the outcomes is, I don't know whether I love or hate. One is paralyzed. To end the paralysis, one of the things you do is to get to that "NO." I believe this is more important than the false "yes" or the partial "yes." That will collapse more or less by itself if you get to the "no." And you have to break through ... and not by force, and not by argument, but by energizing. You have to break through the rationalizations of that "no" that are now internalized. I'm talking about the internalized "no." You have to deal with the external no, too. The patient may be mad at the father who said, "You're a prostitute" and therefore she denied her sexuality or it became blocked. Fathers in Europe say that a little more than fathers in America. Mothers in America say other things.

That's a problem. It's much more easy to see something outside as the enemy than something inside. "Yes, he was awful to have said that to me." What's harder to do is to say, "I don't like sexuality, I've internalized that, I feel I'm a prostitute or would be a prostitute if I were more sexual, or I would surrender to his power if I became vulnerable. So he was mean, I'm not going to be vulnerable to him, I won't feel deeply, sexually or otherwise." And this gets generalized to people, say men, generally. As Mark Twain once said, "A cat that jumped on a hot stove won't jump on a hot stove again, but he won't jump on a cold stove either." [Some confusion, a German translation - Myron is frustrated] Is everybody clear about the goddamn cat? It's very important the way, one way to help somebody distinguish between a hot stove and a cold stove is to hold them over the hot stove until they bring forth all the emotion that they felt when the father said, "You're a prostitute." You understand me? Probably not.

Can you volunteer? Since I'm talking about a prostitute, a woman might be better, or anybody, volunteer for a minute. I would like to demonstrate this. [A young woman volunteers] Good. I won't take a real life example, I'll take this example, ok? She's acting, this is in the theatre: Her father has called her a prostitute. And she has some feeling about that but not a full feeling. That is like the hot stove, she avoids that feeling that she experienced when he jumped on her with that abuse. Is it clear? What I try to do is to get his exact words, as close as I can, and say that to you:

"You're a prostitute." Now, you say "no" to me. [No.] "Oh yes, you are." [NO!] She's actually a professional actress. Try to do it more with your voice; as I get older

I have to cut down on the physical. "You're a prostitute." [No.] "You've always been one." [No!] "I don't want you to be one." [No.] "I want you to be religious." [No!]

I'm not going to do it all because it's complicated. Thank you. [woman sits down] But it has to do with going through those emotions — that's one part of it — that's the part that came from the outside. Come back for a minute: [woman returns] Now just imagine that you think you're a prostitute. Ok. Not a literal one.... but you also debate it. Or you think that, if you were with a man who you weren't going to marry, you'd be like a prostitute. Ok? Or with a man you didn't deeply love. Ok? You don't like that attitude of yourself. Tell me "no"; I'm going to be your inner voice:

"If I go with him, I'll be awful, but I want to go with him, but I don't want to go with him. I'll be awful. I don't want to go with him. But I want to get involved with him, he's nice." Say "no." Say "no" to the debate. Say "I'm sick of it." [No.] Say "I'm sick of it." [I'm sick of it."] Louder. [No!] You have this debate, I have this debate. [No, no, stop it, stop it.!] "I don't know whether to go out with him, I don't know whether to go away with him." [Leave me alone.!] "I could enjoy it, but..." [No, you are a liar. Liar. No!] "I'm your voice. This is what you told me you're thinking." [No!] Ok. Breathe. One of my favorite expressions is "Hate me but breathe." [woman returns to seat]

This goes quite far, this "no" — people do not allow themselves to say "no." I don't mean to say "no, I'm not coming to dinner," but even then they invent a thousand excuses which any fool could see through, but to say "no, I don't want to do something" that I do want to do. I don't want to work tonight, I don't want to go out with her, I don't want to sleep with him, even if there's another side that does. You have to separate those sides and allow the negative feeling to come out in a full expression. Then you can deal with the positive. You can't deal with both feelings at the same time. It's like gridlock — stalemate — on a highway. The cars have to back off from each other, slowly.

If you want to say, "I just don't want to do it" the other side says: "You should do it; look how nice he's been to you." You want to tell your wife or your husband or your parent, "I don't want to do it" but the other side says: "You should do it, how can you feel that way, it's terrible to feel that way, good people don't feel that way." And we're so vulnerable to that argument that we shut up, rather than say just give me the space to express this "no", then I'll make the decision later.

I did find that useful when I was working on the biography of Reich which was often difficult. I would often say, "Oh, I should be doing more, it should go quicker, I should be smarter, I should be more disciplined." And then every time I would switch — a great teacher of mine, not Reich, had a three-step thing of awareness: One is "I don't know what to do" — and that's how I feel in the book, "I don't know how to write this chapter." Then I'd know how to but the next move was "I can't" — "I can't do it, I don't know enough, I'm not good enough." And the third step which gets to — "I won't, I don't want to." You know, the universal "fuck you" or what Reich called more politely, the Big No. And it's a very big step forward when clients can own that, that they are spiteful. None of us like to think of ourselves as spiteful. We like to think of ourselves as somebody who would just love to give, but the time isn't right, the person isn't right, the moment isn't right, the money isn't right, I don't know, any number of things. But we're just loving. Because we basically carry a child's view of themself. And a child is quite loving, very loyal and quite loving. He is a victim. But we're not victims — we are victims in some ways but we're also victimizers in a way a child never, usually isn't. Ok, enough of that one.

I want to go on to another one, about orgonomy [writing on the board]:

Contact with orgonomic paradigm/model

Clarity/clearness of paradigm

Articulation/ development of paradigm

A new paradigm, like orgonomy, develops out of an old paradigm. Is that clear? An old paradigm is like psychoanalysis and dialectical materialism — two paradigms, in fact. And Reich paid a lot of attention as the years went by to distinguishing his paradigm from ideas in psychoanalysis and Marxism that didn't fit his paradigm, that he disagreed with. He did it with classical science, too; he used to call orgone energy in the body "bioelectricity", which is a classical physics term or biological term. And he dropped it because it didn't fit a whole series of findings. So he was very concerned about maintaining the clarity of the paradigm. At the same time, he had quite a bit of interest — and you can see it in him at various places — of articulating, of connecting the paradigm with different phenomena. In some ways, articulation and clarity are functionally identical in the sense that, as you find out more what the paradigm can do, as you articulate it, you help make it clearer. Like oranur and the cloudbusting work help clarify the paradigm at the same time they articulate it. But there's also an antithetical quality between these two concepts. If you articulate too much, you overwhelm your paradigm, it can't handle it. Or the articulations

aren't very good. If, for example, you start using the orgone accumulator and a pyramid structure and six other things, you are not helping necessarily the clarity of the paradigm because we still don't know what the accumulator alone can do. We don't have more than a relative handful of good experiments. It's like the army principle: If you have two half-wits... you know, people with half a brain, somebody who's dumb... If you put two dumb people together, you don't get a smart person. Right? No way! It's often wrong because the principle there is only multiplicative. Like if you multiply halves, what do you get? A quarter, right, you get a quarter worth. And if you put a pyramid and an accumulator together, you may get a quarter of an experiment, not a whole one. Reich tried the accumulator with a hundred things but they want him to have done it with ... I don't know, a vitamin pill or something like that. I'll get to that in a minute about the accumulator — but I feel that, on the other hand, with regard to therapy, there needs to be more articulation with other work because the orgonomic model is strong enough to not be overwhelmed. And to put those findings — though it's always difficult — as subordinate to orgonomy.

This is very important. It's like who's running the show? Who's the director? And what I have in mind by articulation is that orgonomy is running the show. Until it is observed that orgonomy is inadequate, is not good enough to handle certain findings. And if they're major enough, you need a new theory. Not every little thing you can't handle, you don't throw out your theory, but if enough unexplained things get together, you can have a crisis in your theory. If it should happen that we are all reincarnations of people who lived in the past, that would provide something of a crisis for orgonomic theory. Orgonomy hasn't dealt with that topic. And with its rather naturalistic view, it wouldn't be entirely comfortable with it. It might be able to handle it in terms of energy and the cosmic energy ocean, but there would be some difficulty. On the other hand, if the temperature difference in the accumulators disappeared, that might not be a big problem because there's pollution, there's all kinds of environmental factors that may be lessening or eliminating that difference. I'm not saying that's happened.

Say I am a therapist interested in doing the kind of psychodrama I began with her, of her father calling her a prostitute, and getting to her affects. If I just went with that, I'm not in orgonomy, I'm in psychodrama. But if I use that to trigger her rage or her tears and then deepen that in the body, I'm in orgonomy and I may have added a useful tool — I haven't added it, I didn't discover it, Marino did — but I put Marino and Reich together in a certain way. And it might be useful for her but not for him. I know there are people who believe one could get to those affects other ways, just purely through the body. I think that's true, but I also think that some therapists, with some patients can get to them faster using such a technique as psychodrama.

There's a Jewish saying, "'For example' is not proof." If you say, "Does psychodrama work?" Yes, I had a case today and it worked. Well, that's just an example. I don't know whether it works or not from that. It's true we can pile up more numerous cases where things work, but we need to be much more careful in all of this thing of what we mean by "works." And I'm arguing that, particularly in the therapy realm, my viewpoint is something like Ecclesiastes — do you know Ecclesiastes from the Bible — "There is a time for rest, there is a time for play." You know that? "There's a time for speaking, there's a time for silence." You know that? Nobody reads the Bible anymore. There's a place for the Bible, too — in therapy. Well, there's a time for soft bioenergetics which Eva Reich speaks of very highly, there's a time for hard bioenergetics, there's a time for psychodrama, there's a time for talking, there's a time for breathing, there's a time for low charge, high charge, there's times for a bunch of different things, and we've got to figure out which are the times and which are the people that it works best with. And the same thing with the accumulator.

The accumulator is even more of a mystery. Thousands of people are doing some form of body therapy but only a handful are doing anything with the accumulator. The accumulator is nicer in many ways because it does lend itself to a decisive test. But we need to articulate the theory, we need to keep it clear — it's hard to do both, both in terms of time and in terms of the personalities of the people who are attracted to clarification, keeping clarity, and those who are attracted to articulation — they're often different type people. Very few people can do all of this by themselves. So we need working teams. People who tend to focus on clarity get awfully dogmatic; you know, Reich discovered in 1923 this, and in 1926 that, in 1928 that, in 1932 that, 1936 that, and this is this and this is this and this is this, and you go from the eyes down. I mean, they could recite it in their sleep. I'm exaggerating but they do serve a useful function in keeping many things clear. And it's only when you meet some bad articulators that you realize what you left at home was not so bad. Because articulators are bringing in everything — in a chaotic way — and it's not intellectually at all disciplined. It could be very hostile. It could be hostile in the sense that, if you mix everything up.

You know, if I say, you are just like him who is just like him, I'm not seeing any of you. And I often feel that orgonomy is not seen. There's a very nice phrase by a literary critic that you can't see something else unless you're ready to let yourself be seen. And most people are not ready to let themselves be seen by orgonomy — the insights it would reveal about them. Therefore, they can't see it. But it's very important — this isn't just true for Reich — that, whenever you have a new paradigm, vast upheavals are taking place. You have to have a new technology very often, like the accumulator, the Dorbuster, the cloudbuster; you have a new way of thinking — you can't communicate very well with people who are outside your paradigm; they might just as well be in a different culture or speak a different language. You have to start forming bridges so you don't live in isolation without food or water. You need translators who find common words between the two different systems. And you have to do a lot of things to maintain contact ... you have to integrate the old within the new — what's valid in the old. You have to integrate, you have to keep clear, and there's always dangers. If you go toward too much integration and bridges, you can lose clarity.

A very good example, and I believe it's a true story, is that when the Jesuits went to China in the 18th century to spread Catholicism, Christianity, they didn't have any security in China — like many of us, we don't have academic tenure or something — so, they went to China and they didn't have citizenship in China, they didn't even have, like working papers, green cards or red cards or whatever they are. When they got to Peking which was a complicated process, they could have something like citizenship, but that was two years off. They wanted to start right away on spreading Christianity but they knew the Chinese didn't think the same way Christians did. They were very naturalistic, not supernatural, the Chinese. Plus they didn't want to get in trouble, they had no security. So the Jesuits said, Christ was a lot like Confucius, he lived a good life, he taught people to be good, moral, ethical, things like that. And the Chinese thought this was pretty good, you know, like sometimes we can talk about Reich as though he's quite like Freud, not all that different — Marx — when we want to ingratiate ourselves. If we want to rebel, then we say he's totally different. And the Chinese liked the Jesuits. But then when they got to Beijing, they had a press conference, and they said, "Now, there are a few more things we want to tell you about Jesus." You know, his virgin birth, son of God, went to heaven — so they told them the truth. The great danger is, if you pursue this way of making links — of articulating Confucius within Christianity — is that you never say what they said when they went to Beijing. They're so thrilled with the popularity of talking like Confucius that they stay that way.[§]

Ok. I think that's enough. We have time for some questions. Let me just try an experiment, ok? Only half of you will die. Stand up. Can you all stand up? I want you to all say "no." Say "no." [No.] If I tell you to ask me questions on the work, about orgonomy, say "no," you

[§] Editor's Note: The chronic avoidance of Reich's work on adolescent sexuality and orgastic functioning are still widely ignored by many claimed "Reichians" on the therapy/bodywork scene is one example here. Reich's genuine followers who have "gone to Beijing" tend to speak the socially-uncomfortable truths.

don't want to. [No.] Louder. [No!] I'm going to make you ... [No.] ... ask questions... [No.] ... and understand English. Say "no." [No.] Louder. [No!] Give me a cigarette. Say "no." [No, no, no.] Loud as you can. [NO!] Ok, from everybody ... Just say "no." Ask questions. [NO!] Maybe you'll go home and say, you know, I thought of asking but I thought it was a dumb question so I didn't ask, but he didn't give me a chance to ask. Say "no" again. Ask questions. [No!] If you don't ask questions, I'm going to talk for three more hours. [NO!] All right, sit down.

Who's got a question? Who's got a criticism? Who's got a comment? [a man raises his hand] I can't believe it. Yes? [Can you tell us something about orgonomy today in the United States?] You know, the analysts have a good principle that I never use, or rarely use. But it's good on certain occasions and this is one of them. It's very good to use. If somebody asks you something, you respond "what makes you ask." What makes you ask? [I want to know what Dr. Reich has said what has been done to move his ideas forward.] But why do you want to know? I mean, are you just interested in what they're doing, or do you think they're not doing good, or do you think they're doing good, or you know somebody over there, or you want to go there yourself? [Maybe.] You might want to go there? To do what? Study? [Experience.] Just experience ... to become trained as a therapist? Work in a laboratory? [Mainly ... to see does orgonomy exist, or not exist.] I see, you want proof. There are people here who work in orgonomy. Why don't you let them prove it to you, or not? [Yes, I've tried to do it here and there are not as many ...] In America, you think there are more in America? [Yes.] I don't think they're going to be very happy when you come saying, "I'd like you to prove to me that orgone energy exists." [I don't want them to prove, I want to see what they're doing, and think about it, and then decide for me.] I know, but it isn't like that you can just see it, like something at a museum. It's something you have to work with. I mean, if you came to me and said I want to see whether your therapy works, I couldn't show it to you. You'd have to undergo that kind of therapy yourself. Or you'd have to sit in the accumulator every day. I don't mean to be critical of you ... this is a somewhat mechanistic question. It's like we could turn on a button, and the light of orgonomy will shine on your face, like Paul at Damascus, you know. [I didn't mean it like this.] I know you didn't, but that's how it sounded. And as Reich often said, words reflect things of our inner state. You would like to find out if orgone energy exists, and I don't blame you, I'd like to find out, too. But it takes a lot of work, that's what I'm saying, not a visit. Now, here's what they're doing ... But that's a useful question because I get some idea of the background of the question. Questions are rarely just academic, like in Vienna, somebody asked me, "How would Reich deal with phobias?" Later, she told me she had an intense phobia about pigeons which is a very personal phobia, so it wasn't just some general question by a therapist ("How does he deal with ..."), it was a very personal question. So is his question. It doesn't mean that I don't answer, but I answer more knowledgably. Usually if I don't find out what's in the background, I say much too much.

There are some courses with the scientific material that last a week or two weeks[‡] that I think are quite good from what I've heard; I haven't taken them. You can actually get introduced better to the scientific work than you can to the therapeutic work unless you just become a patient, but then you have to stay there at least a year or so. [It's very expensive.] What is expensive? [Therapy.] Everything, all good things are expensive. [At this time, I can't afford it.] Ok, then you can take the science course. Why don't you write and find out when they have the course. I don't have it on me, but there are people here who do have it. I'm not at liberty to give you their names right now, but they're here. Ok? [Ok.] Are you satisfied with my answer? [Yes.] Who is not satisfied?

[I have another question. I observed now your lecture during the last hour and I know that you are talking about something that we did not create a resonance for. And I know that there is the impulse of your side and the impulse of our side, but somehow there's a difference of frequency we are talking about.] That's very good. Did you understand what he asked? [German translation] Why is the resonance lacking? [Because ... what I know from my side ... I don't have a real contact of what is orgone energy. And you have it.] More or less. You've been hearing about orgone energy all day, haven't you? [Yes.] I see, good. [Now my question, has orgone energy something to do with the thinking process mainly? Is that pictures, and thinking, is the substance of that, is that orgonomy?] That's a very good question. And my immediate temptation is to say yes, but I feel that would be stupid. [Will you repeat the question, please?] Yes, are our thoughts made up of orgone energy? I feel it would be stupid because it needs a lot more study; I think it is. Because everything, almost everything that we don't understand, often connects with orgone energy. It's not just made up of it but connects with it. Reich was very concerned with that in his very first methodological efforts, that thoughts unrelated to an excitation of the body — if you're sexually excited, you have pictures of sex, easily; if you're hungry, you have pictures of food. If you've had a full meal, it's hard to get an idea of food. If you've been sexually satisfied, it's hard to get an idea of sex. So there's a relationship between ideas and our vegetative states,

---

[‡] The Orgone Biophysical Research Lab offers a three-week Guided Independent Study Program, specifically designed for hands-on experimental investigation into the central findings of orgonomy. See page 252 for details.

and he actually believed that sexual excitation and orgone energy were intimately connected. And that he was flowing in excitation from the center out to the hands, legs, genitals, everything. So, I think you're right but we haven't done much with that. I mean, it's a difficult question to prove. Reich did prove that, or at least had evidence that, pleasure was connected with a flow of energy from the center to the periphery, from periphery into the stomach. And he demonstrated with measures. But nobody to my knowledge has done even a systematic clinical study of thinking and emotion. And emotion clearly provides articulation for orgone energy ... sadness, pleasure, anxiety. It's a very good question.

END

Published Works by Wilhelm Reich on Orgonomic Functionalism, or as mentioned in the lecture:
- "Biophysical Functionalism and Mechanistic Natural Science", *Int. J. Sex-Economy & Orgone Res.*, 1:97-107, 1942 (Reprinted in J. Orgonomy, 8(1):5-18, 1974).
- "Orgonomic Functionalism, Part 1: Ether, God and Devil", *Annals of the Orgone Institute,* II, 1949 (Reprinted in *Ether, God and Devil/Cosmic Superimposition,* Farrar, Straus & Giroux, NY, 1973).
- "Orgonomic Functionalism, Part 2: On the Historical Development of Orgonomic Functionalism", *Orgone Energy Bull.*, 2(1):1-15, 2(2):49-62, and 2(3):99-123, 1950; continued in 4(1):1-12 & 4(4):186-196, 1952.
- "Orgonometric Equations 1: General Form", *Orgone Energy Bull.,* 2(4):161-183, 1950.
- "Complete Orgonometric Equations", *Orgone Energy Bull.,* 3(2):65-71, 1951.
- *Function of the Orgasm, Discovery of the Orgone, Vol.1,* Farrar, Straus & Giroux, NY 1973.

Published Works by Myron Sharaf:
- "Wilhelm Reich: Listen, little Man!" *Farmand Magazine,* Oslo, Nov. 27, 1948 (Reply to Trygve Hoff's Review ibid., Oct. 18, 1948, S. 13).
- "The First Orgonomic Conference at Orgonon August 30 - September 3". *Orgone Energy Bull.* I(1), Jan. 1949, S.23-29.
- "A Dangerous Tendency in Contemporary Thought", *Orgone Energy Bull.* I(1), January 1949, S.30-33.
- "Erich Fromm: Man for Himself" *Orgone Energy Bull.* I(4), October 1949, S. 193-198.
- "Communication: From the History of Science" *Orgone Energy Bull.* III(1), January 1951, S.35-38.
- "A 'Critique' of Reich's Character Analysis" *Orgonomic Medicine* I(1), June 1955, S. 75-82.
- "Priority of Wilhelm Reich's Cancer Findings", *Orgonomic Medicine,* 1(2):145-150, 1955.
- "Impressions of the Trial of Wilhelm Reich", *Orgonomic Functionalism,* V(3):153-178, 1958.
- "Hiding and Spying: Unorganized and Organized", *Orgonomic Functionalism,* VI(1):7-25, 1959.
- "'Powerdrunkenness' In Some 'Orgonomic' Types", *Orgonomic Functionalism,* VI(2&3):67-75, 1959.

- "Clarifications" *J. Orgonomy* I(1,2), November 1967, pp.182.
- "Some Remarks of Reich: Summer 1948" *J. Orgonomy* II(2), November 1968, S.215-224.
- "Some Remarks of Reich: Summer 1948 (Continued)" *J. Orgonomy* III(1), march 1969, S.116-119.
- "Some Remarks of Reich: Summer and Fall, 1948" *J. Orgonomy* III(2), November 1969, S.247-253.
- "Ollendorff Reich: Wilhelm Reich: A Personal Biography" *J. Orgonomy* III(2), November 1969, pp.254-266.
- "Some Remarks of Reich: Autumn and Winter, 1948 "*J. Orgonomy* IV(1), May 1970, S.126-135.
- "Further Remarks of Reich: Summer and Autumn, 1948 "*J. Orgonomy* IV(2), November 1970, S.250-257.
- "Further Remarks of Reich: Summer and Autumn, 1948" *J. Orgonomy* V(1), May 1971, S.97-106.
- "Further Remarks of Reich: Autumn, 1948, and Spring, 1949" *J. Orgonomy* V(2), November 1971, S.215-220.
- "Further Remarks of Reich: 1948 and 1949" *J. Orgonomy* VI(2), November 1972, S.238-240.
- "Further Remarks of Reich: 1949" *J. Orgonomy* VII(1), May 1973, S.113-116.
- "Further Remarks of Reich: 1950" *J. Orgonomy* VII(2), November 1973, S.254-258.
- "Further Remarks of Reich" *J. Orgonomy* VIII(1), May 1974, pp.90-94.
- "Further Remarks of Reich" *J. Orgonomy* VIII(2), November 1974, pp.225-229.
- "Further Remarks of Reich" *J. Orgonomy* IX(1), May 1975, pp.105-109.
- "Further Remarks of Reich" *J. Orgonomy* IX(2), November 1975, pp.239-240.
- "Further Remarks of Reich" *J. Orgonomy* X(1), May 1976, pp.129-131.
- "Further Remarks of Reich" *J. Orgonomy* X(2), November 1976, pp.271-275.
- "Further Remarks of Reich" *J. Orgonomy* XI(1), May 1977, pp.96-101.
- "Thoughts about Reich" *J. Orgonomy* XI(2), November 1977, pp.240-245.
- "Thoughts about Reich" *J. Orgonomy* XII(1), May 1978, pp.100-103.
- "Thoughts about Reich" *J. Orgonomy* XII(2), November 1978, pp.264-269.
- "Wilhelm Reich's Early Work on Character Analysis" *J. Orgonomy* XIII(1), May 1979, pp.81.
- "Thoughts about Reich" *J. Orgonomy* XIII(2), November 1979, pp.268-284.
- "Thoughts about Reich" *J. Orgonomy* XV(1), May 1981, pp.96-107.
- "Wilhelm Reich and 'The Structure of Scientific Revolutions" *J. Orgonomy* XV(1), May 1981, pp.96.
- "A Writer's Awareness" *Offshoots of Orgonomy* No. 3, Autumn 1981, p.43.
- *Fury On Earth: A Biography of Wilhelm Reich,* St.Martin's/Marek, NY 1983.
- "Conversations with Elsworth F. Baker/Perspectives in Orgonomy, Volume I" *J. Orgonomy* XIX(1), May 1985, pp.144-150.
- "The Articulation of Psychological Knowledge within an Orgonomic Paradigm" *J. Orgonomy* XX(2), November 1986, pp.235-243.

CSICOP, *Time* Magazine, and Wilhelm Reich

by John Wilder*

In the lushly-produced March 29,1999 special issue of *Time* magazine, 100 people, headed by Sigmund Freud, the founder of psychoanalysis, were presented as the 'top' scientists and thinkers of the 20th Century. In a separate, much shorter, top 'Cranks' list of just three people, *Time* placed Freud's star pupil, Wilhelm Reich.[1] Since after the 1960s psychoanalysis was largely replaced by the widespread use of psychotropic drugs, it is somewhat odd that psychoanalysts would head both lists. I wrote to *Time* magazine and asked what criteria had been used to select the top scientists, thinkers and cranks of the 20th century, and by whom. *Time* replied with silence. The 'whom' probably includes contributing editor Fred Golden, a protégé of former *Time* sciences editor Leon Jaroff. More recently, Jaroff himself took a jab at Reich.[2]

Few of *Time*'s readers are aware that veteran science writer, editor, and publisher Leon Jaroff has long been an important member of *CSICOP,* the self-appointed *Committee for the Scientific Investigation of Claims of the Paranormal,* or that for many years Jaroff has been promoting CSICOP's views from his bully pulpit at *Time.*[3] Jaroff joined Time, Inc. in New York in 1951, working as a reporter at *Life* until 1958 when he moved over to *Time* magazine. By 1966 Jaroff was *Time*'s chief science writer, and was appointed to Senior Editor in 1970.

Who was Wilhelm Reich and what is CSICOP? A little history here may help the reader understand what is at stake for science and for culture.

In 1929 Sigmund Freud's most promising 'third generation' student, Wilhelm Reich, returned home to Vienna from an official visit to the Soviet Union. Soviet physicians and social workers knew that Reich had done more than anyone else to turn psychoanalytic theory into productive clinical practice and that Reich was keenly aware of how society affected the health of his patients and, in turn, of how society was affected by the health of his patients. Soon after returning, Reich was invited to speak to Freud's inner circle to discuss his Soviet trip.

At the meeting Reich strongly presented his argument that psychological health is based on sexual health,

and, if it is to survive, there must be a radical change in childrearing practices. Furthermore, a supportive social and economic environment not then present in western civilization, nor, for that matter, in any civilization on earth must be obtained. Reich argued that a radical, 'bottom-up' social restructuring of civilization could be brought about by a new, more dynamic merger of Marxism and psychoanalysis.

It is likely that Reich presented the same thesis to the Soviet leaders he met. Joseph Stalin, who fully believed in the authoritarian, 'top-down' control of society by an elite, surely would have rejected Reich's ideas. Interestingly, Reich's suggested 'new beginning' did find political adherents, especially in central Europe. One result seems to have been 'integral socialism,' itself an antecedent of later anti-Stalinist Eurocommunism.

Like Stalin and his cohort, Freud and his inner circle fiercely rejected Reich's proposal. Freud was greatly disturbed, and in answer to Reich, Freud wrote his well-known 1930 essay *Civilization and its Discontents*, stating his belief that "the human animal, with its insatiable needs, must always remain an enemy to organized society, which exists largely to tamp down sexual and aggressive desires." Interestingly, *Time*'s editors have selected Freud's reaction to Reich's ideas, *Civilization and its Discontents*, to be one of the 20th Century's top-ten, required-reading pieces of nonfiction.

For his part, Reich, through his clinical and sociological studies, had come to a more naturalistic understanding of the function of the human animal's sexual health and its underlying role in supporting a healthy society. In 1930, as the Great Depression began to take hold, Reich moved from Vienna to the international city of Berlin, arguably at that time the cultural 'capital city' of the world, to study first-hand the surfacing of the corrupt and brutal realities which were behind the facade of idealistic western civilization. He developed street clinics in an experimental attempt to attack at the roots the developing twin social pathologies of German fascism and Soviet Stalinism. Reich's prescient observations made during this period would later be collected and published together in 1933 as *The Mass Psychology of Fascism.*[4] This was the same year the German masses voted Hitler into power, and the same year the German federal police, the Gestapo, put Reich on its secret death list and began burning his books. Also, during this same

*John Wilder is an educator in the Midwest with a long-time interest in the works of Wilhelm Reich. He can be reached at: JWildResearch@netscape.net

Not to be outdone by CSICOP Fellows working at *Time magazine, Skeptical Inquirer* magazine (Jan/Feb. 2000) presented its own list of "The 10 Outstanding Skeptics of the Twentieth Century", a lineup which included (according to number of votes received): James Randi, Martin Gardner, Carl Sagan, Paul Kurtz, Ray Hyman, Philip J. Klass, Isaac Asimov, Bertrand Russell, Harry Houdini, and Albert Einstein. One is led to wonder, how the last three individuals, dead for many years, would have felt about being included on such a list.

period, both the Communist International and the Psychoanalytic International expelled Reich from their organizations and publications. Meanwhile, in America in 1933, Soviet communist apologist Corliss Lamont published the *Humanist Manifesto I*,[5] the founding statement of the Humanist movement, attacking capitalism and promoting Soviet top-down solutions to the world's economic and social problems.

Today Reich is acknowledged, usually grudgingly and in private, to have been an important factor in the development, from the middle 1920s to the middle 1930s, of both Freudian psychoanalytic practice and of Marxist politics. However, by 1935 Reich abandoned both approaches as insufficient, and he increasingly turned to experimental biophysics. Years of hands-on studies of human emotional pathology, both on the couch and in the street, had convinced him that the so-called 'progressive' socialists, in fact politicians in general, had made a tragic *biological miscalculation*[6] by not recognizing the very limited ability of adult humans to change their pathological personal and social structures — both extremely stubborn structures, bioenergetically rooted. Reich termed this illness and its aggressive defense the Emotional Plague.

To better treat this rather unyielding disease within

the individual, Reich deepened his character-analytic therapy into the body's physiology itself and called it *vegeotherapy*. In fact, this treatment went much deeper than the 'mind-body' dualistic approaches of psychosomatic medicine; Reich had found, embraced, and understood the emotional and bioenergetic core of plasmatic pulsation.

Now under constant attack by thought-control and body-control agents of the Nazis, of the Stalinist-controlled Communist International, and of the Psychoanalytic International, Reich moved his laboratory from Germany to Norway. There, assisted by physicians and lab workers, Reich discovered microscopic proto-life forms which he termed *bions*. Later, he discovered a glowing radiation emanating from some of the bion cultures. After much observation and measurement, he reached the conclusion that this radiation is the physical and energetic reality behind the aether and life energy hypotheses. Reich termed his discovery the *orgone*.

In Europe, in the late 1930s, physiologically and mentally 'armored' intellectuals, such as those in the nationalist-socialists leadership (both Nazis and Stalinists) were threatened when Reich's revealing work disturbed their emotional and ideational rigidity. Hoping to defame him, fascist 'scientists' and 'reporters' of both left and right spread false rumors to the ignorant and the anxious masses, especially through the press. Brave independent scientists like the Dutch biophysicist W.F. Bon and the English anthropologist Bronislaw Malinowski (who had taken his Ph.D. in physics) tried to defend Reich and his new discoveries. However, this firestorm of rumor and slander in the media, fed by fascists, who were themselves agents of the disease he was attacking, *the Emotional Plague*, forced Reich to flee Norway to America — just months before the Soviet Union and Germany officially joined their forces in the late summer of 1939 — with the intention of dividing up control of Europe, and the world, between them.

Reich arrived in America as a hunted refugee in 1939. Working quietly for a few years in New York City, he earned a living by lecturing at the *New School for Social Research*, by treating patients, and by training many physicians. In his lab at home Reich constructed a small chamber to observe and measure further the unusual radiation he had discovered in Norway. Wanting high-quality peer review, Reich approached the physicist Albert Einstein with his discovery, and Einstein, clearly impressed, invited him to his Princeton home to discuss the matter in person. After several hours of discussion with Reich, Einstein asked for a replica of the experimental chamber so he could study the phenomena at length. Reich's unusual and innovative thinking intrigued Einstein, as it had Bon, Malinowski, A.S. Neill, and other original thinkers of that turbulent period.

In early 1941 Reich complied with Einstein's request by building another experimental chamber and delivering it to Princeton. Einstein spent two weeks in his own lab in Princeton studying Reich's device and observing the unusual temperature effects. Reich's chamber was constructed of alternating layers of metallic and non-metallic materials, a design similar in some respects to the then top-secret 'atomic piles' at nearby Columbia University which were, in some cases, also chambers simply constructed of alternating metallic (uranium) and non-metallic (graphite) materials. Einstein confirmed the temperature difference found within Reich's chamber, but a lab assistant offered a different explanation of the finding, which Einstein forwarded to Reich. Reich studied this alternative explanation, redesigned his experiments, retested, and, to his mind, was able to rule out the alternate explanation. Reich then forwarded his new designs and results to Einstein by mail. A year's silence followed, despite repeated requests by Reich for a reply.

Einstein's secretary, suspected to be a Stalinist agent by the FBI, had full power over what mail Einstein read, what went unread into the files, and what went directly into the trash. She is on record as saying she protected Einstein from 'cranks' by filtering out their mail. Years later, a letter would be received by Reich from Einstein's office asking that Reich cease attempting to contact Einstein, but it would not be signed by him. It is reasonable to speculate that, on her own, Einstein's secretary may have deliberately cut off Einstein's contact with the well-known anti-Stalinist Wilhelm Reich. By the late 1940s the FBI investigation of Einstein's secretary would be closed with the given reason being that it was believed she was no longer an active agent serving the interests of a foreign power.

Reich had observed Stalin's bloody 1930s purge trials, his immoral two-year alliance with Hitler, and his approval of the 1945 rape of Berlin (intended to crush the non-Stalinist German left as well as the Nazis). In 1946 Reich published in English the strongly anti-Stalinist edition of *The Mass Psychology of Fascism*.[4] His book quickly became the most sought-after book in the New York Public Library, and it quickly provoked a defensive knee-jerk reaction from Stalinists in America. Both Reich and his scientific work became the focus of their intense hatred, which, as in Norway, would be expressed through underhanded rumor campaigns and through slanderous articles in magazines — written by journalists with agendas, including the pro-Communists Frederick Wertheim and Mildred Edie Brady. New evidence that Brady was a Stalinist agent with deep influence within the FDA is collected in *Wilhelm Reich and the Cold War*.[10]

Time has been a 'safe house' for journalists with agendas. Soviet agent Whittaker Chambers became a senior editor at *Time* in the 1940s before testifying against his friend, the well-protected Soviet super spy Alger Hiss. Chambers' testimony against Hiss earned him the enmity of many of *Time*'s leftist staffers, including a close friend of Mildred Edie Brady's, *Time* associate editor Leon Svirsky. The following direct quotation from a letter dated December 27, 1944 describes Svirsky, and his relationship to Mildred Edie Brady.

> *"[Regarding Time Magazine]*
> *re Leon Svirsky, an Associate Editor:*
> *He used to work on the old (N.Y.) World Telegram; I saw him several times as he dropped in at the A.S.A. office or at lunch with Kallet. (At the time, I did not know Kallet was in or even specially close to the party.) He was also a close personal friend of Mildred Edie, left-winger, dropped with her husband Brady from the O.P.A. several years ago. Svirsky was certainly a leftist though I had no idea how far left. However, he was an intimate friend of Kallet, and I would say he would be willing to cooperate in any sort of left-wing intrigue. He was not, however, a strong or energetic fellow — seemed a rather weak and undetermined type."*[7]

As a 'far' leftist in a position to influence the course of one of the most important trials of the 20th century, Svirsky "became an adjunct of the Hiss defense, canvassing employees past and present for damaging reminiscences [of Chambers]"[8] Svirsky, who was working hard to protect the Soviet spy Alger Hiss, left *Time* and joined the staff of *Scientific American* during these years. It is interesting that the 'Godfather of CSICOP,' Martin Gardner, a major opponent of Reich's work dating from at least 1951, counted Svirsky as his personal friend,[9] and as his first editor at *Scientific American,* Brady, Svirsky, and Gardner seem to have traveled the same journalistic roads, with the same political agenda.

By 1957 Reich had been railroaded into an American federal prison via a campaign of media propaganda attacks and questionable legal tactics. Readers seeking more details on the political 'take-down' of Reich should read Jim Martin's *Wilhelm Reich and the Cold War*,[10] and Jerome Greenfield's *Wilhelm Reich Vs. The USA*.[11] Reich's books and inventions were burnt in four separate bonfires, the last in 1961, at the direction of senior FDA officials beholding to Mildred Edie Brady. She had been instrumental in writing and orchestrating the passage of the 1938 federal laws that had given the FDA the much larger scope and enforcement powers it later possessed in the 1950s.

After Reich's death obscurity threatened his work. Most historians, fearing retribution, avoided mention of him, except with a large dose of derision. Recently, for example, the psychoanalytic historian Peter Gay made no mention of Reich in his massive biography of Freud, despite Reich's obvious importance to Freud and to clinical psychoanalysis.

On May Day in 1976, as the Soviet Communists

were celebrating their favorite holiday in Red Square in Moscow, the American Humanist Association held its annual meeting in San Francisco. Marxist-Humanists Paul Kurtz, Martin Gardner and a group of like-minded intellectuals met and founded the *Committee for the Scientific Investigation of Claims of the Paranormal.* Their acronym, CSICOP, indicated their apparently conscious intent of becoming the scientific 'psychic cops' or 'thought police' of a brave new world.

One founding member of CSICOP, the Marxist-Humanist philosopher Paul Edwards, respected editor of the 1967 *Encyclopedia of Philosophy,*[12] had been a patient of two physicians trained by Wilhelm Reich. Edwards publicly credited Reich and his "brilliant therapy" with giving him greater insight into the mind-body problem than anyone else.[13] As Edwards was a leading philosopher, and as the mind-body problem is the central problem of philosophy, this is, of course, a great compliment.

The 1933 *Humanist Manifesto I* stated, *"Holding an organic view of life, Humanists find that the traditional dualism of mind and body must be rejected."* Furthermore, a quote from *A Humanist Wedding Service* (1972) says, *"Humanism sees man as an active and inseparable unity of body and personality. Reason is the guide, but reason never separate from the emotions and strivings of the whole person..."* [14]

It's not easy to walk your talk, however. Philosophical methods and discussion did not, do not, and cannot resolve the mind-body problem. Again, recall Reich's *biological miscalculation.* As an active healer, Reich worked with the patient to integrate his or her conceptual 'seeing,' emotional 'believing,' and biological 'feeling' into a functional whole, with a healthy spontaneous emotional and sexual economy underlying and giving a seamless intuitive meaning to the patient's logical, rational thought. Reich found that the mind-body split was a deep biophysical wound traced to ignorant and/or abusive childbearing and child rearing practices. This wound could be somewhat modified in the adult through the unique biophysical therapy he had invented, the therapy Edwards says he experienced with great benefit, especially with regard to integrating his mind and body.

Although Edwards still (in an interview with me in 1999) says he strongly believes that Reich's therapeutic inventions are far more effective than the 'talking cure' of orthodox Freudians, he says that Reich's late 1930s claims of discovering the bion and orgone energy trouble him. Edwards admits that sitting in an experimental orgone accumulator many years ago gave him conjunctivitis, a puzzling effect of an experimental apparatus that he is highly skeptical of; yet, nevertheless, conjunctivitis is a symptom predicted by Reich to be an unwanted side-effect of this invention. Privately, Edwards says that while he still thinks that Reich became a crank in the last six years of his life (beginning in 1951), Reich may eventually be proven right in all of his work, not just the psychiatric.

In the 1960s, several years following Reich's death in an American federal prison, Edwards agreed to aid one of Reich's students, psychiatrist Elsworth Baker, MD, prepare Baker's book *Man in the Trap*[15] for publication. Edwards says that Baker mostly declined his suggestions; however, perhaps coincidently, Baker did drop references to *orgone energy* in his book, adopting the less provocative term 'life energy.' Some say life energy is just another name for orgone: "What's in a name: that which we call a rose By any other name would smell as sweet...." Others say 'life energy' is just a concept, a vague hypothesis; while orgone is a perceptible reality, a demonstrated, proven theory.

Interestingly, Edwards now decries what he calls the 'right-wing' politics of Baker and others of Reich's students in America, as he believes they have missed the contributions of Reich's 'Marxist' period. The reader should recall that Reich, himself, dismissed this part of his work as a 'biological miscalculation,' as immature, as being insufficiently aware of the of the extreme stubbornness of the Emotional Plague.

Edwards, as a founding member of CSICOP, has long contributed to CSICOP's magazine, *The Skeptical Inquirer.* Despite Edwards lukewarm admiration of Reich, CSICOP seems to be populated with men who adhere to modern civilization's mind-body split, a split which underlies the mechanistic-mystical dichotomy that fuels CSICOP's engines. 'Alternative' sciences and 'New Age' religions have inched forth since the early 1970s as the body-mind split has begun to soften here and there, probably due, in part, to the influence of Reich's work. However, despite being parented by the Humanist organization which says it philosophically rejects the mind-body split, CSICOP appears have taken offense to this early, somewhat muddy tide of mind-body merging. The CSICOP leadership seems to view the mind as a rather fancy computer and the body as a complicated robot, thus attempting to solve the mind-body problem in an oddly mechanistic way.

The membership, organization, and style of CSICOP reveal its traditional patriarchal, 'top-down' authoritarian character. Its membership, according to Hansen, is 95% composed of 'white' males; and nearly 100% of its members are intellectuals, mostly drawn from the non-scientific disciplines, despite CSICOP claiming 'science' as its patron. Few active research scientists belong. The membership at large, the 'Fellows,' has little, if any, power to formulate or change policy. Thus, organizationally, there is little if any democracy, as policies are developed top-down by a small board of directors (Councilors) which is not elected by the membership at large, but which instead selects its own members. This small governing board has been dominated by one man since its inception 25 years ago — Chairman Paul Kurtz.

Sometimes life imitates art.

In Joseph Conrad's story *Heart of Darkness*, set in Africa in the late 1880s,[16] a fervent, idealistic proponent of western civilization, Kurtz, is sent by his company into the primitive jungles of central Africa to trade for ivory. Greatly disturbed by what he sees as the African natives' profoundly uncivilized, impulsive, and irrational behavior, Kurtz becomes thoroughly corrupt through his increasingly brutal efforts to promote and retain the power and control of his rigidly-idealistic, 'civilized' vision. To intimidate and terrorize the natives, Kurtz cuts off the heads of those who oppose him and sticks their heads up on stakes around his compound.

Kurtz becomes very ill. Nearing the end of his life, there on a boat in the depths of Africa, Kurtz cannot see the soft, flickering flame of a candle held but a foot away. Although blind, he stares with hardened, piercing eyes into what he fears is the very heart of nature, penetrates it, and finds it terribly dark. Dying in the grip of the unbearable recognition that it is he, not Africa, who is darkly hollow at the core, he whispers, in a commingling of desire and hate, "The horror! The horror!" Left behind is a report that Kurtz has prepared to be sent to the *'Society for the Suppression of Savage Customs'*.

Fast forward 80 years. In the late 1960s, in 'real life,' in the depths of capitalist America, Marxist-Humanist philosopher Paul Kurtz, the future Chairman of CSICOP, watches in horror as his hometown of Newark, New Jersey is set on fire by the aroused and angered African-American working class of that city. Kurtz, a Marxist-revolutionary during his own young adult years,[17] watches in further horror as screaming, chanting mobs of European-American students, led by 'new left' radicals, take over many college campuses. In Paris tens of thousands of French 'new left' students nearly topple the French government; the students, ignorant of Reich's turn away from political solutions, ignorant of the *biological miscalculation*, wave copies of Reich's early Sex-Pol writings as banners of revolt. In China millions of students organized into Red Brigades force the Communist bureaucratic elite to work with their hands in the fields and the factories, turning Chinese society upside down.

Facing these unexpected outbreaks of apparently irrational behavior in the masses, facing what Reich had faced in the early 1930s (due to what Reich termed *the biological miscalculation*), Kurtz struggles to reforge his Marxist-Humanism into a weapon of control and repression. While Reich had turned away from politics to supporting changes in child rearing, to advocating sexual reform, and to studying biophysics, Kurtz, still at his core a political man, seeks elitist political and social solutions to suppress these uncontrolled, 'unscientifically' emotional horrors emanating from the masses. In 1973, Kurtz republishes, in his own Prometheus Books, the *Humanist Manifesto I* and publishes the *Humanist Manifesto II*, of which he is the co-editor.[5] In the next year, Kurtz would publish Wolfgang Leonhard's *Three Faces of Marxism: The Political Concepts of Soviet Ideology, Maoist, and Humanist Marxism.*[18]

Also in 1974, Kurtz would sponsor his friend, the pro-Communist Corliss Lamont, to be the Honorary President of the *American Humanist Association* (AHA), a group Kurtz has come to dominate.[3] Lamont had been identified as a Communist in the late 1940s by former Soviet agents Louis Budenz and Hede Massing. Lamont's own parents (his father was Thomas Lamont, the Morgan Bank chief executive) had written to him that Lamont's vocal pro-communism would lead anyone to believe that Lamont was, in fact, a Communist. Fearing McCarthy's anti-Communist crusade, Lamont finally publicly rejected Communism in a 1952 tract.[19] Still, for the rest of his life Corliss Lamont would continue to find much that he liked in Communism, and in 1976 he would publish a pamphlet he wrote praising the economic structure of Communist China, a tract written shortly after Kurtz had sponsored him to the AHA presidency.[20] Years later, when Lamont died, the journal *Human Events* headlined an article *"New York Times* Honors Memory of Stalinist Corliss Lamont," an indication that Corliss Lamont's place in history will be near that of Alger Hiss and Robert Oppenheimer.

What Marxist-Humanists find appealing in Communism, social restructuring controlled by an elite leadership, goes deeper than political philosophy. There is the anxious urge to control everything, especially the emotional and the 'spiritual,' and the effort to destroy originality and spontaneity, including entrepreneurship, often by means of deceitful ambush. Once in political or economic power, this fearful, biophysically-armored elite would move to establish absolute control (regulation) over all natural processes.

Kurtz proposed, in another 1974 book, *The Fullness of Life*:

"With the death of God and the obsolescence of nationalism, the next move should be towards the building of one world." (p.190) and *"If one world cannot be achieved within the UN...then it should be achieved outside of it. Massive effort is needed in every possible direction."* (p.194)[21]

Here, Kurtz's goal resembles A-Bomb physicist J. Robert Oppenheimer's 1960s proposal that the 'irrational' nation-states and their politicians be replaced by a world government of an elite world-wide network of rationalistic scientists.

Reich himself had hoped that eventually the whole world would become a 'work-democracy,' composed of the fluent teaming of biophysically-healthy, open-minded investigators — but not a structured knowledge empire ruled by a distant elite of dogmatic academics.

Kurtz further observed:

"Looking to the 21st century we may list four areas in which some of the most significant developments are likely to occur...

*1. Increased **control** over nature...*

*2. **Control** of human behavior....The methods nearest at hand are those of operant conditioning and reinforcement in behavioral psychology (B.F. Skinner), and of electrical, chemical, and thermal stimulation of the brain...(See Jose M. R. Delgado, "Psychocivilized Direction of Behavior, The Humanist, March/April 1972)...*

*3. The genetic **control** of evolution...*

A CSICOP Vision of the Future?

A monkey with cranial-implanted electrodes learns to press a lever to get its food (above) while a human (below) gets a similar experimental implant. *"...it is already possible to equip animals or human beings with minute instruments called 'stimoceivers' for radiotransmission and reception of electrical messages to and from the brain...Behavior such as aggression can be evoked or inhibited. In patients, the stimoceiver may be strapped to the head bandage."* (From J.M.R. Delgado, *Physical Control of the Mind*, Harper Collins, 1969, pages 89-91. Copyright © 1969 by J.M.R. Delgado. Reprinted with permission of HarperCollins Publishers.)

4. The colonization of space..."

[Above citation by Kurtz; Bold-face emphasis added, J.W.][21]

Control by whom and for what purpose? Does Kurtz's respect for Delgado rest on Delgado's mind control experiments? In one experiment, Delgado inserted a small electronic device into the brain of a bull.[21] After being teased into charging, the bull was stopped dead in his tracks when Delgado pushed a button that sent a radio signal to the electronic device in the bull's brain, which, in turn, stimulated a terror response in the bull. This is Delgado's, and Kurtz's, "Psychocivilized Control of Behavior." Delgado's book shows photographs of similar experiments with captive monkeys and with institutionalized humans.[22]

Kurtz also praised B. F. Skinner, the behavioral psychologist, whose famous isolation chambers deprived patients of all sensory contact with the outside world. Skinner argued that there is no free choice, that control is everywhere, that we can change mankind by controlling the environment.[23] Skinner's device and techniques were the basis for several mind control and 'brainwashing' experiments, some of which may have resulted in death. Beginning in 1945, Skinner isolated his own infant daughter in such an isolation chamber for two years. She became a suicide in her 20s. D. Ewen Cameron, an intellectual descendent of Skinner's, took the "Skinner Box" to an even further extreme, subjecting — apparently without informed consent — human subjects to long periods of experimental sensory isolation followed by intense brainwashing. Cameron became head of the APA in the 1950s and publicly denounced Reich.[24]

What is the goal here that Kurtz appears to embrace? Genetically-modified, chemical- and radio-controlled, psycho-civilized 'robocops' whose purpose is to establish **control** over life on earth by an elite band of supervising 'scientists,' and then to extend that **control** throughout the universe? Is this an embryonic BORG Collective in the making, a mostly-machine, cyborg, Rationalist 'civilization' (with a faint remnant of humanity) that will put Star Trek's mostly 'Shakespearean,' emotionally-charged human heroes down for the cosmic count? *Is resistance futile?*

In recalling his years as a Communist agent, the author Arthur Koestler wrote that in Stalin's Communist underground the most forbidden word was '*spontaneous.*' Interestingly, in the film epic *Star Wars* it was Luke Skywalker's spontaneous intuition that defeated the forces of the Dark Side. Paul Kurtz, CSICOP's dark advocate of psycho-civilized control, has denounced the spontaneity-filled film *Close Encounters of the Third Kind* as a "sequel to the *Ten Commandments, Ben Hur,* and other religious extravaganzas."[3] What seems to be in conflict here is the beginnings of a spontaneous, rhythmic recognition of a 'spiritual' and physical unity versus the split body-mind (mechanized-mystical) controlled march into the gas chambers of the future.

Kurtz and CSICOP have already extended their efforts to control scientific research well beyond the borders of the USA. French scientist Jacques Beneviste, MD, winner of the *Medaille d'Argent (Medal of Silver) du CNRS* for the discovery of the Platelet-Activating Factor in the blood, was attacked by Leon Jaroff in the pages of *Time* for his work with the 'memory' property of water. Beneviste responded by writing:

> *"What Jaroff printed in Time magazine reflects Jaroff's obsessions and has nothing to do with informed and objective journalism. The surprise is that a magazine of the reputation of Time opens its columns to such a gross disfiguration."*[25]

Examining the claims of astrology, another French scientist, the statistician Michel Gauquelin, found, to his own surprise, statistically-significant evidence that athletes are more likely to be born under the 'influence' of the planet Mars than under that of other planets.[26] Gauquelin published this statistical finding and CSICOP quickly took up this 'paranormal' claim for investigation, the one and only scientific investigation into a claim of the 'paranormal' it has attempted in its many years. CSICOP code-named this study *sTARBABY*. CSICOP leader Dennis Rawlins, a planetary astronomer and a statistician, did a sophisticated mathematical analysis of Gauquelin's 'Mars effect' data and found, much to his own surprise, that his results supported Gauquelin's hypothesis. Rawlins reports[27] that Chairman Kurtz reacted in horror to this news, and that Kurtz and other board members then tried, underhandedly, to suppress the publication of Rawlin's analysis of Gauquelin's research. This dishonesty offended Rawlins' sense of scientific honor and he resigned from CSICOP in disgust. Previously, sociology Professor Marcello Truzzi had been forced to resign from CSICOP, due to the fact that as editor of CSICOP's journal, Truzzi had wanted, in fairness, to publish responsible rebuttal articles to skeptical articles attacking paranormal research. Thus, both Truzzi and Rawlins, two co-founding scientists and leaders of CSICOP, were forced to leave CSICOP due to disagreements over integrity and fairplay, namely CSICOP's apparent lack of both qualities.

CSICOP attacks those who disagree with its way of thinking with derisive ridicule, denigration, and character assassination — rather than with scientific evidence or rational argument. Efforts are not made to discover any truth in what CSICOP has sought to marginalize and to suppress as 'alternative science.'

Because of personal attacks in the media by local French 'Skeptic clubs' associated with CSICOP, Gauquelin's professional reputation was quickly destroyed. CSICOP's leadership remained silent as local 'Skeptic' thugs did the dirty work. Finally, completely

Rock singer Alice Cooper prepares for a mock decapitation by guillotine while James Randi, CSICOP-Fellow and mock-executioner, waits in the shadows in his role as the "Robespierre of Scientific Rationalism".

isolated from his profession, Gauquelin could only find work teaching high school mathematics, and then this, too, was lost. At this point Gauquelin fell into despair and committed suicide, a victim of a relentless campaign of character assassination and of academic 'shunning,' having its origins in CSICOP's leadership.[28]

The rational purpose of skepticism is to wash clean the 'baby' of living truth that cries out within the muddied and muddled conceptions of fumbling scientific investigation, not to toss out the truthful 'baby' with the bath water, as CSICOP presently advocates. When faced with a scientific analysis of the 'Mars Effect' by one of its own leaders, an analysis that supported the very research it was attacking, CSICOP's bosses tossed out sTARBABY's truth with the feared stardust and initiated a persecution that drove Gauquelin, the principal investigator, to his death.

Three hundred years ago, Sir Francis Bacon, the founder of scientific method, wrote in *The Advancement of Learning*:

> *"Surely to alchemy this right is due, that it may be compared to the husbandman whereof Aesop makes the fable: that, when he died, told his sons that he had left unto them gold buried underground in his vineyard; and they digged all over the ground, and gold they found none; but by reason of their stirring and digging the mould about the roots of their vines, they had a great vintage the year following: so assuredly the search and stir to make gold hath brought to light*

a great number of good and fruitful inventions and experiments."[29]

CSICOP is an organization increasingly populated by magicians, philosophers, psychologists, and science writers rather than by working research scientists. Not surprisingly, CSICOP publicly abandoned its promise to sponsor scientific research into the 'paranormal' in 1982 (See its publication *Policy on Sponsoring*). Since that time, if not before, CSICOP has functioned as a social and political action committee, an authoritarian association of hard-headed intellectuals engaged in non-scientific propaganda and back-room politics. 'Spin-doctor' propaganda, verbal denigration through journalism, and control of the media, rather than scientific inquiry, have been CSICOP's operating principles, as it seeks to control the definition and the future direction of scientific investigation.

Bold from successful media campaigns, other science editors and writers besides *Time*'s Jaroff now openly acknowledge their allegiance to CSICOP. Editors Gerald Piel and Sergei Kapitza of *Scientific American*, and aerospace writer Philip J. Klass are just three of a long list of media men who appear to have secured increasingly larger roles in CSICOP's unscholarly and unscientific censorship and propaganda campaigns. As former CSICOP board member Dennis Rawlins writes, "a Committee that lives by the media will inevitably be ruled by its publicists, not by its scholars".[27]

CSICOP had its gun sights on Reich's orgone energy discovery from the very beginning. On the day CSICOP was founded, May 1, 1976, *The New York Times* reporter Boyce Rensberger described the new organization's objectives in an article entitled "Paranormal Phenomena Facing Scientific Study".[30] In the "L" edition of the *NYT* Reich's 'orgone energy' is clearly named as an object of CSICOP's concern, repeating the announcement made by Paul Kurtz in the May/June 1976 issue of *The Humanist*[31] which identified 'orgone energy' as a topic of concern. Interestingly, however, in the later "L+" *NYT* edition all references to 'orgone energy' are dropped — the only topic of study removed from this list. After noting the discrepancy between these two *NYT* editions, I was able to contact, shortly thereafter, a CSICOP official, philosopher Lee Nisbet, and ask him about this odd change. Nisbet replied that while their minds were not yet made up, they eventually wanted to investigate orgone energy when money permitted.

Money may be a big problem indeed if debunking Reich's real scientific investigations into important biophysical questions is the aim. Fifty years ago, in the early 1950s, the FDA spent millions of 1950s dollars, a big percentage of its budget at that time, sponsoring a series of physical and medical experiments intended to discredit Reich's scientific work in court. The results of these studies were never presented in court, as Reich was convicted on legal-technical grounds and not on

scientific grounds. Fifty years later, only a few scientists have reviewed these FDA-sponsored studies[32] — which, to my knowledge, have not been made available to the general public.[33] My own efforts to obtain copies of these studies were unsuccessful, as my repeated requests ended up on an FDA lawyer's desk. In the early 1970s two medical doctors, both students of Reich's later work, did obtain copies of these studies from a SUNY professor who in the 1960s had been granted access to the files of the FDA's five 'most famous cases.' The doctors wrote in the *Journal of Orgonomy*[32] that the FDA-approved studies that they had reviewed were, on the whole, improperly designed and poorly carried out. This may be the reason why the FDA still keeps these studies tightly under wraps nearly a half-century after Reich's death.

Aside from the cost of mounting serious studies, scientific investigations of Reich's work will not be sponsored by CSICOP's current leadership, in any case, as, after the sTARBABY fiasco, Kurtz and his board decided to give up sponsoring any further scientific investigation. Instead, as discussed earlier, they have replaced scientific investigation with outright political propaganda.

The model for CSICOP's propaganda campaigns is the work of Martin Gardner, the 'Godfather of the movement.' Growing up in Tulsa, Oklahoma as the son of a petroleum geologist, the teenage Gardner rejected atheism and joined a series of fundamentalist Protestant Christian sects, one of which included George McCready Price. Price convinced Gardner for a time that the world's fossil deposits were from the Flood, the same Flood that Noah survived. Gardner was convinced that evolution was a satanic myth. However, in the late 1930s, in his fourth year at the University of Chicago, Gardner recanted his religious fundamentalism and rejected Christianity altogether. (Recently, however, in an interview with Kendrick Frazier, Gardner said he still believes in God as this belief helps him escape a deep-seated despair.)

Gardner says he became a radical socialist and a 'fellow traveler' with friends in the Communist Party.[34] Over the years, however, he says that reading Arthur Koestler, Irving Howe, and others convinced him that Stalinism, though not socialism, was a failure. Today, Gardner points out with pride that Norman Thomas' Socialist Party platform of the early 1930s can be easily found within the present-day Republican Party's platform.

For awhile after college, Gardner worked for the U. of Chicago and as a magician publishing several books on tricks. However, since the early 1950s, Gardner has been the foremost advocate of atheistic scientific orthodoxy, of the science of his patriarchy. In 1952, encouraged to greatly expand an essay entitled "The Hermit Scientist", published 1950-51 in the *Antioch Review*,[35] Gardner wrote *In the Name of Science*[36] which put

Wilhelm Reich and his work into the company of scientific cranks and strange cults. Oddly, free copies of Gardner's book were given away with subscriptions to the *Village Voice*, then, as now, a periodical aimed at the counter-culture and the avant-garde.

As Gardner says he thinks that all psychoanalysts are basically cranks, including Freud, why attack Reich in particular? Gardner wrote, "In view of the fact that Reich has in recent years acquired a devoted band of disciples [Gardner said his friend Paul Goodman was one such 'disciple'—Gardner interview] his theories are worth a more extended treatment."[36] 'Treatment?' Treating the masses via the media, with free copies of the book distributed with the newspaper, is applied mass psychology, or propaganda.

Prior to publication, Gardner says he sent a draft of his 'Orgonomy' essay to Reich for comment and that he received it back with Reich's positive commentary and only a few suggested changes — which he says he made. However, Gardner didn't advise Reich of the contents of his other essays, nor of the overall design of his projected book, nor had Reich been told of Gardner's hidden purposes, one of which would be expressed by him in the first line of the Preface, "Not many books have been written about modern pseudo-scientists and their views."[36] When Reich saw that Gardner had placed his essay on Orgonomy between essays on 'Eccentric Sexual Theories' and 'Dianetics,' it became clear to him that Gardner was attempting to deceive the public with a propaganda technique: *guilt by association*. This 'trick' has been practiced since at least the time of Pontius Pilate.

In the first chapter of this 1952 tract Gardner lists five ways to identify the paranoid pseudo-scientist. It may be enlightening for you, gentle reader, to judge both Reich and Einstein by the essential elements of Gardner's list.

1. He considers himself a genius. [Einstein and Reich both did, and both had good reasons to do so.]

2. He regards his colleagues, without exception, as blockheads. [Einstein and Reich both esteemed some of their colleagues, but not others. Both appear to have esteemed each other in 1940-1941.]

3. He believes himself unjustly persecuted and discriminated against. [Both Einstein and Reich had to flee Nazi-controlled Europe to America; due to their scientific beliefs both had been physically threatened and had their books burned in official bonfires. For the duration of WW II Einstein was denied a security clearance by the U.S. government; In late 1941, Reich was awakened and arrested at 2 AM and held without charges for three weeks by agents of the U.S. government. Later, Stalin's secret agents, working through the media and official U.S. government channels, secured Reich's arrest and imprisonment.[10]]

4. He has the strongest compulsions to focus his attacks on the greatest scientists and the best-established theories. [Einstein attacked Newton's theories as insufficient, and Einstein was in a long-running conflict with Planck and other proponents of the quantum theory. Reich declared Freud's and Marx's theories as insufficient; his discovery of the bion upset germ theorists; his discovery of a physically measurable, dynamic aether upset the mid-20th century 'empty space' crowd.]

5. He often has a tendency to write in a complex jargon. [Few people can decipher Einstein's complex mathematical 'jargon'; Reich's terminology appears to be more approachable. Furthermore, it was far more customary in German science than in American science to invent new words and phrases to describe new phenomena or understandings. Gardner shows an American bias against new scientific language here and is thus guilty of cultural jingoism.]

There are real cranks, people whose scientific work is fundamentally nonsense, though exceedingly complex and heavily defended. However, there are also 'cranky' genius scientists, like Nikolai Tesla, whose amazingly creative scientific work forms part of the foundation of the modern world. It is the scientific work that must be examined scientifically, not the person who created it, 'cranky' or not. Gardner recognizes how hard it is to distinguish genius from crankery — 'the 'Demarcation Problem,' as Karl Popper called it — but Gardner says that real scientists, like his friend Roger Penrose, the founder of the 'Twister Theory' in physics, live normal lives. That would definitely leave out Tesla, and many others, too. Gardner says that if the whole of scientific orthodoxy declares the lone revolutionary to be fraudulent, then it is so.

As mentioned earlier, besides Gardner, CSICOP has had quite a few other magicians, or former magicians, associated with it. Why magicians? Magicians do not trust what they see; indeed, they actively pursue the art of fooling people, of illusion, of making people question what they see, of creating distrust in the appearances of the natural world. For magicians seeing is not believing, and this psychic, mind-body split can be deeply disturbing. Psychologist Ray Hyman, a CSICOP official, once observed, in a moment of clarity, "As a whole, parapsychologists are nice, honest people, while the critics are cynical, nasty people".[3] Professional magician and former CSICOP Fellow James Randi may have revealed the end result of CSICOP cynicism when he toured the U.S.A. with the Alice Cooper Band, playing the Executioner, the man who completely separates the head from the body.

A recent newspaper review of an Alice Cooper retrospective tour gives the essence of Randi's experiences with Cooper on stage: "[Cooper] dallied with a dominitrix during 'Go to Hell,' played with decayed parts of family members in 'Pick up the Bones,' stuck his sword through a two-headed mutant for 'Dead Babies,' was restrained in a straightjacket in 'The Quiet Room,' and lost his head to a guillotine as the band played Devil's Food....Cooper sat down for a less than sensitive take on power ballads that describe violence against women, 'Take It Like a Woman' and 'Only Women Bleed.'" Cooper, by the way, was born Vincent Furnier, the son of a minister.

Randi, who grew up in Toronto before moving to Greenwich Village in New York City,, said in a recent interview (*Skeptic*, vol. 8, No., 4, 2001) about his early years:

"...it taught me what the real world was all about – it is tough, it is unyielding, and it can turn on you when you least expect it. You've got to make the best out of it that you can and you've got to mold it, and to beat it – nature is merciless and doesn't give a damn about you."

Enlightening, also, is the savage 10-year media propaganda campaign conducted against Tufts University researcher Thereza Imanishi-Kari and her scientific collaborator Rockefeller University president David Baltimore. Their subsequent political 'take-down' by the National Institute of Health's 'Office of Scientific Integrity,' apparently urged on by several cabals of hidden interests, illuminates the dangers of putting propaganda and politics above scientific inquiry. After a change of political stewardship, with Republicans replacing Democrats, Imanishi-Kari and Baltimore, having already sustained severe damage to their reputations and careers, were cleared of the decade-old charge of intention to commit fraud. According to economics columnist David Warsh (of the *Boston Globe*):

"Ned Feder and Walter Stewart, the self-styled 'fraudbusters' of the National Institutes of Health, have been reassigned to other work and are now widely regarded as cranks [themselves]. The 'Office of Scientific Integrity' has been renamed the 'Office of Research Integrity' and reorganized — its procedures are being extensively rethought."[37]

Warsh closes his column with the argument that science in a democratic, free-market economy is largely self-correcting, and that *"science doesn't need cops to make it work."*

CSICOP in Isaac Newton's times would have been incensed by Newton's fundamentalist Protestantism, and by his decades-long investigations into alchemy. Acting as the 'thought police' of that time, they surely would have sought to prevent the printing of any and all of his works, thereby removing from influence one of science's greatest geniuses. Einstein, another man CSICOP presently acknowledges to have been a scientific genius, welcomed Wilhelm Reich into his home as a scientist and gave Reich's orgone discovery at least two weeks of serious lab study. Who in CSICOP has done or would do the same? Where is their data? Citing the FDA orgone accumulator studies is without value as these apparently flawed studies haven't yet been made available to the general public for examination. In fact, the published results of independent studies on Reich's later work done over the years in various parts of the world largely support Reich's claims. The leadership of CSICOP, however, acting unscientifically with *a priori* knowledge, with prejudice, has ignored these studies.

Paul Kurtz wrote in CSICOP's founding statement that *"We wish to make it clear that the purpose of the Committee is not to reject on a priori grounds, antecedent to inquiry, any or all such claims, but rather to examine them openly, completely, objectively, and carefully."*[31] Distressingly, in their brutal attempts to promote the power, spread, and control of CSICOP's vision, Kurtz and his followers have surged far from this decent path and gone headhunting instead.

The recent ambush of Wilhelm Reich in the pages of *Time* magazine[1] should remind us that, although the pandemic Stalinist and Nazi variants of the Emotional Plague may be greatly reduced, mutant descendants do carry on in other disguises. Reich was murdered 45 years ago, and many of his later works are destroyed or out of print, but his name and his work can still arouse anxiety, horror, and reactive hatred in modern 'hard-headed' intellectuals. While these armored intellectuals and the organizations they control may not have the familiar Nazi or Stalinist surfaces, their manner and their methods of operation are often similar. Valuing the rigid, the tightly-controlled, and the anti-spontaneous, they thrive politically in our democracy by operating within 'front' organizations, from which they viciously ambush their far more creative, productive, and disturbing victims. These elitists seek a unified, mechanized world dominated by their own dry, unemotional, computer-minded, behaviorally-modified kind. Daily they are promoting chemical, electrical, and physical controls on all life, including human life.

Wilhelm Reich identified the Emotional Plague as a real and pervasive social disease, physiologically and energetically rooted in the soma of mankind and potentially operating within all human organizations. By describing what I believe to be one current organizational tool of the Emotional Plague, CSICOP, by showing how it has developed and how it operates through fronts like *Time* magazine, perhaps this essay can begin the process of reducing the Plague's negative effects and promote a healthier and more responsible social functioning in this new century.

Editor's Postscript: CSICOP, Prometheus Books, Pornography and... the *Journal of Pedophilia?!*

Prometheus Books, technically separate from CSICOP but run by CSICOP Chairman Paul Kurtz and publishing many titles by CSICOP Fellows, sells books which range far beyond mere interests in "Scientific Rationalism", but which steer directly into pornography, and beyond. For example, the "Human Sexuality" section of Prometheus Books catalog is edited by CSICOP Fellow and International Academy of Humanism Secretariat Dr. Vern Bullough, a prolific and controversial writer on sexual subjects, who also wrote the introductions to books making uncritical, borderline-advocacy misportrayals of "consensual" adult-child sex, and of human-animal sex. He also was listed as a member of the Editorial Board of the pseudo-scientific *Padika: The Journal of Pedophilia*, on that organization's internet site.* Here is a sample of titles from the Fall-Winter 2000-2001 Prometheus Books Catalog:

* *S&M Studies in Dominance and Submission*, by Thomas S. Weinberg
* *A Youth in Babylon: Confessions of a Trash-Film King*, by David Friedman & Don DeNevi
* *The X-Rated Videotape Guides: Volumes 1 - 8*, by Robert H. Rimmer
* *The X-Rated Videotape Star Index: Volumes 1 - 3*, by Patrick Riley
* *Raw Talent: The Adult Film Industry as Seen by its Most Popular Male Star*, by Jerry Butler
* *The Horseman: Obsessions of a Zoophile*, by Mark Matthews, Introduction by Vern Bullough
* *Children's Sexual Encounters With Adults, A Scientific Study*, by C.K. Li, D.J. West and T.P. Woodhouse
* *Dirty Talk: Diary of a Phone Sex Mistress*, by Gary Anthony & Rocky Bennett
* *Whips & Kisses: Parting the Leather Curtain*, by Mistress Jacqueline
* *The Q Letters: True Stories of Sadomasochism*, by "Sir" John

One Prometheus title, *PORN 101* (J. Elias, G. Brewer, V. Bullough, et al, Editors), was apparently drafted as a college textbook, highlighting a seminar of similar title (*Porn 101: Assimilating Pornographic Material in the Classroom*) which was presented at a recent "World Pornography Conference" sponsored by Bullough's *Center for Sex Research* at the University of California at Northridge. The "Conference" included as speakers many of the above authors, as well as various porn stars aping as "academics". Another Prometheus title, *Children's Sexual Encounters with Adults* gathers and unscientifically misrepresents the historical and cross-cultural evidence regarding childhood sexuality, to white-wash pedophilia under the guise of "scientific rationalism". Such books are promoted and sold on internet sites which openly endorse all kinds of sexual pathology, including pedophilia. All of the above titles were gathered on the last pages of the Prometheus catalog, as if to conceal their existence from the casual reader who might be interested in their other titles, but offended at the more outrageous pornography.

Given that Prometheus Books has several hundred titles on its list of publications — including many excellent classics and titles by well-known authors including various CSICOP Fellows and officers, plus some very important books critical of authoritarian religious dogma — with so many other excellent manuscripts begging for a publisher, one can only wonder what the motivation is to include such extreme pornographic materials in their listing. The personal interests in these materials by some of America's leading "skeptics" appears quite clear. It therefore does not appear accidental that CSICOP and Prometheus Books should also be the central-most sources of attack-and-ridicule disinformation directed towards Wilhelm Reich and his contemporary advocates: It was Reich, after all, who wrote extensively about genuine sexual liberation and adolescent sexuality, but who also roundly condemned the pornographer as being anti-sexual in nature, and pedophiles in particular as being deeply sexually sick, requiring police intervention to keep them away from children. Reich observed: The pornographer destroys the more gentle and emotional-romantic side of sexuality just as surely as the church moralizer destroys the erotic-passion side of sexuality. Sexual health is composed of equal parts of both loving tenderness and eroticism. Both the church moralist and the pornographer express hatred towards natural loving sexuality in general, and towards the opposite sex in particular, differing only in the methods used to smash down natural heterosexuality. Unfortunately, the most vocal critics of the contemporary academic-pedophile movement are from the religious right-wing, who offer only their own brand of antisexual religious moralism as an alternative substitute (ie., the distortions that childhood sexuality does not exist, that contraception, abortion and divorce should be restricted again, and that adolescent lovers — ie., Romeo and Juliett — should be thrown into prison along with the pedophiles). Reich's sex-economic discoveries gain little support from either of these extremist camps, but rather stand as a deeper truth and common functioning principle underlying the two antithetical expressions, both of which are saturated with hatred towards love and sexuality.§

---

* For more information, see the chapters by Edward Eichel in *Kinsey, Sex and Fraud* (Lochinvar-Huntington House Publications, 1990), and *Kinsey - Crimes and Consequences* by J.A. Reisman, et al. (Inst. for Media Education, 1998). Bullough wrote Introductions for *Dares to Speak : Historical and Contemporary Perspectives on Boy-Love*, J. Geraci, Ed. (Gay Men's Press, 1997), and for *The Horseman: Confessions of a Zoophile*, by Mark Matthews (Prometheus Books, 1994)
§ See "Wilhelm Reich's Discovery of Human Armoring" in J. DeMeo, *Saharasia*, Natural Energy, Ashland, 1998, pp.17-46.

References:

1. "100 Scientists and Thinkers of the 20th Century," *Time* magazine Special Issue, March 29, 1999; see, especially, pp. 64-69 and p. 196 (Also, see same article on-line at www.time.com).

2. *Time* magazine, November 9, 1999, page 77.

3. Hansen, G. P.: "CSICOP and the Skeptics: An Overview," *The Journal of the American Society for Psychical Research*, Vol. 86. Jan. 1992. See pages 22, 30.

4. Reich, W.: *Mass Psychology of Fascism*, 1946 Orgone Institute Press (reprinted 1970, Farrar, Straus & Giroux, NY).

5. Lamont, C.: *Humanist Manifesto I*, in *Humanist Manifestos I and II*, edited by Paul Kurtz, Prometheus Books, Buffalo, NY, 1973.

6. Reich, W.: "Biological Miscalculation in the Struggle for Human Freedom", in *Mass Psychology of Fascism*, 1946 Orgone Institute Press (reprinted 1970, Farrar, Straus & Giroux, NY).

7. The original of this document is in the *Consumer Research Archive* located at Rutgers University, in box 521, Folder 1, index #335.9127 A-Z, part of a letter to Major Consodine. December 27, 1944 orig. f. 050.1 T.

8. Tanenhaus, S.: *Whittaker Chambers*, 1997, page 342.

9. Author's interviews with Martin Gardner, 21-22 August 1999.

10. Martin, J.: *Wilhelm Reich and the Cold War*, Flatland Books, Mendocino 1999.

11. Greenfield, J.: *Wilhelm Reich Vs. the USA*, W.W. Norton, NY, 1974.

12. Entry on "Wilhelm Reich", in *The Encyclopedia of Philosophy*, ed. P. Edwards, Macmillan & Free Press, New York 1967, vol. 7, pp. 104-15.

13. Edwards, P.: "The Greatness of Wilhelm Reich: A noted philosopher defends a famous psychotherapist against his detractors" in *The Humanist*, 1974.

14. Lamont, C: *A Humanist Wedding Service* (second revised edition), Prometheus Books, 1972.

15. Baker, E.F.: *Man in the Trap*, Macmillan, NY, 1967.

16. Conrad, J.: *Heart of Darkness*, 1902 (reprinted by Dover 1991); Also see Francis Ford Coppola's modern filmed version of Conrad's story, *Apocalypse Now*, set in Vietnam in the late 1960s.

17. Continelli, L.:, "Dr. Debunker: Philosopher Paul Kurtz Has Built an Empire on Skeptical Inquiry," *The Buffalo News*, Lifestyles section, page 1; 12 June 1994, Sunday, final edition.

18. Leonhard, W.: *Three faces of Marxism: the political concepts of Soviet ideology, Maoism, and humanist Marxism*, Holt, Rinehart and Winston, NY, 1974.

19 Lamont, C: *Memoirs of Corliss Lamont*, Horizon Press, NY, 1981. (See esp. pp 46-48).

20. Lamont, C.: "Trip to Communist China", *Basic Pamphlets -21*.

21. Kurtz, P.: *The Fullness of Life*, Prometheus Books, Buffalo, NY, 1974, pages 190 and 194.

22. Delgado, J.M.R., *Physical Control of the Mind: Toward a Psychocivilized Society*, Harper & Row, 1971.

23 Skinner, B.F: *Beyond Freedom and Dignity*. 1971.

24. Marks, J, *The Search for the Manchurian Candidate*, Times Books, 1979 (See esp. Chapter Nine). Available online at http://www.druglibrary.org/schaeffer/lsd/marks9.htm

25. From "A Warning to All Those Involved in the APS Trial" by Jacques Beneviste and posted on the internet by Marcello Truzzi.

26. Gauquelin, M.: *Cosmic Influences on Human Behavior*, Stein & Day, NY, 1973.

27. Rawlins, D.: "sTARBABY," *Fate, 34*, (pp. 67-98), 1981. Also published on the Internet as http://www.psy.ura.nl/resedu/pn/res/ANOMALUSCOGNITION/starbaby.html

28. Ertel, S., "In Memory of Michel Gauquelin", *Journal of Scientific Exploration*, 7(1): 5-7, Spring 1993.

29. Bacon, F.: *The Advancement of Learning*, Kessinger Publishing, 1997.

30. *New York Times*, 1 May 1976, page 26.

31. Kurtz, P.: *The Humanist*, May/June 1976, p.28.

32. Blasband, R. & Baker, C.: "An Analysis of the Food and Drug Administration's Scientific Evidence Against Wilhelm Reich", *Journal of Orgonomy*, VI:207-231, 1972 and VII:234-245, 1973. Also see: DeMeo, J.: "Postscript on the Food and Drug Administration's Evidence Against Wilhelm Reich", *Pulse of the Planet*, 1:18-23, 1989.

33. A listing of the various FDA documents, by title, with discussion on their ultimate disposition and availability, is found in DeMeo, ibid., 1989, and DeMeo, J.: *Bibliography on Orgone Biophysics*, Natural Energy Works, Ashland, Oregon, 1986, page 50.

34. Gardner, M.: *The Flight of Peter Fromm*, Prometheus Press, 1994. (Only the 1994 edition has the autobiographical Afterword . Also, see. chapters 13, 14, and 23.)

35. Gardner, M.: "The Hermit Scientist", *Antioch Review*, Winter 1950-51, p.447-457.

36. Gardner, M.: *In the Name of Science*, G.P. Putnam in 1952 [revised and republished as *Fads and Fallacies in the Name of Science* by Dover, 1957; see pp. 249-262]. Also in 1952, Gardner, writing under the pseudonym 'G. Groth,' published an article in *Fate*, 5 (pp. 39-43), entitled 'He writes with your hand.' Another of Gardner's pseudonyms is 'I. J. Matrix.' The author also interviewed Gardner on the telephone on 21 and 22 August 1999.

37. Warsh, D.: "Economic Principals: The Fortune that Never Was," *The Boston Sunday Globe*, June 30, 1996. pp. 71 and 73.

Childbirth as a Sexual Process
by Matthew Appleton*

Author's preface: This article was originally written as part of a project about the birth process that I was required to complete during my training as a Craniosacral Therapist. The focus of the article arose as a response to the assumption which prevailed throughout the training that birth is always traumatic for both mother and baby. This was alternatively attributed to the design by nature to toughen up the newborn or as an inherent design flaw on the part of nature of which both mother and baby were passive victims. My own interest in birth grew out of my work with older children, which led me to question the role of birth and other early experiences on their development, and also from supporting my then partner during the birth of our daughter, Eva. We had planned for the birth throughout the pregnancy and knew from our research that birth was not always traumatic and that this not only varied from individual to individual, but also between cultures.

For many years previous to the birth we had both studied the work of Dr. Wilhelm Reich and his discovery of the relationship between sexuality and anxiety, as two basic orientations of life towards it's environment. These were found to be synonymous with an expanding out towards the world and a shrinking away from it. The interplay between sexuality and anxiety in relation to the birth process was already reasonably documented and gave a functional understanding to what otherwise appears to be completely arbitrary and incomprehensible.

I realized when I began writing the article that it might not be considered 'politically correct' for a man to be writing about birth as a sexual process, which is inevitably an aspect of female sexuality. However, I also knew that I had access to knowledge that had been very beneficial in navigating the birth process of my own daughter and might be useful to others. The feedback that I have so far is that this has been the case. My prime

* Matthew Appleton worked as a houseparent at Summerhill School from 1988-97. He is author of *A Free Range Childhood; Self Regulation at Summerhill School* (Solomon Press, 2000). While at Summerhill he trained in psychotherapy at the *Wilhelm Reich Institute of Integrated Therapy* in Germany and in craniosacral therapy with the *College of Craniosacral Therapy* in London. Today he utilizes both disciplines in busy private practices in London and Bristol, England, and is a co-founder of the *Institute of Craniosacral Studies*. He can be contacted by e-mail at:: <mapple@onetel.net.uk>

concern in the writing of this article is the well-being of the newborn, which must be of greater concern than any political concerns. This is not to say that I am not concerned about the well-being of the mother also. However, it is in the interest of the newborn, whose voice is often not heard despite its clarity, that I originally felt the urge to write this article. Female sexuality and the birth process, as the article itself states, have already been usurped by male perspectives too often and I do not want to add to this. My aim is only to pass on knowledge to which I feel everyone should have access. We can then make our own informed choices and understand our experiences from a wider perspective than the one that the medicalized view of birth imposes on us. This is not just about men and women — it is also about the human condition, for birth is a journey we have all made in some form or other.

Introduction

The birth process is often described in purely mechanical, anatomical and physiological terms, or as a medical process in which mother and baby are both passive participants. However for the purposes of this overview I want to dim the lights of the delivery room and send the obstetricians with their gleaming instruments and drugs on a short holiday, so that we can view the birth process in a more human and intimate light. In particular I want to focus on the sexual element of birth and the ways in which larger societal attitudes towards sexuality impinge upon the birth process. Many of the references I use are drawn from the work of medical orgonomists, these being physicians who have been trained in *orgone therapy* developed by the Austrian born psychiatrist and natural scientist Wilhelm Reich. Hence derivatives of the term *orgone* appear at various times. This was the name that Reich gave to the specific life energy which he discovered, but which can be considered to be synonymous with concepts of life energy existing in other cultures, such as *chi, ki* or *prana*.

The term *armoring* which also appears was used by Reich to describe the way in which the body contracts and stiffens against energetic sensations due to external prohibitions or traumas which change these sensations from a source of pleasure to one of anxiety. Because of its effect on the organism as a whole the muscular armor also limits and distorts the capacity for rational thinking and emotional expression. We are all armored to some degree.

Sexual Feelings in Labor

Many women describe their experience of childbirth as being agonizing, anxiety ridden and traumatic. Other women describe very strong sexual feelings. Shelia Kitzinger, mother of five and author of many books about pregnancy and childbirth, writes,

"Childbirth involves waves of energy that are quite different from what most women have been taught in childbirth education classes. The rhythms of uterine contractions are wavelike as women's sexual rhythms are. A woman's sexuality centres around waves of mounting desire, each culminating in fulfillment. That kind of sexual rhythm is what we experience in childbirth. It involves the whole body, not just the genitals." [1]

Orgonomist Michael Silvert describes the following birth process;

"The mother able to yield to the birth process holds lightly to a wall breast-high for support, her elbow bent and relaxed. Her head falls back and her chest goes down softly when she breathes, her pelvis comes forward in a movement suggestive of sexual surrender, knees bent and soft sighs come from her partially open mouth. Color is pink, eyes are bright, and thoughts are equally expressive: "Why this is just like sex. I actually enjoy it. Why don't people know about this, it's wonderful. I'm so happy." [2]

There have been many attempts to make childbirth a more relaxed and pleasurable affair, in particular the natural birth and home birth movements. Pioneer birth researcher Dr. Michel Odent stresses the importance of intimacy, rather than the typical medical setting of bright lights and constant monitoring and interference by obstetricians, nurses, midwives and even birth partners. Shelia Kitzinger takes up the theme of intimacy;

"In an intimate atmosphere the physicality of birth can be close to that of love-making. The swelling uterus straining against the abdominal wall, the woman's quickened breathing, her damp skin and hair and shining eyes, the astonishing urge to push, the energy pours through her, the grunts and moans as she presses the baby down, the bulging perineum, the top of the baby's head like a wrinkled walnut in her vagina, and then oozing through - all these elements in birth are sexual when they are not made medical in the context of hospital care." [3]

She also suggests sexual stimulation or intercourse as means of encouraging contractions if the delivery is overdue.[3] Sexual stimulation leads to the release of oxytocin into the bloodstream, whilst semen is rich in prostaglandins, both of which may be given medically in synthetic form to induce labor. Michel Odent has written of oxytocin,

"Until recently oxytocin was thought of as a female hormone whose only role was to stimulate contractions of the uterus during labor and delivery, and contractions of the breast during lactation. Now it is seen as a male and female hormone involved in all different aspects of sexual life. Its role during sexual arousal and orgasm has [only] recently come to light." [4]

Given that birth is so deeply infused with sexuality it is no wonder that a relaxed and intimate environment is cited by so many as a preferable alternative to the typical medical setting. After all, how many of us would be able to relax into an intimate sexual experience with people coming and going, urging us to hurry up or slow down, and probing us with various medical instruments. However a natural or home birth does not guarantee a birth free of pain or anxiety and it has left many women feeling they had somehow failed when their 'natural' birth did not turn out as some books had led them to expect. At this point we need to look farther afield than the immediate birth environment and take into account the whole physical, emotional, psychological and cultural environment in which sexuality, and therefore the birth process is shaped.

The Glow of Love

Psychotherapist David Boadella, greatly influenced by Wilhelm Reich's findings, wrote:

"To form the body of a new person the germ cells which are embedded in the tissues of the parents have first to be released and allowed to become free floating. These are explosive and climatic events. Ovulation, filmed using optic fibre techniques, is a spectacular and breathtaking process; the sight of the ripe follicle bursting to expel the future ovum brings gasps of amazement and awe from those who see it. The orgasm itself, during which the sperm are flung by the pulses of ejaculation many thousands of times their own length to begin their journey, is capable of spreading a shock wave of excitement through all the tissues of the body." [5]

So begins the birth process in the merging of male and female, a sexual convulsion from which new life will begin to take shape and grow.

"The sexual embrace," wrote Wilhelm Reich, *"if abstracted and reduced to its basic form, represents superimposition and the bio-energetic fusion of two orgonotic systems."* [6]

From then on, if conception occurs, the body of the mother begins to change physically, chemically and hormonally, giving rise to new thoughts, sensations and emotions. From the energetic fusion of sexual intercourse a third energy system is created, interacting with and changing the energetic state of the mother within whom it develops.

"The foetus acts like a stove; it is another energy system in the mother and it energizes the whole mothers being." [7]

This increased orgonotic excitation is clearly visible as the 'glowing' that many people are aware of in pregnant women. It is also visible in the glowing faces of lovers. In either case this lumination occurs as a result of two orgonotic systems mutually exciting each other. Both are essentially sexual.

This energetic expansion and swelling of tissues as the body begins to change shape bears some similarities with the changes that occur during puberty and the body becomes highly sexually charged. Jasmine Lamb, an ex-pupil of A.S. Neill's Summerhill School, describes her experience of puberty as follows;

"It started with a numbness in my stomach when I watched kisses or love scenes in movies and slowly turned, as I grew older, into a throbbing, not just in my stomach, but pulsating across my whole body. Or it would feel like an ocean caught inside me, waves crashing against every cell and capillary. I felt a new longing and loneliness I had never experienced before. I had already spent many, many nights lying in bed wondering what these feelings meant and what this loneliness could be teaching me. As I grew up and into my new body and different emotions, I became more and more relaxed with these feelings. I knew, of course, they were connected with sex and I had an idea that they were what one might call ones sexuality, but I did not grasp the meaning of these desires and longings." [8]

This emotional alertness, along with intense bodily sensation, is not at all unlike the feelings that many pregnant women describe. The yearning often comes even earlier, with pregnancy and babies taking the place of 'kisses' and 'love scenes'. These are powerful desires and many women describe a sense of urgency and sexual incompleteness as they move into their late twenties and early thirties without having given birth.[§] So the birth process itself does not exist as an isolated sexual event, but as part of a sexual continuum that begins long before in the infancy of the mother.

§ Editor's Note: In sex-repressive and armored societies with compulsive familial expectations and unfulfilled marriages (ie, most of the world), the "urge to procreate" often has a deeply neurotic cultural, not biological, background.

Pelvic Armoring

Along with Wilhelm Reich, A.S. Neill, the educator and founder of Summerhill School, vocalized the importance of approving of infantile, childhood and adolescent sexuality. It is important here to stress the word approval, as opposed to interference or even encouragement. The former meets what comes from within as good and natural, whereas the latter imposes from without an adult emphasis, which leads only to precocious behavior and unhappiness. I worked for nine years as a houseparent at Summerhill, where the attitude towards sexuality is one of openness and frankness. The children are able to talk freely about their feelings, and, to the extent that the law allows, express those feelings with each other.

In my experience those children and adolescents who have been most approved of in their sexuality at home are those who are most in touch with their own needs and feelings as a whole. Compared with those kids who have been brought up in sex-negative homes they are more open and affectionate, soft in body and attitude, clear thinking and straight forward, confident, cheerful. On the other hand those kids who have developed a negative attitude towards their sexual feelings tend to be more tense, clingy, fearful and anxious, spiteful, contemptuous, insincere, pornographic, hysterical, unable to concentrate, rigid and 'hard'. The notion that sexuality is in some way a separate compartment from the rest of our lives is a false one. Our sexuality is an expression of who we are and as such sexuality and personality are inexorably entwined.

Whilst at Summerhill I trained in Craniosacral Therapy and worked using the therapy with a wide range of children and adolescents at the school. Craniosacral Therapy is a form of bodywork, in which the therapist tunes into the subtle pulsations of the body with his or her hands and gently stimulates the body's self-regulatory mechanisms to restore balance and health. At the core of this treatment is the 'cranial rhythm' or 'cranial rhythmic impulse', which is described as "a fundamental life force pervading every tissue throughout the body, providing a rhythmic motion not only to every cell, but consequently to every aggregation of cells, and therefore every organ, every organ system, and to the body as a whole."[9] As such the Cranial Rhythm is identical with what Reich called 'orgonotic pulsation'.

One of the children I worked with, a twelve year old boy, had been brought up to have no bad feelings about sexuality and had been allowed to express his sexuality as an infant openly within the home. Nor had he been toilet trained, but was able to regulate his bowels in his own time. (I shall return to the subject of toilet training later.) His whole system seemed very open, with a strong, deep rhythm. When I rested my hands on his illia I was surprised at the degree of expansion and contraction that I felt expressed there. The amplitude was fuller than I had ever felt in any of the other kids I had worked on. The whole pelvis 'breathed' with a softness and certainty I was not used to. In other kids and adults I have worked with I have found the pelvis much stiffer, less mobile, the pulsation agitated or sometimes hardly palpable at all. A few weeks later I happened to see a film of a swarm of jellyfish on television. The clear and rhythmic expansion and contraction they expressed as they moved through the water reminded me at once of the easy and uninterrupted rhythm I had felt in this boy.

In their therapeutic approach, as developed by Reich, orgone therapists identify the armoring as working in a segmental fashion, which transverse the body, interrupting the streaming of energy up and down the body. These segments are described as ocular, oral, cervical, thoracic, diaphragmatic, abdominal and pelvic. The therapist works to release tensions in these segments and to integrate the flow of energy throughout the body. This is done by a combination of direct bodywork and talking, often encouraging emotional expression and pointing out fixed emotional attitudes, such as a false smile, over politeness, whining, swallowed anger or sobbing etc. A lot of emphasis is put on not controlling the breathing, but encouraging full and relaxed respiration. The therapist works methodically, but not mechanically, through the segments, generally in a caudad direction, working on the pelvis last.

> *"The pelvic segment consists of all structures below the pelvic rim, including the lower extremities. Most of the pelvic musculature is involved in the armoring of this segment, but among the most frequently involved muscles are levator ani, the anal sphincters, the bulbocavernosus, the ichiocavernosus (which regulate the erection of penis and clitoris), the gluteal muscles and the thigh adductors. The pelvic segment contains the uterus and ovaries, the male reproductive apparatus, the external genitalia, the urinary bladder, the urethra and the distal portion of the intestinal tract with the rectum and anus."*[10]

Orgone therapist Morton Herskowitz explains,

> *"When one begins to work on the pelvic armoring, one invariably encounters more anxiety than one encountered up until that time before. Because the pelvis is the place where there is the residue of all the sex-negativity, all the sexual repression and everyone in our culture suffers from pelvic anxiety. In addition to the anxiety that is generated when one starts working on this segment, one also see's all the secondary-layer manifestations of the pelvis [distorted expressions of primary needs] which are the rage and contempt that the pelvis holds. It is not by chance that in practically all western cultures the expression 'fuck you' is the most hateful thing one can say."*[11]

We can add to that many other expressions of hate and contempt associated with the pelvis: cunt, asshole, shit, wanker, dick. Yet it is through this segment of the body that we all make our journey into the world, unless, that is, we had a caesarian birth. One can only wonder how far unconscious attitudes towards pelvic functions affects the number of caesarean that are performed. A recent study in the Lancet revealed that of 282 obstetricians questioned 31% of female obstetricians and 17% of male obstetricians would chose a caesarian birth over a vaginal one even if there were no complications.[12]

> *"Anxiety is the hallmark of pelvic armoring. The anxiety.... is a result of the acute fear of strong pleasure. There is rage behind this anxiety that describes the bitter anger at being denied what felt so good."*[10]

This deep anxiety is held at bay by the armoring, but as soon as the armoring is mobilized and the energy begins to stream into the pelvis, the patient begins to experience the deep tensions and anxieties that are held there.

> *"Not untypically,"* explains Dorothea Fuckert, also an orgone therapist, *"patients experience acute anxiety attacks, falling anxiety and fear of dying, sexual impotence or anesthesia (sometimes for the first time in their life)."*[13]

It is little wonder then that there is so much tension and anxiety surrounding birth in our culture.

The etiology of pelvic armoring is not only sexual though. Another important factor to be considered is toilet training and attitudes towards defecation. Children do not need to be toilet trained, but will learn to regulate their bowels themselves, usually between the ages of two and three. Premature toilet training can be particularly harmful, as bowel control is not properly developed until eighteen months to two years old, and the only recourse the child has to soiling itself at this age is to tighten the musculature of the pelvic floor, which in turn becomes chronically anchored armoring.

Parental pressures or disgust at natural bodily functions all add to the armoring process and the infant is wide open and vulnerable to the most subtle influences. Many of the children I lived with at Summerhill brought in with them attitudes of deep disgust and at the same time an unnatural preoccupation with anything anal. All of these attitudes are anchored in the organism itself, in the tight pelvis that squeezes against its own existence in fixed patterns of denial. I have been in orgone therapy myself and remember once towards the end of a session in which I had been expressing a lot of rage and spite from my pelvis, kicking and slamming my pelvis against the couch. As I relaxed I felt a deep warm softness flowing through me, my eyes open and alive to the therapist and pleasurable sensations streaming down from my face and into my pelvis. Then I began to feel the muscles of the pelvic floor tighten up and a deep anxiety that I might break wind. With this tightening up the whole flow of energy became fragmented and diminished. It took me some minutes to pluck up the courage to tell the therapist, but as soon as she assured me it was perfectly okay to break wind the anxiety left me and I began to enjoy the aliveness and softness of my body again. Clearly this was an old anxiety that was rooted in a time when as a child I had not felt so approved of in my body and its functions, so much so that it had become chronically fixed in my pelvis as a tightening up reflex as soon as I felt sensation in that area.

During labor the mother's pelvis has to be able to open up as much as possible to allow the contractions of the uterus to propel the baby on its way. To do this she has not only to bear the natural pain that comes with the spreading of tissues as the baby's head is pushed through, but also the pain of centuries of contempt and disgust heaped upon her genitalia and natural bodily functions. For the newborn this is also the first barrier s/he must cross before passing into a world that will recreate these same patterns of hardness and denial in his or her own soft and open body.

"When a woman comes close to giving birth," says Michel Odent, emphasizing the right to privacy, *"she often needs to defecate. It's not what you do in the presence of your sexual partner, but it's what you do in the presence of your mother as a child."* [14]

But if as a child your mother had her own anal complexes and projected them on to you, the battle becomes even harder. Equally, sex is not something we enter into in front of our doctors, yet birth becomes a medical spectacle.

"A baby passing through the birth canal touches and stimulates the same areas that are stimulated in sexual intercourse." [15]

Again - the battle becomes harder if we have been brought up with harsh and negative attitudes towards soft and pleasurable sexual feelings. Instead of yielding to sensation we tighten up against it.

"Pain occurs only when the uterus contracts down on a foetus that cannot give with the contractions because of lower holding. In many primitive peoples labor is said to be very short in duration and taken rather nonchalantly. Similar cases can occur in our society...... When the cervix is fully dilated and labor

enters the second stage, unarmored mothers have reported feeling a sense of exhilaration and power with no further discomfort. This sense of exhilaration and well-being may last for several hours. It is sometimes accompanied by a feeling of floating and mild ecstasy." [16]

The way in which we raise our children now affects enormously the way in which they give birth in years to come, and so on down the generations.

Anxiety and Modern Obstetrics

I have focused so intently on the pelvic armoring because it is so central to the problems of sexuality and birth, but this is not to suggest that this segment operates in isolation during the birth process. The interplay of different emotions and the body's attempt to contain and restrict them is a continually shifting scenario. The different segments simply represent focal points, with groups of muscles working as a functional group to restrict sensation and emotional expression in that particular area. Within that dynamic relationship certain focal points of restriction will be more deeply and chronically fixed, but they will always belong to a larger constellation shaped and mapped out by a whole life's experience. The anxieties that are bound in the armor and the organism's continued attempt to sequester and control them via the armoring process will all come into play during the birth process.

A birth attendant who has knowledge of natural birth processes and armoring is able to do much to relieve the situation.

"So far as possible we attempt to decrease the intensity of the mother's armoring during her pregnancy. A free chest increases the oxygenation of the blood of mother and baby, augments the mother's energy level, enables her to function more freely emotionally and will be an aid in the expeditious birth of her child. Clearing armor in the eye segment will help her to go through parturition alive to the miracle of the process and ready to greet her child. Above all we attempt to loosen the lower segments, particularly the pelvic segment, so that the pelvis will not contract about the foetus during pregnancy nor hinder the birth process at delivery. In several deliveries performed under orgonomic auspices the obstetrician attended to the actual delivery of the child and the orgonomist kept watch against any tendency to armor, particularly in the eyes." [10]

Two such labors are reported and contrasted in the cases of 'Roxanne' and 'Cynthia' in the *Journal of Orgonomy*:

"As the contractions increased in intensity, the pelvis

mobilized with a tremendous increase in energetic charge. Roxanne's body became erythematous and her energy field highly expanded. A circle of pallor indicating contraction remained, however, around the diaphragm. With each contraction three waves of energy moved through the body ending in the pelvic reflex [a spontaneous tilting forward of the pelvis as in orgasm]........ As energy reached the pelvis, throat and thoracic armoring intensified.... A strong energetic discharge through the genital (orgastic discharge) accompanied the birth..... For about three months postpartum, Roxanne felt 'wide open' in the pelvis and a capacity for intense sexual pleasure in intercourse." [17]

In the second labor described, Cynthia's more severe armoring, particularly in the ocular segment, presented more difficulty:

"She perceived her contractions as strong, although the medical orgonomist felt otherwise, reporting a lack of intensity to her energetic charge and energy field; in particular the latter appeared diffuse and disorganized. None of the pulsatory movements and waves seen in the first case were present, except for an energetic build up with each contraction. The pelvic reflex was absent. ...

As labor progressed, Cynthia experienced episodes of panic and went 'off' in her eyes. Contractions became less effective in moving the baby through the birth canal. Maintaining eye contact with the medical orgonomist, however, helped her to focus resulting in more effective contractions..... As in the previous case there was a palpable discharge of energy at the moment of delivery, although it was not as strong or as complete. Several hours later Cynthia began trembling - a manifestation of the energy remaining undischarged during the actual birth." [17]

The more the mother is subjected to external anxiety provoking stimuli the more her armoring is provoked and the more hypertonic it becomes. She may have heard many frightening stories around traumatic births which have already led her to expect the worst. The presence of bright lights, strange looking metallic instruments, flashing and beeping monitoring devices, nurses and doctors scrubbed up and clothed as if about to perform an operation, the whole medical paraphernalia. These may all add to the sense of dread and bewilderment she feels about what is about to happen. She may find her self being talked to in officious tones, as if she was a naughty schoolgirl. She may have already been poked and prodded around, had her pubic hair shaved, and been subjected to an enema or suppositories, so that her body no longer feels like her own, but belongs now to an anonymous conveyor belt process she has no control over. For some women who already have

a great deal of fear around birth, all this bustling efficiency and high technology may be reassuring, but for many it simply adds more anxiety and therefore more pressure on the already existing armor.

Orgonomist Chester M. Raphael describes one such labor[18]: The 27 year old mother was overdue, but felt that *"there was no need to meddle"*. However, although there were no complications, her obstetrician recommended she be induced. Following a dose of castor oil and an enema *"she had a few contractions and was rushed to hospital. She herself objected that it seemed too early"*. Before her experience of hospital, she was, in her own words *"'... in excellent spirits. I wasn't particularly afraid. I knew that I would have some pain, but I certainly felt I would not find it intolerable'"*. At the hospital she was taken straight away to the labor room where *"'my attitude changed with a suddenness that was startling'"*. From where she was she could overhear two other deliveries that were in progress, along with *"'bloodcurdling screams and pleas for assistance which were coldly regarded'"*. The room was barren, and the sight of doctors in blood-stained uniforms emerging from the delivery room gave the impression of *"'being in a medieval torture chamber'"*. For five hours contractions continued before she was given an injection of demerol and fell asleep.

When she awoke the contractions had almost vanished and her cervix was not dilated. The rest of the day was spent listening to the screams still coming from the delivery room, before contractions began again in the evening. These continued throughout the next day, during which she was disturbed to hear that one of the other women had a stillbirth. The contractions by now were extremely painful, and another enema was given, followed by three injections of 'obstetrical pituitrin'. Finally the obstetrician ruptured the membranes. Dr. Raphael takes up the story.

"When I arrived at the hospital the patient had been in labor for more than 40 hours. Her condition seemed desperate. I found her sitting up, supporting herself with her arms held rigidly against the sides of the bed, her face was ashen, her lips cyanotic, her pulse thready, her hands cold and clammy, her shoulders hunched up acutely. With each contraction, occurring at five minute intervals, she screamed that she could not endure it any longer and wanted to die. Between contractions, her eyes rolled up into her head and her distress was extreme with each contraction. She held her breath and her body stiffened. The picture was one of acute contraction of the entire organism. ...

It took considerable effort to make her lower her shoulders. Succeeding in this, I asked her to breathe more deeply, to prolong her expiration. In less than two minutes her body grew tremulous, clonic movements appeared in the lower extremities and ex-

tended upwards towards her lower jaw and teeth, which began to chatter uncontrollably. She clenched her jaws, but I discouraged it immediately and helped her to let her jaw drop. The spasm in her shoulders and intercostal muscles - which were exquisitely tender - was gradually overcome. Her respiration improved. Then she, herself, complained of a block in the diaphragm. Fibrillations appeared in her thighs, strong sensations of current appeared in her hands and fingers. The severity of the pain of uterine contractions began to subside. ...

The color returned to her face, her pulse grew fuller and slower, and her respiratory movements now proceeded with an involuntary rhythm. She then began to belch and with this the discomfort in the region of the diaphragm subsided. She grew quieter and began to smile. Very quickly the contractions began to occur at two-minute intervals. There appeared to be relatively little discomfort with each contraction and she was able to rest between them. Despite more than forty hours in labor, a good part of it agonizingly painful, she began to look comfortable and pleased."[18]

This account of a hospital birth from 1951 is particularly harrowing, and I am not suggesting that all hospital births are as difficult as this. Nevertheless very many women still recount stories with many of the same elements to them. So why, to begin with, is birth treated more like a sickness than a natural event and an expression of female sexuality? Clearly when used in a rational way modern obstetrics has its place. In particular emergencies lives can be saved. But when studies such as the American *Scientific Research on Childbirth Alternatives: What it Tells us About Hospital Practice* [19] and the more recent *Winterton Report* here in England show us that the modern hospital is not actually the safest place to give birth, despite all its high technology, then we must begin to question the rationale behind obstetrics as practised today. Odent writes:

"The history of obstetrics... is largely the history of the gradual exclusion of mothers from their central role in the birth process. Modern obstetrics originated in seventeenth-century France when male doctors first entered the birthing room and assumed the traditional role of midwives. For the first time women were required to give birth lying on their backs, so that doctors could use their forceps more easily."[20]

With this scenario in mind we need to shift from focusing on the armoring and it's underlying anxiety in the mother to these same problems as they are institutionalized in the practice of modern obstetrics. Odent continues:

"The practice of the medical discipline we call obstet-

rics has never been focused on helping women give birth, but more on just controlling the process. That's why we create midwifery schools so that midwives are no longer mothers helping other mothers, but merely professionals who are being trained to control the process, and that is why doctors have developed the technology to control the process."[14]

This begs the question as to where the need to "control the process" comes from? Stepping back and placing birth in the context of human sexuality the question becomes a broader one; why do we need to control natural human sexual expression, whether it be in the innocent sex play of infants and children, the ripening of the sexual urge in adolescence or in the intensity of giving birth? No other creature on earth attempts to control it's sexual impulses as the human animal does. No other creature on earth has so many difficulties around giving birth. The common principle at play behind our approach to both birth and other inherent sexual expressions lies in the armoring process and in particular the armoring of the pelvis. The armoring is a way of controlling inner sensations, of keeping them at a level that can be tolerated. So the infant who is told that masturbation is 'dirty' or 'not nice' will squeeze his or her thighs tight to kill the sweetness s/he feels there, a sweetness which s/he can only feel now as a source of anxiety. By the same token anything that evokes that anxiety and the emotion of rage at having that original sweetness smothered becomes 'dirty', hateful, contemptuous, to be denied or controlled.

By medicalizing birth we desexualize it. By placing the woman on her back, and subjugating her to the 'wonders of modern technology' the miracle of her own organism is denied.

"Strapped on one's back with one's legs in stirrups is the worst possible position for giving birth. The main veins and arteries are along the spine, and in this position the weight of the baby, the uterus and the amniotic fluid is on the back. Blood clots are frequent in this position." [14]

In a culture in which the male is dominant socially and economically it is inevitable that the sexual anxiety of men will become the most institutionalized. To advocate a prone and passive position for a woman in birth is functionally no different than that of the prone and passive position that many men expect of women during sexual intercourse. Indeed, there are numerous accounts of men becoming sexually impotent when the woman takes the 'dominant' position.

It is also interesting that in cultures where sexuality is more approved of and birth is the domain of women, then female sexuality is equated with lush and curvaceous bodies, broad hips and ample breasts. Female beauty and motherhood are not segregated, but are aspects of each other. In our culture, the modern female ideal, as reflected by fashion models and the media, is emaciated, with thin hips and small breasts, like a young girl or adolescent boy. She looks passive and vulnerable, with none of the power and full bodied sexuality that nature endowed her with. She is more easily controlled.

Conclusion

The birth process and the environment it takes place in both exist in a web of larger cultural mores and societal pressures. There is no one group of people to blame for the situation we have found ourselves in, it has evolved over generations through negative attitudes towards natural bodily functions, in particular, sexual functions. No mother should feel guilty or a failure because she found labor difficult and painful. No man should feel guilty for being a man. We as a society need to recognize and take responsibility for our situation if we are to change it. It is not possible to hope for more relaxed pregnancies and labors unless we look at the sources of anxiety that disturb the capacity for pleasure in all aspects of human sexuality. An understanding of the sexual nature of the birth process and the origins of armoring in the way that children and adolescents are raised to contract against their own sexual natures is fundamental to this hope becoming a reality.

References:

1. "Shelia Kitzinger; On Birth and Sexuality", *Mothering* magazine. Fall 1984.
2. Silvert, Michael: "Orgonomic Practice in Obstetrics", *Orgonomic Medicine*. Vol.1. No.1. June 1955.
3. Kitzinger, Shelia: "Homebirth and Other Alternatives to Hospital", 1991.
4. Odent, Michel: "Hormones of Love", *Caduceus*. Issue 26, 1994.
5. Boadella, David: *Lifestreams. An Introduction to Biosynthesis.*, 1987.
6. Reich, Wilhelm: *Cosmic Superimposition, 1951.*
7. Reich, Wilhelm: *The Cancer Biopathy*, 1948.
8. Lamb, Jasmine: "Perceptions of Human Sexuality", Unpublished college thesis, 1995.
9. Attlee, Thomas: *Course notes*, The College of Craniosacral Therapy, 1996.
10. Herskowitz, Morton: *Human Armoring. An introduction to Psychiatric Orgone Therapy*. Transactions Press, 1999.
11. Herskowitz, Morton: "Psychiatric Orgone Therapy", Transcript of lecture given at universities of Munich, Heidelberg and Hamburg, 1993.
12. "Women Doctors Opt for Caesarian Birth", *The Guardian*. 1996.
13. Fuckert, Dorothea: *"Psychiatric Orgone Therapy"*, Transcript of lecture.
14. Milinaire, Caterine (Ed.): *Birth*, 1987.
15. Liley, A.W.: "The Foetus as a Personality", in *Lifestreams. An Introduction to Biosynthesis*, David Boadella, 1987.
16. Baker, Elsworth: *Man in the Trap*, Macmillan, NY 1967.
17. Blasband, Richard, et al.: "Armoring in Women in Labor", *Journal of Orgonomy*. Vol. 22, No. 1. May 1988.
18. Raphael, Chester: "Orgone Treatment during Labor", *Orgone Energy Bulletin*. Vol. 3. No. 3. 1951.
19. Stewart, D. & Stewart, A.: *21st Century Obstetrics Now, Vol. 1,* NAPSAC Press, 1978.
20. Odent, Michel: *Birth Reborn*, 1984.

Giordano Bruno's Philosophy

by Carlo Albini*

*"Innumerable suns exist;
innumerable earths revolve around these suns
in a manner similar to the way the
seven planets revolve around our sun.
Living beings inhabit these worlds."*
 — Giordano Bruno

Recently, in memory of the 400th anniversary of the death of Giordano Bruno, the Max Planck Institute has published a paper[1] concerning the cosmological discoveries realized by him. With some amazement it has been established that this philosopher of the Renaissance, before Galileo and Kepler, has discovered: the flattening of the Earth at the poles, the rotation of all celestial bodies around their own axis, the presence of other planets beyond Saturn (which was the last planet known at his time), the slowing down of the planets speed with the increasing of the distance from the Sun, etc. All these discoveries had been realized by Bruno without any optical instruments: the telescope was used for astronomical applications firstly by Galileo almost 50 years later.[2]

How was it possible? Let's have a look to Giordano Bruno's life to get some hints of his theories, since as in all great men, the life and the great achievements are deeply interconnected.

Early in the morning of 17th February of 1600, Giordano Bruno was accompanied by a silent procession to *Campo de'fiori* square, downtown Rome near St.Peter's cathedral, to his final destiny. There he was burnt alive together with all his books, and declared heretic — a shameful mark in those times — by the Inquisition. Since his screams could disturb the sleep of the silent majority, his tongue was blocked by a bit. At the last, he was killed, his voice muted after 8 endless years of inquisitions and tortures, burnt with the *silent complicity* of scientists and philosophers.

His death was not only a warning to the whole European sage community, where his death had a deep echo. It was also symptomatic of that historical period, in which future mass murders and religious wars devastated the relationships between Catholic and Protestants.

In fact, even around 1900 the Pope Leo XIII, who

* Consulting Engineer, student of orgonomy, and author of *Creazione e Castigo: La grande congiura contro Wilhelm Reich (Creation and Punishment: The great conspiracy against Wilhelm Reich)*, Tre Editori, Rome, 1997. Email: <carlo.albi@tiscalinet.it>

**Giordano Bruno
1548 - 1600**

published his famous encyclical *Populorum Progressio* expressing the sympathy of the church for the emerging worker's social movement and intent on being an expert in Galileo's theories, exhorted the Catholic congregation to ignore Bruno's philosophy, defaming it shamefully. Pope Pius XII, a few years later (around 1922) asked the Italian prime minister, Benito Mussolini, to destroy Bruno's statue in Campo de'fiori square, erected to remember the man, and that historical event. Mussolini, still fresh from his socialist and anarchic past, refused. As a reaction the pope soon after declared, as a "saint", Cardinal Bellarmino, one of Bruno's inquisitors.

Why? Why this silence? This conspiracy of silence extended like a giant shadow over all European intellectuals, who ignored for centuries the real content of his philosophy.

Looking at the statue, remembering the great man, you could perceive the *fear*, even the *terror* that the political powers and the majority of the intellectuals have felt towards his teachings, even over the centuries.

Filippo Bruno was born in Nola, a little town near Napoli, in 1548. At 17 years he became a monk and took the name of *Giordano*. Immediately he distinguished himself for 2 qualities: great ease of learning due to a wonderful memory, and his unconventional interpretations and criticism of the holy writs. After 2 years he had finished his studies; and was invited by Pope Pius Vth in Rome, to teach the Pope the "secrets" of his memory techniques.

Bruno developed, actually, an *art* to improve the function of the memory: he reached amazing performances (like so many other Renaissance students as Pico della Mirandola). His memory of a subject was actually regulated by *images* of an organic and sequential psychic development. The creation and invention of these mental images were actually an art connected to a general vision of the cosmos. His philosophy developed from this interior art. Therefore memory, invention, cosmic vision and critical intelligence were not separated nor in contradiction, but constituted an harmonic continuity.

Given these facts, he could not negotiate to teach his "secrets" to the Pope, who was only the first of a long tragic-comedic series. Bruno also realized that he could not continue his life as a monk (he was not sexually ascetic), and so he abandoned the monk clothes and began to teach in universities across the whole of Europe.

Following the movements of Giordano Bruno in Europe is like following a current of rich emotions and intellectual achievements, a social flow trespassing borders. Wherever he went, "something" happened: the kings and the powerful, wishing to get his memory "technique" for personal power, invited him; but after his arrival, sincere students and artists groups formed and were fertilized by his teachings.

He arrived in Paris via Toulouse, where he taught with success Aristotle's *De Anima* and a book of memory art (neither book has survived to modern times). In 1581, he taught to King Henry the IVth the art of memory, and dedicated to him *Umbris Idearum*, one of

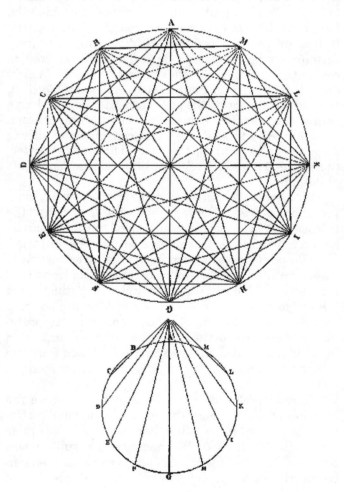

his works; but he published also a comedy, *Il Candelaio (The Candles' Creator)* in which he expressed his acute criticism of the surrounding socio-political world.

From Paris he went to London (1583-1585), contributing substantially to the Elizabethan world, where Italian culture was very much appreciated (Shakespeare was writing his famous works). Bruno had great success and published many of his "Italian dialogues" — in these writings he expressed part of his cosmological vision of the *infinite multiplicity and unity of the universe*,[3] and many artists, philosophers and physicians were inspired by his work.

In 1585 Bruno returned to Paris where he taught his criticisms of Aristotle's physics. The authorities reacted violently, however, so Bruno went to Prague, Wittenberg and Frankfurt, Germany, where he published his *Latin Papers*. He lived in Germany up to 1591, when he was invited to go to Venice from a patrician, Mocenigo. This nobleman wanted to learn his memory "technique" for power-reasons, but Mocenigo was disappointed from Bruno's teachings. Being sure that Bruno was concealing the secrets of his technique, when Bruno tried to turn back to Germany, Mocenigo denounced him to the Saint Office for heretic behavior and teachings.

The 26th May of 1592 marked the start of the inquisition of Bruno in Venice. Soon the Roman Church Court asked for his extradition to Rome, and the request was accepted. After years of incarceration, in 1599 the Cardinal Bellarmino asked Bruno to abjure his teachings. Bruno refused. After the sentence of death, Bruno declared: *"Maiore forsan cum timore sententiam in me fertis, quam ego accipiam"* (*"It's greater the fear in your emitting the sentence, than in my receiving it"*).

Bruno's philosophy continues to be widely misunderstood. Apart from the difficulties of interpretation of some of his writings, particularly his diagrams, and apart from the fact that many of his works are lost, the reason is that students of his works, after centuries of mechanical-mystical deformation of Natural processes, have no coordinate reference point from which to understand it deeply. In fact, Giordano Bruno's philosophy, according physical science — without even mentioning Church doctrine and the Christian misinterpretations — is considered usually only as an anticipation, untidy and mystical, of the more solid and sound physical-mechanical theories and science of Galileo and Newton. This unilateral interpretation has not been, nor is today "casual": It is the painful effort of the modern emotional mind, shaped by empty-space theory (the atomic conception of matter) which places living phenomena in a position of secondary importance by comparison to materialistic inertial phenomena — an effort which has rather successfully worked to conceal and destroy the *Magia Naturalis* vision of the cosmos, typical of Bruno and other important philosophers of the Renaissance.

In fact, it is well established historically that Giordano Bruno belonged to the cultural current of thinkers,

artists and philosophers of the Renaissance, who lived according to a "Platonic" vision of the cosmos, and who believed in a *Magia Naturalis*, something "obscure" for the future Enlightenment philosophy which finally succeeded in deleting from history the actual knowledge of the neo-Platonic vision. To get some hints of these cultural movements we must consider the following:

A) The historical period of the Renaissance, to which Bruno as many other universal genius' belonged (such as Leonardo da Vinci, Raffaello Sanzio, Michelangelo Buonarotti, etc), emerged from a suffocating and oppressive cultural cloak which lasted at least 1000 years. It lasted through the Middle Ages during which the last word in facts regarding not only theology but also physics, astronomy, and psychology were reserved to the Catholic Church, which incorporated and sterilized Aristotle's vision. The cosmos was made immobile, and the universe, the skies, the animal kingdom etc., were all divided into fixed categories. The Church was the navel of the cosmos and the Christ-crucified Catholic interpretation was the only road for the soul "salvation" of a sinful humanity. In this universe there was no place for the concrete human being, in particular for his inwardness, for his emotions and psychology. It was a world of purely static "facts", so similar conceptually to the "positivistic" conception of the 19th and 20th Centuries! (examples: Pavlovian psychology, the behaviorism of Skinner in USA, etc). The cultural movement of the Renaissance amazes us because — look at Leonardo da Vinci and Raffaello's paintings of human expressions, even in saints and angels, and at Michelangelo's statues expressing plastic emotions, at the human characters jumping out from artwork full of intimacy and psychology — at the background was the re-emergence of the Platonic vision, which meant for the great Renaissance movement the recovery of the tangible reality of *ideas* and of the *psychic world*. The *ideas* were not conceived

as a "subjective" phenomenon as mechanical science was inclined, and still tends to conceive. The *ideas* were conceived as physically real, objective energetic *schemata* (Greek word for "dynamic schemes") which lay at the basis, simultaneously, also of *perception and sensation*. For example: Giordano Bruno expressed in philosophic terms, i.e. with a strongly effective style of reasoning, that the cosmos could not be affectively and emotionally perceived and understood without roots in an "always existing" (ie., eternal) intuitive *idea*, which was not to be considered simply as his personal "opinion".[4] Questioning deeply ourselves, making an effort towards emotional attention, man can perceive the reality of the contact-intuition of the following objective primordial phenomenon: No beginning and no end of the real cosmos, which is only conceivable emotionally — and in the context of cyclical creations and deaths, a "cosmic metabolism" in the real animal-vital meaning.[2] The same is true for the *infinity* of the cosmos, or for its *fullness* and for the continuous *movement* of each part of the cosmos in relation to any other part. The universe is concretely (*dynamically or energetically*, in Wilhelm Reich's terms) conceivable only as an infinity of souls integrated simultaneously in *one soul*, similar to the members of one single animal. The "identity of opposites" was one of the first great achievements of Bruno's thought technique, written in a poem (and unfortunately lost) in 1582.[2]

Of course, Bruno did not simply advocate a "return" to the Platonic vision of the cosmos: Bruno's attitude was also critical in many respects toward the old Platonic vision.

B) Bruno's *Magia Naturalis* conception had many sources and roots. Let's say above all it is *not* "superstition" or "supernatural". Let's say also that this is the most controversial and difficult part to understand of his theory. The approach I will use are the following: firstly, the psychological and historical sources in Bruno philosophy, secondly its connections with his cosmic and philosophical vision. In many writings Bruno expressed his interest for the capability of living excitation to reach a *peak of functioning*: For example in moments of "poetic inspiration", of crucial decisions to take affect in short time, of clear reasoning and intuitions, in orgasm, in Bruno's memory performances, and similar excited living functions. For Bruno these functions are not peculiar only to "human" beings, but are present in Nature at large, in the living and in physical Nature. Memory, as an example, can't be improved without a creative process of invented images involving the subject. For memory improvement, the "energetic stimulation" of spontaneous processes are very important. Therefore Bruno conceived that the logic of the living does not follow the "cause-effect" chain, the linear sequence logic. It's not even the circular retroaction ("feedback") process of modern automatic control systems. The *Magia Naturalis* concerns the shape of merging flows between phenomena; in particular the "technical" transactions between man and nature. The technician as a "magician" can't be a mechanical operator having programmed such and such actions to repeat themselves as, for example, the usual modern mnemonic-technique suggests, but involves above all a transformation of the human being, his emotions and whole character, by the use of a dynamic flow of images. And, according to his philosophy, the individual active soul is in resonance with the *anima mundi*, with the cosmic soul: *Magia* has, according to Bruno, the etymological meaning of "mago" = *wise man*.[5] The content of his mnemonic-technique involved the creation (the "painting") of psychic images (*imagines agentes* as Bruno defined them) rich in emotional content and correlated to the object to be remembered: looking today at these images-diagrams, which were and are so confusing for the mechanistic mind, depicted by Bruno in his "Seal of Seals" we have the impression to find something similar to the eastern philosophical "mandala", but with an inner dynamism, since the logic development and the dynamic sequence of these images has to be intrinsic, i.e. of an "immanent necessity", as Bruno said (see. D.W Singer p. 90).[3]

Bruno perceived that the biological functions of memory and emotion, of *reasoning and imagination* were functions of Nature in general — i.e. that the human intellectual functions, of imagination and so forth were potentially present in Nature, and actually realized through infinite variations. His conception of *potential* and *actual* give to his philosophy a sound energetic basis, far from any mysticism, even if his philosophy goes far beyond the words and language form of communication, completely at variance with standard European philosophy. His book *The Seal of Seals* is full of diagram-pictures, to stimulate the emotional function of the mind, of which he took great care also in the editorial phase, and which remained a mystery to the orthodox European philosophy for many centuries, up into today.

The logical result of his philosophy was, and is, against any uniformity in the human consciousness, freedom being an intrinsic necessity and a cosmic universal functional quality. And as history shows, all the changes in relationships between man and the political powers, as advocated by Bruno, were at variance with what would triumph in Europe a few years after his horrible death.

In my opinion only the energetic conception of Wilhelm Reich's *orgonomy*, could give justice to his vision. As examples:

1. According to Bruno organic sensations remain "ineffective" (unconscious!) without the active participation of imagination, and one of the first achievements by the young W. Reich was his conception of the active-perceptual and the passive-sensorial side of pulsation;

2. Bruno's cosmic vision of the universe as an infinite whole of free parts functioning simultaneously and antithetically with the unitary soul of the cosmos, and the observation of the excitation-stimulus effect within living organisms, rising to a peak, is matched by Reich's concept of *orgonotic lumination*, which underlies the orgasm function, sun-planet energetic relationships, and the living qualities of the cosmic orgone energy, with its functional identity of antithetical opposites;

3. The *minimum triple* is Bruno's conception of the minimum "living particles" necessary for an organic *logical* development (in thought, as in mathematics and physics), and the *coincidentia oppositorum* (identity of opposite functions), have similarities to Reich's discoveries on *bions* and the energetic thought technique of *orgonomic functionalism*.

The tragic destiny of the two men, Bruno and Reich, will not be considered lightly by a future, thoughtful world.

References:

1. "Einstein, Bruno und die Zeit", *Sterne und Weltraum, Zeitschrift fur Astronomie*, Max Planck Institut, V.39, Nr. 2-3, Seite 103–204, Februar-März 2000.

2. Anacleto Verrecchia: *Giordano Bruno, Nachtfalter des Geistes* Boehlau Verlag,1999 and Verrecchia Interview in *Ricerrca & Innovazione* N°58, 1999- Torino, Italy.

3. See excerpts in Dorothea W. Singer *Giordano Bruno, his Life and Thought*, Schuman, NY 1950.

4. Giordano Bruno: "De infinito universo et uno" or "De la causa, principio et uno".

5. Giordano Bruno, "De Magia, De Vinculis in Genere".

The writings of Giordano Bruno are mostly available in the Italian language, with a few translations of his works into other languages. For a complete view of Bruno's life and works, the author most highly recommends the writings by Anacleto Verrecchia and Dorothy W. Singer. An internet search of "Giordano Bruno" will bring up thousands of items in many languages, including various books and on-line translations of his once-burned manuscripts.

Studies on the Origin of Life
The Preparation of Primordial Cell-Like Forms
by Bernard R. Grad, Ph.D.*

Introduction

The purpose of this study was to learn something about the processes involved in the transformation of matter from inanimate to the living state. It began with an experiment (Experiment 20, or Exp. XX) reported earlier by Wilhelm Reich in which he claimed that when an autoclaved, microscopically clear, aqueous extract of soil – bion water (BW) – was frozen and thawed, flakes of microscopic size with organic, that is, living form, were obtained.[1] Reich also reported the transformation of the plasmatic flakes into living cancer cells.[1,2]

Encouraged by his findings, I repeated Experiment 20[3] and at my first try I observed his plasmatic flakes in large numbers (Figure 1). However, I also saw other cell-like forms, looking like spores or algae (Figure 2) which were quite different from Reich's plasmatic flakes. Struck by their life-like appearance, I decided to investigate them further.

I did not regard the cell-like forms as being alive when I first observed them but I felt that they may have had some primordial role in the origin of life; hence, I named them primordial forms (PFs). When I showed them to Reich, he asked me to leave some with him. About a year later, he informed me that the PFs were starting to turn green. I felt that the more rapid change in the PFs in the direction of life in Reich's laboratory than in my lab was because of the powerful Oranur effects at Orgonon at that time.[4]

In the mid 1950s Reich was compelled to turn his attention to issues that threatened the continuation of his work and as it turned out, his own survival, and the possibility of my consulting him further on experiments on the origin of life came to an end.

In the years that followed, I continued working on Experiment 20 whenever circumstances allowed, trying to obtain the PFs once again but failing a number of times. Eventually, the problem changed from one of attempting to discover exactly how the PFs were ob-

* Dr. Bernard Grad is an Associate Professor in biology at McGill University, Montreal, Canada. He received his Ph.D. in biology at McGill University in 1949, the year in which he met Reich. Dr. Grad published papers on orgonomy and alternative healing, with about 100 publications on aging and cancer. He retired in 1985, but remains active.   Email: bgrad@po-box.mcgill.ca

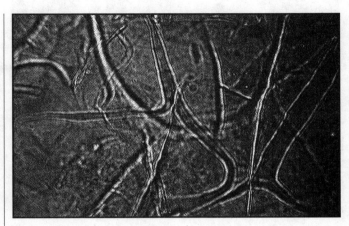

Figure 1: **Plasmatic flakes** obtained on repeating Reich's Experiment 20 (microscopic magnification x 300).

tained in my first trial of Experiment 20 to one of how to obtain the PFs by any means.

Experiments Which Yielded Primordial Form Reproducibility

The solution of the problem of how to prepare the PFs came from the application of the fact that when living tissue breaks down, ammonia (NH_3) and carbon dioxide (CO_2) would be present among other simple products. I assumed that if these substances were brought together, they could again form simple, life-like structures, such as the PFs, and in this way begin again the path of renewal.

Accordingly, three bottles containing BW were stoppered with non-absorbent cotton, autoclaved and placed in a large jar in which carbon dioxide in the form of dry ice and concentrated ammonium hydroxide (NH_4OH) were allowed to interact for several days beforehand. The jar was then sealed with tape and the three bottles remained in the jar overnight at room temperature. The bottles were removed from the jar the next day and placed at about -20°C for six days, after which they were defrosted at room temperature and examined microscopically. (At that time, I ascribed a role to freezing in the formation of the PFs). PFs in large numbers were immediately observed on microscopic examination of the liquid in the bottles. Therefore, allowing ammonia and carbon dioxide to react with BW definitely yielded PFs. This then was one way of bringing together the

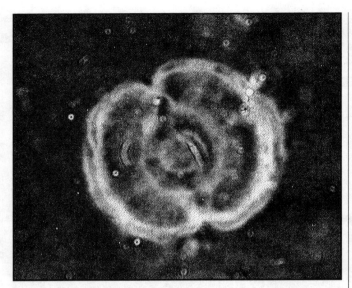

Figure 2: Dividing "spore" with central nucleus observed in my first attempt to repeat Reich's Experiment 20. The negative was used in this figure because it provided a better image of the object than the positive. Magnification x 3200.

basic chemical elements of living tissue, namely nitrogen, hydrogen, carbon and oxygen, thereby beginning the path to regeneration.

In another experiment, BW was exposed to ammonium hydroxide in a jar for about fifteen hours, and a cloudiness was observed within the BW, microscopic examination of which revealed a precipitate in which granule-size bodies were visible. These developed into vesicles, that is, bions, during the next eight hours and continued to swell to become PFs after two days.

In explanation, the first step in the preparation of the PFs was the alkalization of the BW by ammonia for 15 hours but that was insufficient by itself to produce the PFs. Opening the jar to sample some BW for microscopic examination exposed the BW to the air from which it picked up carbon dioxide. This led to the beginning of the growth of the granules and this took several hours because the amount of carbon dioxide in the air was small. However, with time the granules became vesicles and ultimately PFs.

Support for this explanation was provided when BW was exposed to ammonium hydroxide continuously for four days without exposure to air and failed to yield PFs.

To test further whether carbon dioxide might have possibly been this substance, one ml of 25% ammonium hydroxide was added to eight ml of BW and 1-2 hours later a small piece of dry ice was also dropped in, following which the BW became progressively cloudier, at which point microscopic examination showed the presence of large numbers of PFs. This indicated that the addition of carbon dioxide did indeed lead quickly to the formation of PFs in contrast to the several hours it took to pick up carbon dioxide from the air.

Experiments Demonstrating That Soil Bion Water Was Providing Some Substance Essential for Primordial Form Formation

When carbon dioxide and ammonium hydroxide were mixed together in the absence of BW, PFs formation did not occur. Apparently, BW was providing something essential for PFs formation. This was demonstrated by an experiment in which BW was exposed to carbon dioxide and ammonium hydroxide yielding a precipitate containing PFs which were removed from the BW by filtration. The same BW was again exposed to carbon dioxide and ammonium hydroxide which again yielded PFs which were again withdrawn by filtration. When the same BW was exposed to carbon dioxide and ammonium hydroxide for the third time, PFs were not present. Therefore, some substance essential for PFs formation was apparently removed from the BW by repeated exposure to ammonium hydroxide and carbon dioxide and discarding the resulting precipitate.

Identification of the Substance in Soil Bion Water Essential for Primordial Form Formation

To identify in BW the substance essential for PFs formation, 125 ml 100% ammonium hydroxide was added to 2.5 litres of sterile BW and then autoclaved for 15 minutes at 15 lbs pressure and 115°C. Instead of inhibiting the formation of the PFs, the autoclavation of the alkaline BW actually hastened their formation probably by accelerating the uptake of carbon dioxide from the air after autoclavation was completed and the BW was exposed to the air while still hot. A precipitate observed immediately upon removing the flask from the autoclave was separated by centrifugation, washed four times with distilled water and then dried in an oven. Microscopic examination of the dried precipitate revealed masses of PFs. Accordingly, 167 mgm of dried precipitate was subjected to optical spectroscopy and found to contain at least 50% calcium. This was the substance essential for PFs formation which BW provided in the experiments just described.

Subsequent study showed that PFs were readily obtained when ammonium carbonate $(NH_4)_2CO_3$ or sodium carbonate Na_2CO_3 or potassium carbonate K_2CO_3 was mixed with BW.

That is:

$(NH_4)_2CO_3$ or Na_2CO_3 or K_2CO_3 + BW yields PFs
(Eqn. A)

With the information that BW was providing calcium, it became clear that when alkaline carbonates were added to BW, they were reacting with the calcium in BW to form calcium carbonate $(CaCO_3)$ which readily precipitated because calcium carbonate is normally only slightly soluble in aqueous solutions and even less so at a more alkaline pHs.

$$(NH_4)_2CO_3 \text{ or } Na_2CO_3 \text{ or } K_2CO_3$$
$$+ \text{ calcium in BW yields PFs}$$
(Eqn. B)

But:

$$(NH_4)_2CO_3 \text{ or } Na_2CO_3 \text{ or } K_2CO_3$$
$$+ \text{ calcium also yields } CaCO_3$$
(Eqn. C)

That is, PFs prepared in this way are made of calcium carbonate.

The Formation of Primordial Forms In the Absence of Soil Bion Water

An earlier experiment showed that when carbon dioxide and ammonium hydroxide were mixed together in the absence of BW, PFs formation did not occur. In fact, all the experiments described up to this point that succeeded in yielding PFs involved the presence of BW. An experiment showed that this was because BW was providing calcium which was essential for PFs formation. If true, then it should be possible to prepare PFs in the absence of BW provided calcium was provided separately. This was the first experiment in which an attempt was made to obtain the PFs in the absence of BW.

Accordingly, when molar ammonium carbonate was mixed with molar calcium chloride ($CaCl_2$), a precipitate of calcium carbonate appeared at once. Immediate microscopic examination of the precipitate revealed it to be granular (Figure 3) which were reminiscent of Reich's T-bacilli.[1] Within the next few minutes, these granules grew steadily larger to become vesicles (Figure 4) which were Reich's bions.[1] These vesicles continued to grow still larger to yield PFs. They increased in size until they were about the size of cells. Many also had an hourglass shape and a rudimentary nucleus (Figure 5). Many of these forms showed a cleavage in two along the short axis, some even formed tetrads and a few simulated budding (Figure 5). The cleavage became evident early in their formation and appeared more distinct as the PFs grew larger. However, the different parts of the cleaved form were not observed to separate from each other.

These forms were essentially similar to the PFs first seen in BW in 1952,[3] except the ones just described had a less complex morphology (cf. Figures 2 and 5). That is, some constituent(s) in BW other than calcium was probably also making some contribution to PFs formation.

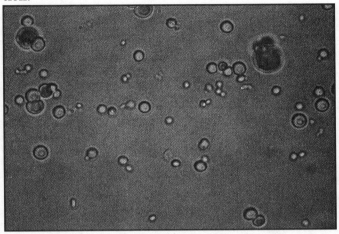

Figure 4: **Vesicles** seen soon after the appearance of the granular precipitate in Figure 3. A few cell-like forms can be also be seen here and there (microscopic amplification x 160).

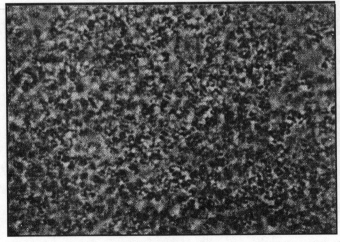

Figure 3: **Granular Precipitate** seen upon mixing 0.25 ml molar ammonium carbonate with 0.25 ml 0.1 M Na_2HPO_4 and then adding 0.5 ml molar calcium chloride (microscopic magnification x 160).

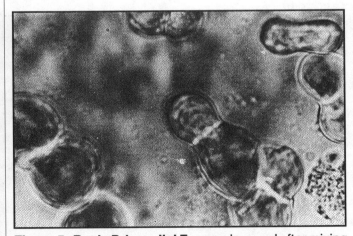

Figure 5: **Basic Primordial Forms** observed after mixing 0.25 ml M ammonium carbonate with 0.25 ml 0.1 M Na_2HPO_4 and then adding 0.5 ml M calcium chloride (microscopic magnification x 400). Note their hourglass shape and cleavage along the short axis of the form.

In the experiment reported earlier[3], the PFs were kept in an incubator at 37°C for several months at which time they began to disintegrate into small pulsating vesicles, that is, into bions, which had wide fields and which alternatively fused and separated from adjacent bions. Because of their attraction for each other, they remained together in heaps for some time and in the same place where the PFs from which they originated were located. However, with time these bions separated from each other and dispersed, leaving the empty structure of the PFs.[3] That is, in the process of PFs disintegration, the PFs became bionous again and had they been observed long enough, the bions should have yielded T-bacilli, as shown by Reich to occur in blood, hay and cancer tissue.[1] This study showed that the process of PFs formation, which involved the development from T-bacilli to bions to PFs, followed the same path but in reverse when the PFs disintegrated.[3]

Moreover, in the formation of the PFs, each bion yielded one PFs but in their disintegration, each PFs yielded a heap of bions. Because of this and because the behavior of the bions that went on to yield PFs was different from that of the bions resulting from PFs disintegration, it was assumed some change occurred in their energetic state during the interval between formation and disintegration.

The chemical reaction between ammonium carbonate and calcium chloride would have been expected to yield only the well-known orthorhombic or hexagonal crystals of calcium carbonate. In fact, these crystals were either not present or present in small numbers during the first few minutes after mixing an alkaline carbonate and calcium chloride to yield a precipitate of calcium carbonate. However, after two hours, the hexagonal crystals outnumbered the PFs, and by twenty-four hours, the hexagonal crystals were in the great majority with only an occasional PFs being observed (Figure 6).

In short, PFs appeared for a brief period soon after mixing an alkaline carbonate with calcium chloride but were only rarely observed twenty-four hours later. Moreover, when this experiment was conducted in the presence of BW, the PFs forms survived indefinitely and the hexagonal crystals of calcium carbonate did not appear at all. The next few experiments sought to clarify this problem.

The Stabilization of Primordial Forms Prepared in the Absence of Soil Bion Water

In the search for a substance to stabilize the PFs made in the absence of BW, it was found that this could be achieved by mixing equal volumes of molar ammonium carbonate and molar calcium chloride in the presence of Krebs-Ringer solution.[§] The process of change from granules to vesicles to PFs was the same as in the absence of Krebs-Ringer except that the newly-formed

PFs did not disappear but persisted indefinitely while the hexagonal crystals did not appear.

Further studies showed that the compound in Krebs-Ringer solution essential for PFs stability was disodium monohydrogen phosphate (Na_2HPO_4). That is, one volume of molar ammonium carbonate mixed with two volumes of molar calcium chloride in the presence of one volume of $0.1M$ Na_2HPO_4 yielded PFs which persisted indefinitely. In short:

$$1M\ (NH_4)_2CO_3 + 0.1M\ Na_2HPO_4 + 1M\ CaCl_2$$
$$\text{yields stable PFs}$$

(Eqn. D)

When disodium monohydrogen phosphate (Na_2HPO_4) was replaced by monosodium dihydrogen phosphate (NaH_2PO_4), a precipitate was obtained from which PFs did not develop. Moreover, calcium chloride mixed with Na_2HPO_4 yielded a precipitate, calcium hydrogen phosphate ($CaHPO_4$), which did not lead to the formation of PFs. Therefore, $(NH_4)_2CO_3$ was always mixed first with Na_2HPO_4: this yielded a clear solution. Then, $CaCl_2$ was added and an amorphous precipitate appeared which developed into PFs. In the presence of Na_2HPO_4, the morphology of the PFs was more cell-like when the volume of molar calcium chloride was twice that of molar ammonium carbonate.

The fact that PFs could be produced in solutions from which BW was absent demonstrated that when PFs were originally obtained in abundance in BW, they were present in BW prior to treatment.

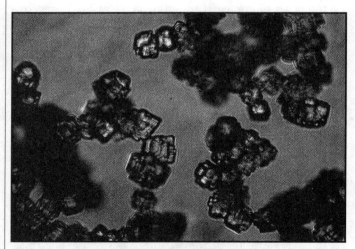

Figure 6: Orthorhombic or hexagonal crystals of calcium carbonate observed after the disappearance of the basic Primordial Forms prepared as in Figure 5 but without Na_2HPO_4 (microscopic magnification x 160).

[§] The Krebs-Ringer solution, which contains physiological amounts of NaCl, KCl and $CaCl_2$, was developed by Ringer to prolong the survival of tissues *in vitro*, and refined by Krebs who added Na_2HPO_4 and NaH_2PO_4 as buffers.

The Role of Disodium Monohydrogen Phosphate (Na_2HPO_4) and pH in the Production of Stable Primordial Forms

Combining ammonium carbonate with calcium chloride resulted in a decline in pH to a minimum of pH 5.15 (without Na_2HPO_4) and pH 5.9 (with Na_2HPO_4) within a few minutes of mixing the chemicals. The next day, the values rose to a plateau of pH 6.7 (without Na_2HPO_4) and pH 7.1 (with Na_2HPO_4) That is, the addition of Na_2HPO_4 to ammonium carbonate with calcium chloride increased the pH.

However, the role of Na_2HPO_4 in producing stable PFs in the presence of $(NH_4)_2CO_3$ and $CaCl_2$ was apparently not due to its capacity to increase the pH because the PFs were not obtained when NaOH or KOH was used in place of Na_2HPO_4 to yield a similar pH curve. Perhaps some atoms of Na_2HPO_4 or of $CaHPO_4$, which may also have formed, substituted for other atoms in the calcium carbonate crystal lattice thereby increasing the stability of the resulting PFs. Another possibility is that atoms of Na_2HPO_4 or $CaHPO_4$ fitted into the space between the atoms of calcium carbonate without replacing them. In this case, the atoms of the "impurity" played an interstitial role with the consequent greater stability of the PFs.

In preparing PFs in the presence of BW, the addition of Na_2HPO_4 was unnecessary, suggesting that the same compound or some other substance serving the same function, was already present in BW, thereby imparting stability to the PFs. Calcium also did not have to be added because it was already present in BW.

Are the Primordial Forms Calcite or Aragonite Crystals?

To determine whether calcium carbonate in the PFs existed in the form of calcite or aragonite, two naturally occurring crystalline forms of $CaCO_3$, one volume of 1M $(NH_4)_2CO_3$ and one volume of 0.1 M Na_2HPO_4 were mixed with two volumes of 1M $CaCl_2$ which produced both PFs and a stippled precipitate. The solution was then adjusted to pH 4.6 at which point microscopic examination revealed that only PFs were present. These were then separated by centrifugation, dried at room temperature and submitted to X-ray diffraction analysis which revealed that the material consisted of calcium carbonate in the form of calcite.

The Preparation of Primordial Forms in the Presence of Substances Other than Disodium Monohydrogen Phosphate

PFs made according to Eqn. D can be considered to be the basic form of the PFs. Experiments now to be described demonstrated that when the reaction between an alkaline carbonate and calcium chloride took

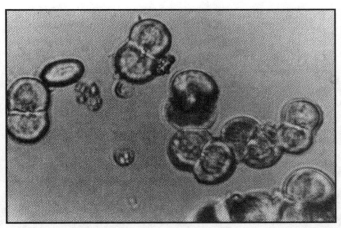

Figure 7: **Primordial Forms** prepared by mixing 0.25 ml M ammonium carbonate with 0.l ml M calcium chloride in the presence of 2.5 ml BW (microscopic magnification x 400). Note their hourglass shape, cleavage along the short axis and rudimentary "nuclei".

place in the presence of substances other than Na_2HPO_4, PFs were produced with a morphology that was more complex in their cell-like structure than the basic PFs.

1) PFs Prepared in the Presence of BW

Having first observed the PFs in the presence of BW, and having subsequently learned how to make them in its absence, it was decided to start a new series of experiments by making PFs once again in accordance with what was learned since the PFs were first observed.

Accordingly, the PFs were prepared by adding 0.l ml 1M $CaCl_2$ to 0.25 ml 1M $(NH_4)_2CO_3$ in the presence of 2.5 ml BW and these yielded PFs which were plumper and with a more granular "cytoplasm" (Figure 7) than the basic PFs (Figure 5). Although a small amount of calcium chloride was included in this experiment, PFs were readily obtained in BW even when $CaCl_2$ was omitted because calcium was already present in BW. Nor was the addition of Na_2HPO_4 necessary to obtain PFs as was the case when preparing the PFs separately from BW. Later, it also was found that the addition of Na_2HPO_4 was also unnecessary when the PFs were prepared in the presence of other compounds.

2) PFs Prepared in the Presence of Sterile, Aqueous Extracts of Peat Moss

PFs were also prepared in the presence of aqueous extracts of peat moss obtained by boiling peat moss in distilled water for an hour (10-20 ml water per gram of peat moss), repeatedly filtering through about two inches of the boiled peat moss till clear of microscopic particulate matter and then autoclaved. In the presence of 2.5 ml of this peat moss aqueous extract (PW), both 0.25 ml 1M $(NH_4)_2CO_3$ and 0.5 ml 1M $CaCl_2$ were found to be essential for the production of PW PFs (Figure 8). $CaCl_2$

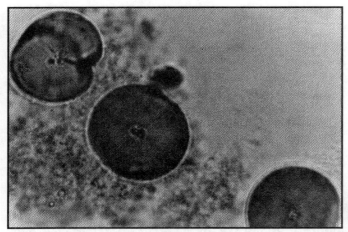

Figure 8: **Primordial Forms** prepared by mixing 0.25 ml M ammonium carbonate with 0.5 ml M calcium chloride in the presence of 2.5 ml PW (microscopic magnification x 400). Note the splitting and rudimentary "nuclei" of these PFs and that their color was more intense than that of the PW solution in which the PFs were prepared. This indicated that the chemical(s) that provided the color in the PW solution was concentrated and trapped within the PFs during their preparation. Note also the difference in the appearance between these PFs and those shown in Figures 5, 7, 10 and 11.

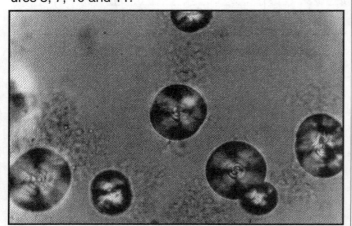

Figure 9: **Primordial Forms** prepared by mixing 0.25 ml M ammonium carbonate with 0.5 ml M calcium chloride in the presence of 2.5 ml PW (microscopic magnification x 160). Photographed through a polarizing microscope. Note the two lines crossing at right angles to each other indicating material inside these PFs was isotropic, that is, was exhibiting uniform physical properties in all directions and therefore, the orderly arrangement of the material inside the PW PFs.

This article, with full-color copies of all photomicrographs, will eventually be posted to:
http://www.orgonelab.org/Pulse5.htm

PF = Primordial Forms

BW = Bion Water extract

PW = Peat Moss aqueous extract

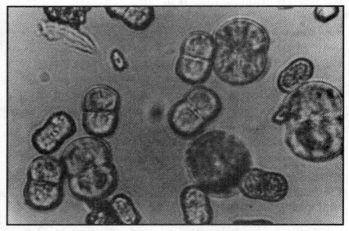

Figure 10: Primordial Forms prepared by mixing 0.25 ml M ammonium carbonate with 0.5 ml M calcium chloride in the presence of 2.5 ml 1% pectin (microscopic magnification x 400). Note their hourglass shape, cleavage along the short axis, rudimentary "nuclei" and the similarity of their appearance to the BW PFs in Figure 7.

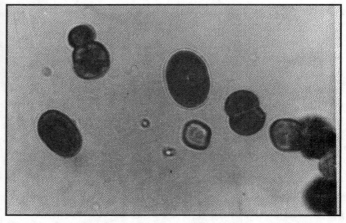

Figure 11: Primordial Forms prepared by mixing 0.25 ml M ammonium carbonate with 0.5 ml M calcium chloride in the presence of 2.5 ml 1% humic acid (microscopic magnification x 400). Note the hourglass shape, cleavage and budding of some of the forms and their rudimentary "nuclei". Note that their color was more intense than that of the humic acid solution in which the PFs were prepared. This indicated that the chemical that provided the color in the humic acid solution was concentrated and trapped within the PFs during their preparation.

had to be added because PW does not contain sufficient calcium, but there was no need to add Na_2HPO_4 as PW apparently contained some stabilizing substance which may be Na_2HPO_4 or some other compound. Moreover, many of the PW PFs were browner than the solution in which they were prepared. This indicated that in the process of making the PFs, the substance that provided the color in PW somehow became concentrated while becoming attached to the PFs. The PW PFs were not only browner than the BW PFs (Figure 7) and basic PFs (Figure 5), but they also had a larger "cytoplasmic" region.

A sample of PW PFs was photographed through a polarizing microscope and revealed a pseudo-uniaxial dark cross indicating that the material inside these PFs was isotropic, that is, exhibiting uniform physical properties in all directions, indicating that the material in the PFs was arranged in orderly fashion (Figure 9).

3) PFs Prepared in the Presence of Pectin

PFs were also obtained by mixing 0.25 ml 1M $(NH_4)_2CO_3$ and 0.5 ml 1M $CaCl_2$ in the presence of 2.5 ml 1% pectin (Figure 10). The appearance of the pectin PFs was similar to that of BW PFs (Figure 7).

4) PFs Prepared in the Presence of Humic Acid

0.25 ml 1M $(NH_4)_2CO_3$ mixed with 0.5 ml 1M $CaCl_2$ in 2.5 ml of an aqueous solution containing 0.1% humic acid also yielded PFs similar to BW PFs, although smaller (Figure 11). Moreover, many of the humic acid PFs were browner than the humic acid solution in which they were prepared. This indicated that in the process of making the PFs, the humic acid was somehow concentrated while being trapped by the PFs.

Additional experiments were also conducted in which the PFs were made in the presence of such biologically relevant substances as DNA, RNA, ATP, albumin, etc. These yielded PFs with features that were still more life-like and intricate; they will be described in a subsequent paper.

Discussion

The basic finding reported in this paper was the one indicating that the elementary chemical reaction between calcium chloride and a carbonate yielded a precipitate that went on to yield forms that were remarkably cell-like in appearance. This was observed when a carbonate was added to calcium chloride which immediately yielded a precipitate , which upon microscopic examination showed that its constituent granules, that were suggestive of Reich's T-bacilli, immediately started to enlarge to become vesicles suggestive of Reich's bions, and then continued to grow until they were cell-like in appearance. This was suggested by their size, their hourglass appearance, their rudimentary "nuclei", their cleavage into two along the short axis, their budding and even cleavage into four. Moreover, when the reaction between calcium chloride and carbonate was made to occur in the presence of more complicated substances, structures with an even more complex cell-like morphology were obtained.

Conventional biophysics and biochemistry has not yet succeeded convincingly in obtaining simple biological structures from the consideration of the conventional geometry of its constituent atoms or molecules. Any structures built up from such constituents may be valuable in explaining its physical or chemical properties but they do not really look anything like the cell from which they may originate.

This is what lends some uniqueness to the finding that an elementary chemical reaction can simultaneously produce cell-like structures. That is, this reaction bridges a gap between chemistry and biological morphology and when examined further was shown to have additional implications to be mentioned later.

Inasmuch as this study began with an attempt to repeat an experiment first conducted by Reich, it is reasonable to look further into Reich's work for an explanation of the findings reported in this paper. The reaction between a carbonate and calcium chloride in aqueous solution can be considered as two energy systems which interact with each other, converge and superimpose. Reich described this superimposition as involving two or more spinning energy streams that come together in a curving path leading to a flow that ends in circular motion with loss of kinetic energy at which point there occurs the "creation of the primordial mass particle".[5]

What evidence does the reaction between a carbonate and calcium chloride reveal that tends to support Reich's speculation? First, there is the creation of the precipitate of calcium carbonate. Moreover, not only did the precipitate appear but when examined microscopically, it was shown to be made up of granules which grew to become vesicles and then primordial cell-like structures.

It cannot be stated at this time that this reaction to create calcium carbonate is unique in regard to its capacity to yield morphological forms of biological relevance; only further investigation will answer that question. Certainly, not all chemical reactions that yield a precipitate result in granules which grow to be vesicles and cell-like structures without further intervention.

An example of this was observed in our experiments when Na_2HPO_4 was introduced to stabilize the calcium carbonate reaction between the carbonate and the calcium chloride. In this instance, it was found necessary that the carbonate and the Na_2HPO_4 be brought together before adding the calcium chloride because if the latter and Na_2HPO_4 were brought together first, there occurred the formation of a precipitate and the further addition of the carbonate did not result in the formation of the PFs.

The connection made in this study, by a chemical reaction between a carbonate and calcium chloride and morphologies with biological relevance, is now open to further investigation.

The PFs resulting from the reaction between a carbonate and calcium chloride in water, with or without the presence of Na_2HPO_4, can be considered as the basic PFs. Moreover, the morphology of the PFs was more complex than the basic PFs when made in the presence of substances more complex than Na_2HPO_4. For example, more complex PFs were made in the presence of such compounds as pectin or humic acid while the morphology of those made in the presence of a mixture of complex substances such as found in aqueous extracts of soil or peat moss was still more so. This is apparent from a comparison of Figure 5 with Figures 7 to 11. Subsequent studies to be described in a later publication describe other even more complex structures.

Because this study took the research into previously unexplored territory between the non-living and living, morphological changes suggestive of those observed in the living were being observed in the PFs that were still apparently not alive. This gave rise to the use of terms suggestive of living structures, such as "cytoplasmic" and "nuclei". However, because they were being described in forms not yet living, they were apostrophized.

The PFs described in this paper were all of microscopic size but studies by others have shown that calcium carbonate precipitation in the presence of silica gel typically formed macroscopically-visible crystal aggregates reminiscent of the exoskeletons of invertebrates.[6] Indeed, calcium carbonate is a major component of the exoskeletons of invertebrates and along with calcium phosphate is a major mineral component also of the skeleton of vertebrates. That is, calcium carbonate may play a primary role in setting the stage for the first steps towards the beginning of life but is also a major component of skeletons of the organisms which subsequently developed. This supports the claim that the reaction between a carbonate and calcium chloride to make calcium carbonate has a very considerable morphogenic potential.

For the PFs to have been observed prior to this report, a stabilizing substance, such as Na_2HPO_4, must have been present for otherwise, the "survival" of the PFs would have been of such short duration that they could have been missed. In any case, even if the PFs were previously observed, this was most likely to have been in a crystallographic context, that is, they would have been examined from the point of view of the development of its different faces and its characteristic interfacial angles. That is, they would have been considered to be a variant or a "habit" of the orthorhombic or hexagonal calcium carbonate crystal and not as a form with a potential for the formation of the biological organisms. This specific attribution to the PFs of prop-erties significant for biology occurred because they were first observed in aqueous extracts of soil in the context of a search for clues to the origin of life.[3]

As discussed elsewhere,[7] the experiments described in this paper also have implications for the phenomenon of pleomorphism which in this context can be defined as the "taking on" of different forms by an individual organism of a species during its life cycle. For example, as described earlier, it was shown that when a carbonate was mixed with calcium chloride, microscopic examination of the resulting calcium carbonate precipitate revealed granules, which grew in size to form small vesicles which then grew still larger to yield PFs. Without the presence of Na_2HPO_4, the PFs would soon have transformed into orthorhombic or hexagonal calcium carbonate crystals.

Just as Na_2HPO_4 prevented the PFs from yielding place to the hexagonal calcium carbonate crystals, it is possible to interfere with the process of change from the just visible granular structures to small vesicles. Indeed, a method for achieving this was already suggested earlier, when in the experiments involving exposure of BW to ammonia, formation of a precipitate which then failed to yield PFs so long as the reaction mixture was sealed so that it could not come in contact with the carbon dioxide in air, which was essential for the reaction to continue. . However, they did eventually become PFs when carbon dioxide became available.

Similarly, by controlling the introduction of still other molecules, the change from bionous vesicles to PFs to hexagonal crystals might also be inhibited. In this way, one could obtain from the same chemical reaction, structures with four different morphologies (barely visible granules, vesicles, PFs and hexagonal crystals). Additional variation in the morphology of the PFs was obtained when the medium in which calcium carbonate was being prepared, also contained other substances. Such PFs were prepared in the presence of pectin, humic acid, BW and PW. If each of these different structures were observed without the knowledge of the presence of the various chemicals in the reaction mixture, it might have been difficult to recognize that all the structures were part of the same process of calcium carbonate formation. By conducting the carbonate-calcium chloride reaction in the presence of even more complex life-relevant chemicals in a study to be described in a later publication, still more intricate biomorphologies were obtained. In short, the chemical reaction which yields calcium carbonate provides a demonstration of the importance of local environmental conditions on the appearance of "pleomorphism" in the non-living realm, mimicking the role of environmental factors on pleomorphism occurring in micro-organisms. Later studies investigated other physical properties of PFs and the findings lent further support to the claim that they could serve as suitable intermediaries in the origin of life.

Acknowledgments

Gratitude is expressed to Harold Brodkin for technical assistance during the time when these studies were first undertaken.

References:

1. Reich, W.: *The Cancer Biopathy*, Orgone Institute Press, New York, 1948, Chapter 2 (Reprinted by Farrar, Straus & Giroux, NY, 1973).

2. Reich, W.: "'Cancer cells' in Experiment XX", *Orgone Energy Bulletin,* 3(1):1-3, 1951.

3. Grad, B.R.: "Wilhelm Reich's Experiment XX", *Cosmic Orgone Engineering (CORE)*, 7(3-4):130-143, 1955.

4. Reich, W.: "The Oranur Experiment", *Orgone Energy Bulletin* 3(4):185-344, 1951 (Partially reprinted in Reich, W.: *Selected Writings: An Introduction to Orgonomy*, Farrar, Straus & Giroux, NY, 1960, 1973).

5. Reich, W.: *Ether, God and Devil / Cosmic Superposition.* Farrar, Straus & Giroux, NY, 1973, pp. 181-183 and 185-186.

6. Garcia-Ruiz, J.M.: "On the Formation of Induced Morphology Crystal Aggregates", *J. Crystal Growth,* 73:251-262, 1985.

7. Grad, B.R., "Calcium Carbonate and Pleomorphism", in: *Pleomorphic Microbes in Health and Disease. Proceedings. First Annual Symposium,* June 18-19, 1999, Montreal, Quebec, Canada. Edited by G.S. Jensen, pp. 55-59.

Some Observations on Reich's Experiment 20*

by Maxwell Snyder, M.S.**

Morphological Differences in Microstructures Produced from Frozen Sterile Hot Water Extracts of Soil, Hay and Green Grass

Introduction

Wilhelm Reich's Experiment 20 (1945, also called *Experiment XX*)[1] represented a significant innovation in the development of his bion experiments (1936-1939)[2]. Instead of producing bions directly from the breakdown and vesicular disintegration of solid material in suspension (as he did in previous bion experiments), Reich found in this experiment a way to induce the formation of a flaky sediment (plasmatic flakes) containing bions, by treatment of a clear sterile filtered hot water extract. Reich prepared such extracts by boiling, or autoclaving, earth in water to induce bionous disintegration, and then filtering off the water and (re)autoclaving it. Such a water extract is therefore called *bion water*. Reich principally used earth to make his bion water, although other materials can be used.

Reich treated bion water to induce flake formation in the following ways:

1) By freezing and later thawing it.

2) By distilling the bion water, and then freezing the distillate.

3) By simply allowing the bion water to stand at room temperature for several weeks.

Reich also reported obtaining flakes without bion water, from ordinary water kept inside an orgone energy accumulator for several months.

Reich considered the energetic charge characteristics of bion water to be a major factor in structure formation. He experimented with fluorometric measurement of bion water, which he regarded as an index of its orgonotic charge. Reich understood fluorescence

as an expression of the orgone energy's property of *lumination*. Evidence for this conclusion came from Reich's finding[3] that the fluorescence of several tubes of bion water showed an almost parallel rise and fall over time, correlating with fair and rainy weather, respectively. Subsequent analysis of Reich's data[4] suggested a similar response of bion water fluorescence to sunspot activity. Furthermore, bions prepared by the Experiment 20 protocol have been found to possess a negative membrane potential[5] and to migrate ten times faster in an electric field than ordinary earth bions.[6] Clearly, bion water and its products have unusual energetic properties.

Reich observed developmental processes in bion water and plasmatic flake samples maintained for several years. After several months he noted the development of small motile protists called *orgonomia*, from bean-shaped forms in the flakes. After five years, Reich[7] found ameboid and amebomastigote (ameboflagellate) forms resembling cancer cells in one sample. The cells were observed to develop from large taut germ vesicles such as those from which protists can develop in grass infusions.

Bernard Grad[8] repeated Experiment 20 in 1952, finding not only plasmatic flakes but also large cell-like structures, 6 - 20 μm (micrometers) in diameter resembling algal spores in frozen and thawed bion preparations. When incubated for several months at 37°C, these cell-like structures broke down into pulsating bions which continually fused with and separated from one another. Grad[9,10] was later able to produce cell-like structures by a specific chemical treatment of bion water, and also entirely without bion water, from known substances.

McDonald,[11] employing earth bion water, and Starz,[12] with hay bion water, obtained preliminary results similar to those of both Reich and Grad in frozen and thawed preparations. In a detailed report based on several years of study of earth bion water preparations, Robert Dew[13] described variations in flakes and microstructures obtained by a variety of methods including freezing, distillation, prolonged standing at room temperature, and orgone accumulator treatment. He observed both the bionous plasmatic flakes described by Reich, and the cell-like structures found by Grad. However, neither Grad, McDonald, Starz, Dew nor this writer has been able to confirm Reich's findings of

---

* A German translation with color photos was also published in *Nach Reich: Neue Forschungen zur Orgonomie* (J. DeMeo & B. Senf, Eds.), Zweitausendeins Verlag, Frankfurt, 1997.

** Pseudonym. Present social conditions force us to withhold the names of some of our colleagues working in academic institutions. The author is a graduate student in biology, and may be contacted through the Editor.

protist development in bion water flakes, even, in some cases, after years of observation. Nevertheless, Dew[13] does describe membrane-bound microspheres (5 - 8 μm diameter) developing from aggregates of small bions found in frozen and thawed distillates of earth bion water preparations maintained in the laboratory for several months. Some of these structures resembled fungal sporangia with sprouting mycelia.

The experiments described below were undertaken to learn more about the influence of the material used to make the bion water on the characteristics of the flakes and microstructures produced when it was frozen and thawed.

Procedures

Earth Bion Water Preparation:

100 g of rich earth from the floor of a redwood forest in Santa Cruz, California

100 ml of tap water

The above were boiled for 45 minutes while stirring, then allowed to settle out. The decantate was poured off and filtered through several progressively finer filters, and finally through a Millipore filter with a pore size of 0.45 μm. The filtrate was poured into six screw-capped test tubes and autoclaved at 15 lbs pressure at 121°C for 20 minutes. The tubes were kept at room temperature for 48 hours, and then two of them were frozen, one for 14 days, and the other for two years. The remaining tubes were set aside as controls.

Hay Bion Water Preparation:

250 g hay, *Avena sativa*, from Kensington, California

250 ml distilled water

The above were autoclaved at 15 lbs Pressure, 121°C for 30 minutes. The fluid was then decanted and filtered through Whatman #1, #2, and #3 filter papers until clear. The filtrate was poured into 20 screw-capped test tubes and autoclaved at 15 lbs pressure, 121°C for 30 minutes. The tubes were kept at room temperature for 48 hours, and then 14 of them were frozen for periods ranging from 24 hours to several weeks. The remaining tubes were set aside as controls.

Green Grass Bion Water Preparation #1:

250 g young green grass seedlings, *Avena sativa*, Menlo Park, California

250 ml distilled water.

The above were autoclaved at 15 lbs pressure, 121°C for 30 minutes. The fluid was decanted and filtered through Whatman #1, #2, and #3 filter papers until clear. The filtrate was poured into 20 screw-capped test tubes and autoclaved at 15 lbs pressure, 121°C for 30 minutes. The tubes were kept at room temperature for 48 hours, and then 14 tubes were frozen for 14 days. The remaining tubes were set aside as controls.

Green Grass Bion Water Preparations #2 and #3:

250 g lawn grass seedlings (in #2); mature *Avena sativa* (in #3)

250 ml deionized water

The above were boiled for 45 minutes while stirring, then allowed to settle out. The decantate was then filtered through successively finer filters, and finally through a Millipore filter with a pore size of 0.22 μm. The filtrate was then poured into 20 screw-capped test tubes and autoclaved at 15 lbs pressure, 121°C for 30 minutes. The tubes were kept at room temperature for 48 hours, and then 16 of them were frozen for 14 days. The remaining tubes were set aside as controls. (This procedure was performed separately for both #2 and #3.)

Observations

Earth Bion Water Preparation:

Earth bion water was a clear yellow liquid with a pleasant sweet odor and taste. Upon thawing, frozen preparations yielded a small quantity of brown flakes, 1-3 mm in length. Under the microscope, the flakes were found to be discretely structured, and of two types: 1) Brown networks of interconnected orgonome forms (Figure 1), and 2) Irregular, clear and gelatinous plasmatic flakes. The fluid contained large motile blue bions also. Some of these free bions were found in heaps. Numerous large (6-20 μm) immobile cell-like structures, identical to the forms first photographed by Grad[8] were found embedded in the flakes. Most of these had two or three 'lobes'. Although their appearance is suggestive of budding and division, these processes were not observed (Figures 2, 3 and 4).

Hay Bion Water Preparation:

Hay bion water was a clear dark yellow liquid with a strong sickly-sweet odor. Upon thawing, frozen preparations yielded numerous small light brown flakes which settled slowly after agitation. Under the microscope, these flakes were found to be diffusely structured, brown, with irregular and orgonome morphologies. They contained numerous large blue bions. Many bions were also found free in the fluid. The bions were highly motile. (Figures 5, 6, 7 and 8).

Green Grass Bion Water Preparation #1:

This green grass bion water was a pale green clear liquid with the odor of cooked spinach. Upon thawing, frozen preparations yielded a small quantity of dark flakes, which settled rapidly after agitation. Under the microscope, these flakes were seen to be discretely structured, black, with irregular morphology. They had a grainy structure and some tiny pale bions. No motile or free bions were observed. Numerous large (5-10 μm) immobile light-refractive cell-like structures were observed embedded in the flakes, which may resemble the *germ vesicles* described by Reich[7] (Figures 9 and 10).

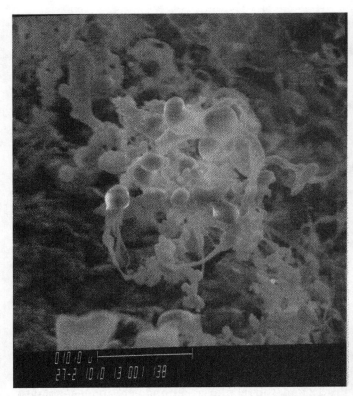

Figure 1: Scanning electron micrograph of flake network, earth bion water preparation.

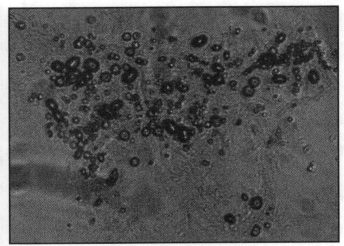

Figure 2: Cell-like structures in gelatinous flake substrate, earth bion water preparation, 150x, brightfield.

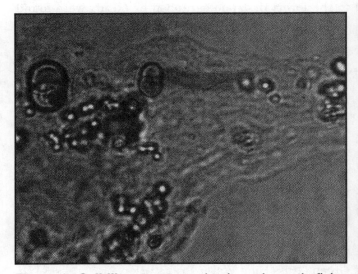

Figure 3: Cell-like structures in clear plasmatic flake, earth bion water preparation, 645x, brightfield.

Figure 4 (right): Bi-lobed and tri-lobed cell-like structures in flake, earth bion water preparation, 645x, brightfield.

This article, with full-color copies of all photomicrographs, will eventually be posted to: http://www.orgonelab.org/Pulse5.htm

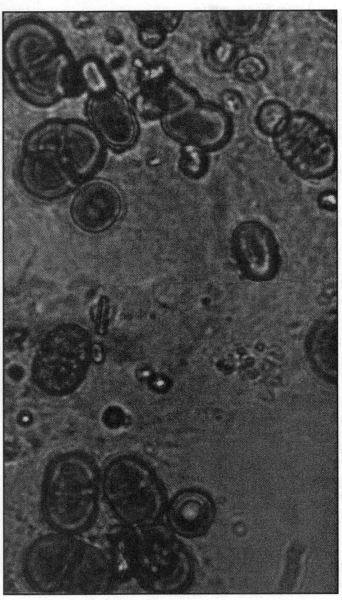

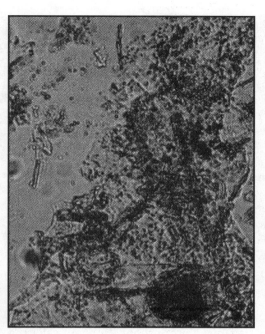

Figures 5 and 6 (above and right): **Bionous flakes**, hay bion water preparation, 150x, brightfield.

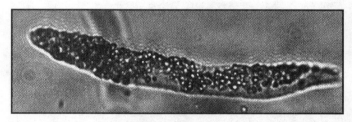

Figure 7: Large light-refractive bions on flake, hay bion water preparation, 645x, brightfield.

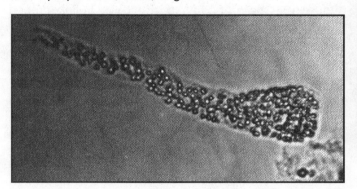

Figure 8: Bionous flake in orgonome form, hay bion water preparation, 645x, brightfield.

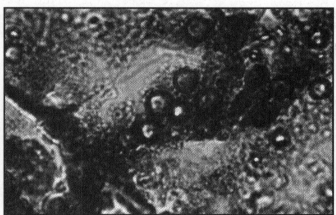

Figure 10: Cell-like structures embedded in flake, green grass bion water preparation, 645x, brightfield.

Figure 9: Discrete flake network, green grass bion water preparation, 150x, brightfield.

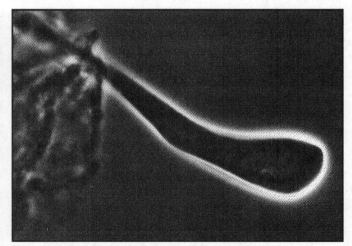

Figure 11: Orgonome form of flake, green grass bion water preparation, 450x, phase contrast.

Green Grass Bion Water Preparations #2 and #3:

These green grass bion waters were pale green clear liquids with the odor of canned green beans. Upon thawing, frozen preparations yielded small amounts of dark flake material. Microscopic observation revealed discrete flakes with a fine grainy structure composed of interlacing orgonome forms. Large cell-like structures (5-15 μm) were found embedded in these flakes in preparation #2, which were identical to those seen in preparation #1 (Figures 11, 12 and 13). Preparation #3 made from mature grass rather than young seedlings, yielded somewhat different structures (not shown) which were more angular, resembling both crystals and the cell-like structures in their morphology. Only a very few tiny motile bions were observed free in the fluid of these preparations.

Discussion

Macroscopic and especially microscopic examination of the thawed bion water preparations reveal striking differences between the three main types. How is one to account for these differences? Detailed information is lacking about chemical composition of all three types of bion water. Additionally, no data on physical properties (such as fluorescence, etc.) of these preparations is at hand. Certain things, however, are known about the starting materials used in making them:

1) Green grass is composed of living plant cells.

2) Hay consists of what is left over when the grass cells die and dry up.

3) Earth contains minerals, decaying organic matter, and a rich microbiota including bacteria, fungi, and protists.

The results of this experiment are consistent with the hypothesis that unique features and characteristics of the starting material are expressed in the resulting flakes.[§] For instance, green grass bion water flakes contain many large cell-like structures, and they are produced from green grass made up of living cells. Similarly, hay bion water flakes which consist of many small vesicular forms and are undergoing structural breakdown, are produced from decaying grass (hay). Earth bion water flakes exhibit both kinds of structure, and earth contains both living cells and decaying matter.

What might mediate this apparent transmission of features through the harsh treatment of boiling, filtration, autoclavation, and freezing to which these preparations are subjected? Obviously, no viable cells can survive it, nor would even dead cells in the size ranges seen have gotten through the 0.22 μm and 0.45 μm

[§] Dew's[13] demonstration of an effect of filter pore size on flake morphology suggests caution in interpreting results of this experiment where pore size was not held constant among the different preparations.

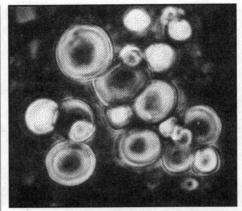

Figure 12: Cluster of cell-like structures in flake, green grass bion water preparation, 450x, phase contrast.

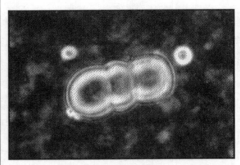

Figure 13: Chain of cell-like structures in flake, green grass bion water preparation, 450x, phase contrast.

filters. Furthermore, flake material was obtained from unfrozen preparations only in extremely minute quantities containing only a few bions, little structure, and no cell-like forms.

Although the work of Grad[9,10] demonstrates the role of specific chemical compounds in formation of the large cell-like structures, the observations reported here are also consistent with Reich's understanding of the function of energetic charge in structure formation. Reich (as given in Raphael and MacDonald),[14] in studies of blood autoclaved in bouillon and 0.1 Normal KCl (potassium chloride) solution — the Reich autoclavation blood test — found that clear fluid, rapid settling of solid flakes, and large blue bions located in the large flakes were indicators of health and energetic charge. Turbid fluid, slow flake settling, and small bions in the fluid and in small flakes were, however, indicative of undercharged biopathic conditions. Similarly, Baker[15] correlated a continuum of discrete to diffuse cloud structures and weather conditions with atmospheric charge and discharge states, as measured with an electroscope/orgone accumulator apparatus.

An Orgone Biophysical Interpretation

Due to the abundance of cell-like structures, discrete flakes, rapid settling, clear fluid, and relative lack of motile free bions, the green grass bion water flakes can be thought of as reflecting the high energetic charge, and tendency toward charging manifested by the vegetative growth and photosynthetic activity of their parent substance.

Hay bion water flakes, on the other hand, due to their lack of cell-like structures, diffuse flake structure, slow flake settling, darker fluid, and abundant motile blue bions, both free in the fluid and in the flakes, reflect the lower charge and tendency toward discharge which would be expected in hay, which is grass undergoing decay.‡

Earth bion water flakes present a more complex picture, with clear fluid, discrete flakes, and large cell-like structures, but also motile blue bions in heaps. This variation in structures may reflect the diversity of soil microbiota, or the presence of both living cells and decaying organic matter in the parent substance. It is interesting that the cell-like structures here show what may be indications of division (or fusion?). Do these characteristics reflect an energetic condition of their parent substance which is at its capacity level, balanced dynamically with both charge and discharge tendencies operative? In many respects, this seems the most alive of the preparations.

Implications

Claymond[16] has already outlined an energetic approach to understanding the fertility of soil. The results of this study raise the possibility that Experiment 20 may be applied as an energetic test of soil fertility, just as the Reich blood tests are employed in medicine.

‡ Starz's report[12] of cell-like structures in hay bion water flakes contradicts the findings presented here.

However, it will be necessary to test this hypothesis by means of standardized trials using different soils of known fertility. In addition, further knowledge of the physical and chemical changes which take place during Experiment 20, in particular those involved in structure formation, promise to be of great value for understanding the self-organization of matter, energy and life.

Appendix:
A Preliminary X-Ray Microanalysis of the Flaky Sediment of Earth Bion Water

The chemical analysis shown graphically below is restricted to the elemental inorganic constituents. The graph shows the largest peaks for potassium and calcium, with smaller peaks indicating the presence of sodium, magnesium, aluminum, silicon and chlorine.

Further microprobe analysis should be conducted, carefully targeting the various types of structures to detect any differences in composition. Additionally, analyses comparing bion water and the structures developing within it, and of bion water sediments derived from different starting materials should be done.

Reich[1] reports evidence suggesting the presence of carbon, sugars, and fats in earth bion water and its flaky sediment. Dew[13] found that earth bion water sediments would dissolve much more readily than grass bion water sediments when treated with hydrochloric acid. Grad[9,10] found that the cell-like structures formed in earth bion water consisted largely of calcium carbonate. The bits and pieces of chemical data cited and presented here support the need for the kind of comprehensive biochemical analysis originally proposed by Reich. Such chemical studies can serve as a valuable complement to functional and morphological studies in the further development of Experiment 20.

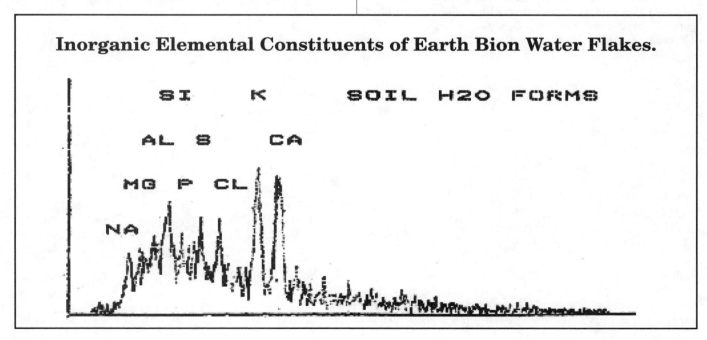

Inorganic Elemental Constituents of Earth Bion Water Flakes.

SI   K   SOIL H2O FORMS

AL   S   CA

MG   P   CL

NA

References:

1. Reich, W.: "Experimental Demonstration of the Physical Orgone Energy", *Int. J. Sex-Economy and Orgone Research,* 4(2-3):133-146, 1945.

2. Reich, W.: *Die Bione,* Sex-Pol Verlag, Oslo, 1938 (Republished as *The Bion Experiments: On the Origin of Life,* Farrar, Straus & Giroux, NY, 1979).

3. Reich. W.: "Meteorological Functions in Orgone-Charged Vacuum Tubes", *Orgone Energy Bulletin,* 2(4):184-193, 1950.

4. Sellers, A.P.: "Bion Water Fluorescence, Sunspots and the Weather", *Offshoots of Orgonomy,* 13:29-31, 1986.

5. Lappert, P.: "Primary Bions Through Superimposition at Elevated Temperature and Pressure", *Journal of Orgonomy,* 19(1):80-91, 1985.

6. Baker, C. & Dew, R.: "Bion Migration", *Annals, Inst. Orgonomic Science,* 1(1):24-32, 1984.

7. Reich, W.: "'Cancer Cells' in Experiment XX", *Orgone Energy Bulletin,* 3(1):1-3, 1951.

8. Grad, B.: "Wilhelm Reich's Experiment XX", *Cosmic Orgone Engineering,* 7(3-4):130-143, 1955.

9. Grad, B.: "Calcium Carbonate and Pleomorphism", in Jensen, G. (Ed.), *Pleomorphic Microbes in Health and Disease, Proceedings of the First Annual Symposium on Pleomorphism,* 18-19 June 1999, Montreal, Quebec, Canada. Holger N.I.S., Port Dover, Ontario, Canada, 1999, p.55-59.

10. Grad, B.: "Studies on the Origin of Life: The Preparation of Primordial Cell-Like Structures", *Pulse of the Planet,* 5:79-87, 2002.

11. McDonald, A.: "A Preliminary Study of Reich's Experiment XX", *Orgonomic Functionalism,* 19(1):165-167, 1961.

12. Starz, K., in Kelley, C.: "Notes and Comment: Biogenesis", *The Creative Process,* 4(1):4-5, 1964.

13. Dew, R.: "Reich's Experiment XX", *Annals, Inst. Orgonomic Science,* 6(1):1-32, 1989.

14. Raphael, C. & MacDonald, H.: "Orgonomic Diagnosis of Cancer Biopathy", *Orgone Energy Bulletin,* 4(2):65-128, 1952.

15. Baker, C.: "The Electroscope, IV: Atmospheric Pulsation", *Journal of Orgonomy,* 11(1):35-48, 1977.

16. Claymond, H.: "Preliminary Indications for an Energetic Concept of Soil Fertility", *Offshoots of Orgonomy,* 11:8-12, 1985.

The Sanal Theory of Bong Han Kim

Bion-like Processes in Acupuncture and Biology

by Dong Chul Kong* and Hyun-Won Kim*

Acupuncture is the representative therapy of oriental medicine, and the principle of acupuncture lies in *meridian theory*. It explains that there are energy transmission lines called *meridians*, which carry life-energy (*chi* or *qui* or *orgone*), and along which the acupuncture points (acupoints) are distributed. By stimulating those acupoints, the bioenergy field of the human body is affected, and a balanced state of the body is restored. However, despite more than two thousand years of history and countless empirical cases, meridian theory is still regarded as a kind of superstition due to the lack of so-called hard scientific evidence. Only recently, the *National Institutes of Health* in the USA announced evidence that the acupoints might really exist. For most oriental people who not only used acupuncture therapy traditionally but also regard *chi* as part of life, this is very funny.

In the middle of the 1960s, there was a North Korean scholar whose name was Bong Han Kim, a professor of Pyongyang Medical School. He not only showed the anatomical entity of the acupoints, but also explained the meridian system as the concrete ductile system in which a certain liquid containing particles called *Sanal* (meaning 'live egg' in Korean) flows. He published five papers from 1961 to 1965. These were: "Revealing the Kyungrak System" (1961), "On the Kyungrak System" (1963), "The Kyungrak Theory" (1965), "Sanal Theory" (1965), and his last paper "Sanal Origin of Blood Cells" (1965). Each of his five papers was revolutionary at the time, and are even today. A North Korean refugee informed me that he died in 1967.

All of professor Kim's papers were published in Korean and appeared only in the North Korean journals. However, his second paper "On the Kyungrak System" was translated into Japanese. Unfortunately, his researches were not published until very recently in South Korea. As both South and North Korea were in a state of tension after the Korean War (1950-1953), it was not easy to study the researches of North Korean scholars. Thus, it was extremely difficult to obtain his original publications. The situation in North Korea was not any better. Since professor Bong Han Kim was expelled from his university post for political reasons,

*Department of Biochemistry, Yonsei University, Wonju College of Medicine, Ilnsandong 162 Wonju Kangwondo 220-701, Korea email: kimhwbio@unitel.co.kr

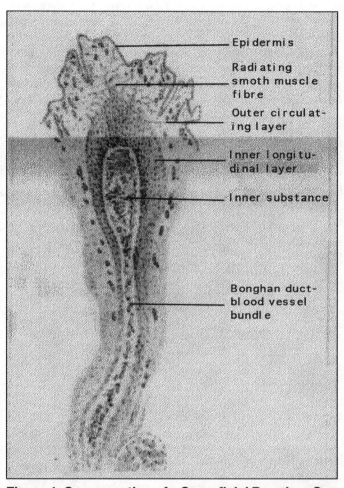

Figure 1. Cross-section of a Superficial Bonghan Corpuscle (skin acupuncture point)

Labels: Epidermis; Radiating smoth muscle fibre; Outer circulating layer; Inner longitudinal layer; Inner substance; Bonghan duct-blood vessel bundle

his research was never pursued by others, even in North Korea. The only research about the Kyungrak system related to Bong Han Kim since 1965 was undertaken by Japanese scholars in 1970, who reported a confirmation of the Kyungrak system exactly as professor Bong Han Kim revealed. Unfortunately, research on the Kyungrak system was still then regarded as superstitious from the viewpoint of current science and medicine. Another obstacle is that even oriental doctors themselves wanted to keep research on the meridians in the world of mysticism, rather than to scientifically investigate it.

One author of this paper, Dong Chul Kong, majored in Electrical Engineering at Seoul National University and was a free-lance writer. His main focus was on alternative science. While reading the English book *Vibrational Medicine* (by Richard Gerber) he was surprised to find a description of the meridian theory of Korean Professor Bong Han Kim. Although it was a brief description, Dong Chul Kong marveled at the theory of Bong Han Kim, whose name was new to him. A scientific investigation began. As South and North Korean relationships were in a state of tension, this was not a easy task. Dong Chul Kong found that Professor Bong Han Kim was a North Korean national hero in the middle of the sixties, but suddenly his name disappeared from all the official pages, and all research related to him was banned. Only one of the review papers of Bong Han Kim could be found, published in North Korea, and also some materials published in

Japan. Collecting all those informations together, Kong published a book, titled simply *Bong Han Kim*. The book invoked much interest from ordinary Korean people, but not from the world of science and medicine.

The other author of this paper, Hyun-Won Kim, received his Ph.D. in Biochemistry from Oxford University. He is now a Professor of Biochemistry at Yonsei University, Wonju College of Medicine. One day, he found the book *Bong Han Kim* and became fascinated at the contents. He contacted the author of the book, Dong Chul Kong. As both of them were graduates of Seoul National University and of similar ages, they became close friends since the first meeting. They decided to reinvestigate Bong Han Kim's research together. A veterinarian, and some oriental medical doctors also joined their group afterwards. Very recently, one North Korean refugee who did research herself as a medical student with Bong Han Kim, made contact with Dong Chul Kong. All of Bong Han Kim's original research team, including most of the medical students of Pyongyang, were politically purged on one day. She could escape the purge only because she was relatively young. After arriving in South Korea, she was very excited to find a name 'Bong Han Kim' whom she so revered, in a bookstore. She was so proud of their research, and has dedicated her life for the resurrection of Bong Han Kim's research.

Bong Han Kim's research could be roughly divided into two categories, the *Kyungrak system,* and the *Sanal theory.* Hyun-Won Kim was more interested in the research into Sanal. While searching the published

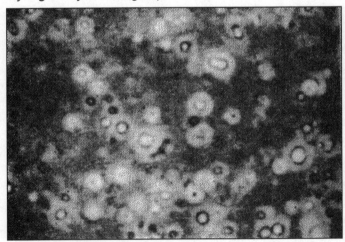

Figure 2. Intravascular Bonghan Duct (from *On the Kyungrak System*, Fig.18)

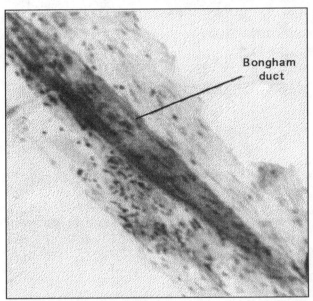

Figure 3. Sanals in Bonghan liquid, by phase microscopy, obtained from the acupuncture meridian system of a rabbit. Sanals move very rapidly at 37°-38°C, *slowing down with heating* and stopping completely above 50°C.

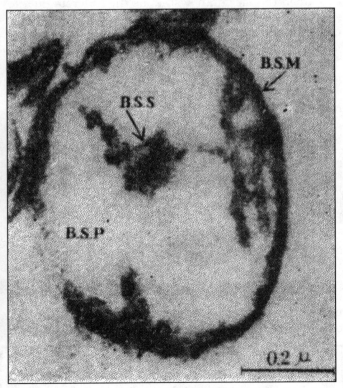

Figure 4. Electron microphoto of a Sanal (117,000x)

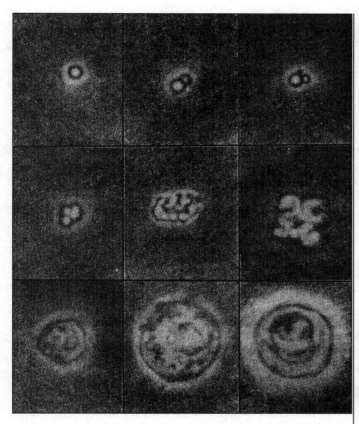

Figure 5. Sanals multiplying and organizing into cells, *in vitro* culture (similar to W. Reich's observed process of *bionous organization*).

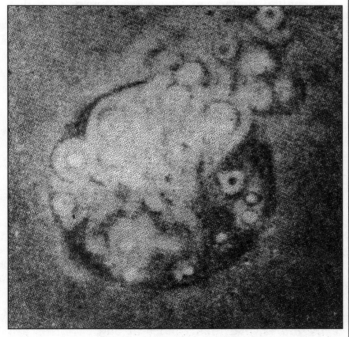

Figure 6. Cell breaking-down and discharging Sanals (similar to W. Reich's observed process of *bionous disintegration* — classically-described today as the phenomenon of *apoptosis*.)

literature, he soon found other great names — Antoine Bechamp, Wilhelm Reich, Günter Enderlein, Royal Rife and Gaston Naessens — who also found the small particles in the living body, and suggested those particles were essential to life. Surprisingly, their revolutionary ideas were all disregarded and they were all persecuted like Bong Han Kim. Now Hyun-Won Kim and his colleagues carry out researches on the Kyungrak system and on Sanal. As expected, a big problem is that they have difficulty getting funds for their research. Professor Kim just wishes things might get better. Bong Han Kim's researches on the Kyungrak System (meridians) and Sanal Theory are too extensive for any detailed description in this article, but an introduction can be given.

Kyungrak System

By applying methylene blue (I%) to the human body, and washing it with warm water, Bong Han Kim could observe blue spots remaining which matched the traditional acupoints. The series of blue spots also followed the traditional acupuncture meridian lines. Other animals also showed the small spots by applying the dye. He injected radioactive phosphorus P^{32} into a rabbit acupoint found by the dye method, and followed uptake of the substance. The P^{32} followed the path of traditional acupuncture meridians. P^{32} levels were negligible in adjacent tissues, away from the meridian lines. These newly found acupoints distributed over the skin are called *Bonghan corpuscles*. By anatomical-histological research, Bonghan corpuscles are classified into A) *Superficial Bonghan corpuscles*, distributed across the skin (Figure I) and B) *Profound Bonghan corpuscles* located deep in the subcutaneous tissues, in and around the blood and lymphatic vessels and around the internal organs. Both of these corpuscles and internal organs are linked by the *Bonghan ducts*.

Bonghan ducts are observed in living specimens as a semi-transparent and somewhat yellowish thread-shaped structure surrounded with connective tissues, and it contains a dense network of capillary vessels. Bonghan ducts are observed to run in general along the vessels in all parts of the body — the head, neck, chest, abdomen, limbs, etc. Thus, skin acupoints (identified as Superficial Bonghan corpuscles) and the internal organs are connected by Bonghan ducts. Bonghan ducts are divided into five different groups:

First is a series of tubules called the *Intravascular Bonghan duct system*. These tubules were found free-floating within the vascular and lymphatic vessels, penetrating the vessel walls at entry and exit points. Fluids within these internal ducts (termed *Bonghan liquor*) were usually found to travel in the same direction as the blood and lymph flow of the vessel, but in certain circumstances, Bonghan duct fluids were found to flow in the opposite direction of blood and lymph. The

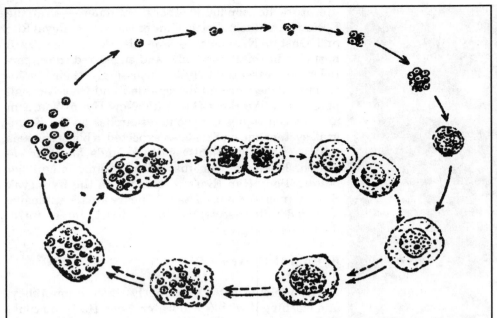

Figure 7. Process of cellular organization and disintegration via Sanal aggregation and discharge, and Sanal participation in cellular division.

fact that these internal ducts penetrate and leave the vessel walls, as well as have their fluids flow sometimes opposite to blood or lymphatic vessels, suggests that the formation of these ducts is earlier than the origin of the vascular and lymphatic systems: Blood vessels and lymphatic vessels appear to *grow around the intravascular ducts at a later stage*. Thus it appears that Internal Bonghan ducts entered and exited the vessels (Figure 2).

A second series of tubules is called the *Intra-Extravascular Bonghan duct system*. These ducts are found along the surface of the internal organs and appear to form a network which is independent of the vascular, lymphatic, and nervous systems.

A third series is known as the *Extravascular Bonghan duct system*. It was found to run alongside the outer surface of the walls of blood and lymphatic vessels. Especially, the Extravascular Bonghan ducts, which are under the layers of skin, correspond to the traditional acupuncture meridian lines.

The fourth series of tubules, known as the *Neural Bonghan duct system*, is distributed in the central and peripheral nervous systems.

A fifth series of tubules are known as the *Intestinal Bonghan duct system*. These are distributed inside the organs: the heart, liver, kidney, etc., connecting to every cell inside the organs. All these ducts are eventually interconnected like the vascular system, in which arterial-venous blood links though capillaries to each organ. The diameter of the Bonghan ducts, though it varies according to its functions and the quantity of its contents, ranges from 10-50 micrometers.

Anatomical identity of the Bonghan duct system has been confirmed by the French scientist, Pierre de Vernejoul. He injected radioactive technetium Tc^{99} into the acupoints of a person, and the radioactivity was followed by gamma-camera imaging. He found the radioactive Tc^{99} migrated along traditional acupuncture meridian lines for a distance of 30 cm in four to six minutes. However, injection of the isotope into random points on the skin, as well as by venous and lymphatic injection, did not produce similar results. These results clearly prove the meridians are a unique and separate morphological entity.

Sanal Theory

A semi-fluid, sticky and of a yellowish color, is observed flowing in the Bonghan ducts. The liquid is named *Bonghan liquor*. The circulation of Bonghan liquor in the Kyungrak system was substantiated by the method of dye injection into the Bonghan corpuscles and Bonghan ducts, and by the use of radioactive tracers. A large quantity of nucleic acids (DNA and RNA), free mononucleotides, amino acids, hormones, and hyaluronic acids are contained in the Bonghan corpuscle and ducts.

Bonghan liquor contains special particles called *Sanals* (meaning *live egg* in Korean). Sanals not only circulate within the Kyungrak system, but also grow within Bonghan liquor. Under certain conditions cells may change into Sanals and enter the Bonghan ducts. In the Kyungrak system Sanals also may change back into cells. It is a continuing process. According to Sanal theory, all the cells in the living body are replenished continuously via Sanals in the Kyungrak system.

To observe Sanals, Bonghan liquor should be extracted from a Bonghan duct or Bonghan corpuscle. Sanals can be observed with a phase contrast microscope (Figure 3). Their size is about 1.2- 1.5 µm. Phase contrast microscopy shows that Sanals have a spherical shape and can be divided into two parts: a dark area in the center, and a surrounding bright area. A detailed structure of a Sanal was made by electron microscopy (Figure 4). However, the striking feature of the Sanals is their movement, which is completely different from random, mechanical Brownian movement. It moves energetically at 37°C, but *keeps slowing down at higher temperatures*, and finally stops at 50°C. Sanals are found not only in the human body, but also in every living creature, every mammal, bird, amphibian, fish, and even in plants.

By ultracentrifugation, Sanals can be precipitated.

Bong Han Kim's research team analyzed the chemical contents of Sanals. Their major contents are DNA and proteins. Less than 1% of DNA are found in the supernatant, indicating most DNAs found in Bonghan liquor reside in Sanals. Notably, each Sanal is reported to contain roughly similar amounts of DNA as an individual chromosome. Some carbohydrates and lipids are also found. Sanals also contain many minerals, such as magnesium, calcium, copper, manganese, zinc, cobalt, etc. Bong Han Kim succeeded with *in vitro* culturing of Sanals. Their culture medium was very similar to that of Bonghan liquor which contains nucleotides, amino acids, sugars, and hyaluronic acids.

Remarkably, Bong Han Kim's research team could observe the changes from Sanals to cells, and from cells to Sanals, which is contradictory to the widely accepted cell theory of Virchow. Cell theory states that all living organisms are made up of cells, the smallest unit of life, and *cells arise only from other cells*. Figure 5 shows the observation of changes from Sanals to cells. A thread-like material comes to the outside of one Sanal. Around this thread-like material, a membrane forms, making a new Sanal. In this way, Sanals keep multiplying. These Sanals are not dispersed, as they are connected with thread-like materials. After sufficient proliferation, the boundaries of each Sanal becomes obscured to form one large nucleated structure. Some homogeneous materials also forms outside this nucleated structure. Finally a cell membrane is formed, creating a new cell out of the Sanals. Bong Han Kim's research team analyzed time-dependent DNA and protein contents of Sanals and cells. During the process from Sanals to cells, the total DNA contents increased sixteen times over the 72 hours after initiation of the process. However, RNA and protein contents kept increasing until 144 hours had elapsed.

Cells newly formed from Sanals sometimes return back into Sanals. First, Sanal particles develop inside the nucleus. Even in the nucleus, Sanals move in a lively manner, and finally cell membranes burst, releasing Sanals to the outside (Figure 6). Bong Han Kim suggested that these two processes, transformation of *Sanals into Cells* and of *Cells into Sanals,* are part of a larger natural cycle which cannot be separated.

Generally, mitotic cell division is known to proceed without rupture of cell membranes. Bong Han Kim explains, however, that the mitotic cell division also involves formation of Sanals, their redistribution to each pole, and reformation of a new nucleus. In cell division, it is generally known that doubled centrosomes are first separated and then move to each pole, forming the nucleus of new daughter cells. Bong Han Kim's research team found that the number of Sanals are similar to the number of chromosomes, and the Sanal DNA contents are similar to that of each chromosome. Bong Han Kim even suggested that Sanals are not different from the chromosomes. In this regard, Sanal theory does not contradict traditional cell division. Cells

are, in fact, explained to exist as a special stage of the grand life cycle of the Sanals (Figure 7).

Bong Han Kim's research team labeled P^{32} to Sanals, and injected them into acupoints. After tracing the radioactivity, they found that the Sanals formed in the intestinal organs flowed into Bonghan ducts, arrived at the Superficial Bonghan corpuscles, and after a certain time returned back to the intestinal organs. While flowing through the Bonghan ducts, Sanals proliferated to form a nucleus-like structure, finally to become cells of certain organs. Sanals isolated in each superficial Bonghan corpuscle (corresponding to acupoints) appear to form different cell types specific for different organs. This confirms traditional meridian theory which postulates that each organ is related to specific acupoints. This means, for example, by stimulating acupoints related to the liver, hepatocytes can be proliferated.

These are brief sketches of Sanal theory. As Sanals could be found in every living creature, including plants, the Sanals found by Bong Han Kim may not be basically different from the *Microzymas* of Bechamp, *Bions* of Reich, *Protids* of Enderlein, and *Somatids* of Naessens. They all investigated their life-essential particles independently. Bong Han Kim is different from these researchers, however, in that he found the Sanals in the Kyungrak system of acupuncture points, meridians, and fluids. This may be the reason for some differences which are noted from the other living particles. We believe Bong Han Kim's researches on the Kyungrak system and Sanal theory are very substantial, and hold a great promise for science and medicine.

General References:

Fujihara Domo: *Great Discovery of Kyungrak System*, llwol Press, Seoul, 1985.

Richard Gerber.: *Vibrational Medicine*, Bear & Company, Santa Fe, 1988.

Bong Han Kim. *On the Kyungrak System*, Foreign Language Publishing House, Pyongyang, 1964.

Bong Han Kim.: "Kyungrak System and Sanal Theory," *Journal of Eastern Medical Sciences*, Pyongyang, 1965.

Bong Han Kim, "Kyungrak System and Theory of Sanal", *Proc. Acad. Kyungrak of D.P.R.K.*, No 2. Pyongyang, Korea: Mod. Science Press 1965.

Dong Chul Kong : *Kim Bong Han*, Hakmin Press, Seoul, 1992.

Wilhelm Reich: *The Bion Experiments: On the Origins of Life* (1938), Farrar, Straus & Giroux, NY 1979.

Wilhelm Reich: *The Cancer Biopathy: Discovery of the Orgone, Vol.2* (1948), Farrar, Straus & Giroux, NY 1973.

Bernd Senf: "Wilhelm Reich: Discoverer of Acupuncture Energy?", *Pulse of the Planet* 2:25-30, 1989.

P. de Vernejoul: "Etude Des Meridiens D'Acupuncture Par Les Traceurs Radioactifs", *Bull. Acad. Natl. Med.*, 169, 1071, 1985.

Bion-Biogenesis Research and Seminars at OBRL: Progress Report

by James DeMeo, Ph.D.*

Bions and the Reich Blood Test Seminars

Starting in Summer of 1996, and for each Summer thereafter, the Orgone Biophysical Research Lab (OBRL) has offered a weekend laboratory seminar on *Bions and the Reich Blood Test*. The basic discoveries of Wilhelm Reich on bions and biogenesis[1] were covered, as well as his findings on the cancer biopathy, and the specific protocols of the Reich blood test[2]. Instructors for the seminar have included Dr. Bernard Grad, Dr. Richard Blasband, Dr. Stephen Nagy and Dr. James DeMeo, who covered a far-ranging subject material: the basics of light-microscopy of living preparations, various experiments and preparations for the creation and observation of Reich's *bions* (orgone energy vesicles), the technique and interpretation of the Reich blood test, reviews of Reich's findings on the *cancer biopathy*, and the relationship of these findings to modern discoveries in biology and medicine. On this last point, for example, Reich's bions appear quite similar to the *extremophiles* and *nanobacteria* of modern biology. In medicine, *mycoplasma* and *cell-wall deficient forms* are suggestive of bionous origins, while the widely-used term "apoptosis" describes a process of cellular disintegration and breakdown into micro-vesicles appearing functionally identical to Reich's discovery of the *bionous disintegration* of cells. For these and other reasons, Reich's findings from the 1930s still attract scientific interest.

Seminar participants came from all over the world, and included physicians and other health care practitioners, university professors, laboratory technicians, and university and high school students. The quality and scope of the seminar was progressively improved with each passing year. Several excellent light microscopes were available during the seminars, plus all basic equipment necessary for making sterile preparations, including autoclave, high-temperature drying oven, and fritted-glass vacuum filtering system using nylon filter disks with 0.2 micron pore size — this is much smaller than the average bacterium or bion, which are around 1 micron in diameter.

All of the photographs presented here were made by myself with a Leitz Ortholux microscope, obtained in good used condition and fitted with top-quality planapo-

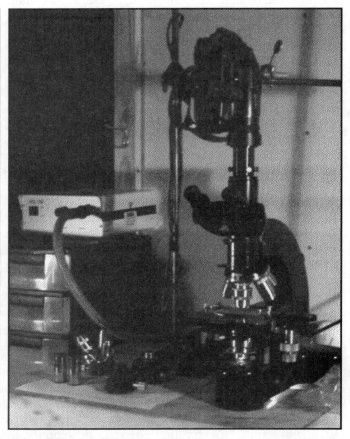

Leitz Ortholux Microscope, with planapochromatic objectives, compensating Periplan eyepieces, apochromatic condenser and halogen fibre-optic light source. Positioned on heavy marble table, with Hi-8 video and 35mm camera recording systems.

Sterilization and Filtration Equipment used for the bion experiments at OBRL.

* Director, Orgone Biophysical Research Lab, Greensprings, PO Box 1148, Ashland, Oregon 97520 USA. Tel/Fax: 541-552-0118 Email: demeo@mind.net

This article, with full-color copies of all photomicrographs, will be posted to: http://www.orgonelab.org/Pulse5.htm

chromatic objectives and compensating eyepieces. These were needed to satisfy the high-magnification, true-color demands noted by Reich in his various publications on the subject.[3] The Leitz scope is capable of magnifications up to 5,000 power using a special 160x planapochromatic objective with 25x Periplan compensating eyepieces, and a 1.25 magnification lens in the central light path. A 3000° halogen fibre-optic light source is used with high-aperture brightfield or darkfield condensers, allowing the microscope to produce spectacular images in true color. A Hi-8 videocamera or 35mm still camera was used for documentation. All the photographs presented here were made with the 35mm camera using tungsten-adjusted film, at exposures between 1/4 to 1/30 second. Regrettably we cannot present the original color images in this publication, but they will be posted to internet.[4]

The Natural Organization of Protozoa

Reich's observations on the *natural organization of protozoa* (protists) have been reproduced by many different scientists and students following up on his work.[5] To refresh the reader, Reich prepared water infusions of dead moss and grass, and observed them microscopically over extended periods of hours and days, noting how the plant tissues would slowly disintegrate into tiny oval vesicles of around 1 micron diameter, which he later called *bions*. The bions would form at the edges of the dead grass; the formerly living material slowly disintegrated into bionous vesicles which would fill the water infusion, and the inner cellular materials would spill their bionous contents out into the water. The bions would show subtle movements, and had a bluish glow. Over time, the bions would form into clusters or heaps, which progressively developed new membrane structures and increasingly life-like movements. New microorganisms emerged from this process, indistinguishable from similar microorganisms in soils or pond water.

Reich's critics claimed he was only observing "air germs" and other contaminating common bacteria, cysts and spores. He countered with various control experiments which heated various preparations to very high temperatures, and which even more quickly produced bions (see the Incandescence Experiments, below). He also made time-lapse photographs of the process, demonstrating the bionous disintegration of plant tissues, with the subsequent reorganization of bions into more complex life forms.[6] Reich also noted his critics rarely looked at living organisms under the microscope, but rather dried and stained everything, killing the life process. Reich was emphatic, *one could not follow the process of bionous disintegration and re-organization by looking at only dried, fixed and stained preparations.*

These basic observations have been made repeatedly by many individuals, though to my knowledge,

Bionous Disintegration of Grass (1 & 2) with subsequent bionous re-organization of various Protozoa (3 through 5 & 6). (after Reich[7]) Other forms are also possible.

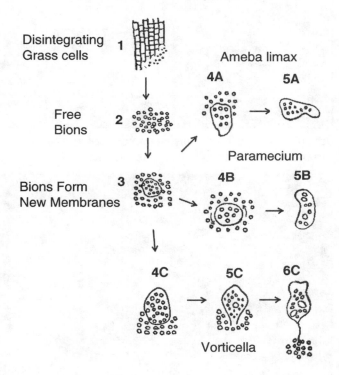

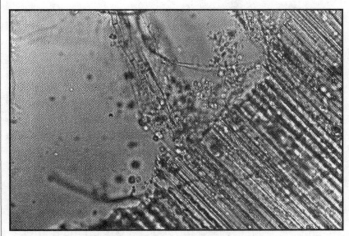

Bionous disintegration of dead grass after 3 days in water (not autoclaved). Vesicles form at the edges of the broken grass blades, and spill out from dead interiors of cells. 500x

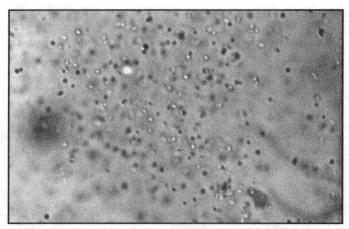

After autoclavation, massive numbers of free blue-glowing bions can be seen in the grass infusion. 2000x

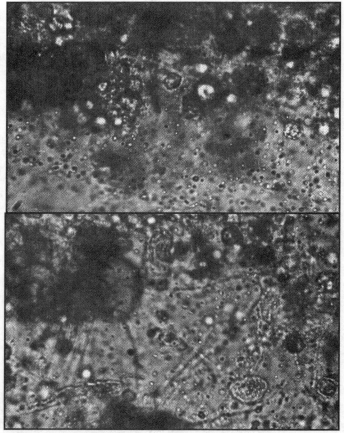

After several weeks, the autoclaved grass-water infusion develops numerous highly-organized forms, which appear to emerge from the background sea of bionous aggregations. Classical biology says these are the products of "cysts" and "spore", or "air germs" — *but, is this uniformly true, even in preparations subjected to high temperature and pressure sterilization? Or do some of them derive from bionous disintegration and re-organization?* (above two photos 1250x).

neither Reich nor other bion experimenters have observed the development of protozoa within autoclaved preparations as described here — and for this reason I wish to emphasize the *preliminary nature* of the results of the autoclaved grass infusion experiments presented here. It may be that the exceptionally high quality mountain well water used, the favorable environmental conditions at the OBRL Greensprings Center facility, or some other factor was involved.

At OBRL, we routinely autoclave grass infusions and other preparations in either screw-top test tubes or glass petri dishes at 26 psi, 130°C for 1 hour — well above what is necessary for killing most common microbes. If the preparations are observed shortly after autoclavation, it is clear this procedure does, in fact, kill virtually all higher living forms — but it also *increases* the production of vast numbers of bions. In fact, for most preparations, there are *more bions after autoclavation* than in similar preparations not autoclaved. For the grass infusions, within a short period of days to a few weeks after being prepared, the experiments conducted at OBRL demonstrated the progressive development of more complex life forms. This was true whether the preparations were autoclaved or not, though the autoclaved preparations took longer for organization to develop. Massive numbers of bions appeared as disintegration progressed, and round membranous forms appeared within the "bion soup", which themselves were filled with bions. Some of these bion-filled membranes began to rotate — firstly slowly back and forth, but then later tumbling with a faster speed — and eventually even to pulsate (expanding, contracting). From such bionous aggregations eventually emerged fully-organized paramecium-like ciliates. Other microbes such as ameba also appeared and proliferated, though following different developmental pathways.

In many respects, the arguments raised by Reich's bion experiments are similar to those which raged in the 1800s between the figures such as Pasteur and Bechamp, or Huxley and Bastian.[8] Reich's methodology brings a fresh empirical perspective to the question, however, and shows the correctness of many of those early biologists who independently observed bion-like, self-organizing microforms.

From the above, we can report the observation that autoclaved grass infusions kept in a closed glass petri dish eventually develop a similar spectra of microbes as seen in those grass preparations not autoclaved. By contrast, control dishes of water open to the air, or even those containing some small amounts of nutrient, fail to show complex microbes such as paramecium and ameba — they only show dust particles and a small number of rod-shaped bacteria and occasional fungal forms. This supports Reich's argument, that the protozoa seen in grass infusions developed through the process of bionous disintegration and re-organization. A time-lapse filming of this entire process is planned for the future.

Incandescence Experiments:
Bions from Iron Dust and Beach Sand

Reich's claim on the natural organization of protozoa from bionously disintegrated moss and grass generated skepticism from his contemporaries, and he countered his critics with increasingly rigorous control procedures. He argued that the bion was a transitory form, existing between the worlds of living and non-living and from which life could emerge under the proper conditions. He argued that the tiny vesicles were not "air germs" nor contaminants. High temperatures, he argued, could speed the process of bion formation. His critics argued he wasn't heating his preparations to a high enough temperature to kill everything in them.

One procedure Reich developed involved heating of inorganic materials such as coal, earth, sand and iron dusts to a white-hot temperature, which was too extreme a temperature for any living thing to survive. While the material was still glowing, Reich would plunge it into a test tube filled with a pre-sterilized potassium chloride solution (0.1 N KCl). These experiments have been performed many times by scientists seeking to replicate these findings, and show an almost immediate development of numerous well-formed bions.[9]

The incandescence experiments undertaken at OBRL focused primarily upon heated iron powder and sand. A 0.1 N solution of KCl was prepared from reagent-grade KCl crystals in distilled water. The solution was firstly boiled and then filtered through a 0.2 micron vacuum filtering apparatus, portioned into 13x100mm screw-top test tubes (~5 ml per tube), which were then autoclaved at 26psi, 130°C for 1 hour. Several tubes were observed microscopically before the experiments for signs of any particulate material or life — nothing was observed. (Unused tubes from the same batches were also kept sealed for several months after these experiments, and observed again, with similar negative observations.)

With the KCl solutions prepared, a small amount of dry, unoxidized powdered iron was scooped onto a groved stainless steel spatula of about 3mm width. The spatula with iron particles was then heated over a propane torch

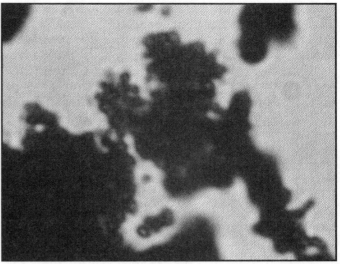

Iron bions created by heating iron dust to a white-hot incandescence over a burner flame, and then quickly immersing the glowing dust into a pre-sterilized 01.N. solution of KCl. Observed microscopically, within a minute after the immersion, one can see bionous aggregations still adhering to the iron particles from which they emerged, looking much like bunches of reddish grapes. 5000x

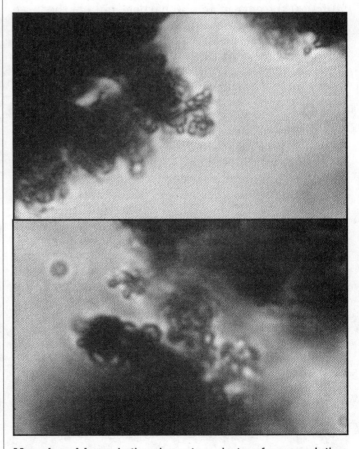

More iron bions, in the above two photos, from a solution prepared as described above, but then autoclaved and kept unopened and sterile for three months. 5000x

for about one minute, until both spatula and iron were glowing orange-white hot. Using sterile technique, the tube containing the KCl solution was opened, and the incandescent iron allowed to gravity-drop into the tube and solution, where the hot material gave a characteristic hiss as the hot metal hit the liquid. The tubes were immediately capped and gently swirled. After about one minute, allowing heavier particles to settle, the suspended fraction of material was taken into a sterile pipette, transferred to a sterile slide with coverslip and observed microscopically. Routinely, from this procedure one immediately sees the edges of the iron particles having broken down into tiny vesicles, of both bluish and reddish color. In some cases, the vesicles appear like "bunches of grapes", with a few identically-appearing bion vesicles floating free in the solution.

It is clear, the iron bions — which except for the reddish colors appear similar to the bions from disintegrated grass in water — are the product of the intensive swelling and cooling process brought about by the high temperatures and quick immersion into the KCl solution. This fact is determined by looking firstly at control tubes of KCl solution, by itself, and secondly by looking at the *unheated* iron powder in a similar KCl solution. In the latter case, one may see an occasional individual vesicle at the edge of an iron particle, but not the large numbers and clusters of numerous bions.

Reich argued that potassium ions from KCl encouraged a general expansive quality within living organisms, being responsible for muscular relaxation. His later experiments on biogenesis, notably Experiment 6 to be discussed momentarily, included a richer variety of chemical nutrients, and hence, more life-like qualities. The iron bions appeared life-like in structure, but had only the most limited movements. We found that iron bions could be produced with more bluish coloration (less reds) and in much greater abundance, if the tube containing the incandesced iron powder was afterward autoclaved, and then allowed to sit undisturbed for several months. More life-like movements and structures could be seen the longer it was allowed to "incu-

bate" after sterilization.

Reich prepared a similar experiment using incandescent beach sand, which is also heated white-hot and plunged into a 0.1 N KCl solution. In the photos shown here, we used sand from a clean beach on Maui, Hawaii, brought by one of our seminar students. The sand showed a strongly vesicular quality after the incandescence and swelling in solution. If subsequently autoclaved and kept sealed for several months, the sand bions showed organized or elongated structures which gave the appearance of life. Single sand bions would clump together and sometimes elongate a bit, though

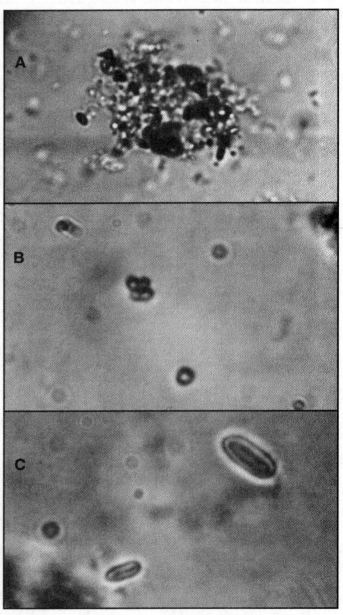

Sand bions in the process of organization. A shows a cluster of autoclaved sand bions after 3 months (1250x); **B** and **C** show single and quadruplet sand bions, and elongated bionous forms, from the same preparation as **A**, photographed at the same time. (5000x)

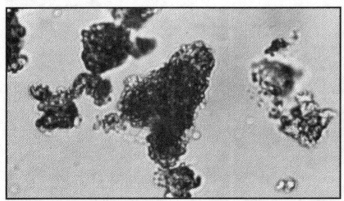

Maui Beach Sand, heated white hot to incandescence, then immersed into a KCl solution. Observed within a minute, the sand shows a highly vesicular structure. 490x

never forming long rod-forms or chains typical of known bacterium. Individual bions would develop in large numbers, being freed from the sand crystals, and some of these would organize into quadruplets. Reich noted sand bions would characteristically group in clusters of four, and also be culturable, but this latter aspect has never been tested at OBRL where our incandescence experiments did not include nutritive chemistry, only KCl. By itself, KCl is not a particularly good nutrient medium for microbiological growth.

The next steps in our bion research program will include an attempt to culture the various microforms observed from the incandescence experiments.

Experiment 6: Vesicular Masses from Sterilized Nutritive Media

Here, I report a variation of one of Reich's bion experiments which utilized a mix of sterilized chemicals and nutritive substances which over time yielded life-like structures.[10] Early in his work, Reich noted that certain chemical groups had a general sympathetic (contractive) stimulus upon life and tissues, while others had a general parasympathetic (expansive-relaxing) stimulus.[11] Calcium ion groups were sympathetic in their action, while Potassium ions were parasympathetic. Cholesterin and Lecithin had similar antithetical properties, as did other ionic combinations. Reich combined various antithetical chemical groups together with the assumption that antithetical expansive-contractive pulsatory movements could be stimulated to occur within raw bionous materials, and from there, to life itself. Pulsation, he argued, was the key to how simple bions developed into more highly organized forms.

In the Experiment 6 replications undertaken at OBRL, we could not easily find many of the original materials designated by Reich in his 1938 protocols, where nutritive microbiological preparations were apparently made "fresh in the lab."[§] I also was concerned that commercially available microbiological preparations might carry contamination from biochemical pollutants not widely present in Reich's day. Animal or vegetable protein from the 1930s and 40s contained no growth hormones or antibiotics, and very little in the way of pesticide/herbicide contaminations, much less nuclear contamination as is the case today. Nor was the water supply so widely contaminated with industrial chemicals and chlorine disinfectants, and other contaminants. I therefore undertook Experiment 6 using the most clean and natural substitute products we could find. Well water was used from the OBRL remote mountain-top laboratory, which is clean of chemical contamination. Some ingredients used, such as beef and vegetable bouillons, corn starch, eggs and milk products

were purchased from local health food stores and organic groceries which follow the strict California and Oregon organic standards — these are much stricter standards of purity than those set by the FDA or USDA.

From the gathered materials, I firstly prepared a *Special Broth* of nutritive ingredients, according to the following formula, which will produce 100 or more 13x100mm test tubes of the nutritive broth, at ~5 ml per tube (depending upon how much loss occurs during filtration). It is a modern-day replication, as close as I could come using natural ingredients, to Reich's original Experiment 6:

Special Broth Ingredients: Experiment 6
1 Liter excellent well or spring water, unchlorinated.
1/4 teaspoon organic beef bouillon soup stock
1/4 teaspoon organic chicken bouillon soup stock
1/4 teaspoon organic vegetable bouillon soup stock
1/4 teaspoon potato starch
20 drops organic cream/milk ("Half and Half")
1/4 teaspoon egg albumen
1 drop egg yolk
1/4 teaspoon granulated dry lecithin
1/4 teaspoon granulated cholesterin (reagent grade)

Procedures:
The water was heated in a clean glass pot with pouring lip, into which the above ingredients were added and stirred. The mixture was brought to a boil, then covered and simmered for one hour, then allowed to cool and settle. The liquid portion was decanted through a stainless-steel strainer and coarse filter paper, then diluted with an equal portion of 0.1N KCl solution previously prepared. The new filtered mixture was boiled again, to further precipitate any protein components, allowed to cool and settle, and then decanted again

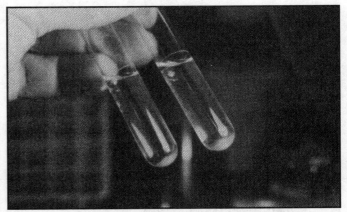

Reich's Experiment 6: Growth (or precipitate?) at the bottom of test tubes containing previously boiled, filtered and autoclaved Special Broth. The preparations were sealed in the tubes during summer of 1998, but significant growth was not observed at the tube bottoms until a year later. The photos show two years of growth.

[§] Quote from Ilse Ollendorff, in a letter to Maxwell Snyder. In later years, Reich did use commercial preparations.

through coarse filter paper. The mix was then autoclaved in a glass beaker covered with inverted petri dish, at 25 psi, 120°C for 30 minutes to precipitate remaining solids, then cooled and decanted through coarse filter paper, and then through medium-grade and fine-grade filter paper. Finally, the remaining solution was pulled through sterile 0.2 micron filter disks using appropriate sterile apparatus and vacuum pump. After filtering, the remaining fluid was pipetted into screw-top test tubes and capped without tightening fully. The racked test tubes were then autoclaved once more, this time at 130°C, 26psi, for 1 hour. After cooling in the autoclave, the caps were twisted shut, and the racks set aside on lab tables.

When this *Special Broth* is prepared, it appears clear with a slight brownish hue. If the sterilization procedures are adequate, one will observe there is no particle debris apparent when the tubes are held up to sunlight, and none of the tubes will develop growth film typical of air deposition. You can open several of the tubes to the air, and observe typical contamination growth fairly quickly, within a day or two. However, none of the sealed tubes containing the sterilized and 0.2

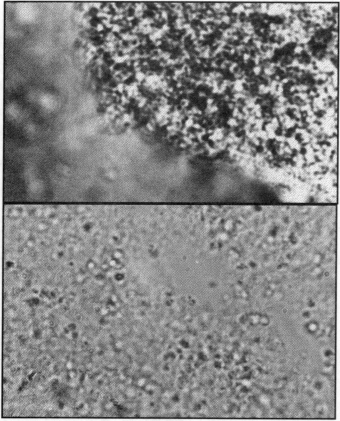

Bionous-vesicular material in the sealed tubes after two years of growth, aggregated into congealed masses. (Top-1250x, Bottom-3000x, high-contrast image enhancement applied)

micron filtered solutions will develop such growth, even after months. When observed microscopically, one can observe the immediate presence of occasional very small vesicles, some of which appear to have both inner and outer membranous structures (unfortunately we did not get photos of this early protocellular appearance). The speed of development of these tiny particles progresses over time, suggesting that the chemical mix in the Experiment 6 Special Broth is spontaneously creating small protocellular vesicles, all on its own.

The OBRL reproduction of Experiment 6 was firstly undertaken in summer of 1998. Using a vacuum pump, Whatman 0.2 micron nylon filter disks and a fritted glass filtering system, we were able to undertake the procedures beyond merely autoclaving the solutions at high temperatures. A large quantity of tubes containing the Special Broth were prepared for the summer seminar, in excess of what was needed, and the extra tubes were kept sealed and sterile over the year.

During the preparations for the 1999 lab seminars, I noted the sealed Special Broth tubes from 1998 were showing a slight growth at the bottom of the tubes. This "contamination" was present at the bottom of every one of the approximately 50 sealed and unopened 1998 tubes. I immediately opened one of the tubes to the air, and observed it microscopically. An abundance of vesicles could be seen, but none were moving, and there were no motile forms in the middle or upper parts of the tube, as would be typical for rot bacteria. Within a day of being open to the air, however, the tube of Special Broth began to swarm with rod-shaped bacteria. Within a week, the surface of the opened tube was covered with both white and black colonies of bacterial-fungal growth. None of the sealed tubes showed this kind of surface growth, only a small quantity of whitish material at the bottom of the tubes. Given the pressures to prepare for the 1999 seminars, I simply put away the Special Broth tubes from 1998, with plans to look at them later on.

A year later, in summer of 2000, I finally got around to looking again at the sealed tubes remaining from the 1998 seminar preparation. By this time, two years later, all the tubes were showing a significant amount of whitish matter at the bottom of each tube, indicating a slow-going precipitation of material, or organismic growth, or both.

Once again, several of these tubes were opened and examined microscopically. None showed bacterial growth, but the precipitate at the bottom of the tubes showed dense aggregations of vesicular bionous forms. None were motile, and they tended to aggregate into masses or clumps of material with the appearance of vesicular protoplasm.

We have not yet attempted to culture these forms to evaluate their potentials for reproduction and growth, nor to undertake evaluation for the presence of DNA, but plans are underway to do so. New equipment will be required at OBRL in order for this to be accomplished.

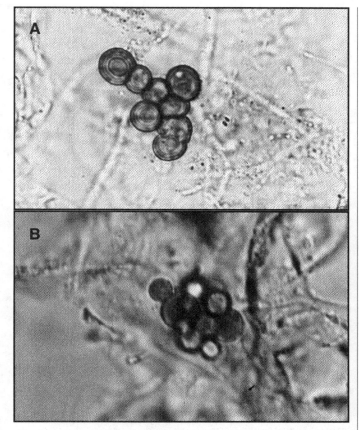

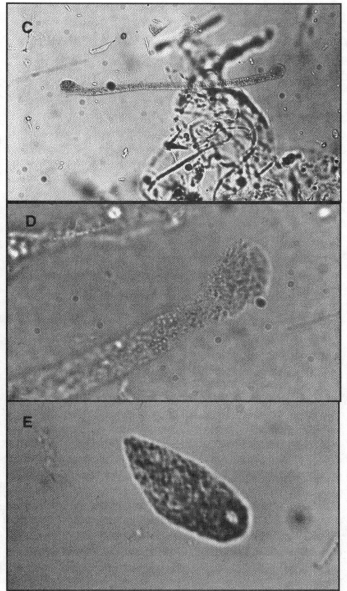

Plasmatic flakes and other cell-like forms from autoclaved, filtered and frozen bion water. The two top-left slides (**A**, **B**, at 1250x) show elongated branching fibres, with clusters of protocellular forms. The two top-right slides show more of the fibrous mass, and an elongated appendage structure (**C**, 250x), one end of which is magnified (**D**, 900x). The bottom-right slide is a *pseudo-ameba* (after Reich) which gave the clear appearance of an ameboid form, but did not move (**E**, 1250x).

In the meantime, samples of the tubes have been sent to microbiological experts, for outside opinions and evaluations. For the present, we simply report these very interesting observations as a basic confirmation of Reich's original observations from 1938.

Experiment 20: Frozen *Bion Water* Yields Life-Like Structures

Reich's Experiment 20 (or, *Experiment XX*)[12] involved boiling ordinary soil, then putting the liquid portion through a series of increasingly fine filters, and then autoclaving the final filtrate, and freezing it while still under sterile conditions. This particular experiment has been replicated many times, and routinely shows a variety of remarkable protocellular forms.

The Experiment 20 replications undertaken at OBRL have been restricted to microscopical observations, without as yet addressing the issues of culturability. A small handful of soil from the evergreen forest floor near the OBRL Greensprings Center (a very pristine environment characterized by old-growth pine and cedar trees) was boiled for approximately 30 minutes in a ceramic pot with about 500 ml of well water. After boiling and with lid in place, the soil solution was allowed to cool and settle for about 2 hours, after which the resulting soil extract was decanted away from the solid portion. First steps of filtration involved pouring the fluid through a fine kitchen-type stainless steel strainer and several selections of increasingly fine filter paper. A final filtration was undertaken using 0.2 micron filter disks through a vacuum apparatus. The resultant liquid was portioned into screw-top test tubes, and autoclaved for 1 hour at 130°C, 26 psi. Tubes were allowed to cool inside the closed autoclave, after which caps were fully tightened. The sealed tubes containing the soil extract, called *bion water*, were then placed into a freezer.

Tubes of frozen bion water were allowed to sit from several days to several months before being allowed to thaw for microscopic examination. The tubes of frozen bion water contained fractured clear ice at the edges of the tube, but brown-colored ice crystals in the center, suggesting freezing which started at the edges of the tube, slowly sweeping various chemical constituents in the bion water towards the central parts of the tube where a final freezing-aggregation took place. When the tubes were allowed to thaw, this central aggregation of flaky material held together as a fibrous mass, which broke into smaller particles only upon shaking. However, it did not dissolve back into the water.

Examined microscopically, the bion water showed numerous varieties of *plasmatic flakes*, as Reich called them, things that looked very cellular or protocellular and life-like, but as yet showed no living motility. These included rounded singular and clustered forms, appearing very much like yeasts or fungal spores, long fibres similar to algae or fungi branches, strange plasmatic membranes, rounded and elongated, containing numerous individual bions inside, and even *pseudo-ameba* (as Reich called them) which looked like ameba, but were non-motile for the periods when they were observed.

The forms were all much larger than the filtration limit of 0.2 micron which the entire solution was forced to pass. Whereas an ordinary bion as seen from iron-powder or grass disintegration would typically form at around 1 micron in diameter, the plasmatic flakes and other life-like forms seen in Experiment 20 appeared at sizes from 50 microns to several hundred microns in size. Given the intensive boiling, filtration and auto-clavation procedures employed, and the fact that the preparations were observed microscopically within only a few minutes after they were removed from sterile conditions, these could not be the product of some hypothetical "contamination". Nor could they be the surviving remnants from killed soil microorganisms, as none would have passed through the filter.

A special distillation procedure was also employed by Reich in the Experiment 20 procedures. These were also attempted at OBRL, but did not yield results which could be reported at this time. In this procedure, the boiled and rough-filtered bion water is distilled through an apparatus which allows only the gaseous water vapor from the original bion water to pass through the apparatus, leaving behind all of the original solid portion, plus any chemical fractions which cannot be rendered into a gas at temperatures of only 100˚C. In the OBRL distillation experiments, where the final distillate was caught into test tubes and then frozen, the thawed solution appeared almost totally clear of any structures, save for a few exceedingly faint and transparent flakes for which we could not rule out the possibilities of dust contaminants from the slide and/or cover slips. This procedure will be attempted again in the near future.

The Reich Blood Test

The procedures for making the Reich blood test[2] have been presented at the OBRL seminars each year since 1995. The test is demonstrated, and participants are then allowed to make it on themselves — only a small finger-prick is necessary. The test is generally performed using a 40x planapochromatic objective (with total magnification of around 400x - 600x) for better depth of field, and can be performed with or without cover slip. Higher magnifications are used to highlight specific features. The microscopes used during the seminar — the OBRL Leitz microscope previously described, a Nikon scope with planapochromats brought by Dr. Nagy, and a Reichert scope fitted with planapochromats provided by Dr. Blasband — allowed unparalleled viewing of the red blood cells *in their living state*, to include observation of their glowing blue energy fields. Depending upon the type of objective and condenser employed, one could make the blue energy fields around the red blood cells either diminish or intensify, but it could hardly be totally extinguished. With the Leitz microscope, at higher magnifications one could also see the micro-constituents of blood plasma even in brightfield. Normally these constituents are only observable in darkfield observation.

Blood cells could also be displayed on a television monitor through a videocamera hookup in the microscope camera tube, allowing a single red blood cell to appear the size of a grapefruit, with a 3-dimensional quality. While classical optical theory claims all powers above approximately 1500x are only "empty magnification" with no added resolution, we found this to be only partly true. The superior optics of the microscopes in use at OBRL did appear to bring out details not observable at lower magnifications — as with the smaller constituents in blood plasma. However, the main function of the higher magnifications was to observe the fine

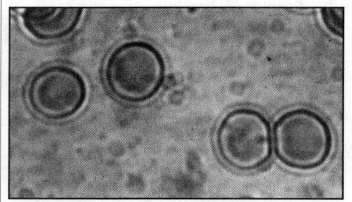

Red blood cells in normal plasma showing distinct energy-fields, appearing a distinct blue in the original photos. 40x Planapochromat oil-immersion objective with Berek Condenser. Total magnification around 1250x using 25x Periplan eyepiece in the camera tube. High contrast enhancement applied to make fields more apparent.

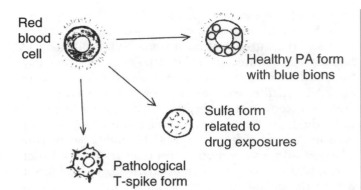

Red blood cell → Healthy PA form with blue bions

Sulfa form related to drug exposures

Pathological T-spike form

Red blood cells, once removed from the body and placed on a microscope slide, slowly break down into various forms, with a speed and percentage distribution that reflects the overall vitality of both the cell and the person. (after Reich[7])

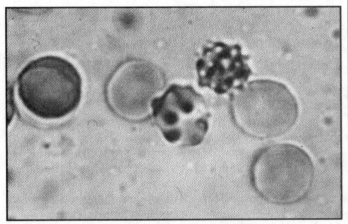

Red cells in different states of disintegration in physiological saline solution. Two center cells show vesicular bionous breakdown, into bionous PA forms as described by Reich. 40x Planapochromatic objective with oil immersion, and oiled condenser. Total magnification around 1250x using 25x Periplan eyepiece.

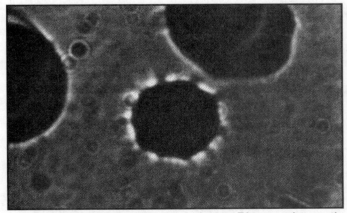

T-spike red blood cell (in center). 90x Planapochromatic objective with oil immersion, and oiled condenser. Total magnification around 2000x.

pulsatory movements within individual microorganisms and blood cells. Red cells observed at such high magnifications would typically show wave-like undulations, pulsations and resonances sweeping across their surfaces, causing their outer membranes to visibly shimmer and vibrate. One could easily differentiate these kinds of cellular movements from mechanical shaking. The lab, in any case, has a concrete floor, and the heavy marble microscope table dampens all but the most intensive mechanical vibrations.

The Reich blood test typically involves mixing a tiny drop of blood (from a finger-prick) with several small drops of physiological saline solution. Both the solution, as well as the glass slide and any coverslip to be used must be pre-warmed to body temperature, as a means to move the blood cells from the body to the slide with a minimum of shock and disturbance. If the slide is cool or cold, the cells immediately contract (as would a person cast into a freezer), invalidating the test. There are other technical points involved besides temperature — pH of the saline solution and glassware surfactants, for example — and these are found in various publications on the subject.[2]

When performed correctly, the Reich blood test shows a patterned disintegration of red cells which reflects the overall vitality and energetic charge of the organism — the red blood cells of healthy organisms show a predominance of typical "donut" or "life preserver" shapes, with a taught exterior ring, depressed center, and bluish energy field. Undercharged organisms may show cells looking slightly-deflated with narrow energy fields. When blood cells are subjected to stress, as from physiological saline solution used in the test, the red cells deteriorate into different bionous forms, with a speed dependent upon the overall health and vitality. Healthy red cells with a strong blue field tend to resist the saline and remain in their original condition for a longer period, and even after an hour on the microscope slide may look relatively unchanged. By contrast, energetically-weakened cells deteriorate within minutes. The bluish orgone (life-energy) field of the red blood cell has a strong correlation with the tendency of the cell to remain in its original form. From this perspective, the orgone charge of the red blood cell is a directly-observable expression of what Reich called the *resistance to disease*. Today, this term has been supplanted by the *immune system*, and so it is reasonable to view the energy field of the red cell, and its tendency to deteriorate slowly or quickly on the microscope slide, as directly-observable expressions of a person's immunity.

During the process of deterioration and disintegration on the microscope slide, red blood cells form three basic morphological structures: *PA* or *"packet" forms*, *Sulfa-forms* and *T-spike* forms. PA forms develop from healthy cells with a strong energy charge, and the charge aggregates into larger bluish bions within the existing red cell membrane. PA-cells appear lumpy, like a sack containing many large balls which appear bluish with the proper microscope optics. T-spike forms appear from energetically weakened and unhealthy red cells, appearing badly shrunken with sharply protruding points. The "T" comes from German "Tod", meaning death; the tips of T-cell spikes typically break off with time, forming what Reich called *T-bacilli,* which are themselves toxic and carcinogenic.[2] Sulfa forms appear as a consequence of the influence of certain pharmacological drugs. In general, the longer it takes for the red blood cells to deteriorate, and the higher the percentage of PA forms over t-spike forms, the better the overall prognosis of the individual. This assumes, of course, that one's technique is satisfactory and that artifacts are not created by faulty procedures.

Mainstream classical hematology and medicine generally interpret the PA form of red blood cell, and the T-spike cell, as the result of mechanical osmosis or "faulty drying-out" of the slide — and so they speak about "crenated" or "burr cells" — rarely attributing significance to these differences except as expressions of microscopical techniques. Consequently, they place little emphasis upon *living blood,* and have entirely missed the rapid deterioration of the blood of cancer patients, or cancer mice, as compared to healthier organisms. Some hematologists and physicians today will confess, privately at least, that with all the emphasis upon fixing and staining dead preparations, they have *never seen a living blood cell under the microscope.*

The Reich blood test also employs an autoclavation test, where several large drops of blood are captured in a test tube filled with a mixture of 0.1N KCl and nutrient

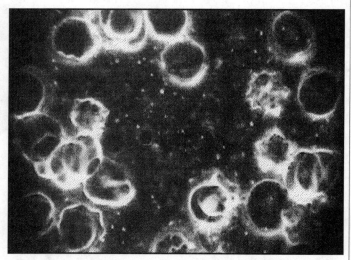

Living Human Blood viewed in darkfield, highlighting the smaller constituents of blood plasma. Red cells are about 8 microns in diameter, suggesting the smaller vesicles are less than one micron. They are called *somatids* by Naessens, and *protids* by Enderlein. Classical hematology calls them *chylomicrons,* and relates them to dietary factors. Hence, they might be defined as *food bions* from the perspective of Reich.

broth. The tube is then autoclaved for around 30 minutes. When this is done, healthy blood amazingly tends to resist the autoclavation process. One can look at healthy blood under the microscope after its autoclavation, and see many whole red cells, with most others in the PA form, filled with large blue bions, and with many free blue bions in the solution. Blood from a biopathic individual, or from a cancer mouse, will show a much greater amount of deterioration after the autoclavation process, with a very high percentage of T-spike forms and T-bacilli. After autoclavation, healthy blood forms a tight clot at the center of the tube which resists easy breakup from minor mechanical shaking, and it smells fresh like a good soup. Biopathic blood, by contrast, forms a clot which crumbles easily with the slightest shaking, and smells rancid, like rotten eggs. These and other factors were worked through by Reich in his blood test, and are part of the reason why he called cancer the *premature putrefaction (rotting) of the organism*, while it was still alive.[2]

The International Symposia on Pleomorphism

All the above photomicrographs, and others, were presented by myself to the *Second International Symposium on Pleomorphic Microbes in Health and Disease*, held in Ashland, Oregon on 19-20 October 2000.[13] The Symposia was attended by health-care practitioners and biologists from North America and Europe; discussions were open and friendly, but pointed and challenging on research and technical issues. Reich's findings fall within the definition of pleomorphic changes in microbes (as with bions clustering to form protozoa, or whole cells disintegrating into individual bions) and showed many points of agreement with the observations of other presenters, but also posed some challenges to their theories.

For example, there were many presentations on the properties of blood as viewed under the microscope in the living condition, which agreed with Reich's findings. Advocates of the Enderlein method of live-cell blood diagnosis, for example, also advocated allowing the blood to slowly deteriorate on a microscope slide, with the complexity of blood forms subsequently developing used for interpretation of human health and sickness. However, their methodology employed use of whole blood without physiological saline, and this takes many hours to disintegrate significantly, as compared to 20-30 minutes for the typical Reich blood test. Also, because the Enderlein method does not incorporate the phenomenon of bionous disintegration and natural organization of protozoa within its theoretical structure, advocates of that theory interpreted the bionous PA and T-spike blood cells forms as evidence of "blood parasites". One researcher was able to show, that bionously-deteriorated red blood cells carried measurable quantities of DNA beyond what might be expected from bone-marrow residues (they have no nucleus, and do not divide or replicate independently, being formed only in bone marrow). Within his own theoretical structure, this important observation supported the concept of "parasites", but viewed from the perspective of bionous disintegration, it suggested bions forming within red blood cells might be *creating their own DNA*. This clear difference in theoretical interpretation was openly discussed, and underscored just how much work remains to be done, to reconcile the competing theories.

It is important to note, there are today several schools of thought about the micro-constituents of blood plasma, developed by clinicians who made extensive observations of living blood. Reich noted red cells deteriorated into bions and T-bacilli, and these could break free of the cells to exist independently within blood plasma, where they might give the appearance of being new living forms. Elongated spicules extending outwards from T-cells can occasionally appear as new flagellated microorganisms, though they are in fact red blood cells with a significant bionous deterioration. Other theorists may observe bionous structures in blood plasma, but give them different names as if they were unique "parasitic" microorganisms, or blood forms such as mycoplasmas.

On the one hand, there is confirmation for Reich in the writings of Enderlein[14] on the *protid*, or from Naessens[15] on the *somatid*, and support for his findings also from the earlier work of Bechamp[16] on the *microzymas*. All of these researchers, like Reich, describe a similar indestructible particle in blood, which also exists elsewhere in nature.[§] On the other hand, none of the above theorists incorporates the finding of bionous disintegration as the source of the particles, nor do they resolve the issue of *biogenesis* with the same clarity and specificity that Reich provided. Only Reich informs us about how the natural organization of protozoa in nature (soils, ponds) parallels the process of cancer-cell formation within the body of humans and other mammals. So while I wish to celebrate the work of these other researchers, for their own empirical contributions to science and biology, I also must emphasize *it would be imprecise to simply claim all the terms and theories being discussed were equally accurate descriptors of what goes on in nature*. We may elaborate further on this consideration.

Raw blood plasma is filled with large quantities of tiny vesicles, of a size around 1/10th of a red cell, and numbering perhaps 20 to 50 for each red cell. They dance around in living blood with an intensity I have not seen with any other slide preparation, and appear immediately in the blood plasma as viewed at the microscope, suggesting they are *not* related to bionous disintegration of red blood cells as is typically observed in physiological saline solutions with the Reich blood test. Naessens and Enderlein both viewed these particles as having a central importance for human immune functions, but their abundance appears connected to dietary factors as well. One microscopist informed me, that after eating a big steak dinner with all the trimmings, his blood was swarming with these small particles. Another said that after going on a fast for several days, her blood plasma was relatively clear of them, to the point where followers of Naessens were worried this signaled a pathological condition (they interpret an abundance of somatids as a sign of good health). Classical hematology calls these small blood particles *chylomicrons*, or *chylous* material,[17] describing them as basically "particles of digested lipids" (fats) composed of triglycerides and phospholipids with a smaller fraction of cholesterol and protein, and which course through blood and lymph, transporting fatty acids and fat-soluble vitamins to the various tissues.[23] They are acknowledged to have an important role in human energy, but classical biology has basically failed to give them sufficient study, especially as seen in living blood. It is unquestionable, as viewed in living blood, these small particles have a dynamic of behavior and structure which challenges any simple definition of them as merely being "fat particles" — orthodox medicine and biology continue to make their definitions by looking only at dead specimens, and so have missed out on something quite important!

Reich, to my knowledge, said nothing specifically about these smaller blood particles that classical biology calls chylomicrons, as he focused upon the qualitative-energetic and bionous phenomenon in blood which could be clearly observed and documented, and for which a strong correlation to general immunity was noted. However, his views do appear compatible with some parts of both the Enderlein and Naessens theory, in that bions, like somatids and protids, are considered fundamental "particles of life". In this respect, Reich's overall theory is much broader than those of Naessens or Enderlein, in that it provides a bridge to similar discoveries of "life particles" from inorganic sources — such as the *jeewanu* discovered by Bahadur[18] — and additionally incorporates the full range of his prior findings on the unity of psyche and soma, the specific psychosomatic mechanism which encompasses emotion, respiration and sexual functioning, and the even wider realm of cosmic life-energy (orgone) functions.

Reich's ideas also fit with some aspects of the classical view; the idea that the abundance of chylomicrons is a consequence of diet indirectly confirms Reich's view that foods in the gut are themselves bionously disintegrating, with certain bionous forms passing from the gut directly into the blood, where energy transfer occurs. This is only a cursory discussion of a complex matter,

§ The preceding article in this issue of *Pulse* presents yet another independent, and quite remarkable set of observations of a similar biological particle, the *Sanal*, as discovered by Korean researcher Bong Han Kim.

however, and precise comparisons of findings from the various live-blood researchers and classical hematologists must wait for experimental and empirical proofs.

In any case, viewing these tiny blood particles, as well as the larger vesicular forms occurring within disintegrating red blood cells as the products of bionous decay was a brand-new idea for most of the Symposia participants. And it was a unique experience for me to interact with these other highly-skilled and experienced professionals, and to discuss these phenomenon without the usual derisive reaction which too often accompanies the mention of Reich's name at scientific meetings.

In closing, I came away from this Symposia with a greater appreciation of Reich's original findings on bions, and on the superiority of the Reich blood test over many other live cell tests in use today. Researchers following the approach of Naessens and Enderlein have much to learn from Reich, mainly on the issue of bionous disintegration as the source of many of the microforms observed in human blood.

On the other side, followers of Reich's method can learn a lot from the various biologists undertaking research on pleomorphic organisms, and other live-cell diagnostic methods. It is a fact that use of physiological saline mixed with blood speeds up the disintegration process on the microscope slide over other methods that use only whole blood by itself. However, for making observations of blood, and defining its properties, it must be acknowledged that the added saline is by itself an additional artifactual influence which confuses the determinations of the natural quantity of vesicular forms at or below 1 micron, and so caution is required before saying just what is, or is not, a "natural" or "unnatural" phenomenon within blood plasma. Also, if DNA can be demonstrated to exist inside bionously-disintegrating red blood cells, it raises an intriguing possibility, that DNA or its precursors might also be detected in the raw bionous material derived from the iron and sand incandescence experiments. If so, that would go a long way towards proving that bions are indeed the bridge between the living and non-living worlds. It would also help to build a bridge between Reich's original findings of the 1930s and 40s, to modern biological research where everything from deep-sea hydrothermal vents to boiling hot springs, to deep glacial ice and Martian meteorites, are found to contain bionous forms. Indeed, an entire new classification of life forms — the *Archaea* — has been proposed, and many Archaea appear quite similar to Reich's bions in their origins from incandescent and/or frozen sources.

Orthodox biology of the mid-20th Century has not anticipated any of these fantastic discoveries, but has in fact been seriously challenged by them. By contrast, Reich's original findings on the bions, from the early 20th Century, have anticipated these and similar discoveries of life forms where according to the classical dogma of his time, life "should not exist".

Acknowledgments

My thanks to Dr. Richard Blasband, Dr. Bernard Grad, and Dr. Stephen Nagy for their personal engagement and contributions to the OBRL laboratory seminars, and to Dr. Nagy in particular for his assistance with development of the Leitz microscope system. Thanks to Dr. Louisa Lance, Dr. Morton Herskowitz, and others who donated significant amounts of labware and apparatus over the last years, helping greatly in this effort. Thanks also to Dr. Gitte Jensen, for inviting me to present this controversial material at the *Symposium on Pleomorphism*, providing a stimulus to undertake the photographic documentation.

References:

1. Reich, W.: *Die Bione,* Sex-Pol Verlag, Oslo, 1938 (Republished as *The Bion Experiments: On the Origin of Life*, Farrar, Straus & Giroux, NY, 1979).

2. Reich, W.: *The Cancer Biopathy*, Orgone Institute Press, New York, 1948, p.170-171 (Reprinted by Farrar, Straus & Giroux, NY, 1973); Raphael, C. & MacDonald, H.: *Orgonomic Diagnosis of Cancer Biopathy*, Wilhelm Reich Foundation, Rangeley, Maine, 1952; Blasband, R.: "Cancer Research: A Comment on the Literature", *Orgonomic Medicine*, II(1):75-81, 1956; Baker, C.F., Braid, B., Dew, R. & Lance, L: "The Reich Blood Test: 105 Cases", *Annals, Inst. Orgonomic Science*, 1:1-11, Sept. 1984.

3. Reich, 1938, ibid, p.7; Reich, 1948, ibid. p.16; Reich, W.: "The Old Question of Magnifications Over 2000x", *Int. J. Sex-Economy & Orgone Res.*, 1:276, 1942.

4. http://www.orgonelab.org/Pulse5.htm

5. Reich, W.: "The Natural Organization of Protozoa from Orgone Energy Vesicles", *Int. J. Sex-Economy & Orgone Res.*, 1:193-225, 1942 (Reprinted in Reich, 1948, ibid, p.48-60); also see: Reich, 1938, ibid., p.25-54. Also see: Dew. R.: "An Air Germ Experiment", *Annals, Inst. Orgonomic Science*, 4:15-42, 1987; Dew, R.: "Further Observations on the Air Germ Experiment", *Annals, Inst. Orgonomic Science,* 7:1-8, 1990.

6. The time-lapse films made by Reich were recently transferred to videotape, and have been on display at the Wilhelm Reich Museum, Rangeley, Maine.

7. Raphael & MacDonald, 1952, ibid, p.72 & 84.

8. Strick, J.: *Sparks of Life: Darwinism and the Victorian Debates over Spontaneous Generation*, Harvard U. Press, Cambridge, 2000.

9. Reich, 1938, ibid, 99-114; Reich, 1948, ibid, p.25, 81-82. Also see: Lappert, P.: "Primary Bions through Superimposition at Elevated Temperatures and Pressures", *J. Orgonomy*, 19(1):80-91, 1985; Carey, K. & Dunlap, S.: "Culturing SAPA Bions", *J. Orgonomy*, 22(1):68-75, May 1988.

10. Reich, 1938, ibid, pp.54-83.

11. Reich, W.: "Der Urgegensatz des vegetativen Lebens (Basic Antithesis of Vegetative Life Functions)", *Zeitschrift für Politische Psychologie und Sexualökonomie*, 1:29-43, 1934 (Reprinted in *Bioelectrical Investigation of Sexuality and Anxiety*, Farrar, Straus & Giroux, 1982; also in *Pulse of the Planet* #4, 1993).

12. Reich, W.: "Experimental Demonstration of the Physical Orgone Energy", *Int. J. Sex-Economy and Orgone Research,* 4(2-3):133-146, 1945; Grad, B.: "Wilhelm Reich's Experiment XX", *Cosmic Orgone Engineering* 7(3-4):130-143, 1955; Dew, R.: "Reich's Experiment XX", *Annals, Inst. Orgonomic Science,* 6(1):1-32, 1989.

13. http://www.holgernis.com/conferences/2000/description.html   See: *Pleomorphic Microbes in Health and Disease, Proceedings, First Int. Symposium,* Gitte Jensen, Ed., McGill Univ., Montreal, Canada.

14. Bleker, M.: *Blood Examination in Darkfield according to Prof. Dr. Günter Enderlein,* Semmelweis-Verlag, Hoya, Germany, 1993; Enby, E.: *Hidden Killers: The Revolutionary Medical Discoveries of Prof. Guenther Enderlein,* Sheehan Communications, 1990.

15. Bird, C.: *Persecution and Trial of Gaston Naessens,* Kramer, Tiburon CA, 1990.

16. Bechamp, A.: *The Third Element of the Blood,* J. Ousley, London, 1912. Also see: Grad, B.: "Bechamp's Microzymas and Reich's Bions", *J. Orgonomy,* 24(1):125-131, 1990; Blasband, R.: "Transformations in Microbiological Organisms", *J. Orgonomy,* 22(2): 293-300, 1988.

17. A recent internet search on the term "chylomicrons" yielded over 4,700 web pages, whereas "bions", "somatids" and "protids" yielded 279, 74, and 4 sites, respectively.

18. Bahadur, K., Ranganayaki, S., Folsome C. & Smith, A.: *A Functional Approach to the Origin of Life Problem,* National Academy of Sciences, India: Golden Jubilee Commemoration Volume, 1980.

Dayton Miller's Ether-Drift Experiments: A Fresh Look*

by James DeMeo, Ph.D.**

"The effect [of ether-drift] has persisted throughout. After considering all the possible sources of error, there always remained a positive effect."
— Dayton Miller (1928, p.399)

"I believe that I have really found the relationship between gravitation and electricity, assuming that the Miller experiments are based on a fundamental error. Otherwise, the whole relativity theory collapses like a house of cards."
— Albert Einstein, in a letter to Robert Millikan, June 1921 (in Clark 1971, p.328)

The history of science records the 1887 ether-drift experiment of Albert Michelson and Edward Morley as a pivotal turning point, where the energetic *ether of space* was discarded by mainstream physics. Thereafter, the postulate of "empty space" was embraced, along with related concepts which demanded constancy in light-speed, such as Albert Einstein's relativity theory. The now famous *Michelson-Morley experiment* is widely cited, in nearly every physics textbook, for its claimed "null" or "negative" results. Less known, however, is the far more significant and detailed work of Dayton Miller.

Dayton Miller's 1933 paper in *Reviews of Modern Physics* details the positive results from over 20 years of experimental research into the question of ether-drift, and remains *the most definitive body of work on the subject of light-beam interferometry.* Other positive

Case W. R. U. Archive

Dayton Miller's Light-Beam Interferometer, at 4.3 meters across, was the largest and most sensitive of this type of apparatus ever constructed, with a mirror-reflected round-trip light-beam path of 64 meters. It was used in a definitive set of ether-drift experiments on Mt. Wilson, 1925-1926. Photos courtesy of the *Case Western Reserve Univ. Archive.*

* Previously presented to the *Natural Philosophy Alliance*, 2000, and published in *Infinite Energy* #35, Summer 2001. Also posted to www.orgonelab.org/miller.htm
** Director, Orgone Biophysical Research Lab, Greensprings, PO Box 1148, Ashland, Oregon 97520 USA. Tel/Fax: 541-552-0118 Email: demeo@mind.net

**Dayton Miller
1866-1941**

ether-detection experiments have been undertaken, such as the work of Sagnac (1913) and Michelson and Gale (1925), documenting the existence of light-speed variations (c+v > c–v), but these were not adequately constructed for detection of a larger cosmological *ether-drift*, of the Earth and Solar System moving through the background of space. Dayton Miller's work on ether-drift was so constructed, however, and yielded *consistently positive results*.

Miller's work, which ran from 1906 through the mid-1930s, most strongly supports the idea of an ether-drift, of the Earth moving through a cosmological medium, with calculations made of the actual direction and magnitude of drift. By 1933, Miller concluded that the Earth was drifting at a speed of 208 km/sec towards an apex in the Southern Celestial Hemisphere, towards Dorado, the swordfish, right ascension 4 hrs 54 min, declination of -70° 33', in the middle of the Great Magellanic Cloud and 7° from the southern pole of the ecliptic. (Miller 1933, p.234) This was based upon a measured displacement of around 10 km/sec at the interferometer, and assuming the Earth was pushing through a stationary, but Earth-entrained ether in that particular direction, which lowered the velocity of the ether from around 200 down to 10 km/sec at the Earth's surface. Today, however, Miller's work is hardly known or mentioned, as is the case with nearly all the experiments which produced positive results for an ether in space. Modern physics today points instead to the less significant 1887 work of Michelson-Morley, as having "proved the ether does not exist".

While Miller had a rough time convincing some of his contemporaries about the reality of his ether-measurements, he clearly could not be ignored in this regard. As a graduate of physics from Princeton University, President of the American Physical Society and Acoustical Society of America, Chairman of the Division of Physical Sciences of the National Research Council, Chairman of the Physics Department of Case School of Applied Science (today Case Western Reserve University), and Member of the National Academy of Sciences well known for his work in acoustics, Miller was no "outsider". While he was alive, he produced a series of papers presenting solid data on the existence of a measurable ether-drift, and he successfully defended his findings to not a small number of critics, including Einstein. His work employed light-beam interferometers of the same type used by Michelson-Morley, but of a more sensitive construction, with a significantly longer light-beam path. He periodically took the device high atop Mt. Wilson (above 1800 m, or 6000 ft elevation), where Earth-entrained ether-theory predicted the ether would move at a faster speed than close to sea-level. While he was alive, Miller's work could not be fundamentally undermined by the critics. However, towards the end of his life, he was subject to isolation as his ether-measurements were simply ignored by the larger world of physics, then captivated by Einstein's relativity theory.

After his death in 1941, Miller's work was finally "put to rest", in the publication of a critical 1955 paper in *Reviews of Modern Physics* by Robert S. Shankland, S.W. McCuskey, F. C. Leone and G. Kuerti (hereafter referred to as the "Shankland team" or "Shankland" paper), which purported to make a fair and comprehensive review of Miller's data, finding substantial flaws.

Lloyd Swenson's *Ethereal Aether* (1972) presents a cursory discussion of Miller and his "inexplicable" positive results, giving a high degree of significance to the Shankland team's critique. Swenson wrote:

"...Shankland, after extensive consultation with Einstein, decided to subject Miller's observations to a thoroughgoing review ... Einstein saw the final draft [of Shankland's manuscript] and wrote a personal letter of appreciation for having finally explained the small periodic residuals from [Miller's] Mount Wilson experiments." (Swenson, p.243)

In August of 1954, Einstein replied to Shankland:

"I thank you very much for sending me your careful study about the Miller experiments. Those experiments, conducted with so much care, merit, of course, a very careful statistical investigation. This is more so as the existence of a not trivial positive effect would affect very deeply the fundament of theoretical physics as it is presently accepted. You have shown convincingly that the observed effect is outside the range of accidental deviations and must, therefore, have a systematic cause [having] nothing to do with 'ether wind', but with differences of temperature of the air traversed by the two light bundles which produce the bands of interference." (Shankland, 1973a, p.2283)

From the above accounts, it certainly would appear

that the case was finally closed on Miller, and that all the lose ends were finally cleaned up. With the strongest support for cosmological ether-drift swept aside as the alleged product of temperature errors, Einstein's theory of relativity continued to grow in popularity and dominance.

Here, I will compare the Shankland team's 1955 criticisms to what is actually contained in Miller's published works, notably his 1933 paper which summarized his work on the subject. It is my contention, the Shankland paper, published 14 years after Miller's death, attempted to resurrect speculative criticisms which had previously been raised and rebutted when Miller was alive, and not given serious credibility except among anti-ether fundamentalists. The Shankland paper also misrepresented Miller's data in several ways, and furthermore misrepresented itself as a definitive rebuttal, which it most certainly was not. In order to properly address this major issue of science history, I will also recount the central facts of Miller's work.

The basic principles of light-beam interferometry for detection of ether-drift are described in most textbooks, albeit with typical factual errors (ie, the slight positive result of the Michelson-Morley experiment is nearly always misrepresented as a "null" or "zero" result) and so will not be repeated here. However, there were novel methods introduced by Miller into the discussion of ether-drift, along with interferometer construction features and principles of operation which are not widely known — these will be detailed.

Miller's Work with Interferometry

Miller began his work on the question of ether-drift and light-beam interferometry with Edward Morley, from 1902 to 1906, using an apparatus three times as sensitive as the original interferometer used by Michelson-Morley in 1887. In later years, from 1921 through 1928, Miller made additional refinements for sensitivity, obtaining increasingly significant positive results. His interferometer was the largest and most sensitive ever constructed, with iron cross-arms 4.3 meters across, and standing 1.5 meters in height. Four sets of mirrors were mounted on the end of each cross-arm to reflect light beams back and forth 16 times horizontally with a total round-trip light path of 64 meters, starting from the same light-source, and finally recombined to form interference fringes whose movement relative to a pointer was read through a magnifying telescope. The large apparatus was floated inside a circular tank of liquid mercury, providing a frictionless base for rotation. Fringe-shift movements (in tenths of a fringe, plus or minus in direction) were observed by one person who walked around with the apparatus while it turned, speaking out the readings at the ring of bell which automatically sounded when electrodes made contact at 24° intervals (dividing the circle into 15 parts). An

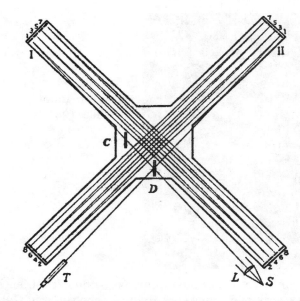

Light Paths of the Michelson-Morley and Miller Interferometers, as seen from above. Source (S) generates light which passes through lens (L) and is then split by half-silvered mirror (D). Beams then reflect back and forth along beams (I and II) to mirrors (numbered 1-8) before finally being recombined by half-silvered mirror (D) and reflected to small telescope eyepiece (T) where interference fringes are observed.

Light-Interference Fringes as seen in the Interferometer telescope. Magnified by an eyepiece with precise graduated markings, one could read the lateral movement or shifting of fringes as the instrument was rotated. Miller's larger apparatus used a 50x telescope, allowing magnified readings down to hundredths of a fringe-shift, though readings were typically recorded in tenths.

assistant then noted the readings on paper. The readings, from consecutive turns of the apparatus were then organized into "sets", which were made at different times of day and at different seasons of year. Data sets were then averaged according to a sidereal time clock, which was correlated with external celestial coordinates. Miller became convinced of an ether Earth-entrainment effect, which necessitated using the apparatus at higher altitudes (to reduce the anticipated entrainment-effect of sea-level environments), and he additionally undertook the experiments in structures where the walls at the level of the light-path were open to the air, covered with canvas. Only glass, or glass and light paper covers were used along the light-beam paths, with all wood or metal shielding removed. By contrast, the original Michelson-Morley interferometer had a round-trip light path of around 22 meters (Michelson 1927, p.153), and the experiments were undertaken with an opaque wooden cover over the instrument, situated in the basement of one of the large stone buildings at Case School in Cleveland.

In his 1933 paper, Miller published the most comprehensive summary of his work, and the large quantity of data which supported his conclusions. A total of over 200,000 individual readings were made, from over 12,000 individual turns of the interferometer, undertaken at different months of the year, starting in 1902 with Edward Morley at Case School in Cleveland, and ending in 1926 with his Mt. Wilson experiments. These data do not include many rigorous control experiments undertaken at Case School Physics Department from 1922 to 1924. More than half of Miller's readings were made at Mt. Wilson using the most sophisticated and controlled procedures, with the most telling set of experiments in 1925 and 1926. By contrast, we can mention here, the original Michelson-Morley experiment of 1887 involved only *six hours of data collection* over four days (July 8, 9, 11 and 12 of 1887), with a grand total of only 36 turns of their interferometer. Even so, as shown below, Michelson-Morley originally obtained *a slight positive result* which has been systematically ignored or misrepresented by modern physics. As stated by Michelson-Morley:

"...the relative velocity of the earth and the ether is probably less than one-sixth the earth's orbital velocity, and certainly less than one-fourth. ... The experiment will therefore be repeated at intervals of three months, and thus all uncertainty will be avoided." (Michelson-Morley 1887)

Unfortunately, and in spite of all claims to the contrary, Michelson-Morley never undertook those additional experiments at the different seasonal configurations, to "avoid all uncertainty". However, Miller did. Over many years, he developed increasingly sensitive apparatus, using them at higher altitudes and in open structures, making clear and positive detection of the ether. His experiments yielded systematic periodic effects which pointed to a similar identifiable axis of cosmic ether-drift, though of a variable magnitude, depending upon the season, time of day, density of materials shielding or surrounding the apparatus, and altitude at which the experiment was undertaken. He argued that basement locations, or interferometers shielded with opaque wood or metal housings, yielded the most tiny and insignificant effects, while those undertaken at higher altitudes and in less dense structures yielded more readily observable effects. The

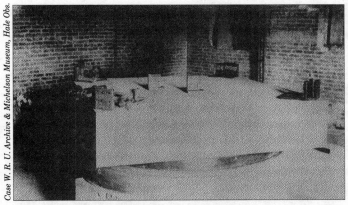

The Michelson-Morley Interferometer with an approximate 22-meter round-trip light-beam path, mounted on a concrete platform in the basement of the old Case School Physics building (today, Case Western Reserve University). This interferometer was about one-third as sensitive as the 64-meter interferometer constructed later by Miller. A protective wood cover over the light-beam paths was removed for this photograph. Such dense coverings and stone-basement shielding, as Miller showed, slowed down the movement of the ether. These problems, along with a relatively short light-path, and placement at a relatively low altitude basement location, virtually guaranteed only a small (but never "null") measured result.

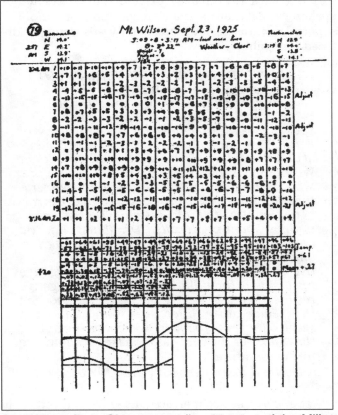

Mt. Wilson Data Sheet, recording 20 turns of the Miller interferometer, in this case, on 23 September 1925, 3:09 to 3:17 AM. Over 300 of these data sheets were recorded by Miller at Mt. Wilson alone, covering more than 6000 turns of the interferometer.

Michelson-Morley experiment, by comparison, was undertaken in the basement of a stone building closer to sea-level. Even so, it produced a slight positive result which was in agreement with Miller's results.

Miller's observations were also consistent through the long period of his measurements. He noted, when his data were plotted on sidereal time, they produced *"...a very striking consistency of their principal characteristics...for azimuth and magnitude... as though they were related to a common cause... The observed effect is dependent upon sidereal time and is independent of diurnal and seasonal changes of temperature and other terrestrial causes, and...is a cosmical phenomenon."* (Miller 1933, p.231)

Debates with Einstein

There are several newspaper accounts indicating a certain tension between Albert Einstein and Dayton Miller, since the early 1920s at least. In June of 1921, Einstein wrote to the physicist Robert Millikan: *"I believe that I have really found the relationship between gravitation and electricity, assuming that the Miller experiments are based on a fundamental error. Otherwise, the whole relativity theory collapses like a house of cards."* (Clark 1971, p.328) Privately, in letters and in spoken words, there was a struggle going on for philosophical dominance, and occasionally this struggle surfaced into public view:

> **GOES TO DISPROVE EINSTEIN THEORY**
> **Case Scientist Will Conduct**
> **Further Studies in Ether Drift.**
> **Einstein Discounts Experiments**
> *Speaking before scientists at the University of Berlin, Einstein said the ether drift experiments at Cleveland showed zero results, while on Mount Wilson they showed positive results. Therefore, altitude influences results. In addition, temperature differences have provided a source of error. "The trouble with Prof. Einstein is that he knows nothing about my results." Dr. Miller said. "He has been saying for thirty years that the interferometer experiments in Cleveland showed negative results. We never said they gave negative results, and they did not in fact give negative results. He ought to give me credit for knowing that temperature differences would affect the results. He wrote to me in November suggesting this. I am not so simple as to make no allowance for temperature."*
> *(Cleveland Plain Dealer, 27 Jan. 1926)*

The above newspaper account is significant, as it demonstrates that Einstein was pushing the "thermal artifact" argument against Miller's results as early as 1926. There are other accounts of Einstein's discontent with Miller's results in "Conversations with Albert Einstein" written by Robert Shankland in the years after Miller's death. (Shankland 1963, 1973b)

Miller's Control Experiments. Top Photo: A wooden platform has been supplied for the mirrors and optics of the interferometer, inside a building at Case School. Bottom Photo: A concrete platform supports the mirrors and optics of the interferometer, inside a small shelter on the grounds at Case School.

Case W. R. U. Archive

Miller's Fully-Insulated Interferometer as it was finally employed at Mt. Wilson, c.1925, fitted with 1 inch insulating cork panels covering the metal support structure, and glass and light paper coverings along the light-beam path (paper removed for the photograph). These steps eliminated any significant influences of ambient temperature differences upon the apparatus and the air within the light-beam path, but still allowed the movement of ether-drift.

Miller's Control Experiments

Miller was fully aware of the criticisms being made against his findings, that his interferometer was responding to one or another mechanical, magnetic or thermal influence. Given its large size and sensitivity, it required a careful set-up procedure prior to each use. Setting screws with extremely fine threads were used to adjust the mirrors, and the final adjustment could isolate 100 wavelengths of light by just a 16° turn of the screw. Even this was insufficient for the final adjustment, which was made by adding small weights of around 100 gram to the ends of the cross-beam, which was sufficient to cause a micro-flexing of the iron supports by only a few wavelengths. Only then would the interference fringes come into view. And once in view, additional care had to be taken to prevent distortions from mechanical vibrations. Consequently, from the very beginning of the ether-drift experiments, Miller undertook extensive control experiments and procedures to guard against laboratory artifacts, and to objectively determine just how sensitive his apparatus was to external influences.

Especially between 1921-1924, Miller's control experiments were most rigorous, aimed at addressing the criticisms he had received following the earlier work, to make the apparatus as sensitive as possible only to ether-drift. A special interferometer of aluminum and brass was constructed, to guard against the possible effects of magnetoconstriction (the measured periodic ether-drifting was the same as with the original iron interferometer). Procedures were made to judge the effects of mechanical vibration — such as using a loose or tight centering pin. Bases made of wood, metal or concrete were floated in the mercury tank, to judge and correct for the effects of strain and deformation. The apparatus was not touched when operating, but rather gently pulled in a circle by a thin string, slowly accelerated to the desired velocity of rotation while floating in the mercury tank. Different light sources were tried, mounted on different locations on the apparatus. Light sources outside the structure were also tried, including Sunlight, but finally an artificial light source located above the central axis of the instrument was used.

Possible temperature effects were evaluated by using radiant parabolic heaters to artificially heat the apparatus and the air through which the light-beam passed. These experiments showed the interferometer clearly was sensitive to artificial heating, and so steps were taken to eliminate the effect. Strong radiant heat sources, it was learned, would badly skew the apparatus if focused upon only one arm or pair of arms of the iron cross-beams. Equal heating of the apparatus had no such effect, but the metal arms were nevertheless covered with a one-inch cork insulation to guard against radiant thermal effects. The light-path was given a glass housing, which stabilized the temperature inside,

Miller's Interferometer House on Mt. Wilson, with canvas-covered windows all around, and "beaverboard" walls (wood fibre composite). The bottom photo shows the same house fitted with a tent cover over the roof and walls, to further stabilize temperatures.

Case W. R. U. Archive

Miller's Interferometer House perched high atop Mt. Wilson (at arrow) at a place later known as "Ether Rocks". Today, I am informed, there is no record of Miller's extensive work at Mt. Wilson, only a memorial plaque dedicated to Michelson and Einstein.

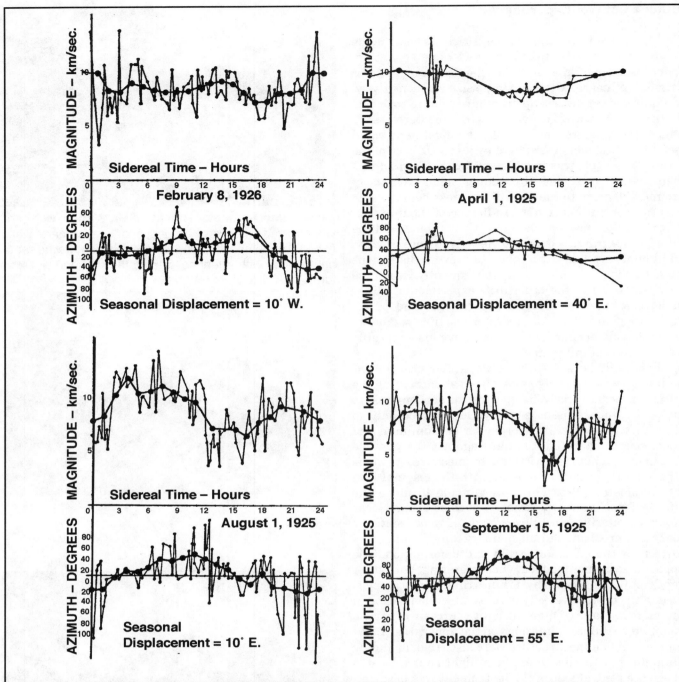

Figure 1. VELOCITIES AND AZIMUTHS OF ETHER-DRIFT, from the four 10-day epochs of measurement at Mt. Wilson, 1925-1926. The figure captions are re-drafted from the originals in Miller, 1933, p.229.

and later, a light corrugated paper cover was added over the glass cover, which did not affect the ether-drift, but further protected against possible temperature variations. Low-level thermal effects were also evaluated, as from human body heat, by having the recording assistant stand in different locations while the apparatus was turned and operated.

Temperature effects from the larger environment were evaluated as well. Early ether-drift experiments, including those of Michelson-Morley and Morley-Miller,

were undertaken inside basement locations with relatively stabilized temperatures, but shielded from the ether-drift as well due to heavy and dense building materials. Miller's ether-drift experiments atop Mt. Wilson required a different approach, and a special house was constructed to shelter the interferometer. It had a floor, walls and roof, and canvas-covered windows all around at the level of the interferometer light-beam. During his last set of Mt. Wilson experiments in 1925-1926, a tent-like covering was erected over the roof and

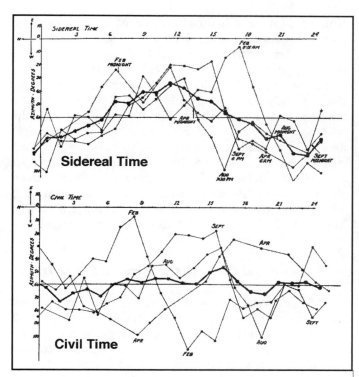

Figure 2: PERIODICITY OF GLOBAL ETHER-DRIFT, from Dayton Miller's Mount Wilson Ether-Drift Experiments, 1925-26. The *Top Graph* plots the data from four separate epochs, measured at different times of the year and organized by sidereal time, showing a definite periodic curve. The heavy line is the mean of all four epochs. The *Bottom Graph* plots the same data organized by civil clock time coordinates; here, the plotted data spreads out along the graph, without apparent periodicity. This demonstrates, the detected axis and periodicity of ether drift is the same for different times of year, but can only be seen when the data is viewed within a cosmological, sidereal coordinate system. (From Miller 1928, p.362 – Note: These data curves are organized along azimuthal means which were later recomputed for Miller's 1933 publication, as given in Figure 1.)

Figure 3: AVERAGE VELOCITY AND AZIMUTH OF GLOBAL ETHER DRIFT, from Dayton Miller's Mount Wilson Ether Drift Experiments, 1925-26. *Top Graph*: Average variations in observed magnitude of ether-drift from all four epochs of measurement. Maximum velocity occurs at around 5 hours sidereal time and minimum velocity occurs around 17 hours sidereal. While Miller's 1933 paper assumed the Earth was *pushing through the ether* and moving towards Dorado, near the southern pole of the Plane of the Ecliptic, the movement and direction of ether-drift past the interferometer was *exactly opposite* to this, towards Draco near the northern pole of the Plane of the Ecliptic (17 hours right ascension, declination of +68°). It is important, *from the standpoint of his working theory* to clarify the concepts of the "net motion of the Earth" versus the "direction of ether-drift". However, *if the ether itself is in motion, acting as a cosmic prime-mover, the direction of ether-drift and the net motion of the Earth would be identical, though at different velocities.* *Bottom Graph*: Average variations in observed azimuth readings according to sidereal time. This graph uses the same average data curve from Figure 2 (top), above, published by Miller in 1928 (p.363) but which was at that time given a different baseline average. The same graph is presented here, for the first time, using Miller's revised seasonal averages as published in 1933 (p.235), which help define the axis of ether-drift. Amazingly, the independent averages for the four epochs provided by Miller (Feb.=-10° west of north, April=+40° east, Aug.=+10° east, Sept.=+55° east) to-

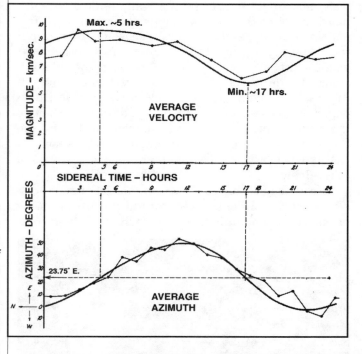

gether yield *a mean displacement 23.75° east of north.* This is very close to the Earth's axial tilt of 23.5°, and can hardly be coincidental. More discussion is given on these issues in a paper by the author, to follow. (DeMeo 2002; Graphic adapted from Miller 1928, p.363 and Miller 1933 p.235).

A Model Constructed by Miller, displaying the axis of ether-drift for the four seasonal epochs of the Earth moving around the Sun. The axis of drift, in this model, appears to be roughly perpendicular to the plane of the ecliptic.

walls to provide additional shielding from direct Sunlight, to diminish thermal variations or radiant heating effects from the walls. Miller noted, at no time during his entire work on the question did he ever observe any periodic effects expressing themselves according to civil time coordinates, as would be present if a thermal effect was radiating from a specific wall, related to solar heating. Since the measurements were made at different times of day, and at different seasons, their amplitude would vary, but the direction of the ether-drift would shift only to the same average points along a sidereal azimuth. This is graphically demonstrated in Figures 1, 2 and 3. The measurements were latitude-dependent as well, and when analyzed with attention to the Earth's rotation, axial tilt, movement around the Sun, and Sun's movement through galactic space, finally revealed a common sidereal cosmological axis of ether-drift.

From reading his publications, one gets the impression of Dayton Miller as a very careful and exceptionally patient experimentalist, someone who took every pos-

Dayton Miller (left) **and Albert Michelson** (right) at a *Conference on the Michelson-Morley Experiment* held at Mount Wilson Observatory, February 1927.

sible precaution to insure his apparatus was detecting only the phenomenon of interest. He also appeared to be quite content with the possibility that, having undertaken all the various controls to shield the apparatus from thermal effects in the measurement room, he might finally get a true "null" or "zero" effect — he did not appear to be a "believer" in ether-drift who would succumb easily to bias. He was a genuine scientist, dedicated to finding the truth of the matter. A null result was not observed, however, and his efforts to control out mechanical and thermal artifacts never eliminated the observed periodic sidereal variations, which persisted throughout his experimental work. More will be said about Miller's control procedures below.

Michelson, and Others, Confirm an Ether-Drift

Miller's work did finally receive an indirect support from Albert Michelson in 1929, with the publication of "Repetition of the Michelson-Morley Experiment" (Michelson, Pease, Pearson 1929). The paper reported on three attempts to produce ether-drift fringe shifts, using light-beam interferometry similar to that originally employed in the Michelson-Morley (M-M) experiments.

In the first experiment, undertaken in June of 1926, the interferometer was the same dimensions as the original M-M apparatus, with a round-trip light path of around 22 meters. A fringe shift displacement of 0.017 was predicted, but the conclusions stated *"No displacement of this order was observed"*. The second experiment, undertaken on unspecified "autumn" dates in 1927, employed a slightly longer round-trip light path of around 32 meters (given as 53 feet for an assumed one-way distance). Again, *"no displacement of the order anticipated was obtained"*, and the short report did not give details about the experimental surroundings or locations.

The third experiment was undertaken on an unspecified date (probably 1928) in *"a well-sheltered basement room of the Mount Wilson Laboratory"*. The round-trip light path was further increased to approximately 52 meters (given as 85 feet for an assumed one-way distance). This time, having moved the apparatus to a higher altitude and using a longer light-path, a small quantity of ether-drift was detected which approximated the result observed by Miller, although the results were reported in negative terms:

"... precautions taken to eliminate effects of temperature and flexure disturbances were effective. The results gave no displacement as great as one-fifteenth of that to be expected on the supposition of an effect due to a motion of the solar system of three hundred kilometers per second. These results are differences between the displacements observed at maximum and minimum at sidereal times, the directions corre-

sponding to ... calculations of the supposed velocity of the solar system. A supplementary series of observations made in directions half-way between gave similar results." (Michelson, Pease, Pearson 1929)

One fifteenth of 300 km/sec is 20 km/sec, a result the authors dismissed as they apparently had discarded the concept of an Earth-entrained ether, which would move more slowly closer to sea level. A similar result of 24 km/sec was achieved by the team of Kennedy-Thorndike in 1932, however they also dismissed the concept of an entrained ether and, consequently, their own measured result: *"In view of relative velocities amounting to thousands of kilometers per second known to exist among the nebulae, this can scarcely be regarded as other than a clear null result".* This incredible statement serves to illustrate how deeply ingrained was the concept of a static ether.

Michelson, Pease and Pearson went on to make speed-of-light measurements in a one mile long partially-evacuated steel tube lying flat on the ground, oriented roughly southwest to northeast. While the purpose of these experiments was not to measure any ether-drift or variation in the speed of light, such variations in fact were observed and reported in their paper. (Michelson, Pease, Pearson 1935) A newspaper account of these experiments, published after Michelson's death in 1931 but prior to their final publication of results reported: *"Dr. Pease and Mr. Pearson say the entire series of measures, made mostly between the hours of 7 and 9 PM, show fluctuations which suggest a [variation] of about 20 kilometers per second."* (Dietz 1933) Miller commented on these results, suggesting they would have measured a stronger ether-drift variation if they had taken their interferometers outside of the basement structures and steel pipes:

"If the question of an entrained ether is involved in the investigation, it would seem that such massive and opaque shielding is not justifiable. The experiment is designed to detect a very minute effect on the velocity of light, to be impressed upon the light through the ether itself, and it would seem to be essential that there should be the least possible obstruction between the free ether and the light path in the interferometer." (Miller 1933, p.240)

Miller had, by this time, acquired a lot of experience working on Mt. Wilson, using his large interferometer in the specially-constructed interferometer house. With a light path of 64 meters, Miller's apparatus was still significantly more sensitive than the best rotating interferometer of Michelson-Pease-Pearson. Given that

Michelson-Pease-Pearson did make some small detection of an ether-drift from their efforts at Mt. Wilson, in spite of the fact that it was located in a basement location, their report of detectable sidereal fringe displacements supports Miller's findings. It is also notable that this was the second time Michelson's work had significantly detected an ether, though in the first instance of Michelson and Gale (1925) the apparatus could only measure light-speed variations along the rotational axis of the Earth. These papers by Michelson and also by Kennedy-Thorndike have conveniently been forgotten by modern physics, or misinterpreted as being totally negative in result, even though all were undertaken with far more precision, with a more tangible positive result, than the celebrated Michelson-Morley experiment of 1887. Michelson went to his grave convinced that light speed was inconstant in different directions, and also convinced of the existence of the ether. The modern versions of science history have rarely discussed these facts.

Shankland Team's 1955 Critique of Miller

As previously pointed out by Swenson, Shankland's 1955 critique of Miller's work was undertaken with "extensive consultations" with Einstein, who like Newton and others before him had assumed only a static or

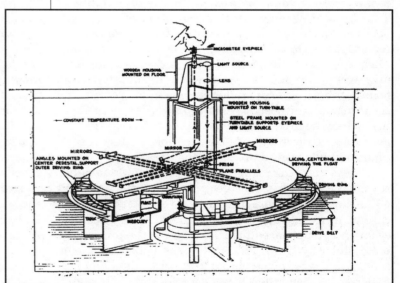

Michelson-Pease-Pearson Interferometer, used in their successful detection of an ether-drift of some unspecified quantity just under 20 km/sec at Mt. Wilson, as reported in their 1929 paper. This positive result was inappropriately dismissed as a "negative" result because the experimenters had prematurely discarded the conceptual implications of an *Earth-entrained ether*. This experiment used the largest light-beam interferometer ever constructed by Michelson, with a 52-meter round-trip light path, coming close to the sensitivity found in Miller's 64-meter interferometer. It is shown here, situated in a basement location, in the ground, which, by itself, would also predictably reduce the measured result.

stagnant ether, through which the Earth passed without material affect and, hence, without entrainment close to the Earth's surface. Shankland in fact was Miller's student for many years, and only emerged to become a professional advocate of Einstein's relativity after the death of Miller in 1941. Shankland became Chairman of the Physics Department at Case following Miller's retirement and death, building his professional career upon publications misrepresenting the Michelson-Morley experiments as the most solid evidence on the question, and publishing widely-read interviews with Einstein (Shankland 1963, 1964, 1973a, 1973b). Shankland later took up administrative positions within government agencies developing nuclear energy — he rarely discussed Miller's positive ether-drift measurements in any of these papers except in the 1955 paper under discussion here. In this sense, it is legitimate to view Shankland, and other members of his team (all Einstein advocates from Case) as very biased reviewers of Miller's work.

The very first sentence in the Shankland team's 1955 paper began with the falsehood, now widely parroted in nearly every physics textbook, that the Michelson-Morley experiments had a "null" result. The third sentence in the Shankland paper was similarly false, claiming that *"All trials of this experiment except those carried out at Mount Wilson by Dayton C. Miller yielded a null result within the accuracy of the observations."* This kind of chronic misrepresentation of the slight positive results of many interferometer experimenters, including Michelson-Morley, Morley-Miller, Sagnac, Michelson-Gale, and Michelson-Pease-Pearson, suggests an extreme bias and deliberate misrepresentation. The fact that this is a very popular bias does not excuse it. By redefining all the positive results observed by what may in fact have been the majority of ether-drift researchers, as mere expressions of "observational inaccuracy", Shankland narrowed his task considerably.

These and other sentences in the Shankland paper revealed its bias from the get-go, and gave it the spirit of an autopsy, where Miller was dissected without careful concern, and certainly where no advocate of ether theory appeared to be involved in the process. It is possible, by the 1950s, there was nobody left who could fill Miller's shoes to make an adequate defense. Ether-theory was then being compared to "the search for perpetual-motion machines" (Swenson 1972, p.239), and such ridicule surely must have had a silencing effect upon the entire fields of physics and astronomy. Swenson also suggests that, during his later years, Miller was largely ignored and isolated. This appears to be correct, as according to an interview with Shankland made in 1981, shortly before Miller died he gave all of his interferometer data sheets — hundreds of pages of measurements — to his one-time student Shankland, with the somewhat bitter statement that he should "either analyze the data, or burn it" (Kimball 1981, p.2). In that

same interview, Shankland also blamed Miller for having blocked the awarding of a Nobel Prize to Einstein for his relativity theory — clearly, Miller's work was a major obstacle to the Einstein theory of relativity, and for that reason may have given Einstein and his followers sleepless nights.

The title of the Shankland paper, and its overall representation suggests the authors had made a serious review of *"the* interferometer observations" of Miller, to include some kind of comprehensive and inclusive evaluation — but this was not the case. There were two basic approaches to the Shankland team's analysis: 1) a search for random errors or statistical fluctuations in Miller's data, and 2) a review of selected data sets which they claimed demonstrated significant thermal artifacts in the data. We can review these claims.

Shankland Team's Evaluation for Random-Statistical variations

The Shankland paper did present a statistical analysis of a portion of Miller's published 1925-1926 Mt. Wilson data, concluding that his observations "...*cannot be attributed entirely to random effects, but that systematic effects are present to an appreciable degree*" and that "*the periodic effects observed by Miller cannot be accounted for entirely by random statistical fluctuations in the basic data*". (p.170) Also, the Shankland team admitted they "...*did not embark on a statistically sound recomputation of the cosmic solution, but rather [looked for]...local disturbances such as may be caused by mechanical effects or by nonuniform temperature distributions in the observational hut.*" (p.172) In short, they admitted the harmonic patterns in Miller's data could not be due to any systematic measurement error, nor result from any mechanical flaws in the interferometer apparatus itself — while simultaneously admitting a disinterest in computation of any potentially validating ether-drift axis ("cosmic solution") from his data. These were important admissions, as the suggestion is, unless they could find some other fatal flaw in his data, Miller had really got it right, and measured a real Earth-entrained ether drift.

Of interest from the perspective of the politics of science, is the fact that *this statistical analysis was not undertaken by any of the four members of the Shankland team listed as authors of the paper!* The analysis was in fact undertaken by Case physics student Robert L. Stearns, for his Master's Thesis (Stearns 1952) — Stearns was given only a footnote credit in the Shankland paper.

Stearns, who performed the analysis, informs us about the large amount of data gathered by Miller. He mentions (Stearns 1952, p.15-17) the existence of "316 sets of data...by Miller in 1925-26" for the centrally-important Mt. Wilson experiments. Each data set was composed of 20 turns of the interferometer, with sixteen data points per turn (a total of 320 data points per data set). Miller noted his work at Mt. Wilson was undertaken at four different seasonal "epochs", each of which encompassed a period of around ten days, centered on the following dates: April 1st, August 1st, and September 15th, 1925 and February 8th 1926 (Miller 1926, 1933). It must be kept in mind, that these Mt. Wilson data from 1925 and 1926 provided the most conclusive and foundational observations for Miller's ether-drift calculations and conclusions, as presented most clearly in his 1933 paper. As detailed below, the Shankland team mentions these Mt. Wilson data, but in a manner which confuses them with his earlier and less significant efforts, including various control experiments conducted at Case School. The significance of this confusion of dates will be highlighted momentarily.

Shankland Team's Assertion of Temperature Artifacts

Regarding possible temperature artifacts in Miller's data, this objection was raised early on in the history of ether-drift interferometry, and specifically rebutted by Miller when he was still alive. A letter exchange between Miller and Georg Joos from a 1934 issue of *Physical Review* records part of this debate, and appears to be one of the few *published* criticisms on the temperature issue Miller ever received while still alive. Miller had this to say about the problem:

"When Morley and Miller designed their interferometer in 1904 they were fully cognizant of this...and it has never since been neglected. Elaborate tests have been made under natural conditions and especially with artificial heating, for the development of methods which would be free from this [thermal] effect". (Joos and Miller, 1934)

The Shankland critique never made any systematic evaluation of possible thermal artifacts using a larger set of Miller's data, as was done with the statistical evaluation. Instead, they appear to have "gone fishing" in Miller's data for something by which they could simply dismiss him. For example, Miller's own 1923 temperature-control experiments were brought into discussion, where radiant parabolic heaters were used to artificially create a general doubling of the size of interference fringes. Miller describes these experiments:

"Several electric heaters were used, of the type having a heated coil near the focus of a concave reflector. Inequalities in the temperature of the room caused a slow but steady drifting of the fringe system to one side, but caused no periodic displacements. Even when two of the heaters, placed at a distance of three feet from the interferometer as it rotated, were adjusted to throw the heat directly on the uncovered

steel frame, there was no periodic effect that was measurable. When the heaters were directed to the air in the light-path which had a covering of glass, a periodic effect could be obtained only when the glass was partly covered with opaque material in a very nonsymmetrical manner, as when one arm of the interferometer was completely protected by a covering of corrugated paper-board while the other arms were unprotected. These experiments proved that under the conditions of actual observation, the periodic displacements could not possibly be produced by temperature effects." (Miller 1933, p.220)

Perhaps without intending to do so, after examining Miller's laboratory notes for the Cleveland temperature control experiments, the Shankland team confirmed Miller on this point:

"In the experiments where the air in the optical paths was directly exposed to heat, large second harmonics (0.35 fringe for one heater, and about twice this value for two heaters) were always observed in the fringe displacements, and with the expected phase. Shifting the heaters to a different azimuth produced a corresponding change in the phase of the second harmonics. When the optical paths and mirror supports were thermally insulated, the second harmonics were greatly reduced to about 0.07 fringe." (Shankland 1955, p.174; emphasis added, J.D.)

This statement confirmed the wisdom of Miller's approach. The added insulation reduced the thermal effects from a nearby radiant heater to only 20% of the un-insulated readings. I have an ordinary commercially-available electric radiant parabolic heater at my home, and it gets so hot you cannot stand closer than 30 cm without burning yourself, or possibly catching your clothing on fire. If Miller had used a parabolic heater even half as strong as this, it would certainly have been a source of heat much stronger than anything present in his Mt. Wilson experiments, particularly at night, during foggy or overcast conditions, and when the entire interferometer house was covered over with a tent, with the apparatus and light-beam path covered with cork, glass and paper insulation. Consider a radiant heater at several hundred degrees C, creating a steep thermal gradient but only a 0.07 fringe shift in the insulated interferometer. How much *less* of an effect would be produced by a human body, or even from the inside of a solar-heated wall? Assuming an environmental thermal effect only one-tenth that seen with the parabolic heater (a wood composite wall radiating inside the structure at perhaps 50°C?), fringe shifts of *only 0.007* would have been produced, *well below observational detection.* Miller's data sheets, for example, recorded observations *"in units of a tenth of a fringe width"*, though readings down to hundredths of a fringe were possible with care. Overall accuracy of the ether-drift measurements also approached a hundredth of a fringe after mathematical averages of many readings were extracted.

The Shankland paper nevertheless used these control experiments as a weapon against Miller, claiming without evidence that heater-type effects *might* have occurred in his Mt. Wilson experiments, even where no such heater or remotely similar heat source was present. But why would the Shankland team shy from undertaking a more systematic evaluation for temperature artifacts? They could have, for example, evaluated only Miller's daytime interferometer experiments, and looked for a thermal effect from the solar-heated southerly wall of the structure during the various epochs — if they could have shown an effect present in daytime data which was not present at night, it would have devastated Miller's claim, and proved their case. However, this obvious analytic procedure was not done, or if it was done, not reported.

The Shankland paper also resurrected the temperature criticisms of Joos (1934), but without reference to Miller's rebuttal in the same published exchange. If the periodic effects observed by Miller were the product of temperature variations, as was claimed by Shankland and Joos, then why would that variation systematically point to the same set of azimuth coordinates along the celestial *sidereal clock*, but *not* to any single terrestrial coordinate linked to civil/solar time? Miller repeatedly asked this question of his critics, who had no answer for it. The Shankland team likewise evaded the question.

It is clear Miller had been deeply engaged on the problem of temperature effects, and worked hard to know exactly how they might be produced, and how to eliminate them. The Shankland paper, however, seized upon Miller's open acknowledgment fringe-shifts from air heating by powerful radiant heaters during control experiments, and a few other sentences written in his lab book, and tried to claim thermal anomalies were probably the source of whatever periodic effects were subsequently measured by Miller at Mt. Wilson, when no radiant heaters were used, and when the empirically-developed control procedures were put in place. Without some kind of independent experimental evidence to support such a claim of a thermal influence, their dismissal was illogical.

The Shankland paper also went through a series of arguments about the interferometer house, how the wall materials, roof angles, interferometer glass housing, etc., might result in a definable effect upon the air temperature in the light beam path, concluding only they could not rule out such an influence — that it "...*is not in quantitative contradiction with the physical conditions of the experiment*". (p.175) Given their ignoring the sidereal nature of the periodicities, this statement could hardly be taken seriously, and certainly did not constitute a rebuttal of Miller's data.

The Shankland paper finally attempted to correlate several selected daytime interferometer runs with temperature measurements made at the same time. They acknowledged difficulty in correlating low fringe-shift values with low temperature differentials, but found one set of high fringe-shift values correlated with slightly higher temperatures, even while noting another set where high values correlated with lower temperatures. Finally, they complain that "...*no temperature data are available to reveal thermal conditions at the roof, which may be responsible for the large fringe displacements at the times of highest altitudes of the Sun.*" (p.176) If this sounds confusing, a reading of the full original text provided little clarification.

Failing to show anything damning from daytime data sets, when temperature gradients inside the interferometer house might be expected to be at a maximum, they turned their focus to nighttime data sets. Once again, only a few of Miller's data sheets were selected out to prove their case. Data from two nights (30 Aug. 1927 and 23 Sept.1925) with stable air temperatures were reviewed — these nights showed very clear and systematic fringe variations (Fig.4, p.176), but because the azimuth of the fringes changed minimally over the approximate 5 hours of observation, the critics complained "it *would be extremely unlikely if the fringe shifts were due to any cosmic effect*" (p.177). Apparently, the Shankland team was so locked into the older "static ether" assumptions of the original Michelson-Morley experiment, they were unclear about what they should have seen in Miller's data. In 1927, at a *Conference on the Michelson-Morley Experiment* held at Mt. Wilson Observatory, where Michelson, Lorentz, Miller and others made presentations and engaged in open debate, Miller addressed this question: "*Observations were made for verifying these [static ether] predictions ...but it did not point successively to all points of the compass, that is, it did not point in directions 90° apart at intervals of six hours. Instead of this, the direction merely oscillated back and forth through an angle of about 60°...*" (Miller 1928, p.356-357) The reason for this is, Miller's detected axis of ether-drift is oriented reasonably close (within 60°) to both the Earth's axis of rotation and the axis of the plane of the ecliptic.

Another important fact which nearly escapes detection in the Shankland paper is that the 30 August data were made in Cleveland, while the 23 Sept. data were from Mt. Wilson, and *neither were a part of the published Mt. Wilson data Miller used for calculations of the ether-drift* — both dates are well outside of the 10-day epochal periods identified by Miller. Furthermore, not all of the interferometer data sheets for a given date — which presumably would have had similar weather and temperature conditions — were included by the Shankland team for critical review. They selected only those data sets which appeared to support their argument of a claimed thermal anomaly. For example, they selected "ten sets of observations, Nos. 31 to 40 inclusive, made in the hut on the Case campus between midnight and 5:00 AM on August 30, 1927" and "...runs 75 to 83 inclusive taken from 12:18 AM to 6:00 AM on September 23" (p.176-177). Other than making the *claim* these selected data gave them the *impression* of being the result of temperature errors, they had no other stated criterion for bringing them into discussion. This biased data-selection, or rather *data-exclusion* procedure forces one to ask: *What about data sets Nos.1 to 30, and runs 1 to 74?* Similar unexplained data selections or data exclusions occur throughout the Shankland paper, leaving one to wonder if the *unselected and excluded* data, which constituted the overwhelming majority of it, simply could not provide support for their criticisms. One can imagine the howl of protest which would have occurred if Miller had taken this approach, arbitrarily excluding data from his calculations which superficially suggested something other than a real ether-drift.

A third data set from 30 July 1925 was highlighted by the Shankland team as it contained one extremely large peak where Miller noted "Sun shines on interferometer". This data does appear to have been a part of Miller's published Mt. Wilson analysis. However, the Shankland team extracted only *"observations Nos. 21 to 28 inclusive, made between 1:43 AM and 6:04 AM on July 30, 1925."* Obviously, at around 6:00 AM the sun rose and caught Miller and his assistant off-guard. What about observations Nos. 1 to 27, or other early-morning data, where the sun *didn't* shine on the inter-

Case W. R. U. Archive

Robert S. Shankland, former student of Dayton Miller and Chairman of the Physics Department at Case Western Reserve University. Shankland's academic career soared after he organized a post-mortem on Miller's work, pronouncing it worthless, and after Einstein later granted him a series of widely-published interviews. Shankland subsequently became a bureaucrat within the emerging atomic energy infrastructure. Intimate with Einstein, in a 1981 interview Shankland claimed Miller's work on ether-drift had probably cost Einstein the Nobel Prize for relativity theory (Einstein did later get a Nobel Prize, but for his other theoretical work). Just before Miller's death in 1941, he entrusted his extensive data archive on ether-drift experiments performed since the early 1900s to Shankland, to include over 300 data sheets from his extensive Mt. Wilson experiments, plus many experimental notebooks. All of this material vanished under Shankland's care.

ferometer? These other data were not brought into discussion, except they did note that the runs prior to the sunshine incident demonstrated "...an extremely erratic behavior...we have no ready explanation for this apparent departure..." Here, the Shankland team basically confesses their grab-bag of "ready" explanations was empty, and the idea that those data were expressing a real ether-drift was simply too "impossible" for them to consider. The fact that Miller included the note about the Sunlight on this data sheet speaks to his honesty.

The Shankland team also identified data sets Nos. 56-58 from 8 July 1924, which was part of Miller's control experiments made in a basement location at Case physics laboratory — the temperatures were very stable, and the fringe oscillations were quite small, and they argued these data were a proof for thermal effects on the apparatus. However, it was this very problem of basement and dense surrounding materials which led Miller on the path to use the apparatus in locations not subject to significant ether-shielding or Earth entrainment. After 1921, Miller only used the Case School laboratory to undertake control experiments, and that is why those particular data were never published.

The Shankland paper concluded its temperature criticisms by discussing a few additional data sets: Nos. 113-118 from April 2nd, Nos. 88-93 from August 8th, 1925, and Nos. 84-91 from February 11th, 1926 (p.177). Here, the amplitudes and phases were claimed to have been "nearly alike", but insufficient detail was given to allow a review of the critic's claims, and it did appear they were once again incorrectly misinterpreting Miller's data along the lines of static ether assumptions.

As in almost all the cases given above, *none of these data were analyzed systematically*, nor were they presented in such a manner that the author's criticisms could be factually reviewed. I got the impression, they simply scanned through a pile of Miller's data sheets, and with a wave of the hand, picking and pointing to only selected parts, dismissed it all as the product of thermal artifacts. Miller's detailed control experiments were basically ignored, as was the fact that, for all these experiments, the interferometer was enclosed in a small house covered over with a tent, while apparatus was shielded with cork insulation, and the light-beam path covered with glass and paper panels — with a full rotation occurring in less than a minute, one is left to wonder how any observable thermal variations could develop within Miller's data, especially variations with a sidereal-cosmic component.

For the casual reader, who had not undertaken a careful review of Miller's original experiments, the Shankland paper might appear to make a reasoned argument. However, the Shankland paper basically obfuscated and concealed from the reader most of the central facts about what Miller actually did, and in any case was so unsystematic and biased in its approach, excluding from discussion perhaps 90% or more of Miller's extensive Mt. Wilson data, as to render its conclusions meaningless.

As a final note, I must regrettably inform the reader, that my own search of available archive materials for both Miller and Shankland at Case University failed to discover even a single one of the hundreds of missing data sheets or laboratory records from Miller's years of hard work. Perhaps, Shankland finally did burn them?

Conclusions

My review of this important but sad chapter in the history of science left me both astonished and frustrated. Miller's work on ether drift was clearly undertaken with more precision, care and diligence than any other researcher who took up the question, including Michelson, and yet, his work has basically been written out of the history of science. When alive, Miller responded concisely to his critics, and demonstrated the ether-drift phenomenon with increasing precision over the years. He constantly pointed out to his critics, the specific reasons why he was getting larger positive results, while others got only minimal results. Michelson and a few others of the period took Miller's work seriously, but Einstein and his followers appeared to view Miller only as a threat, something to be "explained away" as expeditiously as possible. Einstein in fact was catapulted into the public eye following the end of World War II. Nuclear physics was then viewed as heroic, and Einstein fast became a cultural icon whose work could not be criticized. Into this situation came the Shankland team, with the apparent mission to nail the lid down on Miller's coffin. In this effort, they nearly succeeded.

The Shankland conclusions against Miller were clearly negative, but the one systematic statistical analysis of his Mt. Wilson data merely confirmed what Miller said all along, that there was a clear and systematic periodic effect in the interferometer data. The Shankland paper also confirmed Miller's contention that this periodic effect was *not the product of random errors or mechanical effects*. The Shankland team subsequently searched for temperature artifacts in Miller's data, but failed to undertake any systematic analysis of his centrally-important Mt. Wilson data in this regard. Instead, they made a biased selection of a few published and unpublished data sets obtained from different periods in Miller's research, from different experimental locations, including from his control experiments at Case School.

Miller's most conclusive 1925-26 Mt. Wilson experiments encompassed a total of 6,402 turns of the interferometer, recorded on over 300 individual data sheets. That was the data the Shankland team should have been focused upon and evaluated systematically. Instead, only a few of Miller's data sheets from these most centrally-important experiments were selected — certainly less than 10% of the data available to them was brought into discussion — and then only after being firstly dissected to select those data which could most easily be misconstrued as "evidence" for presumed temperature anomalies. For certain, some of the data held up for public critique came from Miller's control experiments at Case, or possibly from trial runs when technical "bugs" were being evaluated and eliminated. Miller is no longer alive to inform us about his data, but the Shankland team willy-nilly lumped together both published and unpublished data, without comment.

Even though they were content to pick and choose data as they wished, they could not come up with a coherent and solid critique by which Miller's work could be conclusively dismissed — some of the data they selected merely confirmed Miller, though the Shankland group seemed ignorant of the basic ether-drift astronomy by which such an interpretation could be made. When alive, Miller openly addressed and corrected for thermal effects upon the apparatus, and yet the periodic elements of his measurements persisted — the Shankland paper ignored Miller on this important point.

The Shankland group undertook no new experiments of their own, neither on the question of ether-drift, nor on the subject of thermal perturbations of light-beam interferometry — they made essentially an "armchair analysis" of Miller's data. Only *some* of Miller's original data was carefully selected to make a rather unbelievable claim that small natural ambient temperature gradients in Miller's Mt. Wilson observation hut *might* produce fringe shifts in the insulated interferometer similar to what Miller himself previously observed in his control experiments using strong radiant heaters. The Shankland paper argued there *must have been* "thermal effects" in Miller's Mt. Wilson measurements, but provides no direct evidence of this.

At no time did the Shankland group present evidence that temperature was a factor in creating the periodic sidereal fringe shifts observed by Miller in his published data, even though this was their stated conclusion. In fact, they presented evidence from Miller's own lab notebooks which implied thermal gradients in the Mt. Wilson interferometer house would have been *below the observational limits* of the insulated apparatus.

The larger issue of periodic or harmonic effects in the data, expressed in nearly identical cosmic sidereal coordinates at different seasons and at all hours of the day, was never addressed or evaluated by the Shankland group. Neither was any attempt made to show *exactly how* an external temperature phenomenon could affect the interferometer readings to yield such a systematic sidereal effect. This issue was almost totally avoided by the Shankland team.

A reading of Miller's 1933 paper shows the picayune and biased nature of the Shankland team procedure, as the systematic sidereal periodicities observed by Miller expressed themselves nearly uniformly across the board, though at differing magnitudes. From 1906 to 1926, Miller undertook over 200,000 separate readings, over 12,000 turns of the interferometer demonstrating harmonic periodicities constantly pointing to the same general axis of ether-drift in the cosmos — a factor which was completely independent of the time of day, or season of year in which the experiments were undertaken. At best, the critics provided only an *ad-hoc argument*, a claim or suggestion without substance, that some small part of Miller's data *might* contain an undefined temperature effect.

From all the above, it appears the Shankland group, with some degree of consultation with Einstein, decided that "Miller must be wrong" and then set about to see what they could find in his archive that would support that *a-priori* conclusion — which is not a scientific method.

As I have discussed previously, Miller found the ether-drift effect to be stronger at higher altitudes and also to be small when the experiment was undertaken in heavy stone buildings or when the interferometer light-path was encased in wood or metal shielding. In my studies over the last 30 years, I've found many examples from the fields of biology, meteorology and physics that independently support the assertion of a subtle energetic force with similar altitude-dependent and metal-reflective properties. (DeMeo 1979, 1989, 1991, 1996) Likewise, there are many new findings in astrophysics, where anisotropy of cosmological factors have been discovered which are congruent with Miller's identified axis of ether-drifting. (Miller 1933 p.241, Allais 1997) Whereas most of these phenomena are today ignored, or interpreted as the consequence of the "big bang" theory, or of Einstein's relativity theory, they may also find an explanation rooted in dynamic drifting within an energetically-rich cosmological medium.

To close, I ask the reader to imagine that Michelson-Morley's 1887 experiment, which ran over only 6 hours on four days, had resulted in a claim that "the ether has been detected", and that Dayton Miller had undertaken his years of work with 200,000 observations showing "the ether cannot be detected". It does not take much consideration to conclude that — in such a fictional case — Miller would today be cited in every physics textbook as having "proved the ether did not exist", and nobody would refer to Michelson-Morley. The fact that the present-day situation is totally opposite of my example is a testament to the intensely political nature of modern science, and how major theories often develop into *belief-systems*, which demand the automatic suppression of any new finding which might undermine the faith and "popular wisdom" of politically-dominant groups of academics. And that "wisdom" today is: *Space is empty and immobile, and the universe is dead.* I submit, these are unproven, and even *disproven* assertions, challenged in large measure by Dayton Miller's exceptional work on the ether drift.

References, Organized Chronologically:

* 1887: Albert A. Michelson, Edward W.. Morley, "On the Relative Motion of the Earth and the Luminiferous Ether", *American Journal of Science*, Third Series, Vol.XXXIV (203), Nov. 1887.

* 1905: E.W. Morley, Dayton Miller, "Report of an Experiment to Detect the FitzGerald-Lorentz Effect", *Proceedings, Am. Acad. Arts & Sciences*, 41:321-328, August 1905.

* 1907: E.W. Morley, Dayton Miller, "Final Report on Ether-Drift Experiments", *Science*, 25:525, 5 April 1907.

* 1913: M. G. Sagnac, "L'Ether lumineux Demonstre par l'effet du vent relatif d'aether dan interferometre en rotation uniforme", *Comptes Rendus,* 157:710, 1913, and "Sur la preuve de la realite de l'ether lumineux par l'experience de l'interferographe tournant," *Comptes Rendus*, 157:1410-1413, 22 Dec. 1913; Also see John Chappell, "Georges Sagnac and the Discovery of the Ether", *Arch. Internat. d'Histoire des Sciences*, 18:175-190, 1965.

* 1922: Dayton Miller, "The Ether-Drift Experiments at Mount Wilson Solar Observatory", *Physical Review*, 19:407-408, April 1922.

* 1925: Dayton Miller, "Ether-Drift Experiments at Mount Wilson", *Proceedings, Nat. Acad. Sciences*, 11:306-314, June 1925.

* 1925: Michelson, A.A., H. Gale & F. Pearson: "The Effect of the Earth's Rotation on the Velocity of Light" (Parts I and II), *Astrophysical Journal*, 61:137-145, April 1925. Also see: "Letters to the Editor: The Effect of the Earth's Rotation on the Velocity of Light", *Nature*, 115:566, 18 April 1925.

* 1926: Dayton Miller, "Significance of the Ether-Drift Experiments of 1925 at Mount Wilson", *Science*, 63:433-443, 30 April 1926.

* 1927: Michelson, A.A.: *Studies in Optics*, U. Chicago Press, Chicago, 1927.

* 1928: Dayton Miller, untitled lecture in "Conference on the Michelson-Morley Experiment", *Astrophysical Journal*, LXVIII:341-402, Dec. 1928; also in *Contributions From the Mount Wilson Observatory*, No.373, Carnegie Institution of Washington.

* 1929: Michelson, A.A., Pease, F.G. & Pearson, F.: "Repetition of the Michelson-Morley Experiment", *Nature*, 123:88, 19 Jan. 1929; also in *J. Optical Society of America*, 18:181, 1929.

* 1930: Dayton Miller, "Ether Drift Experiments in 1929 and Other Evidences of Solar Motion", *J. Royal Ast. Soc. Canada*, 24:82-84, 1930.

* 1932: R. J. Kennedy and E.M. Thorndike, "Experimental Establishment of the Relativity of Time", *Phys. Rev.* 42 400-418, 1932.

* 1933: Dayton Miller, "The Ether-Drift Experiment and the Determination of the Absolute Motion of the Earth", *Reviews of Modern Physics*, Vol.5(2), p.203-242, July 1933.

* 1933: David Dietz, "Case's Miller Seen Hero of 'Revolution'. New Revelations on Speed of Light Hint Change in Einstein Theory", *Cleveland Press*, 30 Dec. 1933.

* 1934: Georg Joos, Dayton Miller, "Letters to the Editor", *Physical Review*, Vol.45, p.114, 15 Jan. 1934.

* 1934: Dayton Miller, "The Ether-Drift Experiment and the Determination of the Absolute Motion of the Earth", *Nature,* Vol.133, p.16-27, 3 Feb. 1934.

* 1935: Albert Michelson, F.G. Pease, F. Pearson: "Measurement of the Velocity of Light in a Partial Vacuum", *Astrophysical J.,* 82:26-61, 1935.

* 1951: Wilhelm Reich: *Cosmic Superimposition,* Orgone Institute Press, Rangeley, Maine. Republished as *Ether, God and Devil / Cosmic Superimposition,* Farrar, Straus & Giroux, NY 1973.

* 1952: Robert L. Stearns, *A Statistical Analysis of Interferometer Data*, Thesis, Case Institute of Technology, Physics Dept. 1952.

* 1955: R.S. Shankland, S.W. McCuskey, F.C. Leone and G. Kuerti, "New Analysis of the Interferometer Observations of Dayton C. Miller", *Reviews of Modern Physics*, 27(2):167-178, April 1955.

* 1963: Robert Shankland: "Conversations with Albert Einstein", *Am. J. Physics*, 31:47-57, Jan. 1963.

* 1964: Robert Shankland: "The Michelson Morley Experiment", *Am. J. Physics*, 32:16-35, 1964; "The Michelson-Morley Experiment", *Scientific American*, 211:107-114, 1964.

* 1971: Ronald W. Clark: *Einstein: The Life and Times,* World Publishing Co., NY 1971.

* 1972: Loyd Swenson, *The Ethereal Aether: A History of the Michelson-Morley-Miller Aether-Drift Experiments*, U. Texas Press, Austin, 1972.

* 1973a: Robert Shankland: "Michelson's Role in the Development of Relativity", Applied Optics, 12(10):2280-2287, October 1973.

* 1973b: Robert Shankland: "Conversations with Albert Einstein. II", *Am. J. Physics*, 41:895-901, July 1973.

* 1979: James DeMeo, "Evidence for the Existence of an Interconnecting Principle...", Appendix to *Preliminary Analysis of Changes in Kansas Weather Coincidental to Experimental Operations with a Reich Cloudbuster,* Thesis, University of Kansas, Lawrence, Geography-Meteorology Dept., 1979.

* 1981: Margaret Kimball "An Interview with Dr. Robert S. Shankland, Subject: Dayton Miller", Transcript of audio tape, 15 Dec. 1981, original with hand-corrections, from R.S. Shankland Archive, University Archives, Case Western Reserve Univ., Cleveland, Ohio.

* 1989: James DeMeo, Chapter on "Independent Discovery of An Unusual Energy" in *The Orgone Accumulator Handbook,* Natural Energy, Ashland, 1989.

* 1991: James DeMeo, "The Orgone Energy Continuum: Some Old and New Evidence", *Pulse of the Planet*, 1(2):3-8, 1989; German translation "Alte und neue Beweise fur das Orgon Energie Kontinuum", *Lebensenergie*, 2:13-20, 1991.

* 1996: James DeMeo, "Independent Discovery of a Dynamic Bio-Cosmic Energy in Space and Atmosphere", & "Dayton Miller's Discovery of the Dynamic Ether Drift", Proceedings, SW & Rocky Mountain Division, *American Association for the Advancement of Science,* 72nd Annual Meeting, Northern Arizona Univ., Flagstaff, Arizona, 2-6 June 1996. *Program and Abstracts, pp.41-42, 1996.*

* 1997: Maurice Allais, *L'Anisotropie de L'Espace:La nécessaire révision de certains postulats des théories contemporaines,* Clément Juglar, Paris, 1997.

* 1998: Maurice Allais: "Experiments of Dayton C. Miller (1925-1926) and the Theory of Relativity", *21st. Century Science and Technology,* Spring 1998, p.26-34.

* 1999: Maurice Allais: "Des régularités très significatives dans les observations interférométriques de Dayton C. Miller 1925-1926", *Comptes Rendus L'Académie Sciences,* Paris, t.327, Série IIb,p.1405-1410.

* 1999: Maurice Allais: "Nouvelles régularités très significatives dans les observations interférométriques de Dayton C. Miller 1925-1926", *Comptes Rendus L'Académie Sciences,* Paris, t.327, Série IIb, p.1411-1419.

* 2000: Maurice Allais: "L'origine des régularités constatées dans les observations interférométriques de Dayton C. Miller 1925-1926: variations de température ou anisotropie de l'espace", *Comptes Rendus L'Académie Sciences,* Paris, t.1, Série IV, p.1205-1210.

* 2000: James DeMeo: "Critical Review of the Shankland, et al, Analysis of Dayton Miller's Ether-Drift Experiments", Presented to the *Natural Philosophy Alliance,* Berkeley, Caif. May 2000.

* 2002: James DeMeo: "Reconciling Miller's Ether-Drift with Reich's Dynamic Orgone", *Pulse of the Planet #5,* in *Heretic's Notebook: Protocells, Ether-Drift and Cosmic Life Energy,* Natural Energy Works, Ashland, Oregon.

Note about publication of this article:

In June of 2000, I contacted the editors of *Reviews of Modern Physics* — the same journal that published the original Miller 1933 paper and the Shankland, et al. 1955 paper — informing them I wanted to submit my paper for publication consideration, giving them the title and an abstract. The editor replied quite negatively, but with a Freudian slip. He showed no interest in the findings whatsoever, claiming his journal did not go into such "historical materials", but he concluded by saying "Thus, I *do* think (sic) it would be suitable for our review format." Upon my follow-up inquiry, he corrected himself, saying he meant to say "I *do not* think it would be suitable." The bottom line is, the editors of *Reviews of Modern Physics* refused to even look at the paper. The article was subsequently accepted for several non-mainstream publications which are not threatened by the idea of an ether or ether-drift.

The Experiments of Dayton C. Miller (1925-1926) and the Theory of Relativity*
by Maurice Allais**

Einstein's theories of special and general relativity rest on the allegedly null results of Michelson's interferometer experiment. Here, a French physicist and Nobel Laureate in economics, demonstrates that Michelson's results were not null, and that the interferometer experiments of the American scientist Dayton Miller produced positive results, thereby invalidating the foundation of the Theory of Relativity.

Introduction

The interferometric observations of Dayton C. Miller in 1925-1926 reveal a very real internal coherence, independent of any spurious effect. They demonstrate that the velocity of light is not the same in all directions, and that it is possible to determine the motion of the Earth in its orbit from purely terrestrial experiments. Accordingly, Miller's experiments invalidate the very foundation of the Theory of Relativity.

1. The Genesis of the Theory of Relativity

In 1900, it was considered, as "well-established," that all attempts to detect, by purely terrestrial experiments, the motion of translation of the Earth had failed. To explain this negative outcome, Lorentz presented *his hypotheses of the contraction of bodies according to their velocities and the local time,* and, following Lorentz, Einstein developed his Special Theory of Relativity (1905), and subsequently, his General Theory of Relativity (1916). From the formulation of the Special Theory of Relativity stem both the impossibility of detecting the Earth's motion in its orbit, and the invariance of the velocity of light in all directions. Today, it is everywhere admitted without reservation, *as postulates,* that the velocity of light is independent of its direction, and that no *purely terrestrial* experiment can detect the velocity of translation of the Earth, or even simply its position in its orbit.

* Reprinted from *21st Century Science and Technology* (www.21stcenturysciencetech.com), Spring 1998, p.26-34, with kind permission of the author and editors.
** Physicist and Nobel Laureate in economics (1988), living in France. Contact by email through H. Aujard <haujard@aol.com >

2. The Reputedly 'Negative' Outcome of Michelson's Experiment and Miller's Experiments

The principle of Miller's experiments is the same as for Michelson's experiments. According to this principle, the interferometer makes it possible to measure *the difference of the velocity of the light for two perpendicular directions.* In his 1933 paper, Miller presented his observations in the form of eight figures, *four for the azimuths and four for the velocities, in sidereal time, for four periods of continued observations during ten days* (Miller 1933, p. 229). *Any appreciation of the scope of Miller's observations boils down to three utterly fundamental questions:*

First Question: Do Miller's observations result from mere disturbances (of temperature, for example), or do they *present a very real internal coherence?*

Second Question: Do they permit us to detect variations in the velocity of light according to its direction?

Third Question: Is it possible to deduce the Earth's position in its orbit from these observations?

3. A Very Remarkable Coherence Underlying Miller's Observations Excludes Spurious Effects

A very marked coherence appears when one considers the variations in the azimuths and velocities, not in civil time, *but in sidereal time.* Figure 1 represents the fittings, with sinusoids *of a period of 24 hours,* of the curves representing velocities and azimuths *in sidereal time. They are on the whole very remarkable.*

The sidereal time θ^* for which the velocity is minimal, and the sidereal time θ^{**} for which the azimuth A is equal to its mean value, and for which $dA/dt < 0$, are *very similar* for the four considered periods (Table 1).

The top pairs of Figure 2 represent the hodographs of velocities for the four periods on the basis of the hourly values of velocities and azimuths in sidereal time. (A hodograph is the curve traced out in the course of time by the tip of a vector representing some physical quantity.) On each graph the $\bar{A}$ mean value is represented.

It is remarkable that on the whole the figures representing the hodographs are approximately perpendicular to the directions of the $\bar{A}$ mean azimuths. The bottom pairs of Figure 2 represent the hodographs deduced from the sinusoidal fittings of the velocities and azimuths. For the four periods, the *calculated hodo-*

Table 1
Observations of Miller: Sinusoidal Fittings with a 24-hour Period

Velocities (corr. coef.)

	R	$1-R^2$
February 8	0.361	0.869
April 1	0.981	0.0377
August 1	0.882	0.223
September 15	0.854	0.271

Azimuths (corr.coef.)

	R	$1-R^2$
February 8	0.856	0.267
April 1	0.939	0.118
August 1	0.970	0.0593
September 15	0.927	0.141

Estimations of θ^* and θ^{**} (in sidereal time)

	θ^*	θ^{**}	$\theta^{**}-\theta^*$
February 8	17.65	18.56	0.91
April 1	14.55	15.48	0.93
August 1	16.50	15.83	−0.67
September 15	17.59	17.78	0.29

R = correlation coefficient
θ^* = sidereal time of the velocity maximum
θ^{**} = sidereal time of the equality $A=\bar{A}$ with $dA/dt<0$

Sources: Calculations of Figure 1. Correlations were calculated by the author in February 1996.

Table 2
Fundamental Figures of Miller: Graphical Estimations of Velocities and Azimuths

Velocities (in km/sec)

	V_M	V_m
February 8	10	7.3
April 1	10	7.8
August 1	11.6	6.5
September 15	9.8	4.2

Azimuths (in degrees)

	A_M	A_m	$\bar{A}$	A_M^*
February 8	15	−40	−12.5	27.5
April 1	60	20	40	20
August 1	45	−20	12.5	32.5
September 15	90	20	55	35

V_M and V_m : maximum and minimum values of velocities
A_M and A_m : maximum and minimum values of azimuths

$$\bar{A} = (A_M + A_m)/2 \qquad A_M^* = (A_M - A_m)/2 \qquad A^* = A - \bar{A}$$

Source: These estimations of V_M, V_m, A_M, and A_m were deduced graphically from photographic enlargements of Miller's figures (Miller 1933, p.229), independently of any hypothesis. These estimations were made in June 1995, and have been used for all the calculations of Table 3.

---

graphs are almost exactly *perpendicular* to the mean $\bar{A}$ directions of the azimuths and *symmetrical relatively to those directions*. Indeed that is an *even more remarkable circumstance*. Finally, the figures change gradually from one period to another. They attain their maximum dimensions around Sept. 21, which corresponds to the autumn equinox, and their minimum dimensions around March 21, corresponding to the spring equinox. *They are therefore dependent on the Earth's position in its orbit.*

All these properties, which indisputably correspond to a very marked coherence underlying Miller's observations, allow us to give an unquestionably affirmative answer to the first two fundamental questions of section (2) above. It is therefore *absolutely wrong* to conclude that Michelson's experiment, as taken up by Miller, gives a negative outcome.

4. A Very Significant Correlation of Miller's Observations with the Earth's Position in Its Orbit

The most significant parameters characterizing Miller's eight fundamental figures are the maximum and minimum velocities V_M, and V_m', the $\bar{A}$ mean values of the A azimuths, and the amplitudes A_M^*, of their variations around their mean values.

Table 2 gives the direct estimations I made graphically of these parameters through the photographic enlargement of Miller's eight fundamental figures (original observations and running averages of Miller's figures), and that were arrived at *quite independently* of any hypothesis or any theoretical interpretation whatsoever.

A thorough harmonic analysis of these parameters shows that *all have a marked semi-annual or annual periodical structure. The maximum and minimum values of the corresponding sinusoidal fittings all occur around the March 21 equinox.* For lack of space, I must limit myself to commenting on the fittings of Table 3 of the observed data with sinusoids for a period of six or twelve months, *all having their maximum on March 21.* (Allais 1997, p.469-492)

Although each of the two groups of fittings corresponding to six- or twelve-month periods relates to *only one reference sinusoid with a maximum on March 21,* all the correlation coefficients are relatively high. They are all the more significant as the considered parameters do not correspond to isolated observations *but*

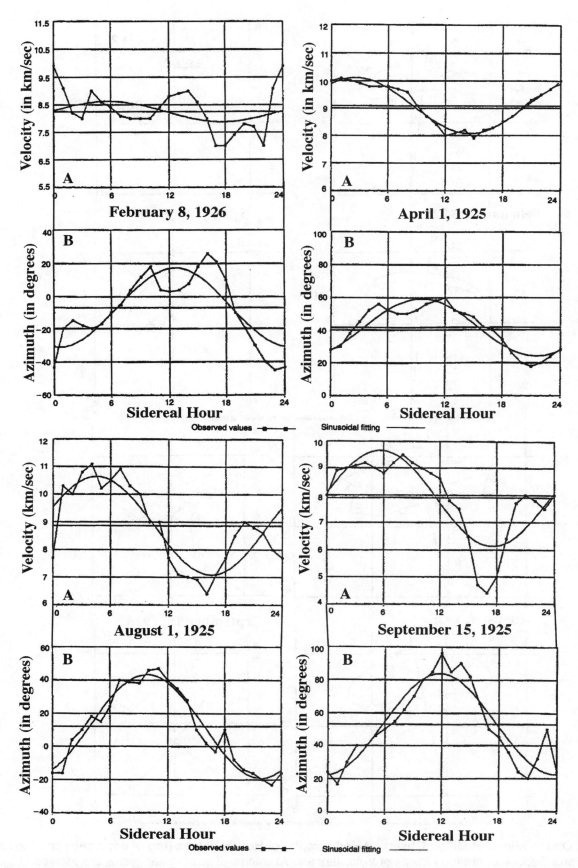

Figure 1. Hourly Observations of Miller: Matched Pairs of Daily Velocity (A) and Azimuth (B) Curves, in Sidereal Time, for four measurement epochs of ~10 days centered on the given dates.

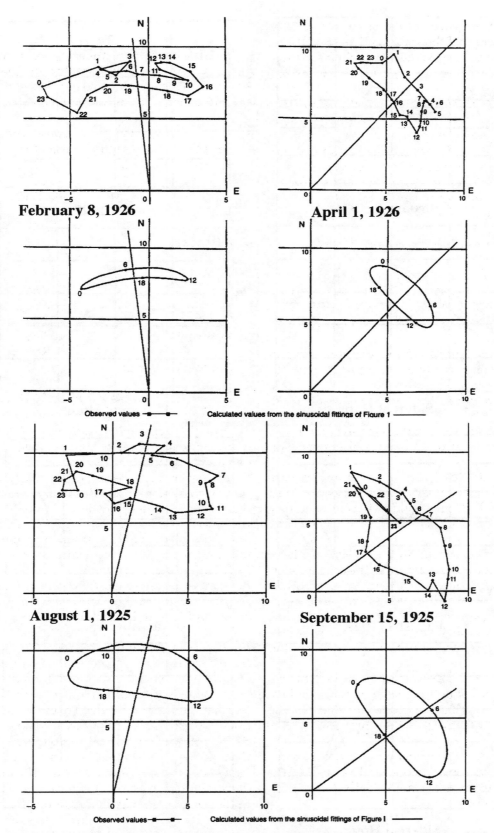

Figure 2. Observations of Miller: Observed Hodographs of Hourly Values (top of each pair) and Calculated Hodographs Deduced from the Fittings of Velocities and Azimuths. The irregular circles are marked in sidereal hours, while the intersecting vector line points to the average azimuth $\overline{A}$ of ether-drift for that given seasonal epoch. Source: Figure 1 data.

to the averages of very numerous observations. The statistical significance of the whole of these results, for semi-annual or annual periods corresponding to fittings *to the same functions, is very high,* and amounts to a quasi-certainty.

Thus it may be considered as perfectly established that the observations corresponding to the four series of experiments have a semi-annual or annual periodicity centered on March 21, the date of the spring equinox, and that it is possible through purely terrestrial experiments, to determine the Earth's position in its orbit.

An affirmative answer must therefore be given, *in all certainty,* to the *third question* of section (2) above.

5. Interpretation of Miller's observations

The above analysis leads to a fourfold conclusion:

* First, there is a *considerable and absolutely indisputable coherence* between Miller's interferometric observations, and it *corresponds to a very real phenomenon.*

* Second, *it is quite impossible* to attribute this very marked coherence to fortuitous causes or to spurious effects (of temperature, for example).

* Third, *the velocity of the light is not invariant in all directions.*

* Fourth, all Miller's observations display *a very marked correlation* with the Earth's position in its orbit.

These conclusions are *independent* of any hypothesis and of any theoretical analysis whatsoever. Most of the results, on which these conclusions are founded, particularly the most significant ones, *were not perceived by Miller.*

On the basis of his own analysis, Miller considered it possible to provide an estimation of the cosmic velocity of the Earth in relation to its orbital velocity (Miller 1933, pp. 230-237). *However, Miller's analysis only considers the $A - \bar{A}$ differences, and does not provide any explanation for the mean deviations $\bar{A}$ of the azimuths and their variations from one period to another* (Miller 1933, pp. 234-235).

Consequently, the interpretation given by Miller to his observations cannot be considered as valid. In fact, it is possible to show that the observed velocities and azimuths can be explained by the conjunction of two effects:

* *an optical anisotropy of space in the direction* $\bar{A}$;

* *an effect proportional* to the total velocity of the Earth (orbital velocity + cosmic velocity toward the Hercules constellation).

6. Significance and Scope of Miller's Observations

The very basis of the Special and General Relativity Theory rests on a triple postulate: the reputedly "negative" result of Michelson's experiment; the invariance of

---

Table 3
Observations of Miller: Semi-Annual or Annual Dominant Periodicities
Fittings to a sinusoid of a period of 6 or 12 months with its Maximum on March 21st.

Series	Period in months	Correlation coef. (R)	$1-R^2$
V_M	6	−0.772	0.404
$(V_M + V_m)/2$	6	−0.607	0.632
$\bar{A}$	6	+0.834	0.306
$\bar{A} + A_M^*$	6	+0.744	0.447
$\bar{A} - A_M^*$	6	+0.880	0.225
Averages:		+0.767	0.403
V_m	12	+0.880	0.225
$V_M - V_m$	12	−0.9994	0.0012
V_m / V_M	12	+0.980	0.041
A_M^*	12	−0.924	0.145
Averages:		+0.946	0.103
Overall Averages:		+0.847	0.269

Source: Est. of Table 2 & Allais 1997, p.469-492.

---

the speed of light in all directions; and the impossibility of detecting the absolute motion of the Earth, through any purely terrestrial experiment.*

However, *with regard to the analysis above,* it is certain that *it is impossible* to maintain that interferometric experiments provide a *"negative"* outcome, that the velocity of the light is *invariant in all directions,* and that any purely terrestrial experiment *cannot determine* the motion of translation of the Earth.

Consequently, the Special and General Theory of Relativity, resting on postulates invalidated by the observation data, cannot be considered as scientifically valid. As Einstein himself wrote in 1925 in a review in *Science*: *"If Dr. Miller's observations were confirmed, the Theory of Relativity would be at fault. Experience is the ultimate judge."* The *positive* outcome of Miller's experiments means that *there is no distinction to be made between the rotation of the Earth and its translation* as maintained by the Theory of Relativity. *Both* can be detected through purely terrestrial experiments.

Rejection of the Special and General Theory of Relativity as being incompatible with observational data *cannot in any way mean that all Einstein's contributions should be rejected.* It means only that all theoretical developments based on data invalidated by experimental data should be discarded as such. Those contributions of Einstein *that appear to have been confirmed by experience* should naturally be preserved, *but, quite obviously, they must be given a theoretical justification other than that of the Theory of Relativity.*

A theory is only worth what its premises are worth.

If the premises are wrong, the theory has no real scientific value. Indeed, the only scientific criterion of the scientific validity of a theory is its confrontation with experimental data.

Postscript:

The materials in this article are a condensation of a more in-depth presentation by Prof. Allais on the subject of Dayton Miller's findings, and the larger subject of gravitation, as contained in his 1997 book *L'Anisotropie de l'Espace*. In 1999 and 2000, Prof. Allais published new materials with the *French Academy of Sciences* (in *Comptes Rendus de L'Académie des Sciences*). While these newer materials have not yet been fully translated, we can report that, as with the case of the new hodographs presented in the above article, Prof. Allais has found even more hidden structure and regularities within Miller's original data. He states:

"These new regularities, which are truly quite extraordinary, provide total confirmation... It is absolutely impossible to attribute these new regularities to any effects of temperature or tortuitous causes." (Allais, 1999b)

" *1. Miller's interferometric estimates of light velocity are entirely valid.*

2. Shankland et al's conclusions on the temperature effects are based on shaky hypotheses and reasonings. They are totally unfounded.

3. ...the averages of the four series of observations present in sidereal time regularities which do not exist in civil time. As a result these regularities have a cosmic origin independent of any temperature effect.

4. The interferometric observations later than Miller's have been limited to a given time in order to test specific hypotheses, whereas Miller's experiments are based on continuous day and night observations during four periods of six to eight days during a year, in order to determine the exact nature of the diurnal and seasonal variations of velocities and azimuths. The interferometric observations earlier than Miller's, the observations of Michelson and Morley and those of Morley and Miller, have displayed velocities of 8 to 9 km/sec which entirely confirm Miller's observations of 1925-1926. At the time these velocities have been [wrongly] attributed to fortuitous causes.

5. The highly significant regularities displayed by Miller's observations do correspond to a very real phenomenon which cannot by any means be attributed to temperature effects. Consequently, the light velocity is not invariant to its direction over time. As a result Einstein's special theory of relativity is based on a principle, the invariance of light velocity, which is contradicted by observational data". (Allais 2000)

More information about the works of Maurice Allais, including full copies of the French Academy papers mentioned here, can be found at his internet web site:

http://allais.maurice.free.fr/English/index.htm

We hope to present more information on this subject, and on Prof. Allais' research findings, in future editions of *Pulse of the Planet*.

General References:

Maurice Allais (1959): "Should the Laws of Gravitation be Reconsidered?" *Aerospace Engineering*, Sept., No. 9, pp. 46-5L Oct., No. 10, pp. 51-59 Nov., No. 11, p. 55.

— (1997): *L'Anisotropie de L'Espace: La Necessaire Revision de Certains Postulats des Theories Contemporaines*, Clement Juglar, Paris.

— (1999a): "Des régularités très significatives dans les observations interférométriques de Dayton C. Miller 1925-1926", *Comptes Rendus de L'Académie des Sciences,* Paris, t.327, Sèrie II b, p.1405-1410.

— (1999b): "Nouvelles régularités très significatives dans les observations interférométriques de Dayton C. Miller 1925-1926", *Comptes Rendus de L'Académie des Sciences,* Paris, t.327, Sèrie II b, p.1411-1419.

— (2000): "L'origine des régularités constatées dans les observations interférométriques de Dayton C. Miller 1925-1926: variations de température ou anisotropie de l'espace", *Comptes Rendus de L'Académie des Sciences,* Paris, t.1, Sèrie IV, p.1205-1210.

Conference on the Michelson-Morley Experiment (1927): *Astrophysical Journal*, Vol. 68, (Dec.), pp. 341-402.

James DeMeo (2001): "Dayton Miller's Ether Drift Experiments: A Fresh Look", *Infinite Energy*, Vol 38, p.72-82; also in *Pulse of the Planet* #5, p.114-130, 2002.

Albert Einstein (1904): "Electromagnetic Phenomena in a System Moving with Any Velocity Smaller Than That of Light", in *Koninkijke Akademie van Wetenschappen te Amsterdam*, Proceedings of the Selection of Sciences, Vol.VI, p.809.

— (1905): "Zur Elektrodynamik bewegter Körper." *Annalen der Physik*, Vol. 17, p. 891.

— (1916): "Die Grundlage der Allgemeinen Relativitätstheorie", *Annalen der Physik*, Vol.49, p.765.

A. Michelson (1881): "The Relative Motion of the Earth and the Luminiferous Aether", *American Journal of Science*, Third Series, Vol.22, Art.XXI, pp.120-129.

A. Michelson and H. Gale (1925): "The Effect of the Earth's Rotation on the Velocity of Light", *Astrophysical Journal.* April, pp.137-145.

A. Michelson and E. Morley (1887): "On the Relative Motion of the Earth and the Luminiferous Aether", *American Journal of Science,* Third Series, Vol.24, No.203, Art.XXXVI, pp.333-345.

Dayton C. Miller (1925): "The Ether-Drift Experiments at Mount Wilson" *Proceedings of the Nat. Academy of Sciences*", Vol.2, April, pp.306-314.

— (1926): "Significance of the Ether-Drift Experiments of 1925 at Mount Wilson", *Science,* Vol.63, No.1635, April, pp.433-443.

— (1933): "The Ether-Drift Experiment and the Determination of the Absolute Motion of the Earth," *Reviews of Modern Physics*, 5(3):203-242, July.

Reconciling Miller's Ether-Drift With Reich's Dynamic Orgone

by James DeMeo, Ph.D.

Dayton Miller's extensive research on the subject of ether-drift and light-beam interferometry led him, by 1933, to publish the following conclusions:[1]

A) The ether of space is a real phenomenon which has subtle interaction with matter, can be deflected or blocked by dense materials in the surroundings of a light-beam interferometer, and also may be entrained along the surface of the Earth, moving faster at higher elevations than at lower elevations.

B) Earth and the solar system are moving at a speed of 208 km/sec towards an apex in the Southern Celestial Hemisphere, towards Dorado, the swordfish, right ascension 4 hrs 54 min, declination of -70° 33' (south), in the middle of the Great Magellanic Cloud and 7° from the southern pole of the ecliptic. Miller believed the Earth was pushing "southward" through a stationary but Earth-entrained ether in that particular direction.

C) Light is not constant in all directions, but shows a measurable direction-dependent variance (*anisotropy*).

As I have previously documented,[2] Miller's findings were never effectively rebutted when he was alive, but he was largely ignored, and brushed aside as irrelevant after his death. Mainstream physics was then in a rush to embrace Albert Einstein's relativity theory which demanded, as one of its fundamental assumptions, constancy in the speed of light in all directions. Light-speed variance and a tangible ether filling all of space were incompatible with Einstein's theory. The theory of the *luminiferous ether* — of an all-pervading mass-free cosmic medium through which light waves were propagated, and which played a fundamental role in other material and physical forces — was quickly dropped by most physicists, without serious investigation of Miller's findings. "Empty space" and a dead universe were thereafter considered as proven fact, and defended with great emotional resistance.

Reich's Dynamic and Pulsatory Orgone

Less than 20 years after Miller's milestone research, in the 1950s, Wilhelm Reich was documenting the existence of a unique and new form of energy, called the *orgone*, which existed in living organisms and the atmosphere, and was postulated to exist in cosmic space as well, with properties remarkably similar to Miller's ether:[3,4]

A) Mass-free orgone energy filled all space, much like a cosmic ether. Orgone could penetrate matter easily, but also weakly interacted with it, being attracted to and charging all matter. Organic materials held the orgone charge strongly, while metals rapidly discharged, or reflected it.

B) Orgone energy was postulated to play a fundamental role in planetary dynamics, specifically the rotation of planets on their axis, and the revolution of planets around their suns, and of moons around planets. Orgone energy also was postulated to be the medium of transmission of electromagnetic waves, and of the energetic excitation which led to the *local development of light*.[5]

C) Reich's theory postulated the existence of large

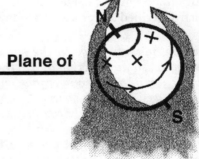

**Draco - Vega - Hercules
North Pole of the Ecliptic**

Plane of   **the Ecliptic**

**Dorado - Great Magellanic Cloud
South Pole of the Ecliptic**

Figure 1: Relative Motion of the Earth and Ether. Is the Earth pushing southward through a passive, stationary ether, or is the ether dynamic, similar to Reich's orgone, streaming northward in a superimposing spiraling spinning-wave, and carrying the Earth-Sun system with it? The "X" marks on the Earth diagram represent Dayton Miller's interferometer cross-arms at different times of day, showing how the movement of ether would vary according to civil time, but still remain constant according to specific sidereal or cosmical coordinates.

** Director, Orgone Biophysical Research Lab, Greensprings, PO Box 1148, Ashland, Oregon 97520 USA. Tel/Fax: 541-552-0118 Email: demeo@mind.net spiraling streams of orgone in cosmic space, notably a streaming motion along the plane of the Milky Way Galaxy, with secondary streams flowing parallel to the Plane of the Ecliptic (of the Solar System), and to the Earth's equator. Reich described these spiral waveforms, giving them the German name *Kreiselwelle* (*spinning wave* or, literally, "gyroscopic-wave"), which he believed underlay various biological, atmospheric and cosmic motions.

The orgone thereby fulfilled the requirements of a cosmological luminiferous ether, though one with specific identifiable properties which expand into the realms of biology and meteorology. However, orgone is not comparable with the older concept of a *static* or *stagnant and immobile ether*, nor fully compatible even with Miller's *passive Earth-entrained ether*. However, it does appear to be compatible with — and this will be the thrust of this preliminary discussion — a *dynamic ether*, something which would also fulfill the role of being a *cosmic prime mover*.

Reich's orgone was a pulsating and streaming phenomenon whose properties had originally been determined from observations of living creatures; he later found similar *orgonotic* expressions in the non-living world as well. His theory of *Cosmic Superimposition*[4] encompassed the phenomenon of cell growth and division, sexual excitation and attraction, emotional phenomenon, cloud dynamics and atmospheric circulation patterns, and finally, planetary movements and galactic structure. Matter was not only created in the universe by streams of flowing and pulsing cosmic orgone energy, but this same energy also acted to move the planets and suns along on their paths in the heavens, much as a ball floating on the water is moved forward by the water waves. Reich described the process as follows:

"The sun and the planets move in the same plane and revolve in the same direction due to the movement and direction of the cosmic orgone energy stream in the galaxy. Thus, the sun does not 'attract' anything at all. It is merely the biggest brother of the whole group. ...

Both moon and Earth spin along in space, with their respective open (not closed) pathways mutually approaching and separating again. Therefore it is not the gravitational masses, but the PATHWAYS of the gravitational masses, which meet.

The moon does not 'circle around the Earth', since the lines of movements are open, spiraling curves. ...

The cosmic orgone energy flow that carries both moon and earth along in the same direction, in the same plane, and in perfect coordination of their speeds, is the true agent of the gravitational free fall. ...

The function of gravitation is real. It is, however, not the result of mass attraction but of the converging movements of two orgone energy streams. From these converging streams the 'attracting' and 'gravitational' masses once emerged and they are still carried along in the universe by the same streams in an integrated, unitary fashion as expressed in their common direction of movement, their common planes of motion, the mutual approach of their centers, and the mutually coordinated speed of their spinning motion".[6]

Reich further compared the spinning-wave to the line described in space by a point near the rim of a turning wheel, or by a rotating top, and as seen in the behavior of pendulums:

"The 'Swing' can be easily visualized as the line described in space by a point on the rim of a wheel rotating forward. In relation to the ground, this point on the rim though rotating with even speed in itself, describes a movement of alternating acceleration and deceleration. In other words, its motion expands and contracts alternatingly. On the forward turn, the point moves faster. On the backward turn, it moves slower. The ratio of speed change depends, of course, on the basic speed of rotation: The faster the rotation, the shorter the contraction with respect to the forward motion.

A spinning top shows the same basic function of speed contraction and expansion. The top will move in a more or less curved line at high speed. The line of motion forward will be more even the greater the speed.

At a lower speed of rotation, the pin on which the top rotates will clearly describe a spinning wave, a KRW (Kreiselwelle) and swings with alternating acceleration and deceleration thus: [see Figure 2, the length of the segments] indicate the acceleration and deceleration.

Alternating expansion and contraction of forward motion may also be easily observed in the movement of swinging pendulums under the condition that the point of suspension moves onward in space, while the pendulum body swings." [4]

These and other descriptions in Reich's writings suggest very real and testable hypotheses regarding planetary movements, some of which already appear to be accepted at a basic level by modern astronomers, though for completely different reasons and certainly without the emphasis given by Reich. For example, it is acknowledged that stars and planets move through the galaxy, and the orbits of the planets describe large spiral-forms in space. However, no special emphasis is placed upon this fact, given the assumption of empty space. Only a few textbooks make mention of it. Reich, by contrast, worked out his own special functional equations of gravitation and pendulum behavior,[4] based

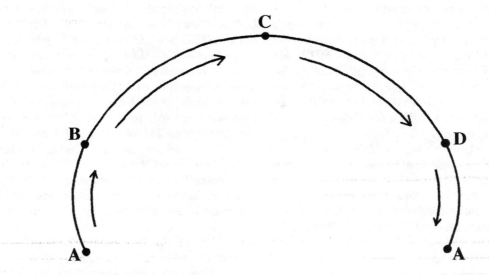

Figure 2. The *Kreiselwelle* or Spinning Wave (Top), as described by a point on a rotating wheel. The points A-B, B-C, C-D and D-A describe equal periods of time along the curve, indicating an acceleration at A-B, B-C, and deceleration at C-D, D-A, with segments B-C and C-D having roughly twice the velocity and distance covered per unit of time, as segments A-B or D-A. The Center-Left figure below presents this idea with the wheel actually drawn in, shown sequentially as it moves from left to right. One might consider the black dot as a planet orbiting a larger body at the center of the wheel, suggesting planets and moons inscribe large swings in space, spiral forms with periods of acceleration and deceleration, and with varying net velocities. If one considers each of the separate circles or "wheels" below to be successively moving out of the page, towards the reader (like a stack of large coins) the context more clearly mimics planetary motions, where central Suns move through space. The Center-Right figure below represents a forward-moving pendulum, where the swings in the forward direction cover a greater distance, with greater velocity, than the backwards swings. The Bottom figure is yet another manner of viewing the orbiting motions of a moon around a planet, or a planet around its central star, with vectors matching our "point on a wheel" or "forward moving pendulum". These figures will gain a larger significance when viewed against the Figures to follow. In all three figures here, the vectors A-B and D-A are shorter than the vectors B-C and C-D. Drawings made after Reich's original figures or concepts, from *Contact With Space*.[4]

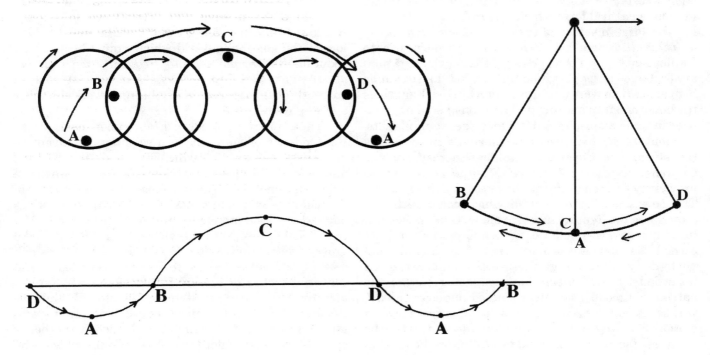

upon his insights on the spinning wave.

As introduced above, the measured observations and ether-theory proposed by Miller have various points of agreement with Reich's orgone: Dense materials affected the speed of movement of both, as did altitude. Both orgone and ether moved faster (or was "more active" as Reich put it) at higher elevations. Both could penetrate matter, though at different rates of speed depending upon density and other factors. Miller's interferometer excluded metal shields and other dense materials over the light-beam paths — a problem with many unsuccessful ether-drift experiments before and after Miller[1,2] — as it would "block the ether"; Reich used a metal-lined enclosure, with other material arrangements, to attract and accumulate, or "trap" the orgone inside, to higher concentrations than was found in the outer environment.

The Ether: Stationary (Static), Earth-Entrained, or Dynamic?

Ever since Isaac Newton, many physicists considered the ether to be a *static* or *stagnant* phenomenon, something which existed throughout the cosmos, but primarily as a *non-moving and immobilized* background medium. A static ether or "Absolute Space" was a necessity for Newton, in large measure to reconcile his mathematical *laws of motion* with his theology. Newton's laws of motion — which can be distilled down to the consideration that *"nothing moves unless something else makes it move"* — eliminates entirely any spontaneous or dynamical qualities to Nature or the ether. By contrast, the ether of Galileo Galilei, who died on the same year Newton was born (1642), was a dynamic phenomenon, a *cosmic prime-mover* which put the heavens into motion, a natural force which was responsible for solving the large mystery of *where all the motion in the universe ultimately came from.* Church theology prior to Galileo and Copernicus portrayed the Earth as stationary in the cosmos, apart from the "perfect" and dynamic heavens, which were put into motion by God. Earth was the home of Satan and sin, and was considered immobilized in the heavens, by contrast to the heavenly planets, Sun and stars, which were pure and daily moved across the skies. The Copernican-Galilean heresy, for the Church, was that it *breathed life* into places where previously Church authority had *declared things dead.* The new scientific revolution which came with and stimulated the Renaissance also made "God" irrelevant, insofar as the cosmic ether or prime mover was concerned. The cosmos was animated by Natural Law, and not by deity. The theologically-preoccupied Newton was unsettled by such ideas, and sought to restore the patriarchal god to his proper role as cosmic clock-maker, who set the universe into motion; his celebrated laws of motion factually worked to *undermine and block* the progress of scientific and social revolution implied within

the writings of heretics such as Bruno, Copernicus and Galileo. Newton appeared motivated to "heal the schism" between Science and the Church, which had developed since Galileo, by *ridding the universe of any notion of cosmic prime mover.* The ether was henceforth declared dead, static and immobile, and God was rescued from the unemployment lines, his role as the source of all universal motion preserved.[8] This viewpoint is not apparent from his mathematics, but is a part of the underlying philosophy which led to Newton's equations being considered "Laws".

Basically, if one assumes space is empty and there is no prime mover, or that an ether exists but is totally static and immobilized in its behavior, then *one must assert some additional principle or metaphysical mechanism for all the observable motion in the universe,* whether it be a metaphysical god, or a metaphysical creation-event such as the "Big Bang", or a mathematical-metaphysical abstraction, such as Einstein's relativity. If the ether exists, and is not static, then Nature simplifies things tremendously, but leaves human metaphysical belief systems even more isolated from reality.

Newton's "Laws" surely hold a strong central truth, in describing how inanimate and dead matter behaves, but they are not absolutes, and fail utterly with respect to the phenomenon of life, emotion, love and sexuality. They also fail with respect to certain dynamical physical processes, such as seen in weather, or solar-geophysical phenomenon. Textbook theoreticians will proclaim this heresy, but the honest weather forecaster, observing a jet stream to "spontaneously" diverge hundreds of miles without apparent "cause" or "reason", or the honest astronomer witnessing solar pulsations suggestive of a heart-beat, or dramatic and surprising solar flares following geomagnetic and not gravitational laws of motion, basically throwing the "Laws of Inertia" out the window, will acknowledge there are dynamical behaviors in the non-living world which cannot be so easily reduced. *Nature moves, and frequently without any apparent physical force to "make" it move* — at least, as currently acknowledged within the framework of "empty space" physics.

The emphasis of modern science upon dead things, the tendency of many modern scientists to invent so many deadly new things which work to destroy Nature, and the tendency for many scientists to be so "up in the head" and emotionally dead themselves — leading them to vicious reactions in opposition to anything which is suggestive of a dynamic living energy principle in Nature — I have discussed elsewhere,[9] as has Reich.[10] The growing perception of modern science as a *belief-system*, or *religion*, quite willing to use the repressive and censorial tactics of the old Vatican hierarchy, stems directly from this constellation of emotional (and motional) factors. It is therefore not accidental that mainstream physicists today emphatically deny the ether of space, in a manner not too different from the way the

American courts decreed *"the orgone energy does not exist"*, ordering Reich's publications (including those cited here) to be burned in incinerators. They will insist with great passion that *ether and orgone "do not exist"*, *and that space is mathematically abstract and totally static, dead and intangible*, as did Einstein.[12] Any scientist whose work suggests otherwise — as with Miller and Reich — is expeditiously isolated and silenced, one way or another.

In fact, Miller's view diverged from the concept of a *static* ether only insofar as was necessary to explain an Earth-entrainment phenomenon, and ether-reflecting capabilities of dense matter which his empirical measurements demonstrated. Consequently, he viewed the Earth as pushing towards the constellation Dorado, near the South Pole of the Ecliptic, through a passive but Earth-entrained ether. Such an interaction was, as Miller argued, the reason why his interferometer detected a flow of ether in a generally south to north (Ecliptic-Pole) direction. Reich, by contrast, put the ether into dynamic motion as his pulsatory and streaming *orgone energy*, which he viewed as THE *prime mover*. Reich's theory demanded the ether (or, orgone) NOT be passive. Reich's prime mover was *flowing and moving*, carrying the Earth along upon its waves of excitation, or capturing the mass of the Earth directly within the streaming flow of its own structure, albeit of a very tenuous and "ethereal" quality. His prime mover, the orgone, also was slowly and dynamically transforming itself from an "ethereal" *mass-free* form, into more substantial *mass-form particles*. In so doing, momentum was imparted to matter, which was one mechanism by which the Earth, Sun and stars were affected by the movements of the energy substrate. Figure 1 gives a rough approximation of the empirical observations derived from Miller, which can be interpreted as Miller proposed, or as Reich proposed. The "X" marks on the globe in Figure 1 represent the interferometer at different positions throughout the day, and one can see how the ether-flow would intersect the interferometer crossbeams at different angles as the Earth rotated. The Figure *suggests* some differences between Miller and Reich which are difficult to reconcile, but this is not necessarily so.

Miller's 1928 Conclusions

As mentioned above, Miller's final conclusions of 1933 were that the Earth was drifting towards a point near the constellation Dorado, close to the South Pole of the Ecliptic.[1] However, his *earlier conclusion* made from the same data, viewed the direction of motion along the *same axis of ether-drift*, but in the *opposite direction*, towards the North Pole of the Ecliptic. As late as 1928, when he spoke at the *Conference on the Michelson-Morley Experiment*,[7] Miller embraced the idea that the Earth-Sun system was moving towards Draco, which is generally close to the northern pole of the ecliptic, 180 degrees opposite of Dorado.

"...variations in the direction and magnitude of the indicated motion are just such as would be produced by a constant motion of the solar system in space... towards an apex in the constellation Draco, near the pole of the ecliptic, which has a right ascension of 255° (17 hours) and a declination of +68°..." ... *"The location of the apex [of ether-drift] in the constellation Draco... is within 6° of the pole of the ecliptic, that is, the indicated motion of the solar system is almost perpendicular to the plane of the ecliptic. The Sun's axis of rotation points to within 12° of this apex".*[7]

Miller's original calculations of this northerly apex appear to be more compatible with a dynamic theory of ether drift, where the ether flowed and moved *from Dorado generally towards the northern pole of the ecliptic (Draco)*, a movement which would carry the Sun-Earth-Moon-Planetary System along with it as it moved, though only a small portion of the ether's velocity could be detected (~10 km/sec) due to Earth-entrainment. The interferometer, as he noted, could determine *"...the line in which the motion of the Earth with respect to the ether takes place, but does not determine the direction of motion in this line."* [1] In his original 1928 paper, he reviewed various observations by astronomers of his day, in their attempts (primarily using measurements of stellar aberration) to fix the direction in which the Sun and solar system was moving. Most of the available studies in the middle of the 20th Century suggested a movement of the Sun and solar system generally towards the northern apex, aimed roughly between the constellations Hercules and Cygnus, and lying within the plane of the Milky Way Galaxy. Today, the calculated direction of solar movement is towards Vega, in the constellation Lyra, which lies in the middle of a small triangle created by the constellations Draco, Hercules and Cygnus. All these constellations are reasonably close to the northern pole of the ecliptic, and to Miller's northern polar axis of ether-drift, and they all are found close to the plane of the Milky Way.

Miller noted, *"The choice between the two possible directions of motion is determined by the consistency of the results in satisfying the original observations taken as a whole, and in connection with known phenomena."*[1] However, even while criticizing static ether concepts, his calculations for determining the final axis of ether-drift, were all based upon static-ether assumptions. In his 1933 conclusions for a southerly apex, he stated: *"...the solar system might be thought of as a dynamic disk which is being pulled through a resisting medium, and which therefore sets itself perpendicular to the line of motion".*[1] He suggested there could be a *relative* motion of the Solar System towards other stars in the more

Figure 3: AVERAGE VELOCITY AND AZIMUTH OF GLOBAL ETHER DRIFT, from Dayton Miller's Mount Wilson Ether Drift Experiments, 1925-26. *Top Graph*: Average variations in observed magnitude of ether-drift from all four epochs of measurement. Maximum velocity occurs at around 5 hours sidereal time and minimum velocity occurs around 17 hours sidereal. While Miller's 1933 paper assumed the Earth was *pushing through the ether* and moving towards Dorado, near the southern pole of the Plane of the Ecliptic, the movement and direction of ether-drift past the interferometer was *exactly opposite* to this, towards Draco near the northern pole of the Plane of the Ecliptic (17 hours right ascension, declination of +68°). It is important, *from the standpoint of his*

working theory, to clarify the concepts of the "net motion of the Earth" versus the "direction of ether-drift". However, *if the ether itself is in motion, acting as a cosmic prime-mover, the direction of ether-drift and the net motion of the Earth would be identical, though at different velocities.* *Bottom Graph:* Average variations in observed azimuth readings according to sidereal time. This graph uses a data curve published by Miller[1] in 1928, but which was at that time given a different baseline average. The same graph is presented here, for the first time, using Miller's revised seasonal averages as published in 1933,[7] which help define the axis of ether-drift. Amazingly, the independent averages for the four epochs provided by Miller (Feb.= -10° west of north, April= +40° east, Aug.= +10° east, Sept.= +55° east) together yield *a mean displacement 23.75° east of north.* This is very close to the Earth's axial tilt of 23.5°, and can hardly be coincidental. (Graphs adapted from Miller[1] p.363 and Miller[7] p.235; also see DeMeo[2] p.121.)

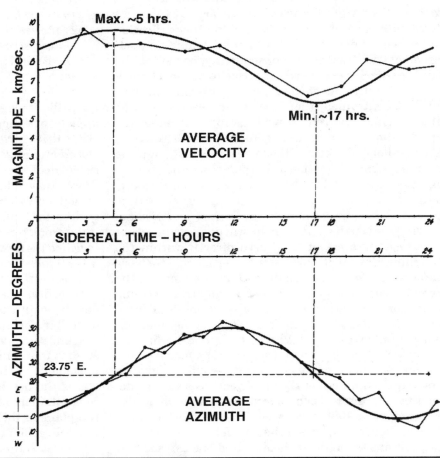

northerly constellations, with the whole group of stars moving in a net sense towards the southerly apex. This was a reasonable conclusion, given the static-ether assumptions. However, there is another way of looking at his data which yields a different conclusion.

One of Miller's data graphs from 1928 is reproduced in Figure 3, presenting the final averages from all four seasonal epochs of his Mt. Wilson data. A deeper understanding of this graph, for those who are not working astronomers, is obtained most simply by use of a standard rotating globe with 23.5° tilt, placed on a table (representing the Plane of the Ecliptic), and fitted with a small X-mark at latitude 34° in California, representing the Mt. Wilson interferometer. With an appropriate mark on the ceiling and floor identifying the axis of ether-drift, and major sidereal hours of 0, 6, 12 and 18 marked on the four walls of the room (in the nature of a

planetarium) the relationships can then be followed as the Earth rotates on its axis over the course of 24 hours. From this graphic, and the model, we can observe the following:

A) At around 5 hours sidereal time, the flow of ether across the Earth's surface at Mt. Wilson is largely horizontally directed (on the globe), thereby creating maximal fringe shifts.

B) At around 17 hours sidereal time, the flow of ether is more vertically-directed, affecting both arms of the interferometer more equally, and thereby yielding minimum fringe shifts. Since the interferometer at the latitude of Mt. Wilson sits "on top" of the Earth at that sidereal time, the mass of the Earth basically shields the interferometer from any measured flow moving "up" from the South Pole of the Ecliptic towards the North.

C) The compass azimuth of ether-drift generally

pointed across a set of coordinates with seasonal variations which ranged from approximately -10° west to +55° east of 0° north, with an oscillating displacement of the drift axis generally towards the east.[1,2] The specific variations are: February -10° (west of north), April +40° east, August +10° east, and September +55° east. A striking fact about these variations is, their average equals 23.75°, *very close to the Earth's axial tilt of 23.5°.* This fact was not mentioned anywhere in Miller's writings, to my knowledge. In the context of our discussion here, it suggests this particular vector is the net result of the energetic streams proposed by Reich[3,4] (elaborated upon below) which move the Earth on its path around the Sun, with a biasing towards the east due to the energetic west-to-east flow along the Equatorial

disk at the Mt. Wilson latitude. A strong energetic streaming within the galactic disk moves the Sun and solar system towards a location in Draco-Vega, while an apparently weaker energetic streaming in the ecliptical disk rotates the planets on their axes, biasing the net detectable ether-drift towards the east by an average angle of 23.75°. The fact that this angle is so close to the Earth's axial tilt of 23.5°, and that the average vector *sustains itself in an easterly deviation* (*without diurnally shifting back 23.5° west of north*) suggests it is *an expression of the causal cosmic-energetic principle responsible for the Earth's axial tilt.*

D) The average directional vector of ether-drift shifts westerly, back towards the north, after 17 hrs sidereal, when the Earth rotation would place the North Pole of the Ecliptic (and North Pole of the axis of ether-drift) in such a due northerly position relative to the interferometer at Mt. Wilson. With further Earth rotation, the vector returns back to 23.75° east at 5 hrs sidereal, and then shifts farther to the east, which is when the northern poles of both the ecliptical plane and ether-drift axis appear on the northeasterly horizon. More discussion will be made on the issue of seasonal variations in ether-drift measurements at a later time.

For these and various other reasons, Miller's original 1928 interpretation of a northerly-directed apex for the net motion of the Earth appears to be more compatible with observed facts, but we must *set the ether into motion as the cosmic prime mover* for this to make any sense. As we shall see, this interpretation brings Miller's empirical work into greater harmony with Reich's theory,

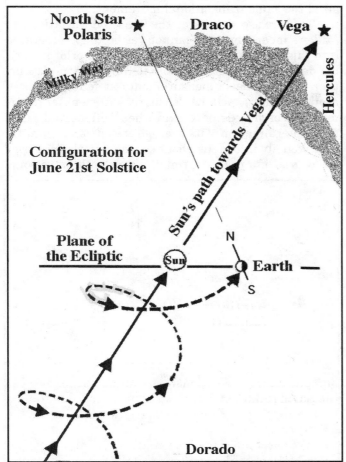

Figure 4. Ecliptical Spiral: The Earth spins on its axis (shown here in summer solstice position), and moves around the Sun in a spiral. The Sun, according to classical astronomical determinations, is moving towards the star Vega. The constellation Draco marks the approximate location of the northern pole of the Plane of the Ecliptic, and the North Pole of Miller's computed Axis of Ether-Drift. The cosmic prime-mover (call it *ether* or *orgone* for the moment) flows in a spinning wave (*Kreiselwelle*) generally towards Draco-Vega, carrying the planets and the Sun along with it, pushing them into spiral motion.

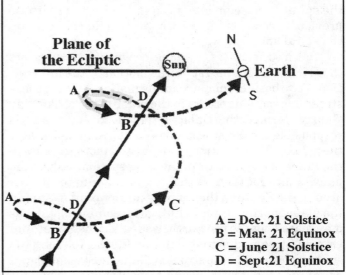

Figure 5: Earth Spiral Movement Around the Sun transverse a greater distance during the period March through September (B-C and C-D) than during the period September through March (D-A and A-B). The line segments can be easily matched with Reich's diagrams, as previously given, regarding the spinning wave.

and more fully integrates both of their works with current astronomical findings.

Spiral Forms in Space

Reich noted[3] that *nearly all cosmic motions are spiral-forms*, inscribing the *Kreiselwelle*, or *spinning wave* across the heavens. There are no "circular" or "elliptical" orbits per se, only large spirals. The Earth may "move around" the Sun, but since the Sun is also moving through the heavens, a large spiral motion is created, as seen in Figures 4 and 5. Here, we can observe there are some seasons when the Earth moves quite a large distance through the heavens, while at other seasons, the Earth moves across only a relatively small distance of space. The distances for B-C and C-D from March 21st through September 21st, for example, are approximately twice those for D-A and A-B, which cover the period from September 21st through March 21st. There is a period of where the Earth accelerates to maximum speed, starting around the time of the Spring Equinox (B towards C) followed by deceleration (C towards D) where the Earth then enters a region where it moves relatively slowly in relationship to the background of space (D-A and A-B). With the cycle completed, there is once again a rapid acceleration the next Spring. It gives the impression of a singular strong energetic wave or pulse, which imparts momentum to the Earth; or, alternatively, the Earth seasonally enters into a region of space characterized by a very high speed of energetic streaming, and then leaves that region to a more slow "backwater" area, as with a circular eddy in an ocean current or river. One can match the letters on the spiral-form segments given in Figure 5, with those previously given on Figure 2, regarding Reich's ideas on the spiral spinning-wave.

Reich's theory of *Cosmic Superimposition* suggests the Earth was put into spinning motion by the intersection of two basic cosmic streaming motions. One of these streaming motions occurs in the plane of the Milky Way Galaxy (termed the Galactic Orgone Stream) and is responsible for the superimposing spiral arm-bands of the galaxy. The other major streaming motion occurs in the Plane of the Ecliptic of the solar system, setting the planets into rotation on their axes and into revolution around the Sun, and their moons into revolution around the planets. This latter Ecliptical streaming motion, as it appeared near to the Earth, was called the Equatorial Orgone Stream, due to its circling the Earth along the equator; he argued the stronger Galactic Stream placed a torque on the rotational axis to yield the 23.5° axial tilt of the Earth which, like a gyroscope, precesses on its axis of rotation every 30,000 years, approximately. In fact, the net resulting motions from these two energy streams are a series of spiral-forms, with the planets making large spirals around the moving Sun, and moons spiraling around each spiral-turning planet. The planets,

such as Earth, appear to come under varying greater or lesser influence from each of the two streaming motions, depending upon seasonal configurations, and these are expressed in the changing velocities and directions the planets take along their spiral-paths around the Sun. Reich noted, a basic west-to-east influence from the Equatorial Orgone Stream, and a southwest-to-northeast influence from the Galactic Orgone Stream, intersecting at a 62° angle. This latter point is standard astronomy, that the Earth's Equatorial Plane is inclined to the Galactic Equator by an angle of 62°. This same set of factors appears to exist in Miller's ether-drift measurements, which "...*oscillated back and forth through an angle of about 60°...*".[7] Reich emphasized the Earth's translational movement through the cosmos, as it spiraled around the Sun, while Miller similarly emphasized the same translational movement.

The precise details of the seasonal variations in Miller's measurements cannot yet be fully integrated into this discussion — as mentioned in a prior paper,[3] his data is no longer available to fully inform us. Further, Miller's basic measurements at four periods of around 10 days each, while clearly sufficient for determination of the existence of an ether-drift, as well as the final determination of its average velocity and azimuth, only vaguely inform us about seasonal variations over the course of a year. Optimally, we should have some

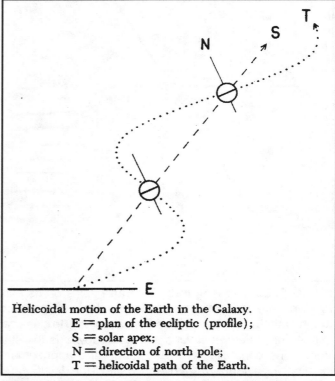

Helicoidal motion of the Earth in the Galaxy.
E = plan of the ecliptic (profile);
S = solar apex;
N = direction of north pole;
T = helicoidal path of the Earth.

Figure 6. Piccardi's Diagram of the spiral motion of the Earth around the Sun. Over the course of a year, the Earth follows a spiral-form trajectory which brings its forward movement through the heavens roughly parallel to the Equator, or parallel to the polar axis. (from Piccardi[13])

ether-drift data for each month of the year. Nevertheless, it is interesting to note periodic variations in velocity, with azimuthal displacements along west-to-east and southwest-to-northeast axes in Miller's data, suggesting alternating influences along a spiral-form *Kreiselwelle* trajectory, similar to what is proposed in Reich's theory. Miller's work has also been the subject of a recent set of papers by Maurice Allais,[12] with added discussion on the question of seasonal displacements.

A similar set of considerations were also pointed out by the Italian chemist, Giorgio Piccardi,[14] whose study of anomalous variations in laboratory phase-change experiments (such as the precipitation of bismuth chloride from solution, or the freezing of supercooled water) suggested similar cosmical factors at work. Piccardi emphasized the helicoidal movement of the Earth around the Sun as a factor which seasonally imparted anomalous variations within tightly-controlled laboratory physical chemistry experiments. The anomaly, he demonstrated, could be affected by metal enclosures very similar to Reich' orgone energy accumulators, and expressed itself globally. That is, the phenomenon affected identical experiments in both the Northern and Southern Hemispheres, in an identical manner, indicating that it was something affecting the entire Earth all at once, and not something related to ordinary seasonal factors, such as temperature or humidity. Piccardi's work was also subject to the academic silent-treatment, and his contemporary advocates were similarly sub-

jected to a blatant censorship after his death, though for a short period of time in the 1950s and 60s, his work did enjoy research support through the UN *International Geophysical Year* science programs. Piccardi noted other aspects to this planetary movement, which are illustrated in his original diagram, presented in Figure 6, and in the provided photos of his 3-dimensional model:

"1) during the month of March the Earth moves in its equatorial plane.
2) during the month of September, the earth moves, if not along its axis, then in a direction not too far removed from that of the North Pole
3) the speed of the Earth's helicoidal displacement varies during the year and phases from a maximum in March (45 km/sec) to a minimum in September 24 (km/sec).
4) the Earth is displaced with the Northern hemisphere leading, except during a small part of[early] March.
If space were empty, empty of fields of matter and inactive, a consideration of this type would be of no importance. But today, we know instead that both matter and fields exist in space. For this reason, the displacement of a body such as the Earth in one direction or another is not inconsequential. Its general physical conditions must vary in the course of a year." [emphasis Piccardi's][13]

Figure 7. Piccardi's Animated Model of the Helicoidal Motion of the Earth around the Sun, presented at the Brussels World-Fair in 1958. (from Piccardi[13])

It is clear, Piccardi's experiments suggest a mechanism similar to that observed by both Miller and Reich.

From the above, we have converging lines of evidence, from three independent sources who do not appear to have been aware of each other's research: Miller, Reich and Piccardi. Miller measured an Earth-entrained ether-drift with seasonal-sidereal components, including lawful episodic displacements along a west-to-east or southwest-to-northeast axis. Reich's study of biological, atmospheric and cosmological factors led him to conclude the existence of streams of cosmic energy in space, moving generally southwest-to-northeast (the Galactic plane or stream of energy) or west-to-east (the Equatorial stream). Piccardi's observations of anomalous variations in phase-change chemistry led to a similar conclusion, regarding energy fields in space which affected basic physical chemistry, depending upon the Earth's velocity through space. He never plotted the axial displacements as they affected his experiments, but a varying south-to-north and west-to-east expression is implied from his materials (Figure 6).

The research findings of Miller, Reich and Piccardi appear to be in general agreement on certain basic points regarding the nature of cosmic space, and the importance of cosmic spatial-geography in the understanding of experimental results, and in formulation of theory.

More detailed discussion on these points must wait for another time. This paper gives only a rough sketch of a complex subject, and patience will be required for development of a more complete understanding of these cosmological factors, and their integration with other empirical facts from astronomy and other branches of science. *We are only now reclaiming and resuscitating entire lines of research which were forcibly demolished by police actions or academic blockades, being closed off to serious investigation during the years c.1930-1960*, a time when many innovative scientists were willfully ignored and censored, or worse: Reich was subject to imprisonment and bookburning, only a few years after writing the materials cited in this article, and this happened with the active participation, or passive consent and approval of the dominant academic mainstream. In this regard, it must be said, things have changed only a little.

The above discussion shows how the addition of the dynamic spiral-form movement into our view of the solar system — of the Sun moving through the heavens and the planets spiraling around in open loops rather than moving in simple closed circles or ellipses — has dramatic consequences for the larger cosmic view. It is as radical a departure from the old way of viewing the Universe, as was the original revolution of Copernicus and Galileo, who put the Earth into motion around the Sun, and helped shake the authoritarian social institutions of their day to their foundations. We can hope for no less.

References:

1. Miller, D.: "The Ether-Drift Experiment and the Determination of the Absolute Motion of the Earth", *Reviews of Modern Physics*, Vol.5(2):203-242, July 1933 (specific refs. to p.231-235).

2. DeMeo, J.: "Dayton Miller' Ether-Drift Experiments: A Fresh Look", *Infinite Energy*, #38:72-82, July/Aug. 2001; *Pulse of the Planet* #5:114-130, 2002. Also at: http://www.orgonelab.org/miller.htm

3. Reich, W.: *Ether, God and Devil; Cosmic Superimposition*, Farrar, Straus & Giroux, NY 1973.

4. Reich, W.: *Contact With Space, Oranur Second Report 1951-1956*, Core Pilot Press, NY, 1957, p.95-110.

5. Reich believed light was a local phenomenon, created from the excitation and lumination of orgone energy per se, with only the excitation being transmitted over a distance, at the "speed of light". See Reich, W.: "Orgonotic Light Functions" Parts I, II, III, *Orgone Energy Bull.* 1:3-6 & 49-51 & 97-99,1949.

6. Reich, *Cosmic Superimposition*, ibid, p.191, 274, 276.

7. Miller, D., "Conference on the Michelson-Morley Experiment", *Astrophysical Journal*, LXVIII:341-402, Dec. 1928; also in *Contributions From the Mount Wilson Observatory*, No.373, Carnegie Inst. of Washington. (specific refs. to p.356-357, 361, and 365-366 of *Astrophysical Journal* version)

8. Stecchini, Livio: "The Inconstant Heavens", in *The Velikovsky Affair: Warfare of Science and Scientism*, A. deGrazia, Ed., University Books, 1966; Kubrin, David: *How Sir Isaac Newton Helped Restore Law'N Order To The West*, unpublished manuscript, 1972.

9. DeMeo, J.: *Saharasia: The 4000 BCE Origins of Child Abuse, Sex-Repression, Warfare and Social Violence, In the Deserts of the Old World*, Natural Energy, 1998.

10. Reich, *Ether, God and Devil*, ibid.

11. Einstein, A.: "Relativity and the Ether", in *Essays in Science*, Philosophical Library, NY 1934.

12. Allais, M.: "Experiments of Dayton Miller and the Theory of Relativity", *21st Century Sci. & Tech.*, Spring 1998, p.30-31 (Reprinted in *Pulse of the Planet* #5:131-136, 2002). cf. *C.R.Acad.Sci. Paris* I. 327 Serie IIB, p.1411-1419, 1999. Also see: Allais, M.: *L'Anisotropie de L'Espace*, Clement Juglar, Paris, 1997.

13. Piccardi, G.: *Chemical Basis of Medical Climatology*, Charles Thomas, Springfield, 1962, p.97-99.

Additional References:

Baker, C.F.: "The Gravitational Spinning Wave", *J. Orgonomy*, 2(1):95-99, 1968.

— : "Mass and the Gravitational Function", *J. Orgonomy*, 2(2):210-214, 1968.

— : "The Red Shift", *J. Orgonomy*, 4(2):183-191, 1970.

— : "The Perihelion Spiral", *J. Orgonomy*, 12(1):55-63, 1978.

— : "The Spinning Wave", Part I and II, *J. Orgonomy*, 13(1):55-80, 13(2):192-219, 1979.

— : "The Orgone Energy Continuum", *J. Orgonomy*, 14(1):37-60, 1980.

— : "The Orgone Energy Continuum: Ether and Relativity", *J. Orgonomy*, 16(1):41-67, 1982.

The Implications of Current Consciousness Research on Orgonomic Theory

by Richard A. Blasband, M.D.*

Since I started my research in 1920, it has always been entirely clear to me that my work was dominated by an objective logic which at first could not be understood, and I felt I was its executive organ. Understanding this logic and rationality in the development of observations, working hypotheses, theories, and new findings in itself forms a major part of my research work. A harmony of subject and object, of observer and observed, that was based on some kind of law, seemed to consistently permeate this logic.
— Wilhelm Reich[1]

Introduction

As noted above, the relationship between the observer and the observed, the investigator and that being investigated, was a dominant theme in Wilhelm Reich's research from its inception. In 1949, with respect to this theme Reich wrote, *"Orgone biophysics operates with organ sensation as a* FIRST SENSE *of a strict physiological nature. In order to investigate nature, we must love — using the word literally — the object of research. Expressed in the language of orgone physics, we must have immediate and undisturbed orgonotic contact with the object."* [2]

While Reich followed his functional path more mechanistically-oriented scientists coming from other disciplines were confronted with experimental anomalies that shook the foundations of their usually accepted view of reality. It began with findings in quantum physics that insisted that the experimenter had to be included in the understanding of certain particle/wave manifestations of light and progressed to anomalous findings in consciousness research that fractured our traditional view of four-dimensional space-time. Reich briefly addresses the significance of the quantum phenomena for his own work but the major findings coming out of the research in consciousness were published after his death. It is the purpose of this paper to review some of these findings and briefly indicate their possible implications for orgonomic theory.

* Director, *Center for Functional Research*, Tiburon, California. www.functionalresearch.org
Email: RABlasband@aol.com

Review of the Literature

In their experiments on Human-Machine interactions, Robert Jahn and Brenda Dunne[3] demonstrated that the distribution of impulses generated by a random event generator (REG) could be anomalously, marginally shifted from normal, either via active mental intention or when passively "attended" either locally or at a distance by someone with no particular conscious intention toward the REG. In both cases, it was established that something having to do with the consciousness of the operator was, in some way, influencing the device. In accounting for this anomaly and the fact that the REG could be influenced at distances of thousands of miles and, in certain experiments, independent of sidereal time, Jahn and Dunne concluded that the effect could not be caused by electromagnetism and defined consciousness as a non-electromagnetic wave, through which a state of "resonance" is established between the operator and the machine.

In their model, Jahn and Dunne define consciousness as all that one identifies as oneself: thought, emotions, physical substance, etc. Since it was demonstrated that the presence of the operator alone, without consciously attending to the REG could affect the REG, we thought that expressed emotions by subjects who had no intention toward the REG might also affect it. In psychiatric orgone therapy intense emotional expression by the patient occurs fairly regularly: it was therefore hypothesized that an REG set up in my therapy office would be anomalously affected during those moments when patients would cry in sorrow, fear, or frustration, or express fear, anger, or pleasure as compared to those times when patients would be emotionally "neutral".

Other than the quantum mechanical theoretical formulations of Jahn and Dunne,[3] there was no reason based upon the findings and theories of classical biophysics and experimental evidence to expect any influence on the output of an REG by a spontaneously emoting individual. Since conducting our experiment, the only relevant experimental findings involve the effects of group emotional expression on the REG.[4,5] A review of the mainstream literature on the biophysical basis of emotions shows that while one can demonstrate myriad physiological parameters that correlate with feelings and expressed emotions, all involved measurements are made either within or on the surface of the body. The only found research indicating possible biophysical factors affecting living systems non-locally (at a distance) was that of Harold Saxton Burr and Wilhelm Reich, both of whom postulated bioenergetic "field" effects in protoplasm.

Burr observed that an electrical field measured a small distance away from the surface of an unfertilized, biologically undifferentiated salamander egg appeared to have a determining effect on the establishment of the pattern of the future axis of the central nervous system.[6] On the basis of these and other experimental observations Burr and F.S. C. Northrop postulated that an electrical field (later defined as a "quasi-electrostatic field") was a primary property of protoplasm, maintaining pattern in the organism in the midst of physiochemical flux.[7]

But, while it is possible that emotional expression could affect an REG through perturbing an electromagnetic field (EM) emanating from the body, or be some component of the elements that generate such a field, the findings and theory of bioelectromagnetism provides no basis for expecting that such a field would extend much further than a few inches from the body. Furthermore, the experimental phenomena documented by Jahn & Dunne and others in their work with REG effects and remote viewing, especially those involving temporal anomalies, cannot be explained by electromagnetism.[3]

A non-EM biophysical basis for the emotions was elucidated by Wilhelm Reich. In his clinical psychoanalytic and later "vegetotherapeutic" and "orgone-therapeutic" work, Reich proposed that emotions were a function of the patient either "expanding" toward or "contracting" away from the outer world.[8] This amoeboid-like behavior confirmed an earlier postulate of Freud that never took serious root in later psychoanalytic theory. When Reich replaced the classical psychoanalytic technique of free-association with the more confrontive technique of character analysis, he noted that patients more readily gave in to the expression of their previously blocked emotions. The emotional expression was accompanied by spontaneous pulsatile movements of the patient's body. These movements were greatly amplified when Reich directly physically released the patient's chronic muscular tension ("muscular armoring") by massage of the spastic musculature. As the characterological and muscular armoring softened in the course of therapy, patients reported feeling "electrical currents" and sensations of something "streaming" through their bodies. This was usually associated with an increase in general vagotonic tone, flushing of the skin, brightening of the eyes, contraction of the pupils, slowing of the heart, and an increase in pleasurable sensations at the skin. The opposite of this state of "bioenergetic expansion" was one of "bioenergetic contraction", usually brought on by

fear or anxiety, and characterized by a general autonomic sympathetic tone with pallor of the skin, narrowing of the eyes, dilatation of the pupils, acceleration of heart rate, and sensations of inner tension.[8]

In order to objectify these observations, Reich measured bioelectric charge on the skin surface of subjects in a variety of emotional states. He found that the subjective perception of anxiety or sadness was "functionally identical," (an energetically, meaningful correlation) with a contractive movement of bioelectricity away from the skin surface toward the bioenergetic "core" of the organism — autonomic neural plexes deep in the abdomen and pelvis. Anger, pleasure, and longing were functionally identical to an expansive movement of bioelectricity from the core outward to the skin surface.[8] A recent attempt to replicate Reich's study with modern equipment confirmed in many respects this basic antithesis between autonomic nervous system functions and their correlation with bioelectric charge on the surface of the skin.[9]

Reich found that a bioelectrical interpretation was not, however, sufficient to explain adequately all the phenomena observed in his bioelectrical studies. He then undertook a series of experiments on the sources of energy sustaining life, which ultimately suggested a non-electromagnetic basis for living processes. In the course of his research, Reich reported experiments in which he postulated a field of mass-free energy, "orgone energy," surrounding and interpenetrating all living things[10]. Reich's principle device for detecting this field, the "orgone energy field meter" could apparently detect the energy field of a lively human at distances up to 6 feet.[§] The effects of spontaneous emotions on the meter were either not undertaken, nor reported, although Reich did report that subjects who were more "vegetatively alive" (capable of the expression of intense emotions) could more readily affect the meter, compared to those who were vegetatively "dead," such as an individual who was catatonic.

Methodology

Details of our method of investigation and results may be found in our original paper published in the *Journal of Scientific Exploration*.[11] In essence the experiment was designed to see if any correlation could be found between the output of an REG and the expression

---

[§] This device consisted of moveable facing metal plates, one of which was connected to the different pole of the secondary coil of an induction apparatus. A 40-watt bulb connected between the plates glows when the primary current is at a certain intensity. The proximity of something living to the upper plate affects the intensity of glow of the bulb. The more "alive" the object the more intense the glow. Reich, W. *The Cancer Biopathy*, Orgone Institute Press, N.Y., 1948.

of overt emotions by patients in psychiatric orgone therapy. An REG obtained from the Princeton University Engineering Anomalies Research (PEAR) lab was hooked up to a computer located 10 feet away from the patient. The REG output was blocked from view by the patient and the therapist by computer software. REG trials were begun when the patient entered the office. Times of emotional expression were noted by the therapist either on a pad or punched into the computer via the F-keys. Software accompanying the REG permitted statistical analysis of the REG output. All analyses were conducted only at the conclusion of each of the two several-monthly periods over which the experiment was conducted. Subjects for the investigation were eight female patients, who had been coming to therapy weekly or twice-weekly for at least one year and had resolved their initial resistances to therapy. Their diagnoses included non-psychotic catatonic schizophrenia, hysteria, and phallic-narcissistic character types as defined by Reich and Baker.[12] This initial experiment was restricted to female patients for several reasons, the most important one being the greater emotionality of women compared to men. The experiments were conducted in two segments of about six months each in 1993 and 1995.

Results

Over the duration of the entire experiment we noted 8 events of the overt expression of hitting and (sometimes) kicking with anger, 30 events of screaming with fear or crying with sadness, anxiety or frustration, and 2 events of crying with longing. Using the statistical method of ANOVA, analysis of variance, the REG outputs associated with anger and crying were compared to each other and to the output corresponding to neutral affect. The latter was best seen in the beginning of sessions when patients usually unemotionally reported events of the previous week.

We found that the mean distribution of REG output when patients expressed emotion was highly significantly different than when their affect was neutral. We also found that the expression of anger was significantly correlated with a "positive" deviation of the mean distribution of the REG output, while the expression of crying with anxiety or sadness significantly correlated with a "negative" output. These results were consistent, "across the board", not due to large deviations of a small sample. A graph of these results may be found in Figure 1, labeled "Combined Cumulative Deviation of REG Output." The parabola defines the

95% confidence level. It will be noted that the combined cumulative deviation (in bits) at the end of 40 to 50 thousand trials (each trial like the flip of a coin), for talking with neutral affect is no greater than that expected by chance alone, while the deviations for the expression of emotions anger is significantly greater (greater than the 95% confidence level) than that expected by chance. In fact these deviations were so remarkable that they would have been expected to occur by chance alone less than once in one hundred trials.

Discussion

It may be speculated that the upward, "positive" deviation shown in correlation with the expression of anger and the opposite deviation correlated with the expression of fear or crying with anxiety, sadness, or frustration, correspond to respective expansive and contractive movement of bioenergy within the expressing organism. However, as tempted as we might be to think that the REG output is a result of a physical energy or "force" emitted or withdrawn during moments of emotional expression it would be difficult to conclude so given the fact that there are several electronic rectifying elements between the power source of the REG and the final REG output. "Positive" and "negative"

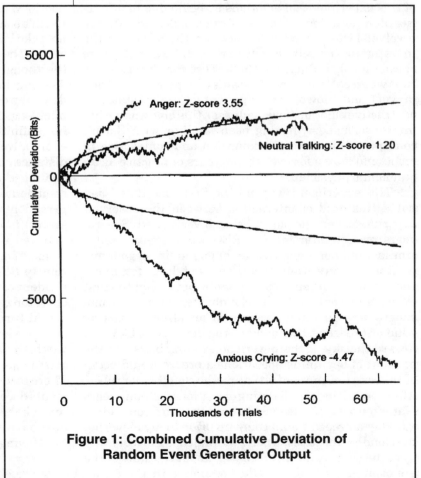

Figure 1: Combined Cumulative Deviation of Random Event Generator Output

REG output are *not* measures of "more" or "less" amounts of electrical energy being ordered out of a state of randomness, but are rather, strictly relative values resulting from a comparison of the actual output with a known template value.

Therefore, if our results (and the results obtained by other investigators in this genre of experimentation, cited above) cannot be explained by some physical energetic "force" emanating from the subject to the REG, we must conclude that some non-physical "agent" or "situation" (in the broadest sense of the term), is involved. Further, whatever this non-physical force, agent or "situation" might be we must account for the possible role of the investigator (myself, in this experiment) in obtaining our results.

Let us address the latter issue first. On the basis of the way in which the experiment was set up and conducted there is no way that we can rule out a possible influence by the experimenter. As demonstrated in previous studies by PEAR and others, cited above, in addition to conscious intentionality the simple presence of the operator without conscious intention toward influencing the REG can be of great importance in the outcome of the experiment. I suggest that until further experiments of this genre are performed and more information is available, that we understand the results of this experiment on emotions as being due to a functional interaction, a state of "resonance" of all the involved factors, the patient-subject, the REG, and the investigator (myself). For even though I was not aware of consciously influencing the REG so that it registered "up" when patients were in states of expansive emotion (anger) and "down" when patients were in states of contractive emotion (fear, sadness), this bias was within my consciousness, having been familiar with Reich's concepts of bioenergetic expansion and contraction in emotional states for over thirty years of practice as an orgonomic physician.

This experiment was not the first time that I had noted this kind of interaction between the observer/experiment and the object being investigated. Several years prior to starting the REG work I witnessed a similar phenomenon while engaged in orgonomic weather modification experiments. I had, for many years while doing such experiments, noted that the first evidence of contact by the cloudbuster with the atmosphere was an intensification of an already existing wind or breeze at the moment the device was elevated toward the sky. If there were no existing breeze at the moment of beginning operations a breeze would begin within a few minutes of elevating the cloudbuster tubes. After conducting cloudbusting operations for many years I later quite spontaneously noticed that on a completely still day a breeze would come up *prior* to my elevating the cloudbuster tubes, when I was at least 100 feet away from the device and only *thinking* about the state of the atmosphere and what could be done with the cloud-

buster. This happened many times when I was working and was confirmed by other cloudbuster operators. I hypothesized that the cloudbuster, the atmosphere, and myself "*cofunctioned*"[¶] with each other and that through thinking I programmed my organism to resonate with the cloudbuster and the atmosphere. It became clear to me then that it was possible that the conduction of experiments in other realms of orgonomic science involved the thought and intention of the investigator in ways that are presently unknown but should be investigated.

In this respect it is useful to review Reich's single investigation into dowsing, a practice that involves an intimate relationship between thought and bioenergetic functioning. After consulting with an effective dowser, and being convinced of the dowser's ability to detect water using a tree branch, Reich successfully tried it himself. His investigation led him to conclude that, "The branch only plays the role of an indicator. It is the organism of the dowser which reacts to the water in the ground" and, "The organism reacts (without any perception) to the spring in the ground with orgonotic excitation, since both the organism and the water are strongly orgonotic and represent two orgonotic systems."[13] In the light of the recent experiments in conscious intention, cited above, and other studies of non-local effects of the mind on matter, we can consider Reich's conclusion to be correct, but limited. Reich does not take into account the role of the conscious intentionality of the dowser to detect, specifically, *water*. Without the thought, "Is there water here?", for example, the dowsing branch, rod, pendulum or any of the other detection devices used in dowsing, will not respond. One might argue that Reich implicitly included thought in his definition of the "organism", but this would not explain the accurate dowsing over a map of targets at distances over 1000 miles away.[14] Nor would it explain healing at a distance,[15] or "remote viewing", the well-documented phenomenon whereby an individual (the percipient) can "know" where another individual (the target) is in space without being given any previous knowledge of the target's whereabouts[3]. It is also extremely important to note that intentional effects on a remote REG and remote viewing can take place independent of sidereal, "here-now", time. That is, the REG operator can effect the REG weeks in advance of the actual turning on of the device and the percipient in remote viewing experiments can know ahead of time where the target will be *before the target is even given his instructions* by a "blind" third party about where to go.[3] There are many other rigorously controlled experiments documenting these and similar phenomena, so as remarkable and unsettling as these effects may be, one may have a high degree of confidence in their reality.[§]

Having documented the above phenomena, what

[¶] I am indebted to Ray Reese for this term.

can we say of their implication for orgonomic theory? In all of the above-stated anomalous phenomena two individuals or individuals and a machine that generates impulses at random are in a kind of "resonant" contact within a realm of functioning that appears to be different than our known four-dimensional space time. Let us discuss resonance first.

With respect to resonance, Jahn and Dunne[3] offer a wave theory of functioning and state that the anomalous REG phenomena only appear when the operator embraces the REG as target with a feeling akin to "love". This reminds one of Reich's functional approach to investigation in the orgonomic realm. "In order to investigate nature...we must *love* the object of research." In *Cosmic Superimpositon*[16] Reich describes a process whereby two mass-free orgone energy streams can superimpose upon each other, creating mass in the process. He describes superimposition as being the primary function when two individuals engage in a loving genital embrace. I suggest that the function of resonance as it manifests in the above-described experiments is a more finely-tuned sub-variation of the deeper, broader, possibly "coarser" function of orgone energetic superimposition.

With respect to the "different" realm of functioning, I suggest that this realm is deeper and broader than the realm of physical reality as we ordinarily know it and that it "informs" and is "informed by" our four-dimensional time/space. It is highly unlikely that the operative force within this realm is electromagnetic energy : The anomalous phenomena show no drop-off of the signal with distance as one always finds with known physical forces and, most telling, there is no known physical force that can explain the well-documented temporal anomalies. We may, however, find an operative "force" in this realm in Reich's "mass-free" orgone energy. Reich describes the "ocean" of mass-free orgone energy surrounding our planet as that place (or realm) from which a "pointed-state" of orgone emerges. It is considered to be a realm of energetic functioning that is the "substrate", so to speak , of our known physical reality, a "place" from which physical matter spontaneously emerges.¶

---

§ Radin states, *"..some individual psi experiments have produced results with odds against chance greater than a billion to one. And the odds after combining thousands of psi experiments are astronomically beyond that."* Radin, D. *The Conscious Universe*, Harper/San Francisco, 1997.
¶ One is reminded here of recent research on "zero-point energy", the energy of the vacuum, where virtual particles spontaneously emerge from a fundamental "ground", that is claimed to be the original "stuff" of which our universe is made. See Haisch, B., Rueda, A. and Puthoff, H. "Beyond E=mc²", *The Sciences*, November/December, 1994 p.26.

"An overall view seems to indicate that *from the general energy substratum of cosmic orgone energy arise and sink back again countless individual, luminating, concentrated orgone energy units*. They separate from their matrix and unite again with it. We could compare this functioning with water waves which arise from an undulating sea under the influence of a stiff breeze, producing white, pointed crests. The waves arise from the sea, live through, each in its own way, a certain lifetime, and sink back, dissolving again into the general substratum. *Thus each unit shows a distinct individuality, a birth, a peak of individual existence, and a decline and death."* (italics Reich's)[16]

Reich describes this process as the "common functioning principles of rise and fall of galaxies, planets, organisms, clouds and primordial cosmic energy".[16]

At this point it is important to note that the usually described qualities of orgone energy, its "blueness", pulsatory and lightening-like luminations in the orgone room, slow pulsatory movements in the atmosphere, "flickerings" in the sky, bioenergetic currents and streamings, "excitations" in the presence of another, etc., are manifestations of orgone energy in the process of or subsequent to its emergence in our atmosphere from its cosmic, mass-free state. Further, the sensing of these manifest orgonotic phenomena is constrained by our armor and the bioenergetic and structural limitations that are naturally inherent in our present state of evolution. On a strictly mechanical level human beings have the ability to directly sense only within a very limited range (perhaps 5%) of the totality of the full range of known measurable radiations, not to mention radiations currently beyond our conceptual and instrumental capacities. The detection of anomalous elevations of temperature and the slowing of electrostatic discharge within the orgone energy accumulator are objective verifications of our perceptions of orgone energy, but are, in many respects the result of the interaction of manifest orgone energy with mass - air molecules and static electrical charge, respectively. The measurement of anomalously huge energetic charges in orgonotically charged vacuum tubes (VACOR tube) and in the accumulator by the Geiger-Mueller counter is closer to the direct measurement of mass-free orgone.[17] What this indicates is that it is unlikely that the soft, slow, pendular, wavy, undulatory functions of manifest orgone energy can be the substrate for the non-local, apparently instantaneous transmission of information seen in paranormal phenomena. But, as we approach the mass-free state and orgonotic functions attending the "pointed" state of orgone energy, we find enormous quantities of energy in action, *as much as 25,000 impulses per second*, as measured with a special variation of a Geiger Counter.[17]

Also, within the mass-free realm of functioning the

potential speed of movement of a signal can apparently far exceed known speeds of mass moving within the constraints of our four-dimensional time/space. Reich describes the "motion" of mass-free orgone as being in the form of a spinning wave, a KRW (Kreiselwelle).[18] Moving along the lines of a spinning wave, mass-free orgone spontaneously pulsates, swinging with alternating acceleration and deceleration. Utilizing a functional variation of the classical wave equation, measurements of the frequency of pulsation of differing lengths of swinging pendulums, and his own, functionally-derived, "Kr^x" number system, Reich generated mass-free equations that indicate that the speed of light is not the limiting speed in the universe.[18]

Conclusion

Evidence from contemporary consciousness research, including my own investigations on correlations between emotional expression and the output of a REG, indicates that contact between living beings and between living beings and machines can be effected at a distance and independent of sidereal time. These phenomena cannot be explained by the well-known theories of electromagnetism. At this time we may best understand these phenomena by postulating a function of "resonance" operating in a realm that is deeper and broader than our four-dimensional space-time. If, as Reich maintains, mass-free orgone energy is the fundamental substrate for all functions within the cosmos, it must in some way be the basis for resonance functioning within this deeper realm. Evidence is presented from Reich's research indicating that mass-free orgone is capable of generating enormous amounts of energy functioning at speeds well beyond that of light. These qualities may, indeed, provide the physical basis for the anomalous transfer of information in question.

References:

1. Reich, W. *American Odyssey*, Farrar, Straus and Giroux, N.Y., 1999 p.406.

2. Reich, W. *Ether, God, and Devil*, Orgone Institute Press, 1949, Rangeley, 1949 p.52.

3. Jahn, R.G. & Dunne, B.J. *Margins of Reality*, Harcourt, Brace, Joanovich, N.Y., 1987.

4. Nelson, R.D., Jahn, R. G., Dunne, B.J., Dobyns, Y.H., & Bradish, G.J. "FieldREG 2, Consciousness field effects: Replications and explorations". *J. Scientific Exploration* 12, 1998, p. 425.

5. Radin, D.I., Rebman, M., & Cross, M.P. "Anomalous organization of random events by group consciousness: Two exploratory experiments", *J. Scientific Exploration*, 10, 1996, p. 143.

6. Burr, H.S., *Blueprint for Immortality*, London, Neville Spearman, 1972.

7. Burr, H.S., & Northrop, F.S.C. "The Electrodynamic Theory of Life", *Quarterly Review of Biology,* 10, 1935, p. 322.

8. Reich, W. *The Function of the Orgasm*, Meridian, N.Y. 1942.

9. Braid, B. & Dew, R., "Reich's Bioelectric Experiments: A review with recent data." *Annals of the Institute for Orgonomic Science*, 5, 1988, p.1.

10. Reich, W. *The Cancer Biopathy*, Orgone Institute Press, N.Y., 1948.

11. Blasband, R.A. " The Ordering of Random Events by Emotional Expression", *J. Scientific Exploration* 14/2 2000 p.195.

12. Baker, E.F. *Man in the Trap*. New York: Macmillan. 1967.

13. Reich, W. "Dowsing' as an Object of Orgonomic Research", *Orgone Energy Bulletin* 3:3, 1951, p. 139.

14. Roberts, K. *The Seventh Sense*, Doubleday & Co., Inc.. Garden City, N.Y.1953.

15. Sicher, F., Targ, E., Moore, D. & Smith, H. A "Randomized Double-Blind Study of the Effect of Distant Healing in a Population with Advanced AIDS". *Subtle Energies a& Energy Medicine* 9:2 1998 p. 83 Originally appeared in the *Western Journal of Medicine* 169 (1998).

16. Reich, W. *Cosmic Superimposition*, The Wilhelm Reich Foundation, Orgonon, Rangeley, Maine, 1951, p.195.

17. Reich, W. "The Oranur Experiment", *Orgone Energy Bulletin*, 3:4, 1951.

18. Reich, W. *Contact with Space*, CORE Pilot Press, N.Y., N.Y. 1957. p.97.

Open Discussion on the New Consciousness Research

James DeMeo: Thank you Dr. Blasband for a fascinating paper, in which I believe you have opened up new territory for us all to consider. Your ideas raise many questions, however, and I'll give you several. Firstly, you discuss several different types of REG phenomenon:

A- Proximal effects by humans on the REG, where the REG apparatus is close to the experimenter or test subject, and yields results at the same time of attempted influence.

B - Distance effects, where there is a large distance between the experimenter/subject and REG, but also with results obtained at the same time of attempted influence.

C- Time-independent effects, where there is both distance and lapses of time between the operation of the REG and the experimental undertaking which is claimed to affect it.

I can immediately accept the results from Type A phenomenon, as it appears quite similar to the effects of a typical healer, who uses energy from the hands to affect another person. Type B phenomenon also have supporting evidence from the field of energy healing, even if it has not been documented to the same level as with Type A phenomenon. Certainly, with cloudbusting, we employ a similar long-distance influence.

For Type C phenomenon, however, my sense is — even if you assume backwards-time or forwards-time direction of causality — the basic phenomenon has yet to be fully demonstrated. For example, if an REG gives anomalous readings outside the framework of the causal initiative of the operator, and one accepts the idea that both Type A and Type B phenomenon also are possible ways to affect the REG apparatus, then how can one tell for sure, if the claimed Type C phenomenon wasn't in fact simply a more localized response (Type A or B) to some other phenomenon that was affecting the background mechanisms? From your own work, for example, a very angry person or crying person "nearby" might affect the REG apparatus unknown to the experimenters, who might otherwise consider it the result of a time-displaced reaction. I also wonder if phenomenon such as solar flares, which Piccardi[§] showed would affect even basic crystallization phenomenon, might also affect the REG. It seems to me, the REG reactions (of "positive" or "negative") are not sufficiently specific to prove the Type C effect, unless specifically-targeted time periods were selected using very tight experimental controls. For example, the experimenter says they will try to affect the REG at 2 pm, five days into the future or five days into the past (using a blinded experimental procedure), and the REG is allowed to operate for many days, showing its only significant reactions at that 2 pm target period. One would have to show long periods of inactivity followed by a burst of activity at a specifically targeted time period, followed by another period of inactivity, and with those maintaining the apparatus doing so in a "blinded" condition, ignorant of the target time period. Has this kind of highly-controlled experimental result been obtained for the Type C phenomenon?

Richard Blasband: Leaving aside discussion on the fundamental nature of time, which is a topic too formidable to entertain in brevity, but is pertinent to our discussion, permit me to address the details which you mention. With respect to the influence of *nearby* others who might also be possibly influencing the experiment, I can, at this point, only agree with Radin. He asked the same question about the results of his own experiments using the REG with groups, where he found spontaneous anomalous changes in REG output when group excitation was high compared to times when it was neutral. His answer is that in the conduct of his experiments, he, *"..assumed that the mental noise generated by everyone else in the world was random in time [emphasis his] with respect to the events of interest in our experiments. Therefore, all other minds did not systemically affect the specific results that we were monitoring. While other groups were undoubtedly involved in many interesting high-focus activities, we assumed that those activities did not occur at the same times as the events in our experiments. In other words, we speculated that we detected field-consciousness effects because we knew precisely when, where, and how to look for them."* (Radin, *The Conscious Universe*, Harper San Francisco, 1997, p.173).

In what would be agreement with you, Radin (op cit p.178) describes over a dozen studies showing a robust correlation between geomagnetic field effects and behavior (including psi). The psi effects improve as geomagnetic fluctuations decrease. Radin also cites some evidence of correlation between psi effects and phases of the moon.

With respect to the temporal anomalies, I do not believe that the experiment you outline has been done, although it would be a good one to do. What has been done, utilizing a plethora of well-thought-out controls, are several kinds of "precognitive" studies, in which a "percipient" tries to "know" what an "agent" in the field is seeing hours prior to the agent going to some place unknown to either. The place is selected by a blinded, third party using a method of random selection. These studies have yielded very robust correlations. (Radin, op cit p.117, Jahn & Dunne, 1987 p. 151). There are also the pre-telekinetic or pre-cognitive effects noted by Jahn and Dunne (1987), where operators influence the REG

[§] G. Piccardi: *Chemical Basis of Medical Climatology*, Charles Thomas Publisher, Springfield, IL 1963.

at a distance and "off-time" by weeks.

James DeMeo: A recent paper in the *Journal of Scientific Exploration* showing unclear or negative results from various REG experiments[¶] as undertaken in different laboratories concluded there was an "inadequate understanding of the basic phenomenon involved and suggested a need for more sophisticated experiments and theoretical models", and I hope your own work in this regard will be given a broader consideration by those undertaking the REG experiments. Specifically, I am wondering if the overall phenomenon might be subject to some of the same problems we face with orgone accumulator experiments — while neither orgone nor REG phenomenon are electromagnetic in nature, the REG test subjects and experiments may in fact be affected by disturbing *oranur*, as from power line fields, fluorescent lights, etc. I know your office is in a very clean environment, energetically speaking, and you got a very good result. Do any other of the REG experimenters take these factors into account? Most typical laboratories these days are highly contaminated, bioenergetically speaking.

Richard Blasband: To the best of my knowledge, while aware of the effects of solar flares and other geophysical events, experimenters in the psi field are unaware of oranur. I am certainly aware of them, but can, at this point, find no correlation between high oranur conditions and REG effects, although this does not rule oranur out as a possible influencing factor. Fortunately, the atmosphere here in the San Francisco Bay area is relatively clean.

James DeMeo: The Z-scores you obtained from REG responses to emotional phenomenon are quite strong — stronger, in fact, than most of the more purely cognitive reactions noted in the consciousness-related literature I am familiar with. It suggests to me, that emotions are more powerful affectors of the local field than are purely cognitive elements. This agrees with the idea that spontaneous emotional phenomenon — which engage both psyche and soma in unitary action — are more highly-charged and carry a stronger affect as compared to more "calculated" or "thought-out" factors which lack an emotional component.

Richard Blasband: You are quite right about the strength of the REG effect with emotions compared to those usually obtained by more cognitive approaches. Indeed, this was in my mind when I started the experiment. Of course we would have to ask whether the obtained results were, in some way, a function of my belief, as I

¶ R. Jahn, et al: "Mind/Machine Interaction Consortium: PortREG Replication Experiments", *J. Scientific Exploration*, 14(4):499-555, Winter 2000.

indicated in the body of my paper. But here we would have to ask what we mean by "stronger". Usually we mean degree of "force", but this might not be the best way to think about what is going on. Another possibility is "greater intentionality", albeit an unconscious process in the case of the emotions expressed in my experiment. This is where interpretation is "up for grabs". At this point we simply do not know. But, it seems to me, that our understanding of this aspect of the phenomenon is crucial for the understanding of how this deeper, broader realm of nature actually functions. In this context it is well to examine our beliefs as to how "local" REG (and healing) effects take place. One can readily assume that an energy is emitted by the operator (or healer) directly into the system in question (machine, man). I believe that this is true to a considerable extent, but there is clearly something else going on, which is generally subsumed under the term, "information transfer". This is necessary to explain not only that an effect (anomalous REG production or healing) is taking place, but the direction of that effect, whether it be unexplainable increase or decrease in REG output or improvement in physical or emotional well-being. Certainly in the case of "non-local" man-machine interactions and healing, we must invoke some other mechanism (or possibly synchronicity) than direct physical energy transfer as it is classically understood.

James DeMeo: One set of experiments I would encourage you to undertake, here at the Greensprings Center if needed using the orgone energy darkroom, would be to evaluate the role of the orgone accumulator and dor-buster in the functioning of the REG apparatus and experiments. For example, what happens when this apparatus is placed inside an accumulator, or under the tubes of a dor-buster? You express the view that the absolute charge does not affect the REG, but has this idea been empirically tested? Also, if the operator was sitting inside an accumulator, would this increase the strength of the REG responses? If so, it would provide good support for the theoretical linkages you are proposing.

Richard Blasband: I have long wanted to put an REG inside an accumulator to see if there was any change in the former's output. Unfortunately the devices are a bit expensive and until recently I had only one of them and have been afraid of "changing" the device a la oranur, and rendering it unsuitable for routine use. I now have two REGs and others built by the same company can be obtained, and will proceed to do what you suggest. No, I have not tested the effect of relative amount of charge (degree of emotional expression) on the REG, but it is an excellent suggestion, which I will try to implement. Having the operator inside an accumulator is another good idea to test.

Orgonometry: A New Detector

by Courtney F. Baker, M.D.*

A number of methods have been used to measure the orgone energy, or at least register its presence, via its conversion into conventional [secondary] energies, or its effect on conventional apparatus. These are summarized below:

1. The human skin potential;
2. Spontaneous charging of rubber gloves, cotton, celluloid in an orgone accumulator (orac) or near bion cultures;
3. Fogging of photographic plates;
4. Spontaneous magnetization of iron instruments in the presence concentrated orgone;
5. Visual impressions of moving points of light which can be magnified with a lens;
6. Charging of the Geiger-Muller counter tubes to register orgone energy;
7. Measurement of the orgone accumulator heating effect (To-T);
8. The magnetic field of the accumulator;
9. Electroscope discharge rates;
10. Charging and lumination within a high vacuum tube.

The reader is referred elsewhere[1,2] for a specific description of each of the experimental situations mentioned above. In general, orgone energy measurements are often difficult and frustrating because of their great variability and difficulty of reproduction. Many of the measurements (especially To-T and electroscope) are highly weather dependent; others which involve biological preparations show an unpredictability of results despite apparently identical experimental conditions. Two of the most reliable measurements are To-T (the orgone accumulator heating effect) and electroscope discharge rates. These two experiments generate data which is generally clearly correlated with the weather.

Physics of Electrostatic Charge

In the conventional realm, the phenomena of electrostatic charge is considered well understood. Charge consists of some kind of "electrostatic" entity bound to material particles (such as the electron or proton) which produces an influence at a distance (indeed, this is how we know of the entity called "charge"). Concentrations of

* Courtney Baker, M.D., is a medical orgonomist, and may be contacted at: 956 Tennis Ave., Ambler, Pennsylvania 19002. Tel. 215-643-1229. Email: <Rafbaker@att.net>

net charge readily demonstrate effects on suitable nearby objects (such as electrostatic attraction for small bits of paper). Such particles and their associated charge when in motion produce in addition magnetic fields and may radiate electromagnetic energy. The electrostatic charge associated with a given particle is exactly the same for each particle and inseparable from it. What exactly the nature and origin of "charge" consists of is unknown. Further, charge is believed to produce its effects through empty space, via massless particles called photons.

While these observations are well established, they constitute only a small subset of the overall phenomena of "charge" *as found in nature*, as revealed by a number of orgonotic experiments. These experiments suggest a much broader concept regarding charge, and shed light on its origin and various stages of transformation from the orgone energy.

The first consideration is that orgone energy is *mass-free*. By this is meant the fact that its existence is not dependent on mass in any form; by contrast, all other energies have a direct, explicit association with matter [heat is the motion of matter; light is radiated from material particles; magnetic and electrostatic fields arise from charged particles of matter; nuclear radiation comes from the atomic nucleus, etc].

The second consideration is that of the relationship of orgone energy to "electrostatic" energy. This question first arose when Reich began to do electroscope discharge measurements, and found that the discharge rate was slower in the orac. Experimental findings and simple reasoning led to his conclusion that:

"...the [orgone] energy is an energy *other than electricity*." [1:109]

He reaffirmed this conclusion again a page later, after considering that the slower rate in the orac was due to concentrated orgone energy and not ionization, since ionization would naturally increase the discharge rate. The concentrated orgone in the orac therefore did not manifest as ionization, but rather reduced the energy gradient between the electroscope and environment. This was a new way of looking at the discharge rate.

It is clear, therefore, that orgone energy, even when concentrated, is not the same thing as electrostatic energy, even though there is a strong relationship between the two, and even through orgone can sometimes manifest with electrostatic effects. Consider the following observations, which suggest that a transformation takes place from biological or atmospheric orgone to "electrostatic" charge:

1) During Reich's work with the bion cultures, strong radiation was discovered coming from them; in some cases his hand showed a local inflammation from exposure to the radiation. Yet, this radiating energy *did not activate the electroscope.* A rubber glove, however, laying near some cultures did unexpectedly show a vigorous electroscopic reaction.

2) Organic substances (plastic, cotton) placed in the orac will, *after a period of time,* activate the electroscope. Since it has already been established that *the concentrated energy in the orac is not ionization,* then again a transformation appears to have taken place, in that the concentrated orgone absorbed onto the organic matter manifests electrostatically.

3) We may readily activate an electroscope by drawing a comb through the hair, which concentrates orgone onto it; in clear, dry weather several thousand volts may be obtained on the comb. Yet, the orgone energy in the hair does not manifest electrostatically (otherwise the hair would be sticking away from the head).

4) Reich was able to concentrate orgone energy in a highly evacuated glass tube (*vacor*) by placing it in an orac for several weeks. The application of high voltage excitation would not only cause the orgone to luminate, but also to produce discharges from a central wire *which would activate an electroscope.*

We are therefore inclined to draw the conclusion that free orgone energy in the air, in the interior of an orac, or within living organisms does not normally manifest as electrostatic energy. By "manifest", we mean simply that the *electroscope reacts,* i.e., behaves superficially the same way as when charged with high voltage electricity. We are not saying that orgone-charged objects have concentrated electrons on them (or a deficit of electrons).

Indeed, more careful observation of electroscope behavior shows that the "electrostatic charge" obtained from orgone behaves differently from electrostatic charge obtained from a conventional high voltage source:

5) Careful analysis of discharge curves of the electroscope sometimes shows two superimposed discharge curves, suggesting a *mixture of different kinds of charge.* That is, drawing the comb through the hair evidently creates both conventional electrostatic ions as well as concentrated/transformed orgone energy charge, both registering as "electrostatic" charge.[3]

6) In dry weather in winter, a comb-charged electroscope may show a *spontaneous increase in deflection,* indicating that it is drawing in more energy. This is a non-mechanical, i.e., *orgonotic* effect.[4]

7) Certain experiments with the electroscope show that comb-energy will pass through (that is, allow the charging or discharging) of insulators such as plastic while ordinary high voltage DC will not pass.[4]

These latter experiments suggest that "electrostatic" charge derived from orgone energy sources behaves differently than conventional electrostatic charge. We strongly suspect that the main differences derives from the mass-free aspect of the orgone, i.e., that it is not tied to material particles. It is thus free to sometimes manifest other orgonotic qualities such as the low-to-high (reversed) flow of energy (example 6 above).

It is therefore necessary to distinguish between three types of "charge":

I. *Free orgone energy,* which does not register electrostatically but nevertheless can "charge" systems with energy;

II. *Mass-free electrostatic charge:* this entails electrostatic effects (i.e., will influence an electroscope) not due to particles, but to concentrated mass-free orgone energy;

III. *Mass-bound electrostatic charge,* such as associated with the well-known elementary particles: electron, proton, positron, etc.

The type II and III charges have in common the fact that they register at conventional electronic circuits. They are nevertheless different, since the mass-free type II charge would not produce the same heating effects (e.g., ohmic heating) as it moved in the circuits (see for example the experiments of Henry Moray[5]); type II charge evidently also retains some orgonotic functions as well (such as the flow from low to high).

The Detection Process

It is clear that electronic circuits, without special modification, are generally useless for detecting orgone energy, since the energy flows through the circuits without significant interaction. One approach to detection, therefore, is any process which would transform the moving orgone energy via stoppage, i.e., such as the rubber-glove and bion observations. One drawback here is the relatively long charging times involved.

A second approach is suggested by the normal functioning of biological systems. It is remarkable that with few exceptions (some enzyme systems) nature rarely uses electron flow; in the vast majority of cases, the "electrical" functioning of nature is via *ions.* Witness the profusion of ions in the body: charged protein ions, electrolytes, ionized layers across membranes, nerve conduction via ionic flow, etc. Evidently orgone energy interacts more readily with whole ions than it does with the solitary electrons. An ionized medium might therefore make a good orgone detector; in fact, the charged Geiger-Muller tube functions via the ionization of the contained gas.

The Detector

The presently described detection system is the outcome of many years of systematic and often frustrating research.[§] A large number of experimental observations were made and recorded until a reliable detector was discovered, and further testing revealed no artifacts were involved. The first crude detector was quickly modified; the first major improvement resulting in a ten-fold increase in sensitivity. Further quantitative and even qualitative improvements have been made since then.

The detector acts by directly transforming the moving orgone energy [entering via the antenna] directly into an electrical potential which will register at conventional electronic circuits. That is, type I charge is transformed into type II charge, which can then interact with the type III charges in conventional electronic circuitry. In this case the conventional circuitry is a millivoltmeter with full-scale ranges from one millivolt to five volts, with a provision for carefully adjusting the circuit to offset any drift. The output is displayed on a microammeter, which can be zeroed at the center of the scale, for easy recognition of polarity reversals. The reading of orgone activity is reported as millivolts (electrical conversion equivalent).

A simple schematic of the detection system is shown below:

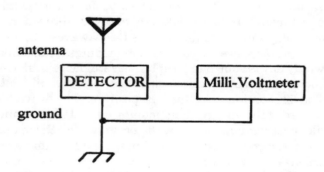

The term "antenna" used in this context means any conductor connected to the input of the detector and used to transmit orgone energy from the outside to the detector itself. In practice, antennas for laboratory work (i.e. such as reading energy emission from a leaf) involves conducting metal receptors (such as a wire or flat plate) from one to three inches in size; for mobile outdoor work, antennas from three to eight inches (a short wire); and for atmospheric work, a fixed shortwave [long wire]

§ Author's note: Since the detector is still under development, details of its construction cannot be revealed at this time. The millivoltmeter was designed for this project and is thus not a commercially available unit; however, it is otherwise unremarkable, being made from standard solid state devices using a straightforward circuit design, with the output displayed on a microammeter.

type of antenna.

The output of the detector is fed through electronic circuits to the microammeter without a net reversal of polarity. Thus, a positive deflection of the meter indicates a positive voltage coming from the detector. In addition, the final reading represents no net amplification of the detector signal. Thus the electrical reading equivalent for the orgone that is reported in millivolts is directly proportional to the electrical value immediately exiting the detector.

With experience, it became apparent that the detector does not measure the normal background level of orgone energy, or any static orgone energy fields. In careful trials outdoors at high scale sensitivities it did not register a nearby ten-fold accumulator, and showed only a very minimal (difficult to distinguish from background noise) response to the body when not moving, i.e., a steady hand held near the detector antenna. On the other hand, even slight motion of the body or hand can produce dramatic deflections of the needle. The detector essentially responds to *moving orgone energy* discharging into (or out of) the metal antenna input.

The Energy Field of the Body

Various configurations of small metal antennas have been tried in the process of studying the energy field of the human body. In general, the detector is extremely reactive to any body motion with antenna sizes ranging down in size as small as an inch.

A standard antenna developed for mobile outdoor work consists of a straight eight inch stiff wire. Hand sensitivity can be judged by waving the hand nearby (i.e., at a distance of one-two feet) using the 200 mv scale. [Remarkably, the sensitivity often seems to depend on the geographic location.] Waving the hand can produce anything from a slight motion of the scale (low sensitivity) to full scale deflections of the meter (high sensitivity). The readings may be taken with the unit Earth-grounded, or alternatively "grounded" by being held in the hand, i.e., the metal chassis "grounds" to the skin surface.

This sensitivity in some cases actually becomes a nuisance, since readings for other purposes have to be taken with the observer absolutely still and no other human movement nearby. On the high sensitivity scales (say, 20-50 mv full scale) it becomes extremely difficult to make accurate readings without tedious repetition, since even the slightest shifting in the chair results in large scale movements of the needle.

Several special observations may be noted. With one type of small antenna partially enclosed in a metal cylinder open at one end (facing outward), the detector was still extremely sensitive to the body field, even when several feet away and Earth-grounded. On several occasions, with this unit held in the lap and the antenna facing outward approximately six inches from the leg, small but clearly discernible pulsations of the needle were observed which correlated exactly with the radial pulse. In this case, it is apparent the unit was registering the QRS complex [of the normal electrocardiogram] as it was manifested by variations in the body energy field. The needle movement represented about five millivolts. By comparison, the amplitude of the QRS complex recorded by Reich in the bioelectric experiment skin potentials was about two to three millivolts.[6]

Another response that is regularly seen with outdoor work with the eight inch antenna is a slow, rhythmic pulsation when the unit is held at waist level with the antenna facing outward. This corresponds to respiration; inspiration gives a slow, negative-going excursion of about 20-50 mv, which then returns to baseline with expiration. That this is not an artefact of body motion is easily tested for by deliberately moving the unit. In these situations the effect is minimized when taking readings by momentarily holding the breath.

The full extent of the body field effect became apparent when a careful trial was done to determine the maximum range of this phenomenon. A test subject stood in front of the unit (eight-inch antenna, 200 mv scale, outdoors on wet grassy area) and waved her arms, giving vigorous needle deflections. She then took successive steps backward and repeated the waving. Small but clearly observable needle deflections were noted up to a maximum distance of 28 feet.

Atmospheric Readings

A long copper wire antenna elevated above the ground is effective for making energetic contact with the atmosphere. Three types of electromagnetic and electrical phenomena in the atmosphere are recognized:

(1) Radio waves, (electromagnetic energy) spanning a huge spectrum of wavelengths. Voltages on the antenna are nominally in the microvolt region, and reception requires some minimum tuning and detecting circuits;

(2) High voltage (hundreds to thousands of volts) transients during local thunderstorm activity. These potentials rapidly rise and fall in magnitude and are easily observed using a gold-leaf electroscope;

(3) The Earth's potential gradient. The fair-weather potential gradient is about 150 volts/meter and is slowly varying (over hours to days). Special apparatus is required measure it, namely, an amplifier with an extremely high input resistance and a source of ionization (usually a radioactive disc).

In the present experiment, a 135 foot copper wire was suspended from 10 to 25 feet above the ground in the open air and connected to the input of the detector in a attempt to measure orgone energy functions in the atmosphere. Grounding was done via a four foot copper stake driven approximately two feet into moist soil. The output from the detector (see diagram above) fed a millivoltmeter which shared a common ground with the detector.

Immediately on setting up this system, a great *variation* in readings was apparent. The meter needle swung back and forth, sometimes slow and sometimes abruptly, and often paused for periods of time at a particular reading only to then resume motion. Frequently the needle crossed zero, indicating reversal of electrical polarity. The rate of motion of the needle was relatively slow, i.e., taking several seconds to rise to a peak, and sometimes staying at a peak for several minutes at a time. It was obvious that a single reading did not adequately characterize what was happening in the atmosphere. For this reason a recording technique was begun in which a continuous series of readings were taken every 15 seconds for at least 10 minutes (i.e., 40 or more readings). Statistical and graphical analysis could then be done on this data, which gave a much fuller *qualitative* picture of the orgone energy activity than any single reading.

On a typical clear, windy day the voltage continually wanders, frequently crossing the zero position and demonstrating 8-12 wave-like changes during a ten-minute recording period, indicating a wave every 50-70 seconds. The waves tend to come in roughly two sizes: infrequent large voltage waves alternating with more frequent smaller waves. On less active days there may be only 7-8 waves per period, about 90 seconds apart, with less variation in size. Thus, highly active days (very windy) may have sharp high peaks and many smaller waves; a quiet day may have fewer, broad slow waves.

The display of 45 consecutive readings on an active, windy day is shown in Graph I. Several large peaks are shown which approach a magnitude of 1000 millivolts. The predominant voltage is positive. The wave-like nature of the energy being monitored is striking, much like observations made at the ocean shore. Reich very aptly referred to the cosmic energy continuum as the *orgone energy ocean*.

This pattern of activity is markedly different from the atmospheric electrical effects mentioned above. The *quality* of the readings is non-mechanical, neither sudden nor sharp but rather slowly undulating wave-like in character. The pattern is furthermore strongly weather-dependent. The *amplitude* is orders of magnitude larger than received electromagnetic radiation, but much smaller than transients or the potential gradient. It is likewise much slower than transient discharges, but much more rapid than the very slow (hours to days) changes in the potential gradient. Other considerations (to be discussed) show characteristics very different from known electrical phenomenon.

On "quiet" days (no wind) the detector output shows infrequent polarity reversal; indeed, in ten readings of quiet days seven of them did not reverse polarity at all. However, as soon as any measurable wind is present, the frequency of zero crossings increases markedly. This is shown in Table 1.

In addition, there is a clear correlation of average detector output (computed by averaging all of the 15 second readings during the ten minute observation period) and weather. Clear weather, or partial cloudiness (fair weather cumulus) show readings in the low positive or even negative regions, and a great deal of needle movement. The magnitude increases and polarity generally remains positive in overcast weather, with reduced variation. This tendency is increased further with precipitation. In some cases (overcast) the needle remained virtually still for the full ten-minute observation period. See Table 2.

Several special observations can now be discussed. On a windy day, rapid swinging of the needle often seems correlated with sudden gusts of wind. The correlation is often just a general impression, although occasionally the rise in the needle appears to *precede* the motion of the trees outside. Other considerations [outside the scope of this paper] suggest strongly that in many cases wind is essentially the result of air set in motion by direct action of the orgone energy, i.e., a macroscopic transfer of momentum to the air molecules. Here, the orgone impulse from the atmospheric orgone

Table 1:
Correlation between polarity reversals and wind.

Wind	Number of Zero Crossings	Average
Calm	7, 2, 0, 5, 0, 0, 0, 0, 0, 0	<2
Breezy	11, 12	11
Windy	9, 20	15
Very Windy	14, 42	28

Table 2:
Correlation between weather and average magnitude.

Weather	Average Magnitudes (mv)	Average
Clear	86, 155	120
Scat. Clouds	432, -120, -182, 212, 34, -57	53
Overcast	545, 776, 836, 1138	824
Rain or Snow	1154, 1993, 599, 953	1175

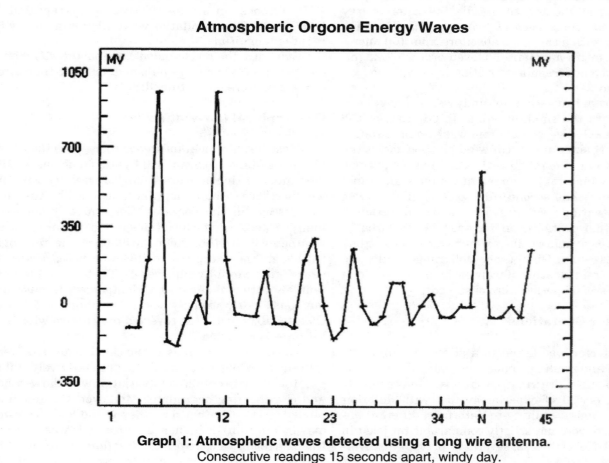

Graph 1: Atmospheric waves detected using a long wire antenna.
Consecutive readings 15 seconds apart, windy day.

into the air substance would very likely be *accompanied by an orgone impulse into other matter as well* (such as the antenna wire). This is an example of the functional pair of charge and momentum:[7]

$$\text{Orgone Impulse} = \int \frac{\ell^2}{t} \int \begin{cases} q = \text{charge [measured at antenna]} \\ mv = \text{momentum [wind]} \end{cases}$$

Diagram 1:
The functional pair of charge and momentum.

The data shows that in overcast or rainy weather states the polarity does not reverse, so a continuous flow of energy in one direction is suggested, reminiscent of a DC flow of electricity. In order to study this phenomenon, a high voltage (i.e. highly insulated) capacitor of .001 microfarads was inserted in *series* with the antenna and detection circuit. Astonishingly, this procedure *had no discernible effect whatsoever on the readings*. This indicates that the energy is capable of flowing without hinderance right through the substance of the capacitor, suggesting the possibility that despite the slow-moving character of the needle, the actual energy movement may consist of *high frequency impulses*. Further testing with a range of capacitors from 100 microfarad to 10 micro-microfarad, [seven orders of magnitude], showed an irregular variation in amplitude by a factor of two.

Strong rapid pulsations in windy weather have been observed with the small antenna. In one case at the shore of Lake George, N.Y., a front was coming through, with overcast skies and a stiff wind blowing across the lake. The water was rough with occasional whitecaps. Using the 500mv range, zeroed at center scale, rapid (approximately one second) full scale oscillation was seen, representing >250mv swings in each direction.

In another instance on an open grassy area in eastern Pennsylvania readings were taken while a strong wind was blowing. On the one volt range, full scale oscillations (representing 500 mv each direction) with a one to four second period were observed.

Cloudbuster Operations

The detector was taken to a site of cloudbusting operations, and readings made over many days before, during and after drawing operations. Unfortunately this was a period of experimentation with different antenna systems, resulting in data from different antennas which were not strictly comparable (at least in magnitude). Nevertheless, several important discoveries came out of this work.

An initial survey of the site (consisting of a large grassy field near a highway, with a small pond, driveway, and second pond) produced consistent differences in the readings near the cloudbuster, and at a distance (50 feet or more distant). Near the cloudbuster readings were low (20-40mv range) but higher elsewhere (up to 160 mv). This was initially attributed to the energy-modifying effect of drawing operations. However, continued readings, particularly after the cloudbuster had been dormant for several days, resulted in the dawning realization that these consistent readings were *a function of the local geography*. This will be discussed below.

Other than geographical readings, two types of cloudbuster operation phenomena were noted. In the first, there were three occasions when the local readings all dropped proportionately (from 25 to 50%) shortly after (10 minutes) starting operations, or after completion. All three cases were followed by rain; in one case by rain in several hours, in the other cases by rain in 24-48 hours.

In the second phenomena, a dramatic oscillation of the detector was noted on several occasions (four readings) adjacent to the cloudbuster after the cloudbuster drawing was stopped, and grounding in the pond discontinued. Here, full scale deflections occurred with a period of about one second (i.e., with the meter zeroed at center scale, the needle would swing from zero to full scale and back). In one case the reading was repeated an hour later and the oscillation was still present, but with reduced magnitude.

Evidently the ungrounded cloudbuster was highly charged, and this energy pulsated for some time after operations were discontinued.

Geographical Correlation

Most measurements of orgone energy functions take place at a stable geographical location (such as a fixed laboratory setting) and are strongly correlated with the weather. This includes familiar functions like To-T and electroscope discharge rates. Consequently one normally expects that the atmospheric variation with weather will be the major variable in the readings. [Although one exception to this was noticed several years ago: a carefully balanced To-T set-up gave consistently negative readings at a Montgomery County lab, but consistently strongly positive readings in a Bucks County lab (which then reverted to negative when the set-up was returned).]

The detector readings at the cloudbuster site were initially puzzling, since they appeared relatively stable over the site with only 25-50% variation with the weather and cloudbusting operations. Moreover, the readings tended to run together, i.e., they would both be lower (say before rain) or higher. Eventually it was realized that the readings were *primarily a function of location*, and secondarily a function of the weather and cloudbusting operations.

Initial location-effect readings were done in open fields, far from trees. Generally open grassy areas show a low reading, but some locations show strongly increased readings not correlated with any obvious environmental features.

This location effect was examined more carefully at a wooded residential property in Montgomery County, at three locations: (1) a grassy backyard area, (2) on a concrete dam and patio next to the dam (five feet away) near a small pond, and (3) at three locations five feet apart at the end of a driveway. Representative readings are shown in Table 3 below:

Several trends are apparent in Table 3. The grassy area shows consistently low readings regardless of weather. In three of four cases where a comparison is possible, the patio only five feet away shows clearly stronger readings than the dam. All three cases of careful driveway measurement showed dramatic changes over a ten foot distance. There is no obvious reason for these differences, particular at the end of the driveway, where there are no changes in feature whatsoever.

In other words, geographic locations are apparently associated with relatively stable energetic patterns. While some variation with the weather is seen, the dominant variable is the location. Furthermore, strong changes in magnitude and even polarity are observed over remarkably short distances.

Antenna Size

It is clear from even a cursory examination of the data that antenna size is not linearly correlated with detector output. For example, the 135-foot antenna, which is more than two hundred times longer than the eight inch antenna, only gives readings a order of magnitude larger. In order to generate a rough analysis of the relationship, the antenna size has been correlated in Table 4 with the average maximum readings. By "average maximum" is meant the average of the largest values that are commonly seen during most readings,

with each type of antenna. In the case of the eight and three inch antennas, direct comparison can be made since at a given location readings by both can be done.

Table 4: Antenna Length Vs. Detector Voltage

Antenna (inches)	Maximum MV
1620	1500
8	250
3	100

A plot of the logarithm of antenna length versus maximum detector output gave a reasonably straight line (r=0.998). This very preliminary finding suggests a strongly nonlinear relationship between detector output and antenna length.

Discussion

In all measurements done to date, including both the long wire readings as well as those from the short antennas, there have been no instances of the absence of readings (including readings during steady rain and snow). Any "zero" readings have been momentary, representing polarity shifts but not the absence of activity. This observation stands in contrast to the case with To-T and electroscope discharge rates, both of which give markedly reduced or zero readings with the onset and arrival of rainy weather. In the latter case, however, the orgone energy has not ceased functioning; the zero readings are merely an indication of the limitation of these two forms of measurement in certain types of weather. The detector, therefore, appears to give a more realistic indication of orgone energy activity, since energy is always moving, even during rain.

The detector output demonstrates both positive and negative polarity. The most likely (but not the only) explanation for this is energy flowing into the antenna versus energy flowing out of the antenna. In the case of

Table 3: Variations in readings due to geographical location (in millivolts)

Date	Weather	Grass	Dam	Patio	Driveway (x3)
9-19	clear, sunny	20	**	-20 var	**
9-19	clear, sunny	+10	+10	+40	+100
10-2	sunny	**	-40 steady	+50 to -100	+60/+40/-20
10-7	clear, sunny	+20	0 to -50 var	0 to -50 var	+50 to +100 0 to -10 -20 to -40
10-20	overcast, wet	+10	-20	-60 to -100 var	+60/-20/-20

hand motion near the small antenna, the swinging of the needle is clearly correlated with the direction of motion, i.e., hand motion toward ("make") or away from ("break") the antenna. Other causes for the polarity variations (weather and location) are not as clear, but may involve pulsatory states of the energy, or sources and sinks of energy relative to the substances of the Earth.

It remains for further research to demonstrate the connection between the clear cut correlation of readings with location, and the energetic landscape of "geoenergy" as is often described by dowsers. They have described streams of energy moving across the surface of the Earth (often erroneously called "ley lines"), sources and sinks of energy, and places of crossing and special intensity ("power spots"). It is tempting to speculate that the stable positive and negative polarities associated with geographic location may in fact correspond to these entities. Only further research will tell.

References:

1. Reich, W.: *The Discovery of the Orgone, Vol. II: The Cancer Biopathy*. New York: Orgone Institute Press, 1948.

2. Reich, W.: "The Oranur Experiment, First Report (1947-1951)," *Orgone Energy Bulletin*, 3:185-344, October, 1951.

3. Baker, C.F. (pseud. Rosenblum, C.F.): "The Electroscope (Part II)," *Journal of Orgonomy*, 4:79-9, 1970.

4. Baker, C.F. (pseud. Rosenblum, C.F.): "The Electroscope (Part I)," *Journal of Orgonomy*, 3:188-197, 1969.

5. Moray, T.H.: *The Sea of Energy in Which the Earth Floats*. Salt Lake City: Cosray Research Institute, 1978.

6. Reich, W.: *The Discovery of the Orgone, Vol. I: The Function of the Orgasm*. New York: Orgone Institute Press, 1942.

7. Baker, C.F.: "The Spinning Wave: II," *Journal of Orgonomy*, 13:192-219, November, 1979.

Orgone Energy Field Observations Using the Dowsing Rod

by Nikolas Nikolaidis B.Eng., M.Eng.*

Introduction

It is widely believed that dowsing is the art of finding groundwater. However, true water-location is only one aspect of this ancient art. Dowsing in general deals with the infinite manifestations of life energy. It has been practiced since ancient times by the Egyptian, Chinese, Greek, Roman and other civilizations. Practicing dowsers are involved in a variety of situations such as groundwater and mineral location, archaeological site excavation, healing, and the location of missing persons.

For a long time dowsing was considered as charlatanry and mysticism, and dowsing remains unexplained and mysterious for conventional science. Wilhelm Reich had only a single observation of dowsing in 1951.[1] He observed a dowser on his farm searching for water and then tried it himself, concluding from the standpoint of orgone physics, that dowsing is an object of orgone-energetic research

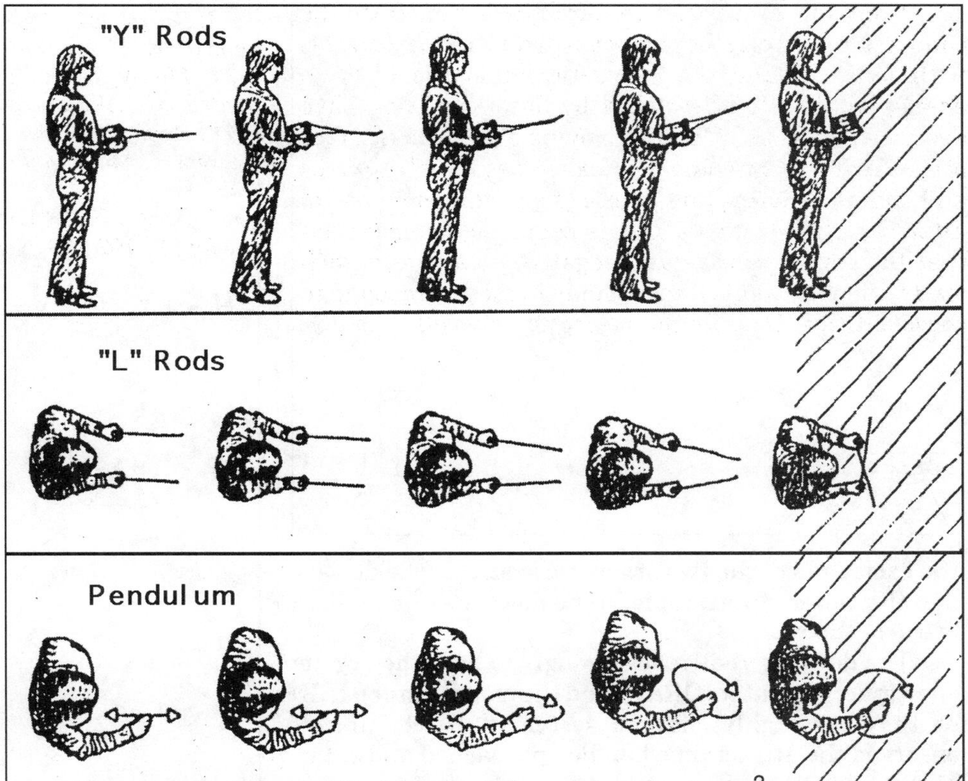

Description

Dowsing is a very simple process in which the dowser holding a "tool" in his hands walks on the ground. Upon approaching groundwater or an energy field in general a movement of the "tool" is observed and felt (Figure 1). A wide variety of tools are used in dowsing, such as L-rods, Y-shaped wires or branches, pendulums, little metal pipes etc. Very sensitive dowsers work with bare hands without any tools. No mystical process whatsoever needs to be involved.

Orgone energy — either free flowing or concentrated — reacts strongly to the dowsing rod. Reich's concept was that the movement of the rod is a result of

* Environmental Engineer, Athens, Greece.
Email: ecosphere@the.forthnet.gr

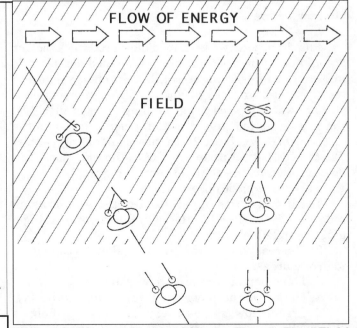

"Y" Rods

"L" Rods

Pendulum

Figure 1. Dowser at Work, using different dowsing tools.[2]

FLOW OF ENERGY

FIELD

Figure 2. Dowser Approaching an Energy Flow-Field from different angles

Figure 3. Dowser Approaching an Energy Center from different angles.

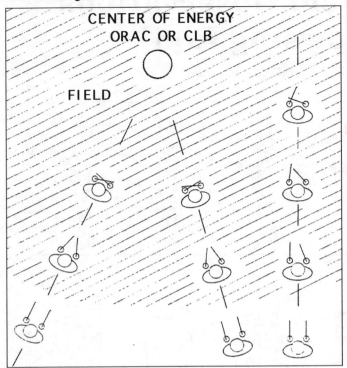

the excitation of the two orgonotic systems (the dowser and the water, for example). The dowser's orgone field attracts the rod.

The dowsing rods react strongly to both the orgone energy accumulator (ORAC) and the cloudbuster (CLB) as they are highly charged systems. Reich himself observed the attraction when he approached and sat in his 20-fold ORAC.

Observations

I have chosen two L-shaped metal rods as a tool for orgone energy field observations. L-shaped rods provide information for both the strength of the energy field and its direction. In case of energy flow (for example a stream, water pipe or the grounding pipes of the CLB) the dowser is "led" to a direction perpendicular to the direction of flow (Figure 2). In case of an "energy center" like the CLB at zenith or an ORAC, the rods "lead" the dowser towards the charged center (Figure 3).

Here are some basic observations:

1. All orgonomic apparatus react to the dowsing rods: the ORAC, the CLB, the DOR Buster, even a single pipe grounded in water.

2. The reaction is stronger in rural areas compared to urban areas.

3. The reaction is related to weather.

4. The size of the energy field varies during the day.

5. Orgone flow creates a very strong energy field as observed during discharging of the ORAC or grounding the CLB in running water.

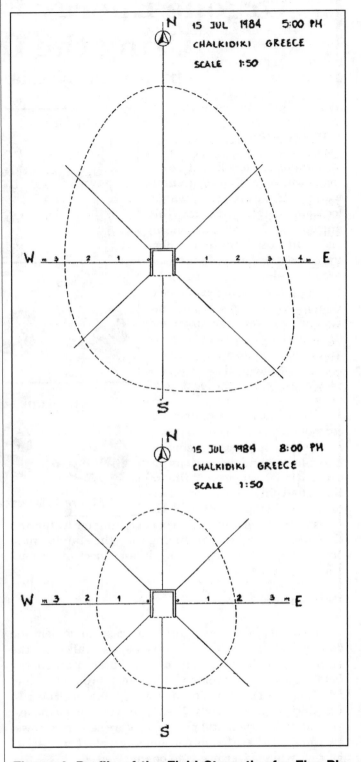

Figure 4. Profile of the Field Strength of a Five-Ply Orgone Accumulator, marking the radius where dowsing L-rods crossed and became parallel. Top Graphic: Field Strength at 5:00 PM, 15 July 1984. Bottom Graphic: Field Strength on same day, 8:00 PM.

6. The size of the energy field around the CLB is related to the water flow of stream or riverd in which the CLB is grounded.

7. The energy field created by an orgone apparatus interacts with the Earth's natural energy fields. Care must be taken so that the experiment is set up in a "clear" spot.

8. Energy charge remains for some time in the area where an orgone apparatus has been situated even after removing it. The remaining energy field is much weaker.

This last observation is known in dowsing as the *after-image*. Experienced dowsers know that reaction does not always determine the presence of groundwater. The excited energy field created by flowing water remains even after the water has left a groundwater table. Various techniques are available for avoiding erroneous conclusions.

Quantification

A quantification of the above observations has been attempted. It has to be made clear that the measurements are only my own and their values are only relative, dependent upon my orgonotic state at that time. The reaction distance varies somewhat from one person to the next. I would call the measurements *objective* but *not exact* — objective because many people can repeat them, but not exact because they will be slightly different between different people.

1. Energy field around the ORAC

I used a very simple experimental set up. After checking the site for an absence of natural energy fields, I assembled a five-fold ORAC in a N-S orientation, without the door, and with the open side facing south. After several minutes a field was created around the accumulator. I took hourly dowsing measurements of the distance at which the two L-rods met and were roughly parallel to each other, or perpendicular to the direction of movement (Figure 4). The energy field profile was determined by using the two main directions (N-S, E-W) and the two secondary (NW-SE, NE-SW).

Daily variations are shown in Figure 5. The energy field is weak at dawn, it expands suddenly at sunrise, it pulsates during the day and then it contracts again suddenly around sunset.

2. Energy field around a single pipe

In this case I used a simple experimental set up based on the functioning principle of CLB. I filled a steel barrel with about 100 liters of water and put a single aluminum pipe 3.00 meters long pointing at zenith (Figure 6A). Water was coming into the barrel through a plastic hose and excess water overflowed. I placed the

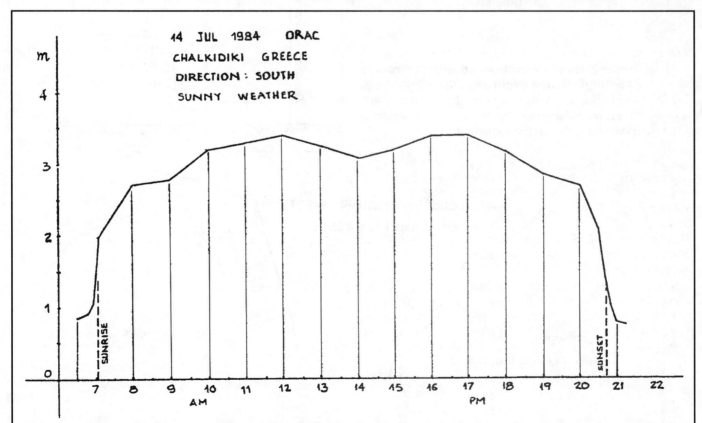

Figure 5. Hourly Variation in the Field Strength of a Five-Ply Orgone Accumulator, southerly component, as determined by measured variations in the radius of dowsing reactions.

water hose in the north direction. Water flow was minimal, approximately 1 m³/hour. It took 5-10 min. for the field to get full strength from the onset of water flow (Figure 6B). I took measurements every hour in general and more frequently during sunrise and sunset. Results were similar to the ORAC energy field observations: a weak field was observed in the morning, with a strong and variable field during the day and weak again in the evening (Figure 7 and Figure 8).

These findings are similar to Wilhelm Reich's observations with electroscopical discharge rates, which he equated with atmospheric orgone charge. He observed a diurnal variation of atmospheric orgone charge for similar weather conditions (sunny-clear weather), which start very weak in the morning, get stronger during the day and then fall in the evening.[3]

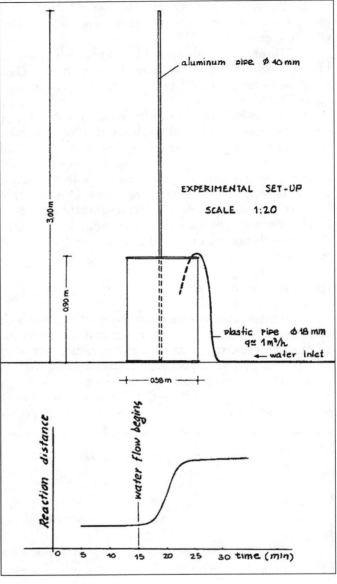

Figure 6A. Diagram of a Single-Pipe "Cloudbuster" (Right Top), grounded into water to create an excited field.

Figure 6B. Graph of the Time to Create an Excited Field (Right Center), from the onset of grounding.

Figure 7. Hourly Variation in the Field Strength of a Single Water-Grounded Pipe (Bottom Left and Right), westerly component, 21 and 22 Sept. 1983, as determined by measured variations in the radius of dowsing reactions.

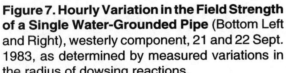

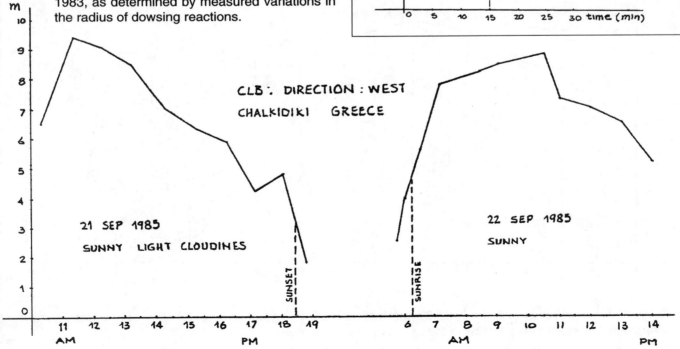

CLB. DIRECTION : WEST
CHALKIDIKI GREECE

21 SEP 1985
SUNNY LIGHT CLOUDINES

22 SEP 1985
SUNNY

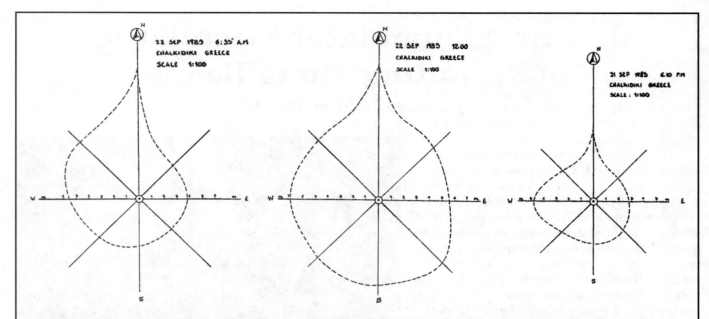

Figure 8. Hourly Variation in the Profile of Field Strength of a Single Water-Grounded Pipe, marking the radius where dowsing L-rods crossed and became parallel. Water is flowing into the barrel at the center of each profile from a hose entering from a northerly direction. Left: 6:35 AM. Center: Noontime. Right: 6:10 PM.

Discussion

The findings presented here are preliminary and incomplete. However, dowsing rods proved to be a promising research tool in orgone biophysics. The process is very simple and easily accessible by many people. The bioenergetic structure of the observer is fully engaged in the experiment, a concept difficult for the modern scientific mind.

Nikolas Nikolaidis, October 1985

References:

1. Reich, W.: "Dowsing as an Object of Orgonomic Research", *Orgone Energy Bulletin*, 3(2):139-144, 1951.
2. Graves, T.: *Dowsing, Radiaesthesia: Technique & Application* (Greek translation by A. Selli), p.81, Makris, Athens, Greece, 1982.
3. Reich, W.: *The Cancer Biopathy*, Farrar, Straus & Giroux, NY 1973. See section on diurnal variations in electroscopical discharge, graphs for 15-25 July 1941 on pp.138-139. For Greek translation by K. Theodorimbasis, (Akmon, Athens, Greece, 1977) see pp.142-143.

Orgone Accumulator Stimulation of Sprouting Mung Beans

by James DeMeo, Ph.D.*

Introduction and Background

A good part of the discussion on Wilhelm Reich's orgone accumulator focuses upon the physical evidence for the orgone energy, in the measurement of temperature, electroscopical discharge rates, Geiger-counter reactions, water evaporation, and the like. However, Reich's original discovery developed from the study of living organisms, and he gave the name "orgone" to the energy for that reason. My earliest research into Reich's monumental body of work was also in the direction of the biological sciences. Some of the most compelling experiments demonstrating the unusual properties of the orgone accumulator come from its observed effects upon living creatures. In the 1970s, I undertook a series of plant growth-enhancement experiments with the orgone accumulator, replicating the work that Reich and others have undertaken on the question, which has shown fairly consistent positive effects.[1] While the physics experiments developed by Reich are very important, the biological effects remain more foundational, particularly given their replicability and useful benefits in the treatment of serious injury and illness. For this reason, I sought to develop an experimental protocol on seed-sprouting inside the orgone accumulator which is fairly simple to reproduce, is highly controlled, and the results of which can stand up against classical scientific objections.

The method employs the sprouting of mung beans, obtained from local health food stores, in shallow glass dishes of water, which are then placed in an orgone accumulator during the period of sprouting. Identical dishes of bean sprouts are placed inside suitable control enclosures, which are of similar thermal dynamics, and do not contain any metals. Both accumulators and control enclosures shield out all light from the growing seeds, which are sprouted in the dark. In 1978, I published an early pilot experiment using this method[2] which showed an average of 74 mm of growth in dishes of control-group mung beans, as compared to 142 mm of growth inside a simple one-ply orgone accumulator, and 201 mm of growth inside a stronger 10-ply accumulator. That's an average of more than twice the

* Director, Orgone Biophysical Research Lab, Greensprings, PO Box 1148, Ashland, Oregon 97520 USA. Tel-Fax: 541-552-0118 Email: demeo@mind.net

Figure 1. Orgone Energy Darkroom: A room-sized orgone accumulator at the Orgone Biophysical Research Lab, Greensprings Center, Ashland, Oregon.

amount of growth inside the orgone accumulators as compared to the controls. In more recent years, this experiment was undertaken again, but with greater rigor and tighter experimental controls than before.

Orgone accumulators are constructed from alternating layers of organic insulating materials and ferromagnetic metals, with either only a few alternating layers or many layers. The more layers, the stronger the accumulator, though the relationship is not exact and depends upon many other factors, to include the local weather and environmental conditions related to atmospheric pollution. One "ply" of an accumulator is defined as one layer of organic insulating material plus one layer of metal. The organic insulating material may also include certain non-organic materials with a high dielectric constant, such as fiberglass or certain plastics, but often simple coarse fabric made from sheep's wool is used. Additional alternating layers of metal and organic insulator can be repeated inside the walls or panels of an accumulator to increase its strength. Usually, steel wool and sheep's wool are alternately layered inside the walls of a more rigid accumulator framework, the interior of which is composed of galvanized steel sheet metal, and the exterior composed of wood or mason board. Coatings of shellac and other high-dielectric materials are often given on the outside of the accumulator to increase its strength. From a casual examination, the accumulator looks like an ordinary box with thick walls and a solid-metal interior, and classical theory anticipates virtually no effects upon plants or animals, much less upon the physical properties of the air inside. Such was, however, the essence of the claims made for over 60 years by Reich and other scientists following in his path. I have already given a complete discussion of the history, background theory and construction principles of the orgone accumulator[3] and so will not repeat that information here.

Experimental Protocol and Control Procedures

In the summers of 1998, 1999 and 2000, with the assistance of various students enrolled in the OBRL Independent Study Program, a new series of seed-sprouting tests were undertaken, using the orgone energy darkroom (a room-sized orgone accumulator) and a special thermally-balanced cardboard, plastic and wood container for the control enclosure. The orgone accumulator darkroom was originally a large wooden "Mini-Barn" of 3.5 x 5 meters dimension, converted into a large one-ply orgone accumulator by adding fiberglass insulation and a final interior covering of galvanized steel sheeting. Inside this metal-lined structure were placed several additional smaller accumulators — these included two multiple-ply human-sized accumulators, each of which contained inside itself a smaller multiple-ply orgone accumulator — this latter innermost accumulator was used for the seed-sprouting experiments. Other orgone accumulators were also located inside the orgone darkroom, to include an additional 10-ply charger and other disassembled accumulator panels, all of which worked to build a fairly high orgone charge inside the structure. It is typical for people who enter the room for the first time to express amazement at the subjective feelings of pleasurable expansion and high charge, which can best be described as what one might feel walking in a grove of giant redwood trees on a sunny day, combined with a mild radiant feeling on the skin.

The placement of the orgone darkroom outdoors, in a natural forested environment, created a strong, yet soft and expansive feeling inside, something which is nearly impossible to obtain when strong accumulators are constructed within congested urban environments, or close to large power lines or nuclear reactors. In fact, the rural forested location of the OBRL Greensprings Center was selected for this very reason: the great distance from significant sources of electrosmog and low-level nuclear radiation, which are known to excessively excite and disturb the orgone energy continuum. Figure 1 shows the interior of the OBRL orgone accumulator darkroom. The two human-sized orgone accumulators can be seen at the back wall.

Open-top glass dishes containing dried mung beans with water, to be described momentarily, were placed inside the smaller charger boxes, which were then placed inside the larger human-sized accumulators inside the orgone darkroom. Total accumulator strengths of 13-ply and 25-ply were thereby achieved for the orgone-charged group of seedlings.

The control enclosure consisted of a series of nested boxes placed under the shade of large trees about 15 meters from the orgone darkroom: the bean-water dishes were placed inside a cardboard box which was sealed with black electrical tape along its seams. Two of such cardboard boxes, containing two dishes of beans, were then inserted inside an opaque plastic storage box which was lined with plastic bubble-wrap for insulation, and the storage box lid was then closed. The storage box was placed on top of a plywood platform which was elevated off the ground by about 15 cm, similar to the Mini-Barn orgone darkroom — a large wood box was then inverted to cover the plastic storage container. The control enclosure was therefore similar to the accumulators, except that it did not contain any metals.

An Extech light meter with external probe was used to measure the presence of unwanted light entering through possible cracks into both the orgone accumulators and control boxes, but both measured at zero lux.

Temperature controls were established empirically, evaluated by direct daily measurements of maximums and minimums, through adjustments in the accumulator and control ventilation and shading before the experiments were started. It was found that nearly identical temperatures could be achieved between the accumulator and control environments by leaving the door to the orgone darkroom ajar by about two centimeters, and by adding a sealed one-gallon jug of water inside the cardboard control boxes holding the seed sprouting dish, to increase their thermal mass. Additional wood shading panels were set around the sides and the top of the control enclosure to shield against diffuse or stray-direct sunlight which penetrated through the forest canopy. Once this was done, the thermal dynamics of the controls and accumulators were brought to within approximately one degree F, on average, as measured with maximum-minimum alcohol thermometers.

Humidity inside the enclosures was assumed to be nearly identical, given the very close interior temperatures, similarity of volumes and the sealed nature of both the accumulators and controls. A layer of plastic was added to the inside walls of the cardboard control boxes to prevent any moisture absorption into the cardboard, to match the situation inside the metal-lined accumulator boxes. In any case, there was no flow of air into or out of either the accumulators or the controls; they received fresh air daily, however, when they were opened for watering, as described below.

The dishes of seedlings were prepared as follows: Round open-faced, flat-bottom Pyrex evaporation dishes of 170 mm diameter and 90 mm height were used. A sample of 100 dried mung beans were extracted randomly from a well-mixed sack of beans, then weighed dry, and placed into each evaporation dish along with 50 ml of untreated well water from an excellent source at the Greensprings Center. The water level was sufficient to cover the dried beans about halfway, allowing them exposure to both air and water. Prior work indicated this method would insure the seeds would not "drown" and thereafter fail to sprout, nor would the dish dry out over a period of 24 hours. Starting at approximately noontime, two glass dishes of watered seeds were placed inside the orgone accumulators, one inside the 25-ply and another into the 13-ply accumulator, with another two identically-prepared dishes placed inside the cardboard-plastic-wood control box. After watering and placement of the dishes and the max-min thermometers, the accumulators and control enclosures were shut closed and sealed, so as to eliminate all light and to conform to the previously-established thermal controls. Twenty-four hours later, the boxes were opened, and the dishes of seeds removed to evaluate their growth and water levels. Water was added daily, on demand, so as to keep a constant and identical level of water at the bottom of all the dishes, even if one dish consumed more water than another. The quantity of water given was recorded, as were the readings on the max-min thermometers. The dishes of seeds were then closed back into their respective enclosures, for orgone-charging, or for controls. After approximately 10 days of this procedure, around the time when the sprouting seeds were pushing up against the interior lids of the accumulator boxes, the experiments were terminated and the seedlings measured.

Experimental Results

For evaluations, the dishes of sprouted seedlings were firstly photographed; then the mass of sprouted seeds was carefully removed from the glass dishes and blotted dry on paper towels for about 10 minutes. After blotting, the mass of sprouted seeds, including roots, were weighed, and the net increase in plant mass calculated by subtraction from the original dry weights. Individual seedlings were then gently teased apart and stretched out along a meterstick, and measured from root-tip to the point just below where the leaves joined the stem of the sprout. Averages and other statistical data were then extracted. Figure 2 shows the results from the three

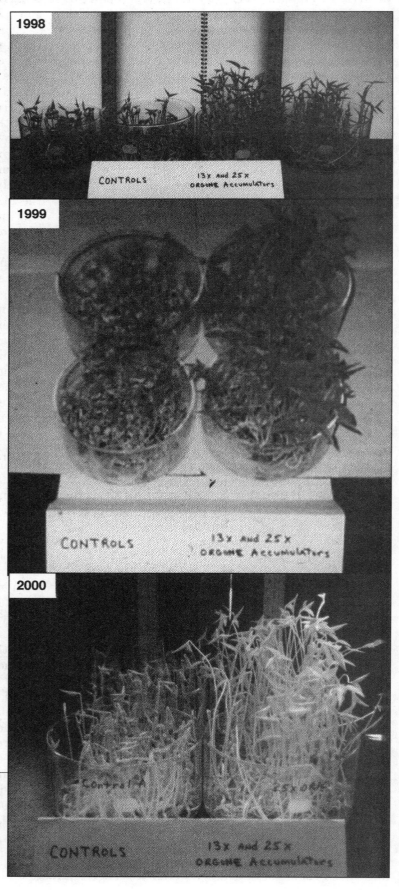

Figure 2. Three Summer Trials of Orgone Accumulator Seed-Stimulation Experiments. Dishes of seeds on the right sides of each photograph, with greater growth, were charged inside orgone accumulators. Dishes on the left sides were the control groups. Top 1998, Mid. 1999, Bot. 2000.

Figure 3. Histograms of Orgone-Charged Versus Control Mung Bean Sprouts. Top: Orgone Charged. Bottom: Controls. Orgone-charged group clearly shows more growth than control group.

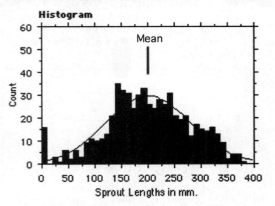

ORGONE-CHARGED MUNG BEAN SPROUTS
3-TRIALS COMBINED (n=600)

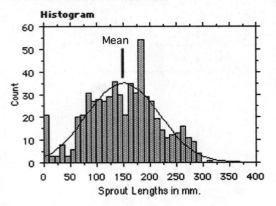

CONTROL (Not Charged) MUNG BEAN SPROUTS
3-TRIALS COMBINED (n=600)

Figure 4. Sprout-Length Cumulative Counts, Orgone-Charged Versus Controls

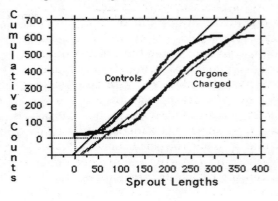

ling was 385 mm, while the longest control seedling was 317 mm This computes to a roughly 34% increase in growth due to orgone-charging.

Another way of viewing these data is given in Figure 4, which orders the data from shortest to longest sprout length, and displays the orgone-charged and control groups on the same graph. Again, one can clearly see the systematic increases in growth from orgone-charging, across the board. The two graphs show widely-separated regression lines, and do not overlap except at the very lowest end of the curve given the fact that both groups had a small percentage of seedlings which did not sprout, and which were identified as "zero" growth. A simple T-test indicates the probability of this distribution happening by chance alone is less than 1 in 10,000, very significant indeed ($p < .0001$).

Germination rates, where any seedling with growth of less than 25 mm at the end of the experiment is considered to be "dead", was 95.8% for the controls and 97.3% for the orgone-charged groups. Orgone charged seedlings also consumed a slightly greater quantity of water than the controls (118.3 ml versus 109.9 ml) and showed a slight gain in weight (53.2 gram versus 49.0 gram). However, these latter characteristics were not as significant as the overall increase in the length of the seedlings. In fact, the orgone-charged seedlings were often quite elongated and spindly, sometimes giving the appearance of being so highly-charged they were racing upwards. The control seedlings were certainly quite vigorous and healthy all on their own, and appeared stouter even if slower-growing. This interpretation is supported by blind experiments performed on the taste of the sprouts — everyone agreed that the control seed-

summertime seed-sprouting experiments at OBRL, for 1998, 1999 and 2000. The orgone-charged groups clearly have grown more than the controls.

Figure 3 presents histograms of seed growth data for the three summers combined, with a total of 1200 individual seedlings from 12 different dishes of seeds. One can clearly see the difference in the distributions of growth between the orgone-charged and control groups. Descriptive statistics indicate the orgone charged group grew an average of 200 mm, while the controls grew 149 mm, the orgone-charged group showing an average of 50 mm of increased length as compared to the controls. The longest orgone-charged seed-

TABLE 1.	Control Groups	Orgone-Charged Groups	Percent Change
Average Seedling Lengths	149 mm	200 mm	+ 34%
Germination	95.8%	97.3%	+ 1.6%
Weight Increase	49.0 gram	53.2 gram	+ 8.6%
Average Water Consumed	109.9 ml	118.3 ml	+ 7.6%
Refractive Index (%Brix)	6.3	5.1	− 19%

lings tasted better, while the orgone-charged group was more bitter. This was confirmed by refractometer readings of the juice from the seedlings, suggestive of a higher sugar content in the control group. The orgone-charged group appeared to be expending more of its sugars in growing to greater lengths. More will be said on this in the conclusions.

Overall results for the three aggregated trials (1998, 1999 and 2000) are summarized in Table 1. A similar analysis of each trial independently has been undertaken (not presented here for space considerations), which gives nearly identical results.

Control Experiments for Temperature

After these data were obtained and analyzed, a question was raised if it were possible for the small residual thermal differences between the accumulator and control groups to yield up such an effect, independent of orgone-charging. Generally, plant growth can be stimulated under warmer conditions, as is readily seen inside a greenhouse. While an *average* daily thermal difference of around 1°F was observed, without systematic thermal bias in favor of either the control or accumulator groups, I felt it important to more thoroughly address this question. A search of published literature failed to locate specific information on the growth re-

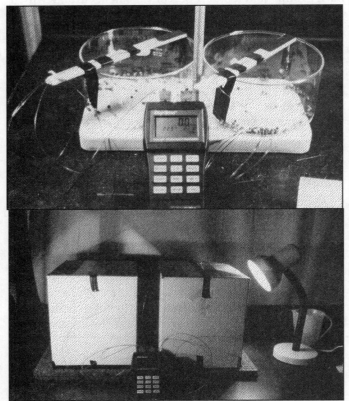

Figure 5. Temperature Control Experiment. Dishes of beans with temperature probes (Top) are placed inside the two boxes (Bottom); one box is heated slightly by the lamp. Differential electronic thermometer at front center.

Figure 6. Histograms of Temperature Control Experiments. Top graph displays growth of beans kept slightly warmer, by 0.5° to 2.8° F, as compared to beans in bottom graph. No significant differences appear between the two sets of data, in stark contrast to the data in Figure 3.

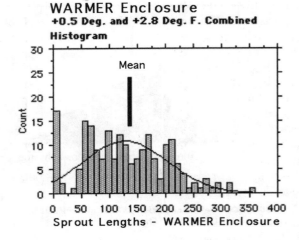

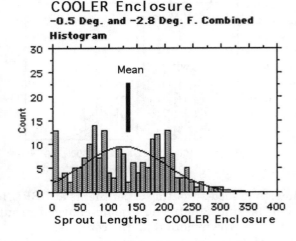

Figure 7. Sprout-Length Cumulative Counts Cooler Versus Warmer Environments

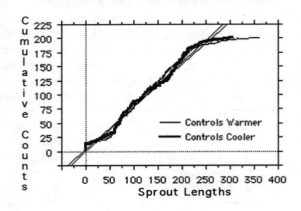

sponse of sprouting mung beans to variable temperature, except for an optimal growth temperature lying between 18-30°C (65-85°F). Consequently, experiments were undertaken to empirically evaluate the differences between groups of mung beans grown under slightly different thermal environments. Early trials using incubator ovens, with heating elements turned on and off by thermostatic controls, yielded erratic results as directly measured with precise thermometers — variable thermal gradients of several degrees F existed between their tops and bottoms, and between the back and front, and so forth. Metal incubator ovens also resemble an orgone-accumulator, which in the context of the present experiment suggested a host of uncontrolled variables and questions, such as the effects upon the seedlings of the proximity of the metal walls of the incubators. Consequently, incubator ovens and other metal "environmental control" devices were abandoned in favor of a method based upon the control procedures of the original seed-sprouting experiment.

Two identical cardboard boxes were placed on a table in a constantly shaded and darkened part of the laboratory. Seed sprouting dishes similar to those described above were prepared, except that a sensitive thermocouple was suspended inside the center of each dish, about three centimeters from the bottom. The two dishes were then placed inside two identical cardboard boxes, closed up and sealed with black electrical tape along the seams. The two thermocouples were attached to a Cole-Parmer *Digi-Sense* dual-channel differential temperature meter, which recorded the data every hour. A 60 watt light bulb was brought close to the side of one of the boxes, from between 10 to 50 cm distance, allowing for a slight warming effect on one of the boxes, as shown in Figure 5. By carefully adjusting the distance between the light and the box, I was able to achieve a controlled slight increase in temperature within the proximate box, even as the temperature inside the laboratory rose and declined over the course of the day. This procedure was performed two times, once with one dish at an average of 0.5°F (0.27°C) difference, and again with 2.8°F (1.5°C) difference. This procedure demonstrated *no significant differences in growth-rate between the cooler and warmer dishes of bean sprouts*, for both the 0.5°F and the 2.8°F trials. The results of these experiments, combined, are shown in Figures 6 and 7. The warmer boxes showed a mean of 127.9 mm of growth, while the cooler boxes yielded 127.1 mm growth, an a difference of only 0.8 mm. The regression lines, seen in Figure 7, nearly overlap, as do the data themselves, which are indistinguishable on the graph. The probability values were also very low and insignificant, with $p=0.91$ on a T-test comparing the two groups. This is clear proof that the small thermal variations which persisted in the experimental set up comparing orgone-charged and control groups — which were on the order of an average 1°F difference — were insufficient to pro-

duce the magnitude of growth-enhancement effects seen in the orgone-charged groups.

Conclusions

The orgone energy accumulator has been shown to work a remarkable affect upon the growth of seedlings, increasing the sprouting length by 34%, and germination rates and overall weights by smaller percentages. However, as mentioned previously, refractive indexes and taste of the sprouts suggest the orgone-charged sprouts had a lower sugar content as compared to the control groups. The orgone-charged sprouts were possibly expending sugars in making additional cellular material, growing to longer lengths. Or, it might be the consequence of keeping the sprouting seedlings inside the accumulator on a constant basis. Prior studies have shown enhanced flowering and fruiting of garden vegetables, with increased sweetness (by taste), in groups which were orgone-charged for considerably shorter periods of time (i.e, a single exposure of only a few hours)[4]. Biomedical experiments also are limited to short daily orgone-charging sessions, as excessively prolonged accumulator usage may lead to temporary unpleasant *overcharge* symptoms, such as headache and nausea. Consequently, while the present experiment provides clear positive proof that the orgone accumulator imparts an increased growing force to seeds sprouted in glass dishes and nourished only by water, this method of prolonged charging in the laboratory *may or may not be directly applicable to increased agricultural productivity*, which has already been shown to benefit from shorter charging periods. The next phase of this laboratory approach should focus upon providing a broader spectrum of nutrients coupled with shorter charging-times in the accumulator.

We might also ask, how does the orgone accumulator create this affect upon the sprouting seedling? This is a question about which we can only speculate. Orgone energy stimulates the parasympathetic nervous system in animals, leading to expansiveness and relaxation, as well as increased energy. How might this apply to seedlings? Orgone is known to have a strong mutual affinity and attraction to water, and it may be that the water is firstly charged, only secondarily to be absorbed by the seedling. Once the seedling is growing and moist, it would then absorb even more energy directly into its structure, and with the increased vitality, push and elongate itself more so than the control seedlings, even to the point of exhausting its available chemical nutrients. Or, it is possible that there is a *field created inside the accumulator, which works against the gravitational force* (as proposed by Reich[5]) thereby helping to "push" the seedlings upward, in a manner similar to the force which moves sap upwards, to the tops of tall trees. One researcher, O. Ed Wagner[6] already proposes an antigravitational function at work in tree-sap mechanisms, and it may be that what is observed inside the orgone accumulator, affecting sprouting mung beans, is a small scale version of that principle, of what happens in living nature, in trees. If so, then it suggests a physical mechanism for levitation independent of the seedling or tree, waiting to be better understood, and harnessed.

As written elsewhere, a primary consideration for replication of this experiment is, aside from the control procedures already discussed, that key attention be given to proper accumulator construction materials, and also, that the local energetic environment must be viewed as an integral part of the experimental setup. One cannot undertake this experiment in highly-polluted regions, within close proximity to large high-tension power lines, or within 25-50 miles of a nuclear reactor, and be certain of repeatable positive results. Indoor environments with background EM fields of even less than 1 milligauss or 1 kv/m may also disturb the energetics within the accumulator, and yield erratic results. Regions characterized by natural forests, and structures similar to an "old barn in the woods" as described in my *Orgone Accumulator Handbook*,[3] are a reasonable description of the optimal environment for biological orgone energy experiments.

It must be additionally noted, that Reich's use of the orgone energy accumulator as an experimental medical device was proven to have positive effects for a wide variety of diseases, including degenerative illnesses such as cancer. This finding was, of course, jumped upon by his critics, and abused by the 1950s Food and Drug Administration as an excuse for the persecution of Reich, and the eventual "banning and burning" of all his scientific books and journals, and his eventual death in prison — all for the technical violation of an obscure FDA labeling law! The reader should know, the orgone accumulator has as powerful an effect upon animal tissues and physiology as upon plants, as demonstrated in a host of clinical reports and controlled studies,[7] including two double-blind controlled studies on the psycho-physiological effects upon human subjects, as undertaken at the University of Marburg, Germany, and the University of Vienna, Austria.[8] Consequently, there is no excuse whatsoever for the hostile smears directed against Dr. Reich and the orgone accumulator, as have continued now for more than half a century. The honest and genuine scientist will take note of this fact. It should also be mentioned that there is an equally large body of published research evidence on the physical demonstration of the orgone energy, from a physics and atmospheric point of view,[9] starting with Reich and continuing down to the present day.

The results presented here, and elsewhere, are unquestionable positive proof for the factual existence of a powerful biologically-stimulating energy within the orgone accumulator, unlike anything presently acknowledged by mainstream science.

Acknowledgments: Thanks to Theirrie Cook of the Orgonics company <www.orgonics.com> for construction of the accumulators used in this study. Also thanks to Alexandre Genest, Jean-Phillippe Lemieux and other Independent Study students at the OBRL Greensprings Seminars for their assistance with the measurements.

References:

1. Baker, C., and Burlingame, P. (1990) Orgone Treatment of Sprouting Mung Beans, *Annals of the Institute for Orgonomic Science*, 7: 9-14.

Claymond, H. (1985) Preliminary Indications for an Energetic Concept of Soil Fertility, *Offshoots of Orgonomy*, 11: 8-12.

Claymond, H. (1986) Some Observations on Orgonotropism, *Offshoots of Orgonomy*, 12: 49-50.

Claymond, H. (1987) The Importance of Randomization in the Conduct of Plant Experiments, *Offshoots of Orgonomy*, 14: 30-31.

Claymond, H. (1987) Effects of the Orgone Accumulator on Potato and Onion Plants, *Annals of the Institute for Orgonomic Science*, 4: 44-48.

Courie, M. (1955) Plant Response to Orgone Energy, *CORE (Cosmic Orgone Engineering)*, 7: 203-204.

DeMeo, J. (1975) Effects of Fluorescent Lights and Metal Boxes on Growing Plants, *Journal of Orgonomy*, 9: 62-68.

DeMeo, J. (1978) Seed Sprouting Inside the Orgone Accumulator, *Journal of Orgonomy*, 12: 253-258.

Dexter, M., Desmond, L., and Coen, K. (1977) Orgone Energy and Plant Growth, *Energy and Character*, 8(3): 79-81.

Espanca, J. (1981) Letters from Portugal, *Offshoots of Orgonomy*, 2: 35-39.

Espanca, J. (1981-1987) The Effect of Orgone on Plant Life, Parts 1- 10, *Offshoots of Orgonomy*, 3: 23-28; 4: 35-38; 6: 20-23; 7: 36-37; 8: 35-39; 11: 30-32; 12: 45-48; 13: 13-17; 14: 19-22; 15: 29-32, 35.

Espanca, J. (1984) Orgone Energy Devices for Irradiation of Plants, *Offshoots of Orgonomy*, 9: 25-31.

Espanca, J. (1986) Orgone Energy and Plant Life, *Annals of the Institute for Orgonomic Science*, 3: 57-62.

Lai, T. and Eberl, D. (1988) Effect of an Energy Accumulator on Phosphorus Availability, *Abstracts, 80th Annual Meeting, American Society of Agronomy*, p.240. (Reprinted in *Pulse of the Planet*, 4: 116, 1993).

Lane, L. (1977) Effects of the ORAC on Growing Plants, *Journal of Orgonomy*, 11: 68-71.

Reich, W. (1949) *Ether, God and Devil*, Orgone Institute Press, New York. (a brief discussion of effects of orgone energy on plants is found on page 81 [page 102 in the 1973 Farrar, Straus, and Giroux edition])

Ritter, P. and Ritter, J. (1954) Experiment Orgone Flower Pot Number 1, *Orgonomic Functionalism*, 1: 323-326.

Schwartz, J. (1986) Some Experiments with Seed Sprouts and Energetic Fields, *Offshoots of Orgonomy*, 13: 18-21.

Sellers, A.P. (1987) The Effects of Orgonotic Devices on Tomato Plant Growth, *Offshoots of Orgonomy*, 15: 20-28.

Shelton, B. (1964) An Experiment Investigating the Effect of the Orgone Accumulator on Plant Growth, *Orgonomic Functionalism*, 10: 63-66.

Wyvell, L. and Strick, J. (1984) Orgonotropism, *Offshoots of Orgonomy*, 9: 7-12.

2. DeMeo, 1978, ibid.

3. DeMeo, J. (1989) *The Orgone Accumulator Handbook: Construction Plans, Experimental Use, and Protection Against Toxic Energy*, Natural Energy Works, Ashland.

4. Espanca, 1981 - 1987, ibid.

5. Reich, W. (1956) *Contact With Space*, Core Pilot Press, NY, p.95-110.

6. Wagner, O. E., (1995) *Waves in Dark Matter*, Wagner Research Laboratory, Rogue River, Oregon.

7. Bio-Medical Research with the Orgone Accumulator (English-language publications only):

Anderson, W. (1950) Orgone Therapy in Rheumatic Fever, *Orgone Energy Bulletin*, 2: 71-73.

Baker, C., Dew, R., Ganz, M., and Lance, L. (1984) Wound Healing in Mice, Part 1, *Annals of the Institute for Orgonomic Science*, 1: 12-23.

Baker, C., Dew, R., Ganz, M., and Lance, L. (1985) Wound Healing in Mice, Part 2, *Annals of the Institute for Orgonomic Science*, 2: 7-24.

Bizzi, B. (1970) Orgone Energy: Life-Force and Morbid States, *Energy and Character*, 1(1-2): 50-61.

Blasband, R. (1972) An Analysis of the U.S. FDA's Scientific Evidence Against Wilhelm Reich, Part 1: the Biomedical Evidence, *Journal of Orgonomy*, 6: 207-222.

Blasband, R. (1973) The Orgone Energy Accumulator in the Treatment of Cancer in Mice, *Journal of Orgonomy*, 7: 81-85.

Blasband, R. (1984) Effects of the Orac on Cancer in Mice: Three Experiments, *Journal of Orgonomy*, 18: 202-211.

Blasband, R. (1988) The Orgone Energy Light: A Pilot Experiment, *Journal of Orgonomy*, 22: 62-67.

Bremer, K. (1953) Medical Effects of Orgone Energy, *Orgone Energy Bulletin*, 5: 71-84.

Brenner, M. (1991) Orgonotic Devices in the Treatment of Infectious Conditions, *Pulse of the Planet*, 3: 49-53.

Cott, A. (1951) Orgonomic Treatment of Ichthyosis, *Orgone Energy Bulletin*, 3: 163-166.

Grad, B. (1986) Orgonotic Functions in Healing by Touch, *Journal of Orgonomy*, 20: 253-261.

Grad, B. (1992) The Effect of the Orgone Accumulator on the Acute Lymphoblastic Leukemia of AKR Mice, *Journal of Orgonomy*, 26: 199-217.

Grad, B., Cadoret, R., and Paul, G. (1961) An Unorthodox Method of Treatment of Wound Healing in Mice, *International Journal of Parapsychology*, 3(2): 5-24.

Hoppe, W. (1945) My First Experiences with the Orgone Accumulator, *International Journal of Sex-Economy and Orgone Research*, 4: 200-201.

Hoppe, W. (1949) My Experiences with the Orgone Accumulator, *Orgone Energy Bulletin*, 1: 12-22.

Hoppe, W. (1950) Further Experiences with the Orgone Accumulator, *Orgone Energy Bulletin*, 2: 16-21.

Hoppe, W. (1955) Orgone Versus Radium Therapy of Skin Cancer: Report of a Case, *Orgonomic Medicine*, 1: 133-138.

Hoppe, W. (1973) The Treatment of a Malignant Melanoma with Orgone Energy, *Energy and Character*, 4(3): 46-50.

Lassek, H. (1991) Orgone Accumulator Therapy of Severely Diseased People, *Pulse of the Planet*, 3: 39-47.

Levine, E. (1951) Treatment of a Hypertensive Biopathy with the Orgone Accumulator, *Orgone Energy Bull.*, 3: 25-34.

Muschenich, S., and Gebauer, R. (1989) The Psychophysiological Effects of the Reich Orgone Accumulator, *Pulse of the Planet*, 1 (2): 22-24.

Opfermann-Fuckert, D. (1989) Reports on Treatments with Orgone Energy, *Annals of the Institute for Orgonomic Science*, 6: 33-52.

Raphael, C. and MacDonald, H. (1952) *Orgonomic Diagnosis of Cancer Biopathy*, Wilhelm Reich Foundation/Orgone Institute Press, Rangeley, Maine.

Reich, E. (1979) I Was the Strange Doctor, *International Journal of Life Energy*, 1: 32-42.

Reich, W. (1942) The Carcinomatous Shrinking Biopathy, *International Journal of Sex-Economy and Orgone Research*, 1: 131-155.

Reich, W. (1943) Experimental Orgone Therapy of the Cancer Biopathy (1937-1943), *International Journal of Sex-Economy and Orgone Research*, 2: 1-92.

Reich, W. (1943) Experimental Orgone Therapy of the Cancer Biopathy (1937-1943), *International Journal of Sex-Economy and Orgone Research*, 2: 1-92.

Reich, W. (1945) Anorgonia in the Carcinomatous Shrinking Biopathy, *International Journal of Sex-Economy and Orgone Research*, 4: 1-33.

Reich, W. (1948) The Cancer Biopathy: Discovery of the Orgone, Vol.2, Orgone Institute Press, Rangeley, Maine. Reprinted 1973 by Farrar, Straus & Giroux, New York.

Reich, W. and Reich, E. (1955) Early Diagnosis of Cancer of the Uterus (Ca V) (Case No. 13), *Cosmic Orgone Engineering*, 7: 47-53.

Silvert, M. (1952) On the Medical Use of Orgone Energy, *Orgone Energy Bulletin*, 4: 51-54.

Snyder, N. (1989) Finger Temperature Effects of the Orgone Accumulator, *Journal of Orgonomy*, 23: 57-63.

Sobey, V. (1955) Treatment of Pulmonary Tuberculosis with Orgone Energy, *Orgonomic Medicine*, 1: 121-132.

Sobey, V. (1956) A Case of Rheumatoid Arthritis Treated with Orgone Energy, *Orgonomic Medicine*, 2: 64-69.

Tropp, S. (1949) The Treatment of a Mediastinal Malignancy with the Orgone Accumulator, *Orgone Energy Bulletin*, 1: 100-109.

Tropp, S.(1950) Orgone Therapy of an Early Breast Cancer, *Orgone Energy Bulletin*, 2: 131-138.

Tropp, S. (1951) Limited Surgery in Orgonomic Cancer Therapy, *Orgone Energy Bulletin*, 3: 81-89.

Trotta, E. and Marer, E. (1990) The Orgonotic Treatment of Transplanted Tumors and Associated Immunological Functions, *Journal of Orgonomy*, 24: 39-44.

Wevrick, N. (1951) Physical Orgone Therapy of Diabetes, *Orgone Energy Bulletin*, 3: 110-112.

8. Müschenich, S. & Gebauer, R.: *Der Reichsche Orgonakkumulator, Naturwissenschaftliche Diskussion, Praktische Anwendung, Experimentelle Untersuchung*, Doctoral Thesis, University of Marburg, Germany, 1986, published by Nexus Verlag, Frankfurt, 1989.

Hebenstreit, G.: *Der Orgonakkumulator nach Wilhelm Reich. Eine Experimentelle Untersuchung zur Spannungs-Ladungs-Formel*, Diplomarbeit zur Erlangung des Magistergrades der Philosophie an der Grung- und Integrativwissenschaftlichen Fakultät der Universität Wien, 1995.

9. DeMeo, J.: *Bibliography on Orgone Biophysics (1934-1986)*, Natural Energy Works, Ashland, Oregon, 1986. This work contains over 400 separate citations by around 100 different scientists and naturalists, most of whom hold the M.D. or Ph.D. degrees An additional large number of publications exist on the subject since 1986 to the present day.

Editor's Note: On the Theoretical Relationship Between Orgone Energy and Cosmic Rays

Classical physics views cosmic radiation as having an extraterrestrial origin. Due to greater ionization effects at higher altitudes (the "natural leak" inside ionization chambers), and higher count-rates within radiation-detection equipment, cosmic rays are assumed to arrive at Earth's upper atmosphere, being greatly diminished closer to the Earth's surface. However, *cosmic rays also decline dramatically above the upper atmosphere, except within discrete and highly-structured "radiation belts"*. Additionally, *the measured directions of cosmic rays at the Earth's surface, as seen in cloud chambers and in directional detectors, are almost wholly random, coming from "everywhere", though with a slight west-to-east bias*. This is assumed to be the consequence of the Earth's magnetic field, which deflects cosmic ray particles according to their positive or negative electrical charges. By classical theory, *primary* cosmic rays in the upper atmosphere are 98% gamma rays and about 2% electrons, and these quickly decay or breakdown into *secondary* particles, which are detected closer to the Earth's surface. These secondary particles are composed predominantly of high-speed protons (hydrogen nuclei) with a lesser portion of helium nuclei (alpha particles), bare electrons, and heavier nuclei of other atoms such as carbon, nitrogen, oxygen, lithium, boron, silicon, calcium, and iron. Among the secondary particles also are abundant, negatively-charged *muons*.

The velocity-energies of cosmic rays are also variable, from low to high ranges, though they are much more abundant at lower energy levels. Low energy cosmic rays occur at hundreds to thousands of events per second within each cubic centimeter of space, even when measured deep under the ocean or in mines, though only the higher end of their spectra can be detected with ordinary Geiger-Müller counters. Scintillation and *Cherenkov* (blue-light) counters, as described in the paper by Dave Marett to follow, detect a higher proportion of these events. High energy cosmic rays, characterized by "bursts" of activity in the counting device over a short period of several seconds or minutes, are much rarer events, occurring only every several days, and there is no dominant theory on how cosmic rays of either weak or strong energies are produced or accelerated through the cosmos. The infrequent nature of high energy cosmic rays does not allow them to be firmly matched to high-energy cosmic sources, such as supernovae or galactic x-ray sources, and they are no more abundant within the disk of our Milky Way Galaxy than outside of it. Given all this seeming chaos in the background cosmic ray environment, *the west-to-east bias in the direction of cosmic radiation remains one of its more constant features*. Also of interest is the inverse variation of cosmic ray intensity to the enigmatic 11-year cycle of sunspot abundance.

From the viewpoint of orgone biophysics, certain components of cosmic ray behavior, if not the entire scope of cosmic radiation itself, are postulated to be an expression of the Earth's excited orgone energy field. For example:

A) Increased orgone energy charges inside strong orgone accumulators have been observed to alter the "background radiation" count-rates of Geiger-Müller tubes, and to similarly affect ionization phenomena within high vacua. This class of anomalistic *oranur* phenomenon, which Reich firstly investigated, suggests that "background radiation" and hence, cosmic rays, are a *local phenomenon*, created within the Earth's atmospheric orgone ocean, and dependent upon factors such as the local charge and excitation of the orgone energy.

B) The blue color of orgone energy as seen in nature and within orgone-charged high vacuum tubes (*vacor tubes*), and the presence of visible bluish-white flashes and flimmering of light corpuscles (*orgone units*) as seen in the open daytime or nighttime atmosphere, as well as on zinc sulfide screens within orgone energy darkrooms, appears functionally identical to classically described *Cherenkov radiation* — bluish glows and flashes of light observed within high-dielectric plastics, and also within the open air, in large bodies of water, or deep in polar ice, but which are attributed to cosmic rays and other mysterious high-energy particles such as neutrinos. Modern cosmic ray detectors utilize this phenomenon, of simple light-flashes in the open air, by using sensitive photomultiplier tubes *without* fluorescing crystals or plastics, and *aimed directly into the night sky*. Detected light flashes are then interpreted as "cosmic rays".

C) The west-to-east bias in the abundance of cosmic rays, detected as subtle blue-white flashes of light in the Earth's atmosphere, or as pulses within ionization-type detectors, is strongly suggestive of Reich's theory of *a west-to-east rotating disk or envelope of orgone energy* moving parallel to Earth's equator and latitude bands, but at a slightly faster speed than the Earth's rotation.

D) The drop-off in radiation counts at the highest altitudes is also suggestive of a role being played by the Earth's orgone envelope, which diminishes at the highest altitudes, in the upper atmosphere.

Much remains to be determined on these matters experimentally, but Reich made a good start, and leaves us with an excellent working hypothesis for further research. The following paper by Dave Marett is an excellent step in this direction.

General References:

Reich, W.: *The Oranur Experiment*, Wilhelm Reich Foundation, Maine, 1951 (reprinted in *Orgone Energy Bulletin* as Vol.3, No.4, Oct. 1951, and partly reprinted in *Selected Writings*, Farrar, Straus & Giroux, NY 1960).

Reich, W.: *Ether, God & Devil* (1949); *Cosmic Superimposition* (1951), Farrar Straus & Giroux, NY 1973.

West-East Asymmetry and Diurnal Effect of Cosmic Radiation

by Dave Marett B.Sc.*

Introduction

Cosmic radiation has remained somewhat of a mystery since its discovery by Hess in 1912. It has been assumed by classical physics that various particles in open space are accelerated to high velocities, possibly by shock waves induced by the explosions of supernovae. These particles in turn pass with great speed and energy through the universe, some of which pass through the Earth's atmosphere, allowing detection. Typically, *primary* cosmic rays decay in the upper atmosphere producing *secondary* showers of particles, classified as muons, which are partly observed in cloud-chambers, triggering reactions on Geiger-Müller and scintillation counters, adding to the general background radiation. Muons in turn exhibit great speed and energy and typically continue through the Earth without losing much of it. To date, there is no definitive proof as to the origin of cosmic rays, and yet millions of them pass through each of us every day carrying about 750,000 joules of energy. Detection of these rapid energetic events requires special sensors, usually clear plastic materials mixed with a fluorescent dye attached to a photomultiplier tube. According to classical theory, the muon polarizes and "pulls" on the carbon ring structure of certain plastics thus generating a UV photon. The dye converts the UV into visible light which can pass through the plastic and be detected by the photomultiplier tube. Another approach is to use a *Cherenkov detector* which employs a lucite cylinder. Muons passing through the lucite at "faster than light speeds" create minute polarizations in the lucite producing detectable photons.

Classical theory in relation to cosmic rays postulates that electroscopic self-discharge occurs as a result of ionization caused by cosmic rays. This thought was supported by experiments performed on the rate of electroscopic discharge at various altitudes using balloons (Hess 1911)[1] (Kolhorster 1914)[2]. In these experiments, it was found that electroscopic discharge rates increased with altitude. Early researchers measured electroscopic discharge rates at various altitudes and surmised that the electroscope discharged more slowly close to sea level and on sunny days because of the increased density of the atmosphere to absorb these radiations. To contrast this, Wilhelm Reich (1947) discovered that orgone accumulators exhibited a temperature rise in relation to ambient which corresponded to the slower electroscopic discharge during sunny conditions. Furthermore, these effects varied diurnally, peaking typically around mid day. Another observation made by Reich was that a moving, wave like pattern could be observed through a telescope, trained on the horizon, moving generally west to east during high pressure conditions.[3]

Many researchers in the past have studied the muon flux in the near vertical and horizontal directions as well as at various intermediate angles. Allen and Apostolakis (1961) using an emulsion spectrograph measured the variation in cosmic ray flux as a function of zenith angle above 1 GeV/c between 65° and 85° from the vertical[4]. Their results indicated a relation of the form

$$I(\o) = I_0 \cos^n \o$$

where $I(\o)$ is the vertical intensity, and n is a constant approximately equal to 2.[1]

Moroney and Parry (1954), Coats and Nash (1962) and Allkofer and Andresen (1967) have performed similar experiments at other angles between 0° and 75° which tend to support the above relation.[5] At angles greater than 75° the density of the atmosphere varies rapidly such that the $\cos^2 \o$ relation could not be expected to hold. In addition to the angular distribution of the cosmic ray flux, an asymmetry along the west-east axis has been discovered. This asymmetry has been postulated to be a result of the interaction of the magnetic field generated by the decelerating particle as it enters the earth's atmosphere with the magnetic field of the earth. This can be described mathematically by the cross product

$$F = qE + q/c \ v \times B$$

which would indicate a net west-bound direction for negatively charged muons and conversely an eastbound direction for positively charged muons. Blackett (1937), Jones (1939) and Hughes (1940) have shown there is an excess of positively charged muons in the penetrating component of the radiation and the ratio has been set as 1.225 +/- 0.049 in the momentum range of 0.4 GeV/c to 20 GeV/c.[6] Classical physics has thereby accepted a net

* Independent Research Scientist, Toronto, Canada. Email: <vortex@eol.ca>

west-to-east bias in cosmic ray flux, based upon the explanation of muon curvature due to the Earth's magnetic field.

Experimental Evaluation

The present experiment focused on three aspects of cosmic radiation: the differences in muon flux as a function of polar direction, zenith angle and time of day. The detection apparatus consisted of two disc-shaped scintillation counters of 14cm diameter and 5cm thickness viewed each by a single photomultiplier tube to one side. These scintillators were placed at opposite ends of a rotatable structure separated by a distance of 160cm and with a 109cm Cherenkov detector (lucite) placed midway between, along the same axis. These three aligned detectors could be rotated as a cylinder in any direction to facilitate zenith angle measurements as well as polar compass direction. The counting equipment consisted of high speed discriminators for the scintillators (0.2V threshold, allowing separation of events in the muon energy range from lower energy events and noise) feeding into a coincidence unit and a linear fan-out so that the top and bottom scintillators could be coincident-recorded on 3 to 5 separate timed scalers. The timing cycle was set so that these scalers would count overlapping time periods of from 10,000 seconds to 20,000 seconds (~3-5 hours). Runs were performed in the four polar compass directions at eleva-tion angles of 0° (horizon), 22.5°, 45°, 67.5° and 90° (zenith) to determine the absolute cosmic ray flux as a function of zenith angle and direction, and to determine the extent of the west-east asymmetry. Also, the scaler data was combined from all directions to determine the average hourly muon fluctuation for a 24 hour period. A schematic of the equipment layout is shown in Figure 1.

Preliminary calibration of the detectors indicated quickly that we are literally "bathed" in a sea of energy. A 24 square inch detector produced roughly 950 events per minute. A total of seventeen runs during the spring of 1987 gave useful data which could be combined to demonstrate the $\cos^2 \phi$ angular distribution. The count data was converted into flux per unit solid angle per unit horizontal area (absolute units $sec^{-1} cm^{-2} sterad^{-1}$) [Equal to the flux of cosmic rays through the full volume of the cylindrical detector per second, for any given angle of observation]. This is described by the expression

$$Ad_\Omega = (\ AA'\,cps)/d^2$$

where $A = \pi r^2$ (the cross sectional area of the scintillator). $A = A'$ since the two scintillators are the same and cps refers to "counts per second". d = 160cm, the scintillator separation.

Taking the zenith data only, an average flux of $1.11 \times 10^{-2} +/- 0.04 \times 10^{-2} sec^{-1} cm^{-2} sterad^{-1}$ was calculated. This agrees closely with the literature value of $1.1 \times 10^2 sec^{-1} cm^{-2} sterad^{-1}$ for the total intensity of the

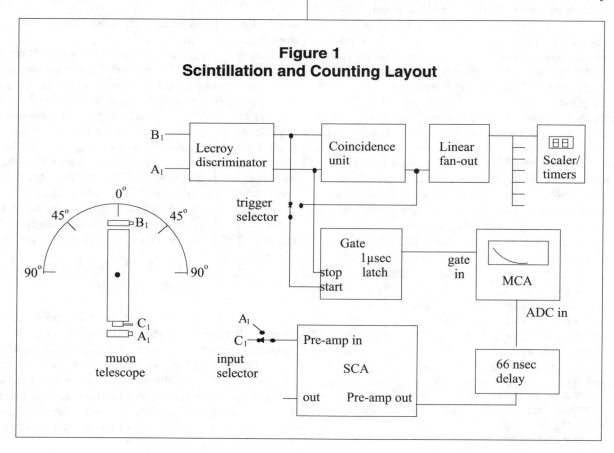

Figure 1
Scintillation and Counting Layout

hard and soft components combined.[3]

The angular distribution of the muon flux followed closely the $\cos^2\phi$ relation to zenith angle with the exception of the west to east flux which was higher by 22%. The values for the angular flux are listed in Table 1. The individual data points that made up the above average were superimposed upon a standard cosine curve ($\cos^2\phi$) in order to show the experimental distribution compared to the theoretical. This curve is shown below in Figure 2.

The west-east asymmetry of the muon flux was studied in some detail to determine its consistency with zenith angle. A total of six runs were performed from the west and five from the east between zenith angles of 90° and 22.5° and these were plotted against $\cos^2\phi$ in order to compare their slopes. The slope from the west was found to be 0.99+/-.03 and from the east 0.81+/-.03, giving a ratio of 1.22+/-.03. Independent researchers have placed the positive to negative muon ratio at 1.225+/-.049 (Thompson) and 1.25 - 1.30 using cloud chambers.[7] Cloud chamber data would tend to support the magnetic field interaction theory. Since the detectors used in this experiment are incapable of discriminating charges, there is no way to conclusively determine the cause of the asymmetry. A graph of the above data is included in Figure 3 as reference.

The occurrence of unusually high muon "bursts" during relatively short time intervals (10,000 seconds, or ~3 hrs), often 200% higher than average (see Figure 2), were detected on five separate occasions. In order to realistically present the diurnal data generated from the overlapping counting cycles, two curves have been plotted, one including the unusually high counts and the other not in Figure 4a and 4b.

Although confirmation of the diurnal phenomena is not complete, preliminary findings show that a peak in

Table 1: Scintillation Readings by Elevation Angle and Direction

flux units sec⁻¹cm⁻²sterad⁻¹			[Burst data in brackets]
Zenith:		$1.11 +/- .04 \times 10^{-2}$	
East	22.5°	$8.83 +/- .34 \times 10^{-3}$	
	45°	$5.53 +/- .22 \times 10^{-3}$	$[6.97 +/- .22 \times 10^{-3}]$
	90°	$1.91 +/- .20 \times 10^{-3}$	
West	22.5°	$1.03 +/- .34 \times 10^{-2}$	
	45°	$6.70 +/- .22 \times 10^{-3}$	
	90°	$1.80 +/- .20 \times 10^{-3}$	
North	45°	$5.21 +/- .25 \times 10^{-3}$	$[7.30 +/- .28 \times 10^{-3}]$
South	45°	$6.22 +/- .23 \times 10^{-3}$	$[8.71 +/- .24 \times 10^{-3}]$

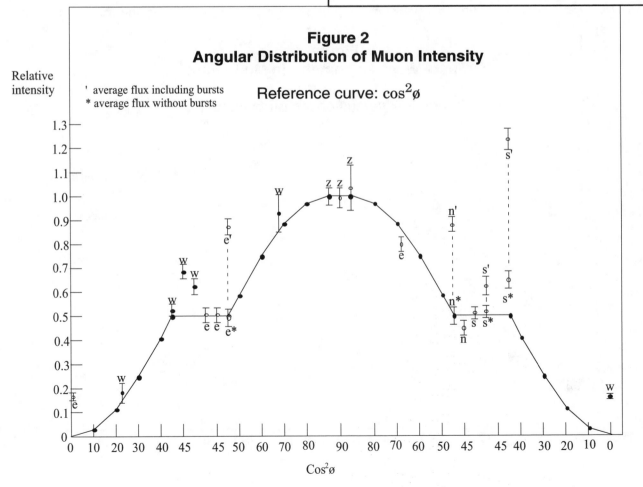

Figure 2
Angular Distribution of Muon Intensity

Reference curve: $\cos^2\phi$

' average flux including bursts
* average flux without bursts

Relative intensity

$\cos^2\phi$

the muon flux occurs at approximately 12.30pm which was 28.4 +/-6.7% higher than the average with the bursts excluded. If the bursts are included, the diurnal effect is far more dramatic with a peak at 13:45 hrs (1:45pm), 2.3 times above the mean. Smaller peaks at 18:30 hrs (6.30pm) and 5.30 hrs (am) are clearly discernible. Diurnal variations in cosmic ray fluxes have previously been reported as 0.3% with the peak during the middle of the morning hours.[8]

In conclusion the west-east asymmetry of cosmic rays and the wave-like west-east phenomena of Reich betray an energetic motion leading the earth in its rotation. The peaking at sunrise and sunset as well as at mid day would suggest that stimulation of the atmosphere by solar radiation may be a factor in the cosmic ray flux. The magnetic interaction theory cannot provide an explanation of the diurnal variations in the flux. Moreover, the high average intensity of the cosmic ray bursts at sunrise midday and sunset suggests, as Reich theorized, a component of cosmic radiation may have a terrestrial origin.

References:

1. Hess, V.F.: "Über Beobachtungen der durchdringenden Strahlung bei sieben Freiballonfahrten", *Phys. Zeits.*, 12 (1911); *Phys. Zeits.* 13, 1084 (1912).

2. Kolhörster, W.: *Phys. Zeits.*, 14, 1066, 1153, (1913)

3. Reich, W.: *The Cancer Biopathy,* Orgone Inst. Press, NY 1948, p.112 & 145.

4. Allen, K.E. and Apostolakis, A.J.: *Proc. R. Soc.* A265 117-32 (1961).

5. Moroney, J.R. and Perry, J.K.: *Aust. J. Cim.* 7 423-36 (1954).

Allkofer, O.C. and Andresen, R.D.: *Nuovo Cim.*ento 51 329-40 (1967).

6. Thompson, M.G.: *Energetic Muons*. Taken from: *Cosmic Rays at Ground Level* ed. by A.W. Wolfendale. Inst. of Physics, London 1973.

Blackett, P.M.S.: *Proc. R. Soc.* A159 1-18 (1937).

Jones, H.: *Rev. Mod. Phys.* 11 235-8 (1939).

Hughes, D.J.: "Positive Excess and Electron Component in the Cosmic-Ray Spectrum", *Phys. Rev.* 57 592-97 (1940).

7. Cosmic Ray Fluxes, *Muon Reference Binder*, Univ. of Toronto Physics Dept., 1986.

8. Hoag, J. B.: *Electron and Nuclear Physics*, 2nd Ed., Van Nostrand, 1938.

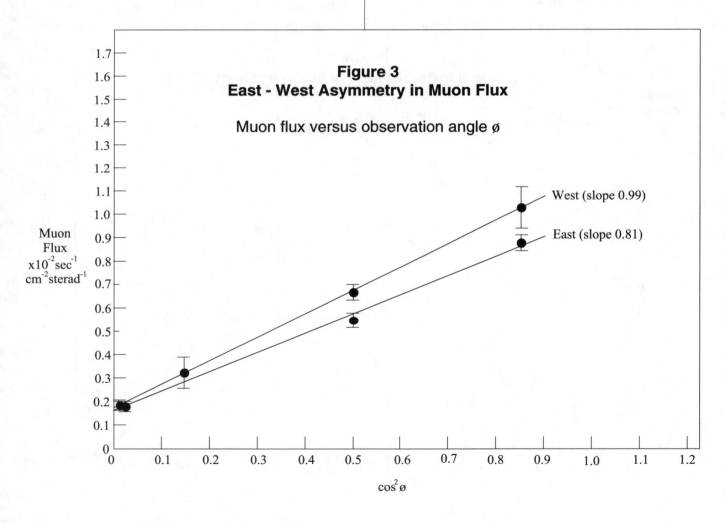

Figure 3
East - West Asymmetry in Muon Flux

Muon flux versus observation angle ø

West (slope 0.99)

East (slope 0.81)

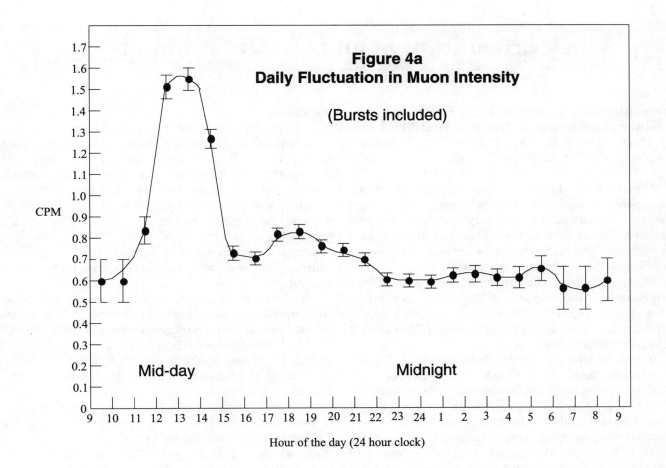

Figure 4a
Daily Fluctuation in Muon Intensity

(Bursts included)

CPM

Mid-day   Midnight

Hour of the day (24 hour clock)

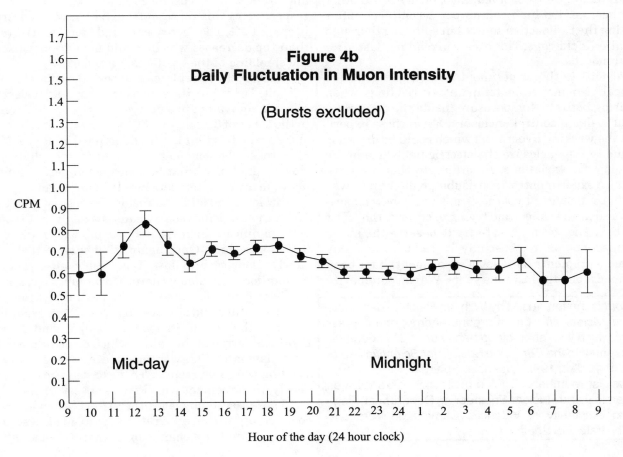

Figure 4b
Daily Fluctuation in Muon Intensity

(Bursts excluded)

CPM

Mid-day   Midnight

Hour of the day (24 hour clock)

Confirmation of an *Oranur** Anomaly

Anomalies in Radioactive Decay Rates and Temperature Measurements Inside a Modified Faraday Cage * * by V. Milián,[1] R. Ranchis,[2] G. Verdú,[2] J.L. Muñoz-Cobos,[2] G. Baeza,[2] P. Kot[2]

Dr. Wilhelm Reich developed a special enclosure which was capable of causing anomalies in response patterns of several devices such as mercury thermometers and Geiger -Müller (GM) counters. This enclosure is like a Faraday cage and all the six faces are built alternating metallic and non-metallic substances.

Reich postulated that those anomalous readings were caused by the response of the meters to what he called *orgone energy*, which was concentrated by the enclosure due to its special configuration. He called it the *orgone accumulator*.

In 1950 he wrote a report called *The Oranur Experiment* (in *Selected Writings,* Farrar, Straus & Giroux, NY 1963). In this report Reich describes dramatic reactions of the GM counters as a response to the presence of radioactive materials inside the accumulator. Counters showed erratic counting rates or seemed to be "dead" for a period. Jamming and fading in counts per second measurements were observed. Also, he described other anomalies, i.e. too high counts per second (cps) after removing the radioactive sources in spite of a thorough ventilation of the cage. This excess in readings lasted for several months.

Previous to this experiment he had also reported significant anomalies in temperature readings when comparing both the temperature inside the accumulator and inside a control enclosure. From these experiments the working hypothesis which could be drawn is that due to the enclosure the electric fields inside the cage allow for variations. According to this, we have performed experiments with a double goal. The first was to try to confirm our hypothesis designing new experiments and at the same time trying to observe the effect of the box. The second was to try to observe the above mentioned anomalies, specially in radioactive decay rates measurements. This set of experiments have been performed along the last nine years. We can summarize

our results:

a) The first experiment consisted in simultaneous temperature measurements using a set of four electronic sensors (Pt-100). The sensors were covered with different materials and gave the same readings outside the box. But when placed inside the box and after adding a radioactive source of 1 microCurie, they slowly increased the differences between each other till 1°C suggesting a change in resistivity. The differences in readings disappeared after removing the radioactive source. This was repeated three times with similar results.

b) Other experiments were simultaneous radioactivity measurements using two independent GM counter tubes. Simultaneous background counts with two GM counter tubes decreased their values from 0.258 to 0.229 cps ($c_1 = 0.03$ cps), and from 0.313 to 0.268 cps ($c_2 = 0.05$ cps) , when the tubes were placed inside the box. This was due to the 20 mm of shielding provided by the metal of the cage's sides. But simultaneous radioactive decay measurements of two sources, namely Ra-226 and Cs-137, when placed inside the box, showed a decrease in their values from 36.04 cps to 35.60 cps ($c_3 = 0.44$ cps), and from 276.40 cps to 273.05 cps ($c_4 = 3.35$ cps) respectively. This represents, in both cases, a decrease in cps of 1.2%. The decreases c_3 and c_4 are much greater than the decreases which should have been caused by the shielding of the box faces, c_1 and c_2.

As we know, the plateau slope of the tubes is 0.04 % per volt. Therefore, the above mentioned 1.2 % decrease in cps is equivalent to a decrease in the applied tension to the tubes of 30 volt, i.e., 5% of 600 volt. These results show a trend similar to that mentioned by Reich. Moreover, these phenomena take place not immediately but slowly, similar to what happens when performing the above mentioned temperature measurements.

Besides, the addition inside the cage of a shielded 100 mCi americium source causes a slight but statistically significant increase in cps of 0.3% for radium and 0.1% for cesium. Once again, this change took place slowly, along several days. Conversely, after removing an additional unshielded natural uranium source, which had been placed for some days inside the cage (accumulator), we still could observe an excess in cps readings of 0.7 % in the case of the radium source, and 0.2% for cesium, referred to the values which could be measured many days later. This was repeated after several months yielding the same results. This excess in cps vanished slowly, in agreement with Reich's observations.

These results suggest either a fluctuation in electric conductivity within apparatus kept inside the accumulator cage, and/or a change in decay-rate constants.

* *Oranur* is the term used by Wilhelm Reich to designate an *anti-nuclear effect* from orgone energy, one expression of which was anomalous behavior of GM counters.
** Presented to the *European Society for Scientific Exploration*, 9-12 Oct. 1998, Valencia, Spain.
1. Physicist, member of CIFA e-mail : vmilián@arrakis.es
2. Chemical and Nuclear Engineering Department, Polytechnic University of Valencia, Camino de Vera s/n. 46022 - Valencia Spain.

Green Sea Eritrea: A 5-Year Desert-Greening CORE Project in the SE African-Sahel [*]

by James DeMeo
Field Operations Team: James DeMeo[1], Ph.D., Theirrie Cook[2], B.A., Aurelio Albini[3], M.D., Carlo Albini[4], and Prof. Dr. Bernd Senf[5]

Following is a report on the first systematic application of Wilhelm Reich's discovered technique of *cloudbusting*, for the purposes of drought-abatement and desert-greening in a region lying immediately adjacent to the Sahara Desert, the largest extremely hyper-arid region on planet Earth. The results of these operations, which spanned five summers of field work in the small nation of Eritrea, are unprecedented and even spectacular. They prove what is possible when controversial and unorthodox research subjects, such as the atmospheric energetic discoveries made by Reich in the 1950s, are given even a small amount of social support and research funding. The results also provide a powerful confirmation for Reich.

Introduction and Background

Starting in 1994, a five-year research program was organized to bring the methods of *Cosmic Orgone Engineering (CORE)*, or *cloudbusting* to the nation of Eritrea, lying at the SE corner of the Sahara Desert. The project idea was initiated in 1992 by Aurelio Albini and Carlo Albini of Italy, who have family ties to Eritrea, and who gained approvals from government officials for the project to proceed. For five summers starting in 1994, two separate expeditions were undertaken each year by teams of volunteer workers from the USA, Italy, Germany and Eritrea, employing from one to three different cloudbusting apparatus at several different sites in Eritrea. The project was formally organized and

* This *Cosmic Orgone Engineering (CORE)* project was the product of the hard work and volunteer efforts of a large number of persons in addition to the field operations team. Special thanks to Adriano Albini, Tekeste Kifle, Enricho Sebastiani, Richard Wilkinson, Martin Zumtobel, and to various representatives of the Eritrean *Ministry of Agriculture* and *Civil Aviation Department*, especially to Semere Amlesom and Asefaw Habtemichael, without whose personal support and engagement this project would never have been possible.

1. Eritrea Project Director, and Director, *Orgone Biophysical Research Lab,* Greensprings, PO Box 1148, Ashland, Oregon 97520 USA. tel-fax: 541-552-0118, Email: demeo@mind.net
2. Director, *Orgonics*, Petaluma, California, USA, Email: Orgonics@aol.com
3. Pediatrician, *Civil Hospital of Ischia*, Naples, Italy. Email: <albiniau@libero.it>
4. Consulting Engineer, student of orgonomy, and author. Email: <carlo.albi@tiscalinet.it>
5. Professor, *Fachhochschule für Wirtschaft*, Berlin, Germany. Email: <senf@fhw-berlin.de>

Cloudbuster *Kiremti* (Tigrinya word for "Good Rains") on the banks of Mainifhi Reservoir (Map point "A", p.184), Eritrea, East Africa, during a 5-year Desert-Greening Project undertaken with the support of the *State of Eritrea*.

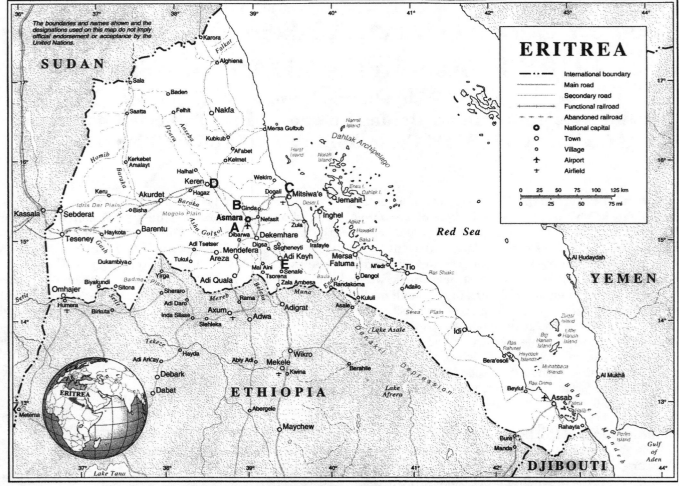

Figure 1. Map of Eritrea, identifying the major cloudbuster operations sites:
A. Mainifhi Reservoir, B. MaiSheka Reservoir, C. Massawa Port, D. Keren Farm, E. Senafe Reservoir

funded as a joint effort between *Eritrea Bahri Kuzli (Green Sea Eritrea)*, in Naples, Italy, and the *Orgone Biophysical Research Lab (OBRL)* in Ashland, Oregon, USA, with shared work-democratic responsibilities by the various members of the field operations team. The project was additionally undertaken with the full approval, and with financial and logistical support, of the *Eritrean Ministry of Agriculture* — as such, the Eritrean operations constituted as much of a social breakthrough as a technical achievement, showing as they did the ability of the cloudbusting method to increase rains even at the edge of the world's largest desert region.

In 1991, following nearly 30 years of oppression by the much larger nation of Ethiopia (a feudal monarchal dictatorship which later degenerated into a brutal communist totalitarian state), the small nation of Eritrea won its struggle for independence. A United Nations referendum in 1992 indicated the Eritrean population wanted full political independence from Ethiopia, and so the old nation of Eritrea was reborn, with international recognitions. Foreign aid began to flow into the nation, and the process of rebuilding began in earnest.

Unfortunately, the region also had suffered under nearly 30 years of drought, paralleling the long period of social turmoil. A visit to Eritrea by the Albini brothers in 1992 indicated the immense difficulties of rebuilding a national infrastructure under conditions of extreme drought. Fortunately, they were aware of the work of Wilhelm Reich on the cloudbusting method, and contacted James DeMeo of the OBRL with a simple question: *What could be done against the seemingly intractable drought conditions?*

Eritrea's Natural Weather Patterns

Research was thereafter undertaken as to the natural climate and weather of the region, to identify those conditions when good rains occurred by nature alone. Applying a mix of information from textbooks, climate records (going back to the early Italian colonial period), direct observations and more recent weather analysis, the specific dynamics of Eritrean weather during wet and dry conditions were clarified, from both classical-meteorological and orgone-energetic standpoints.

The highland region of Eritrea (where the majority of population and agriculture exists) experiences a natural rainy season in summertime, roughly from June through September, when the tropical rainy belt (*Inter-Tropical Discontinuity*, or *ITD*) moves northward to influence Eritrea. The months of October through May are generally dry with little or no rains on the highlands, at the time when the ITD tropical rainy belt shifts southward away from Eritrea, and the region comes under the influence of the Sahara Desert atmosphere. Over the last 30 years, the problematic situation existed wherein the ITD tropical rainy belt moved north during summers only minimally and weakly, leaving the region under predominantly Saharan-dry conditions for years on end. A videotape made of atmospheric conditions in 1992 clearly showed the presence of an extensive *dor-layer* (Reich's term for what is classically called "atmospheric haze" or "desert dusts", but which is partially or even fundamentally composed of stagnant orgone energy, called *deadly orgone*, or *dor*). These and other lines of empirical evidence suggested, if applied carefully and correctly, the cloudbusting method could have a beneficial effect and produce rainfalls similar to what the region experienced during normal to better-than-normal rainy seasons.

Classically, several ingredients were necessary for good rains over Eritrea:

1. Good moisture flow from the Gulf of Guinea, northeast across Ethiopia and Sudan, into Eritrea.

2. Convection of heated air from the southern Red Sea, up the slope of the escarpment into highland Eritrea.

3. Well-developed upper-level easterly jet stream.

The Eritrean-Ethiopian highlands receives some early-season moisture from a southerly or southeasterly vector, out of the Indian Ocean, but the largest rains always occur with the advection of moisture from the southwest, out of the faraway Gulf of Guinea in the southern Atlantic Ocean. This Atlantic moisture will, in good rainy years, move northeast across the Congo region and Ethiopian mountains, sometimes all the way to the southern Red Sea. The Atlantic moisture will then interact with a heated convective current rising up the escarpment from the southern Red Sea, to yield massive cloud development by mid-day. The storms will be especially dynamic when energized by an easterly (east-to-west) jet stream moving high overhead. Convective thunderstorms so generated will then move westward across much of the *Sahel* zone[§] of sub-Saharan Africa, lasting late into the evening, and being continually fed with moisture by the northeasterly flow of moist air from the Gulf of Guinea.

The presence of the Sahara Desert just to the north of Eritrea always threatens to bring drought, however.

___

[§] *Sahel* is an Arabic term meaning "edge" of the Sahara.

The Saharan atmosphere in that region is especially choked with dor-haze, and when the Sahara expands and fails to retreat northward during the months of June through September, it would act to block the northeast-flow of moisture from the Atlantic. An expansive Saharan atmosphere would also cause excessive amounts of dor to spill southward into Sudan and Ethiopia, where it would further block moisture flow from the Gulf of Guinea. Dor-haze also spilled eastward to fill the Red Sea basin, intensifying the already heavy dor conditions along the Red Sea coast, dampening out the usual convective activity, or rendering that convection incapable of forming clouds (in violation of typical adiabatic expectations). For these apparent reasons, the region is known to be one of the world's "problem climates"[1] in that classical meteorological theory fails to fully explain how it functions.

During dry years of Saharan influence, thick and heavy dor-layers would rise up to 20,000 ft (6,000 meters) above the local topography, blanketing the entire region. Under such torrid dor-haze conditions, the easterly jet stream would considerably weaken, or appear only late in the rainy season. Consequently, it became evident from the very beginning, that a lot of dor-busting with the cloudbuster would be needed. Also, a good rainy season in Eritrea also carried with it the suggestion of greater rains across the entire sweep of the Sahel region. Sadly, the 30-year epoch of long-term dryness in Eritrea was correlated to similar dryness across much of the Sahel.

Following our instincts to locate cloudbusting sites that would allow us to draw up moisture from either the Indian Ocean, Red Sea or Gulf of Guinea, with logistical assistance from the Ministry of Agriculture, we sited the cloudbuster at several large Eritrean reservoirs, behind water impoundment dams constructed during the period of Italian colonization. These were primarily at *Mainifhi* and *MaiSheka* Reservoirs, close to the capitol city of Asmara, on the African highland escarpment at approximately 7000 ft (2100 m) elevation. The highland escarpment location at MaiSheka, we would learn from meteorologist Asefaw Habtemichael, was generally known as the *"birthplace of the tropical easterlies"*, in that the global easterly rainy belt simply did not exist farther to the east of that location. (There is no "easterly rainy belt" over southern Arabia or India, for example, and India experiences only a seasonal monsoon). During years of good rains, the tropical easterlies would literally blossom at certain high points along the Eritrean highlands, and from there move due west across most of the Sahel.

A third favored location for the cloudbusting work was at the port city of *Massawa*, on the hyper-arid Red Sea coast. The dor was intensive and oppressive at this location, with sand dunes, high temperatures and humidities which ranged from high to low. Little rain fell there, even though the overheated waters of the Red Sea

Thick Atmospheric Dor-Haze lingering over the country-side, looking east down the escarpment towards the Red Sea (map point "B" in Fig. 1) near MaiSheka Reservoir.

were evaporating tremendous quantities of water into the atmosphere. Figure 1 shows a map of the region, identifying the specific cloudbuster draw-sites. For the 1994 operations, only the one cloudbuster was used, constructed in Eritrea; in later years, additional apparatus would be employed.

Weather Patterns in Late 1993, Early 1994

As is discussed below, Eritrea and surrounding nations, as well as much of sub-Saharan Africa, suffered for the prior 30 years not only from the anticipated October-May aridity associated with the close proximity of the Sahara Desert, but additionally from severe drought, where the much-anticipated June-September rainy season failed to materialize. As the organizational and fund-raising aspects of the Eritrea CORE Project got underway after 1992, it became increasingly clear that the region was suffering from a combined desert-expansion and drought catastrophe which was only getting worse. The following *Drought Emergency Bulletins* [2] were circulated by the Orgone Biophysical Research Lab, to the members of the field operations team and a smaller group of interested supporters, and served to underscore the disastrous situation faced by people in Sub-Saharan Africa and Southern Asia at the time. From these materials, it became clear that the stagnant atmosphere over the eastern Sahara and Arabian Deserts was in a dramatic state of expansion, pushing out beyond its "normal" geographical boundaries, to extinguish or shorten various regional rainy seasons, and otherwise create intensive drought over a vast area.

DROUGHT EMERGENCY BULLETIN
A DEVELOPING DROUGHT SITUATION
ALONG THE CENTRAL & SOUTH FRINGE
OF THE SAHARASIAN DESERT BELT
December 1993 Reports:
EASTERN MEDITERRANEAN/ISRAEL: "Instead of the rain and cold that have come to be expected following two winters of above-average precipitation, this season has been characterized predominantly by clear skies, sunshine and dry easterly winds... Interludes of wet weather have been much briefer than expected or forecast and the rain that has fallen has been absorbed into the earth only to evaporate later, courtesy of the sun and dry winds" (Jerusalem Post, 17/12/93 — situation not substantially changed from that date, though water impounded from prior rainy seasons is sufficient in Israel for most of 1994.)

DROUGHT EMERGENCY BULLETIN
January 1994 Reports:
EAST AFRICA: TANZANIA: "Tanzania's Agriculture minister warned that his country faces a devastating famine following the failure of seasonal crops. Crops are also withering in southern Somalia, renewing the specter of another round of hunger in the beleaguered nation." (Earth Week, San Francisco Chronicle, 8 Jan. 1994)

ARABIAN PENINSULA: "Saudi Arabia's King Fahd bin Abdul Aziz called for rain prayers to be offered throughout the kingdom because this winter's rains did not fall. Similar prayers were offered in the United Arab Emirates last month." (Earth Week, San Francisco Chronicle, 28 January 1994)

WESTERN CHINA: "Half a million people in northwest Chinese province of Shaanxi are without adequate drinking water due to a severe drought that is also ravaging the country's winter wheat crop. Since last autumn, rainfall has dropped by as much as 60 percent from the previous year. Half of the province's wheat crop has withered, and local meteorologists predict the dry spell is likely to continue for several more months." (Earth Week, San Francisco Chronicle, 28 January 1994)

VIETNAM: "20,000 highland tribesmen in the center of the country face famine due to a prolonged drought. About 20 villages in Quang Tri Province are suffering the worst food shortage in memory. Their inhabitants are trying to survive on tropical plants, herbs and the roots of wild banana trees." (Earth Week, San Francisco Chronicle, 8 Jan. 1994)

DROUGHT EMERGENCY BULLETIN
DROUGHT CONTINUES TO DEVELOP AND
SPREAD ALONG THE SOUTH-EAST FRINGE
OF THE SAHARASIAN DESERT BELT
February 1994 Reports:

EAST AFRICA: KENYA & ETHIOPIA: "Three months of drought has brought a million people in parts of Kenya and Ethiopia to the brink of famine. Seven people have already died of starvation, and others have resorted to searching for wild berries and roots to survive. Officials fear that 250,000 head of cattle will die in Kenya's Kajiado District unless rains arrive by the end of March. The presence of about 400,000 refugees from Somalia, Ethiopia and Sudan has made the food crisis in Kenya even more acute." (Earth Week, San Francisco Chronicle, 11 February 1994)

EASTERN MEDITERRANEAN/ISRAEL: "The Kinneret (Sea of Galilee) Authority on Friday announced that so far this has been the driest year for a decade, and if much rain does not fall by the end of April, the Kinneret will probably not reach its optimum level. Authority director Zvi Ortenberg said the lake has risen 29 centimeters since the beginning of the year. Cloud seeding was not undertaken early this year, in accordance with forecasts for abundant rain." (Jerusalem Post, 20 February 94)

PAKISTAN: "A prolonged dry spell in Pakistan has withered most of the country's huge illegal opium crop. 'This was help from God, but we will not pray for it to come again because it also destroys other crops' Interior Minister Naseerullah Khan Babar told a news conference. The drought has destroyed 80 percent of the poppy crop..." (Earth Week, San Francisco Chronicle, 11 February 1994)

DROUGHT EMERGENCY BULLETIN
DROUGHT CONTINUES TO DEVELOP AND SPREAD ALONG THE SOUTH-EAST FRINGE OF THE SAHARASIAN DESERT BELT WITH LIMITED NORTHWARD SPREAD INTO THE MEDITERRANEAN
March 1994 Reports:

EAST AFRICA: KENYA & TANZANIA: "Five million people in Kenya and northern Tanzania face severe food shortages from a drought and intense heat that are killing livestock and shriveling food and export crops. The UN Food and Agricultural Organization has warned that the worst drought in 10 years threatens famine for 2 million people, and it plans to make emergency food shipments. Kenya's tea and coffee export facilities are closing because of the withered crops". (Earth Week, San Francisco Chronicle, 5 March 94)

EAST AFRICA: ETHIOPIA: "Desperate Ethiopians, believing that clouds of smoke would bring an end to their drought, deliberately set wildfires that burned more than 1.5 million acres of forest in the south of the country. The blazes also destroyed standing grain crops and vegetable gardens, as well as a large number of domestic animals and wildlife". (Earth Week, San Francisco Chronicle, 12 March 1994)

THAILAND: "Residents of Thailand's capital have been warned to store fresh water because their taps may soon run dry. An extended drought over much of the country has brought many rivers and streams to dangerously low levels, including the Chao Phraya, which flows through Bangkok. (Earth Week, San Francisco Chronicle, 12 March 1994)

THAILAND: "A freak thunderstorm interrupted the worst drought Bangkok has experienced in decades, soaking the capital and bringing its notorious traffic to a standstill. Despite the dry-season downpour, meteorological and irrigation officials warned that the rain was only a short reprieve from the drought." (Earth Week, San Francisco Chronicle, 25 March 1994)

TURKEY: "Turkey's worst drought in more than 35 years is expected to cut the country's vital wheat export by 500,000 to 1 million tons this harvest. (Earth Week, San Francisco Chronicle, 25 March 1994)

DROUGHT EMERGENCY BULLETIN
DROUGHT CONTINUES TO DEVELOP AND SPREAD ALONG THE SOUTH-EAST FRINGE OF THE SAHARASIAN DESERT BELT WITH LIMITED NORTHWARD SPREAD INTO THE MEDITERRANEAN
April 1994 Reports:

INDIA: "A forest fire raging in India's Similpal national park threatens large numbers of tigers, leopards and elephants. Environment Minister Adwait Singh said the blazes had engulfed 1/10th of the 850 square-mile park about 150 miles southwest of Calcutta. ... the fires...have been made worse by scorching weather." (Earth Week, San Francisco Chronicle, 1 April 1994)

EAST AFRICA: "The failure of seasonal rains in East Africa continues to threaten millions of people from Rwanda to Ethiopia with starvation" (Earth Week, San Francisco Chronicle, 8 April 1994)

MEDITERRANEAN: "Most of the Mediterranean Basin again received little or no precipitation — dry for 8 weeks" (Global Climate Highlights, Weekly Climate Bulletin, 6 April 1994)

CHINA: "Seventeen cities in provinces across northern China face what Beijing authorities are calling 'the drought of the century'. Officials have set up a $3.2 million fund to help pump water to the affected population centers. Key grain producing provinces are among the hardest hit. (Earth Week, San Francisco Chronicle, 8 April 1994)

PAKISTAN: "Pakistani Prime Minister Benazir Bhutto appealed to the nation to pray for rain to end a drought that started last October. The extended dry spell has affected wheat, sugar and cotton crops." (Earth Week, San Francisco Chronicle, 8 April 1994)

EASTERN MEDITERRANEAN: "A freak Saharan sandstorm swept over the Mediterranean Island of Cyprus, turning the spring sky a yellow-gray and threatening air traffic. The 'desert depression' first hit Libya, then blew all the way across the sea to Greece." (Earth Week, San Francisco Chronicle, 8 April 1994)

DROUGHT EMERGENCY BULLETIN
DROUGHT CONTINUES TO DEVELOP AND
SPREAD ALONG THE SOUTH-EAST FRINGE
OF THE SAHARASIAN DESERT BELT
WITH LIMITED NORTHWARD SPREAD
INTO THE MEDITERRANEAN
May 1994 Reports:
EAST AFRICA: "More than 50 people have died in eastern Uganda because of famine caused by drought. In some areas, people are surviving on a water-weed that will soon disappear if river levels continue to drop. Others are subsisting on grass and mangoes. Political rivalries are reported to have prevented relief supplies from reaching the affected areas." (Earth Week, San Francisco Chronicle, 13 May 1994)

SOUTH AFRICA: "Renewed drought in parts of South Africa threatens to wipe out more than half the country's sugar crop. Agricultural officials in Natal province warn that the losses are inevitable if the region does not receive significant rainfall during the next six weeks". (Earth Week, San Francisco Chronicle, 13 May 1994)

DROUGHT EMERGENCY BULLETIN
ANALYSIS: March 1994
Regarding forthcoming work
in Eritrea, East Africa.

The equatorial rainy belt (Intertropical-Convergence Zone) appears not to be moving northward as is usual with the change of seasons. High-pressure drought conditions are replacing the normal low-pressure rainy conditions in that segment of the equatorial region. It would appear that the desert air mass over Saharasia, loaded with stagnant dorish energy, is expanding southeast, with a major component of stagnation working its way eastward across the Indian Ocean to affect South Asia. This may also explain abnormally high levels of dor energy in the Southern Pacific Ocean, which is presently working its way into North America, giving the West Coast of the USA another year of drought.

Whatever the reasons for this expanding drought situation, it poses a grim forecast regarding rains for Eritrea during the summer months. If the tropical rainy belt is not sufficiently energized or northward-moving in its location to bring rains to Ethiopia and Kenya, then it might not affect Eritrea either.

This means our work in Eritrea will be all the more critical, and for June-July 1994, we may possibly find ourselves working under fully-blown drought conditions.

Field Operations in 1994

A period of approximately two years was required to raise sufficient funds to pay for the first year of operations in Eritrea, supplied by both private donors from the USA and Europe, and a small grant from the *Jewish National Fund*. Funds raised were sufficient to pay for transportation of the six-person team to Eritrea, construction of the cloudbuster, and for food, camping gear, rooms in Asmara (the capital city), and so forth. All persons volunteered their time and services, without personal compensation, and the first year of operations got underway in earnest.

The first year of work was mapped out in early 1994, well before any confident forecasts could be made about the forthcoming rainy season, except for the depressing accounts as given in the various *Drought Emergency Bulletins* presented above. Nearly all the nations of the Horn of Africa — Ethiopia, Sudan, Somalia and Eritrea — had been in the grips of social chaos and war for years, and meteorological forecasts were a low priority until such time peace was established in 1992.

The Eritrean government openly gave logistical support during the 1994 operations, providing skilled metalworkers and supplies for construction of the large trailer-mounted cloudbuster. The *Research Division of the Ministry of Agriculture*, under the directorship of Semere Amlesom, and the meteorological analysis branch of the Civil Aviation Department, led by Asefaw Habtemichael, gave extremely helpful, crucial support in terms of short-term weather forecasts, meteorological data and satellite imagery, access to water resources for grounding of the cloudbuster, loan of a 4-wheel-drive truck with driver, and so forth. Several photos are given of the main cloudbuster constructed in Eritrea, and used for the field operations. It was given the name of cloudbuster *Kiremti*, which means "good rains" in the Tigrinya language.

The arrival of the CORE team in June 1994 confirmed the presence of a heavy dor layer, more intensive along the Red Sea lowlands, but also well-developed over the highlands. Dry northeasterly winds, blowing straight out of the Sahara, predominated and worked to push back the moisture into Ethiopia or beyond, and to "knock down" any clouds which would develop. This Northeast wind was itself charged with dor, and gave the feeling of blowing right through your clothing, producing a biological contraction that went deep into the bone. A lot of effort was therefore expended by the cloudbusting team to maintain their health during the difficult operations.

Once the cloudbuster was constructed, it was brought to one of several locations for operation: MaiSheka and Mainifhi reservoirs on the highlands, close to Asmara, or to the port city of Massawa, on the Red Sea coast. The field team would typically travel by truck on unpaved tracks, with the cloudbuster in tow, to a distant location and establish a field-camp, sleeping on the ground or in the vehicle for several days, cooking our meals on an open fire or kerosene stove. Invariably, local villagers would come and visit, their children crowding around and singing songs (for which they got small coins or cookies or fruit), making the entire affair a most interesting if not fatiguing adventure. The cloudbuster would be set up at water's edge, some distance from the campsite, and operated for one to three days maximum, according to the original principles set down by Wilhelm Reich,[3] as applied to the local weather and energetic parameters.

Operations in Massawa, on the Red Sea, required a long drive on a winding narrow road from the peak elevation of Asmara down the escarpment to sea level. Typically we would depart around midnight, and arrive in the early morning hours, allowing us to set up the equipment and seek shade before the temperatures typically soared to around 100°F (38°C).

After several days of such exhaustive work, we would pack up and return back to Asmara, for a hot shower and restaurant meal, before trekking off again to the next location. This method would allow several days of work at one location, with another several days at the next location in short order. As learned from field operations in the USA and elsewhere, operations from any single site for more than a few days at a stretch were avoided – atmospheric energetic overcharge and cloud inhibition would otherwise result – with mobile operations from different sites over the course of several days being the preferred and most effective method.

The main cloudbusting techniques applied were dor-busting, and scans towards the directions where moisture normally came at that time of year, with additional draws to contract the orgone-energy envelope and to stimulate jet-stream movements known to be associated with good rains. Weather data was obtained from a weather station operating at Asmara airport, but more frequently and regularly by fax machine from the USA. During most of the five-year project, one member of the team remained working in the USA at OBRL headquarters. They would obtain African satellite images and weather maps from various sources, and relay them by fax machine to the field team in Eritrea, to the Ministry of Agriculture offices, or to a hotel or other location as close to the operational site as possible. Usually, traveling in the field meant we were totally isolated from classical weather data, except for small weather instruments carried along, and sketchy BBC weather forecasts for Africa.

A small barometer proved nearly useless given the constant elevation changes, but a simple electronic temperature/humidity meter did allow hand-graphs to be constructed, showing changes in *absolute humidity* over the course of the days, and signaling the arrival of moister air masses. Factually, the shortwave radio proved to be a better weather tool in its reception of *static discharges from lightning strikes*. We could count the number of static bursts per minute, and get an idea about how much lightning and thunderstorm activity there was in the local region. In 1994, internet connections by telephone or satellite link were not yet economically feasible on our small budget. The weather-fax method worked exceptionally well, however, as the most

Cloudbuster Kiremti, working at the port city of Massawa on the Red Sea (Top, map point "C" in Fig.1) where a thick dor-haze is apparent, and at the MaiSheka Reservoir (Bottom, map point "B" in Fig.1).

recent forecasts, with a summary of the previous day's rainfalls, were generally waiting for the team just before departing to work in the mornings, or once we returned back to the city.

In 1994, and in each subsequent year, the work was organized into two separate expeditions or phases, timed to maximally benefit local agricultural needs and expectations. Phase I occurred at the start of the normal rainy season to insure a good start to natural rains, while Phase II occurred in the middle of the rainy season, to insure a continuance of rains during the critical pre-harvest fruiting stages of plant growth.

Phase I: 20 June to 3 July, 1994
Phase II: 18 August to 27 August, 1994

It must be pointed out that the actual dates when operations were started were established months in advance, such that we could not possibly know what the subsequent short-term forecasts would be. We would make our airplane reservations months ahead of time, and upon arrival in Africa be confronted with a series of logistical delays and obstacles for getting the equipment

Infrared Satellite Image, 25 June 1994, East Africa (Right), showing the southern Red Sea and Horn Region during a peak rainfall event, Phase I Cloudbusting Operations. Eritrea is located at point A, where a major rainstorm cluster covers the entire western half of Eritrea. Smaller rains fell across parts of Ethiopia, to the north and south of the major highlands area (point B). Moisture flows were confined to a relatively shallow layer, moving around, rather than over, the Ethiopian highlands. The cloud-free area north of the dashed line marks the Sahara Desert air mass, which moves south to cover all of Eritrea during the dry months from October through May. Without moisture from the Southwest, Eritrea would literally become a part of the Sahara.

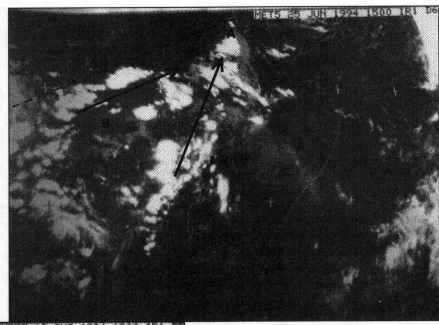

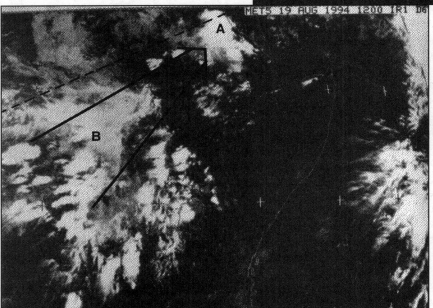

Infrared Satellite Image, 19 August 1994, East Africa (Left), showing the southern Red Sea and Horn Region during a peak rainfall event, Phase II Cloudbusting Operations. A major rainstorm cluster covers nearly the entire nation of Eritrea (point A). Subsidiary rains developed and fell across most of the Ethiopian Highlands, at point B. The general flow of moisture starts on the west coast of Africa, in the Gulf of Guinea, moving northeast to eventually cross Ethiopia and Eritrea, as marked by the arrows. In this image, moisture flow is well-developed into a thick layer, providing exceptional rains for the entire region. Moisture also penetrates northward, beyond the dashed line, into the Sahara region.

in good working order, given that much of it had been in storage for months, sometimes with various parts going missing and needing new construction and repair. It was therefore impossible for us to predict with any accuracy just when we would start our work.

Nevertheless, on the very first day of the 1994 operations, within minutes of setting up and working the cloudbuster, wind-reversals associated with good moisture flow from the Gulf of Guinea developed — in fact, the reversal was so significant and noticeable that a worker in the meteorological division at Asmara airport some 30 miles away became highly excited, and immediately jumped into his car to drive to the field operations site to see for himself what we were doing. He apparently had not seen those moisture-bearing winds for many years, and found it hard to believe our appara-

tus and the onset of work on that same day was truly the cause. However, it was the cause, and both well-developed cloud structures and some small rains occurred at the cloudbuster site within about 30 minutes, spreading to a larger area by that evening, and eventually across Eritrea in the subsequent week as our field operations expanded into other areas.

The dor-busting operations in Massawa proved to be essential, if not dangerous and difficult. Heavy dor-levels increased with humidity and temperature to nearly unbearable levels around the cloudbuster, as the dor-haze slowly was driven towards a moister condition, following a pathway described by Reich some 38 years earlier in his book *Contact With Space*[4] — where *dor converts directly into water*. The physical experience and observations of this incredible process, were of the

Heavy Rains Over Asmara, Eritrea, following cloudbusting operations in Summer of 1994.

brownish-grey dor haze slowly thickening and becoming more milky and opaque in nature, converting towards a foggy condition. Breathing became difficult, and the air surrounding the cloudbuster at the time became unnervingly still, as did the surface of Massawa Bay, with visibilities reduced to less than 10 meters. This conversion, once initiated, continued for some period after the cloudbusting operations ended, and even the Red Sea region experienced anomalous cloud development and rains.

The 1994 operations culminated in heavy downpours of a wide distribution across nearly all of Eritrea and the southern Red Sea region, which soaked deep into the parched earth and filled the many empty or half-drained lakes and reservoirs. Dry river beds in the western parts of Eritrea flowed with water, and the adjacent regions of Ethiopia and Sudan also benefited. In fact, we almost lost the cloudbuster to the bottom of a reservoir when our truck driver failed to return one evening — it had been parked on a small hill deep in the dried-up reservoir, and rising water levels from heavy rains threatened to turn that hill into a small island. Only some heroic action with the 4-wheel-drive truck allowed the cloudbuster to be retrieved before the "island" was swamped! Older residents of Eritrea confirmed to us that these soaking rains, which came

regularly every day and lasted for many hours, spread from horizon to horizon, were like they remembered "from 30 years ago", before the long drought. It was a spectacular result which left our team happy, amazed and humbled, if not frequently soaked and exhausted.

Unfortunately, in 1994 the Eritrean Ministry of Agriculture had not yet established a rainfall-measuring system with any significant number of stations by which to quantify these observations. However, yearly averaged data was available from the World Meteorological Organization which summarized rainfall data for stations over a larger area of the larger Sahel region, to include Eritrea, Ethiopia and Sudan.

Figure 2 presents a *Precipitation Index for the Western Sahel*,[5] a year-by-year graphical representation of rains, revealing the long-term 30 years of drought over the region, as well as the reversal of this disastrous situation, to above-normal rainfalls, in 1994. Since the data constructing this graph is derived from *only the western half of the African Sahel* (20°W - 15°E longitude) we cannot be certain these rains developed as a consequence of cloudbusting in Eritrea (at ~35°E). However, evidence from field observations, from cloud patterns on satellite imagery, and from news reports indicating rains in neighboring Sudan and Ethiopia at that time, suggested good rains across the Eastern Sahel as well.

Figure 3 demonstrates the good rains in the Western Sahel during 1994 were accompanied by a significant northward intrusion of the *Inter-Tropical Discontinuity (ITD)*, or tropical rainy belt, into the Southern Sahara region, starting on the third decade (10-day period) of June, which began on June 20th, but not earlier.[5] The northward intrusion persisted thereafter, for the rest of the 1994 rainy season. Since the cloudbusting operations started on 20 June, this graph suggests *the timing of the good rains across the Sahel were timed to the cloudbusting operations in Eritrea.* Table I produces more direct evidence along these lines, showing 1994 to have a significant northward movement of the ITD tropical rainy belt in the *Eastern Sahel* as well,[5] covering latitudes 20°E to 35°E, inclusive of Eritrea. Taken together, these data confirm the unusually wet conditions, the unusual northward movement of the tropical rainy belt into the Southern Sahara regions during 1994, and strongly suggest the work undertaken in Eritrea that year benefited the entire Sahel zone of Africa.

An indirect confirmation of these unusually wet conditions also came from an acquaintance who lived part-time in southern Algeria, in the center of the Sahara Desert and close to *Tassili n'Ajer*, the old Tuareg "place of the waters" which is today bone-dry, but in the years prior to c.4000 BCE was wet enough to support large browsing animals such as elephant and giraffe, with lakes and streams containing hippo and crocodile.[6] Following the good rains in Eritrea, this isolated part of the central Sahara also got a good rainfall, leading to the

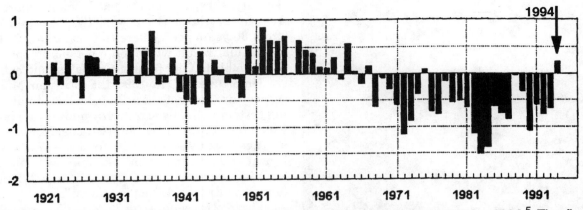

Figure 2: Precipitation Index for the Western Sahel, Sub-Saharan Africa, 1921 - 1994.[5] The first year of cloudbusting was in 1994 (marked with an arrow), shows a reversal of a 30-year drought-pattern to an above-normal rainfall. May through September standardized departures from 1951-1980 mean rainfall, for stations 20°W - 20°E and 8°N - 18°N.

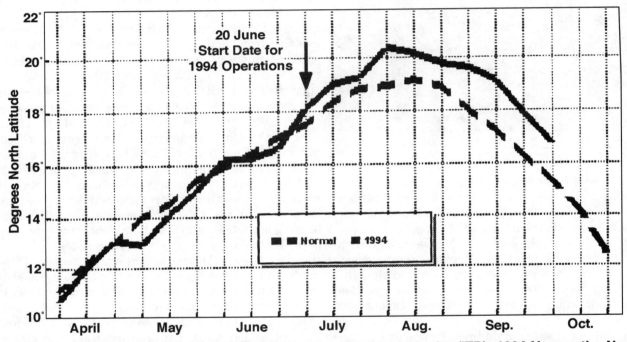

Figure 3: Movement of the West African Inter-Tropical Discontinuity (ITD), 1994 Versus the Normal Condition,[5] dekadal (10-day) average data, for latitudes 10°W to 10°E. Phase I cloudbusting operations started in Eritrea on June 20th. The graph indicates a persisting northward movement of the ITD starting within the third dekade of June, on or after that date.

Table 1: Interannual Variation of the East African (20°E - 35°E) Inter-Tropical Discontinuity (ITD), June-September Average:[5]

Year	1989	1990	1991	1992	1993	1994
Latitude (deg.N)	15.55°	14.35°	15.25°	15.6°	15.25°	16.45°

Asmara, Eritrea is at 15°N Latitude, and 35°E Longitude

widespread appearance of grasses across formerly barren sand-dunes.

Officials in the Eritrean government were sufficiently impressed with the results of our work, that our team was invited back to undertake additional work the next year. A five-year research project was agreed upon, basically on a handshake, organized through the *Orgone Biophysical Research Lab* acting as a non-governmental organization, with our field research team in full command of all aspects of the project. All basic expenses of the project were covered by the Eritrean government, with the goal to empirically evaluate the method of cloudbusting, and its potential benefits to Eritrea. Eritrea was then spending over 100 million dollars per year for the importation of food, and so even a small reduction in this dependency would show a big payoff. From our side, money was never the issue, but a yearly fee of $25,000 was agreed upon, which covered our expenses. While the economic value of the work was certainly well beyond this relatively small sum, we did not ask more from such a small and impoverished nation. If a five-year project in Eritrea worked out well, we anticipated they would provide an introduction of our work to regional organizations devoted to water security in the region, for more ambitious and well-funded undertakings. It was an important first-step, the first time in history that any official government agency had agreed to support cloudbusting research.

Attack of the "Skeptics"

About a week prior to our departure from Eritrea, at the end of the Phase I operations and after some wonderful — indeed, incredible! — rains had fallen, our cloudbusting team and the overall project was subject to an intensive attack by a local academic "skeptic". An American professor on a Fulbright Scholarship working for the Eritrean climatology division, accompanied by one of his students working in the Civil Aviation Department, circulated a vicious letter making personal attacks and ignorant misrepresentations of our work. His goal was to have the entire project cancelled, on the claim it was a waste of money for the government. Interestingly, his own personal $70,000 annual scholarship was nearly three times as large as the entire yearly expense of the Eritrean cloudbusting project. This "skeptic attack" was aimed at persuading government officials that the good rains were only the result of "coincidence". A strong defense of the project was made thereafter, with a written rebuttal and several clarifying Memorandums presented to the Eritrean Ministry of Agriculture, countering the many vicious accusations and responding to a few honest questions — pertinent extracts from those documents are appended to this article. Unfortunately, unethical attacks have too often characterized the academic response to positive results on cloudbusting, and indeed, of nearly every experimen-

Wildflowers and Tall Grasses in the Eritrean countryside, after a season of good *Kiremti* rains.

tal finding which supports Wilhelm Reich. Fortunately, officials in the Eritrean Ministry of Agriculture were persuaded more by the evidence from their own eyes, having personally witnessed the reversal of the long-term drought crisis following the cloudbusting operations, than by the weak arguments and *ad hominem* personal attacks of the "skeptics". The project continued to be supported by the government of Eritrea.

Field Operations in 1995

In summer of 1995, another two expeditions were completed with excellent results, with operations undertaken at the same three field operations sites as in 1994: Mainifhi, MaiSheka, and Massawa.

Phase I: 3 July to 15 July, 1995
Phase II: 30 August to 10 September, 1995

Good meteorological data was finally available in 1995 from the Eritrean government. Figure 4 shows the Daily Precipitation over Eritrea for the months of June through September, from a network of 39 measuring stations.[7] The square boxes mark the dates of operations.

The results from the 1995 operations were very good, though not quite as intensive or widespread as what was seen in 1994. Due to late notifications and logistical difficulties, the 1995 operations began somewhat later than in 1994 (July 3rd, as compared to June 20th). Major rains nevertheless began, as in 1994, only after cloudbusting operations got underway. Rains were in fact scarce and nearly absent over much of Eritrea until the onset of the first cloudbusting operations in early July.

As in 1994, the 1995 operations were followed by many episodes of widespread and long-duration rains, covering most of Eritrea. Reservoirs in many cases were filled to overflowing, as was the case at MaiSheka which was completely filled to the top of the spillway by the 6th of September, having risen by 2-3 meters alone during the Phase II operations. Mainifhi reservoir was also brought up by around 3-5 meters from its original level by the end of July.

The Phase I operations were followed by an intensive cycle of rains which carried over through the end of July and into early August as well, but with a temporary return of dry conditions in early to mid August. Cloudbusting during Phase II had very good initial results, but by early September only isolated showers and thunderstorms occurred, as the larger Saharan system was pushing south once again, greatly limiting the effectiveness of our operations, which used only one cloudbuster.

The 1995 operations clarified several points which were only suggested in the 1994 operations:

A. Early work with the cloudbuster was observed to create pulsations which were separated by a dry period of several days. Continued work narrowed the dry-period between the pulses considerably, such that a pulsation of once every two days would develop. Continued work could increase this tempo considerably, such that more widespread and moderate-to-heavy rains began to occur, with regular daily rainfall of a very widespread distribution. These were the more typical "old time" rains characteristic of the equatorial tropics, and which would, if they persisted for several weeks, literally fill every small pond and large reservoir. With further work, we occasionally observed this atmospheric "heart-beat" or *pulsation* occurring *twice a day*, with one good rainshower starting in the early afternoon, and another one around or after sunset, lasting late into the night as a steady drizzle. Operations at Massawa always appeared crucial for this to happen, as a means for mobilizing the considerable quantities of dor-energy

which collected there. Massawa also had a direct line-of-sight connection to the Danikil Depression to the south, a very hot and arid landscape which lay below sea-level. While we never travelled to that location (we were warned about roaming bands which might rob us of everything), it also appeared to be a "reservoir of dor", with a dominant, semipermanent dor-haze layer. Once this haze-layer in Massawa was diminished, clouds and rains on the highlands around Asmara would blossom in a substantial manner.

B. In September, the Sahara desert would start pushing southward, bringing a very dry influence to Eritrea. Clouds which would form in the morning and early afternoon hours, and which seemed promising for the development of rains, would be literally "blown down" by a strong afternoon push of dry dusty-dorish *hamsin* winds from the north. Once these winds developed, the cloudbuster had no apparent influence except possibly to exacerbate the intensity of the dusty winds. The key seemed to be, to develop strong and widespread rains in the August and early-September period, such that this Saharan-wind phenomenon would be delayed, and appear only in late September or October. Based upon these experiences, in subsequent years, we decided to undertake Phase II operations at an earlier time, in early or mid-August, rather than waiting until the end of August.

C. On occasion, cloudbusting operations were able to develop very good rains, in spite of standard meteorological forecasts for continued dry, high pressure conditions typical of the Sahara. Specifically, meteorologists with the Eritrean Civil Aviation Authority had been closely watching a pattern of anomalous high pressure, which persisted through June and July of 1995, and were so concerned about it that, on the morning of July

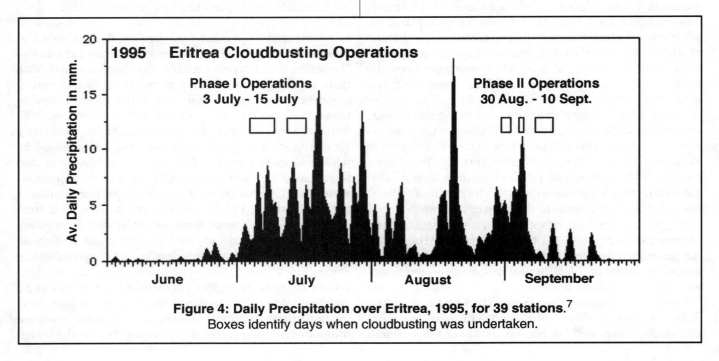

Figure 4: Daily Precipitation over Eritrea, 1995, for 39 stations.[7]
Boxes identify days when cloudbusting was undertaken.

19th (shortly after our Phase I cloudbusting operations had ended), they issued a public forecast and announcement on Asmara radio, stating that the influence of Saharan high pressure would initiate an episode of dry weather over Eritrea for the next week. Fortunately, this forecast did not materialize, as exceptionally heavy rains developed by 11:00 am on that same day, the 19th, with a second episode of rain later in the afternoon. It was one of the heaviest rain days for the season, and the next day (the 20th) saw rains just as heavy and widespread. In some ways, this kind of embarrassment for the meteorological forecasters did not make our cloudbusting team very popular at the Asmara Airport, where the Civil Aviation Authority had their offices, and where we periodically visited to review the weather maps and satellite images.

From the perspective of the field operations team, their forecast for dryness was contrary to observations made in the field: we had been observing the gradually increasing tempo of atmospheric pulsation, expressed mainly in cloud cover but also in the gradually increasing distribution and amount of rainfall. The atmospheric pulsation firstly began on July 5th, shortly after our first cloudbusting operations at Mainifhi reservoir. By the 12th of July, the pulsation increased in tempo, and it increased again on July 19th, as can be seen in Figure 4, showing the regular peaks in the rainfall data. The good rains occurred in spite of the meteorological predictions, which placed a primary emphasis upon the atmospheric pressure patterns. Without going into detail here, it should be stated openly that *the theory of orgone biophysics, which is the operational theory for the cloudbuster, places pressure patterns and atmospheric circulation in a subordinate position to more fundamental energetic processes.* The cloudbuster operations were successful in developing a favorable rainfall regime in Eritrea, in spite of the persistence of the Saharan high-pressure influence. This kind of situation, of good rains developing in spite of the standard meteorological forecast, is fairly typical of cloudbusting operations and has been observed almost routinely during similar work in other regions.

D. Related to the above points, on several occasions during the 1994 and 1995 operations, and during subsequent years, we appeared to witness the direct conversion of hazy dor in the atmosphere directly into liquid water droplets and rains. Reich postulated, in 1956,[4] that under intensive dor-haze conditions of atmospheric energetic stagnation, liquid water and oxygen would dissociate into hydrogen ions and ozone. Under the right orgone-energetic conditions, he speculated that a re-formation of water and oxygen could occur directly from the hazy dor which itself has a very low humidity.

$$H_2O + O_2 \longrightarrow 2H^+ + O_3^- \longrightarrow H_2O + O_2$$

In such cases, and with application of specific CORE techniques, *the greyish dor layer slowly converts into a milky-colored haze, and later into a real fog. In these cases, a very low humidity air mass can be directly transformed into a higher-humidity air mass, without known advection of new moisture from a distant region.*

This conversion of dor into water was previously observed during the 1988 "Miracle March" California CORE operations,[8] and in the 1991-1992 Israel CORE operations,[9] although this particular phenomenon is not always observed. During the Eritrea cloudbusting work, this conversion was observed several times, after which some of the heaviest downpours were observed during the entire five-year project, and under conditions where the rains appeared impossible to explain according to the classical meteorological model — no significant advection of moisture was occurring in such instances, neither at high nor low altitudes, nor was there sufficient moisture already present to make clouds and rains, even if one anticipated the introduction of great instability into the atmosphere from other sources. *The new moisture appeared to develop directly from within the existing air mass; this would invariably be followed by heavy rains; the previous dor-haze vanished from the landscape and atmosphere which thereafter appeared incredibly clear, sparkling and transparent.*

The "Skeptics" Strike Back: Operations in 1996 are Cancelled

During the Phase II 1995 operations, the Director of the Eritrean Ministry of Agriculture asked me to prepare a short statement addressing the mechanism of the cloudbuster, something which could be given to persons who might ask about the device and how it worked. This information was apparently requested as the Ministry of Agriculture was continuing to receive criticisms against the project. Consequently, an additional document with copies of published papers was prepared and sent to the Ministry (parts of this are also appended at the end of this article). The added materials apparently were insufficient to satisfy the critics.

After September of 1995, there was a cessation of all communications from the Ministry of Agriculture, which indicated the project had lost its support. We could only speculate that the skeptics had intensified their attacks against the project, perhaps even distributing to the Eritrean government some of the poisonous materials about Reich which have been published by the "skeptic groups" since the 1950s.[10] Eritrea was at the time receiving significant amounts of foreign aid from European nations, and from the USA, and even the small sum provided to our work in 1995 would have given the critics a clear target towards which they could be anticipated to throw all sorts of mud and slander — James DeMeo and the Orgone Biophysical Research Lab were, at that time, being slandered in widely-distributed magazine articles and on the internet by various "skeptics" and their support network (which, amazingly, included a few claimed "Reichians"). We felt we had done all that was possible to keep the project alive, and so accommodated ourselves to the reality of the situation, being happy to have brought two good years of rain to Eritrea.

Unfortunately, there were warnings of continued drought and food shortages in the Horn of Africa:

"FAO SAYS SHARPLY HIGHER CEREAL PRICES MAKE SUB-SAHARAN AFRICA'S FOOD SECURITY OUTLOOK PRECARIOUS

The ... aggregate cereal production in the Horn of Africa in 1995/1996 [is estimated to be] at 5 per cent below the previous year's harvest. ... Reduced crops in Eritrea, Somalia and Sudan ...production also declined in Kenya.... Large numbers of vulnerable people and those affected by localized crop failure require continued food assistance throughout 1996... There are an estimated 9 million people currently facing severe food shortages in eastern Africa, including some 7 million in the Horn of Africa. Eritrea: Reduced harvest, large number of vulnerable people — Ethiopia: Large number of vulnerable people, localized drought — Somalia: Civil strife, poor harvest — Sudan: Displaced persons, localized food deficits, civil strife" (Press Release, UN Food and Agriculture Org., FAO/3633 29 May 1996)

Eritrean rains in 1996 were poor in both quantity and distribution. The government of Eritrea was once again saddled with huge costs for importation of food, something which had been dramatically reduced following the good rains and harvests in 1994 and 1995. While food imports were on the order of 30 to 50 million dollars per year following the good harvests of 1994 and 1995,

after 1996 they skyrocketed to over 150 million.[11] From this stark reality, underscoring the solid economic value of good rainfall in agricultural regions, there apparently were voices raised in the government, to contact our cloudbusting team and *bring us back to Eritrea*. Consequently, in early Spring of 1997, we received a fax letter from the Eritrean Ministry of Agriculture, *apologizing for their long silence, and inviting us back once again, to continue with the project as originally planned*. One can appreciate, how rare such a reversal in viewpoint is within the chronicles of either science or government.

Figure 5 shows the distribution of rains over Eritrea in 1996. One can easily see, by comparison to the rainfall graphs for 1995 and subsequent years (presented below), the complete *absence of the larger peaks in rainfall* for 1996. Rains occurred either as smaller showers or isolated thunderstorms, but not as large storm complexes with widespread distribution, as is more typical of good *Kiremti*-type rains. The larger peaks in the rainfall, seen in 1994, 1995, and in 1997, 1998 and 1999, when cloudbusting operations continued, were representative a larger quantity and more widespread distribution of rains. Nearly every rainfall measuring station was collecting some amounts of precipitation over periods of several days, as large and well-developed storm complexes moved across the entire nation.

Operations in 1997

The early months of 1997 suggested that the forthcoming rainy season in Eritrea would be poor. Kiremti rains in 1996 had been generally below-average with a poor distribution, and by April of 1997 international climate agencies were issuing dire forecasts of regional drought, based upon a developing El Niño event. The El

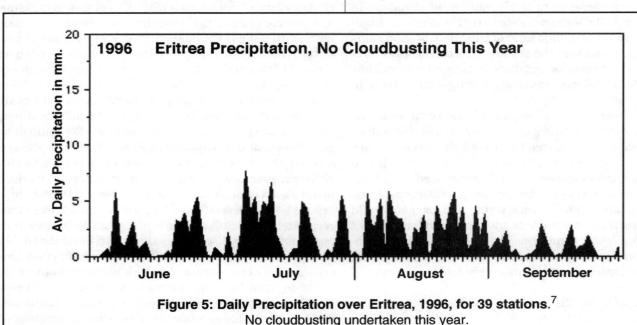

Figure 5: Daily Precipitation over Eritrea, 1996, for 39 stations.[7]
No cloudbusting undertaken this year.

Niño — a warming of waters in the Pacific and Indian Oceans — is generally correlated with poorly-developed Tropical Easterly rains in areas of the African Sahel, and also across the Indian Ocean and SE Asia. Around February of 1997, the *National Oceanographic and Atmospheric Administration, Climate Prediction Center (NOAA-CPC)* in the USA had forecast *"near normal to dry conditions... for central and eastern Sahel"* for June-July-August of 1997, with a specific evaluation of "-1" (slightly below normal) for northern Eritrea. Other areas of Eritrea were not at that time (February 1997) included in their long-term forecasts. However, by April of 1997, El Niño conditions had intensified considerably, and NOAA-CPC issued another forecast for June-July-August 1997, which anticipated rainfall declines of from "-1" to "-7" (slightly to significantly below normal) for the regions immediately to the west and south of Eritrea. Since these western and southern border areas normally feed moisture into Eritrea during the period of Kiremti rains, at the very least the NOAA-CPC forecasts suggested possible drought conditions for Eritrea as well.

By May of 1997, with a significant weakening of Tropical Easterly winds and warming of the Indian and Western Pacific Oceans, NOAA issued an advisory expecting the *"warm episode (El Niño) conditions to intensify during the next several months"*. [12] It was with this background of grim forecasts that the Eritrean Ministry of Agriculture requested a resumption of experimental cloudbusting operations.

By mid-June of 1997, shortly before the start of our field operations, Ethiopian Newspapers reported areas of widespread drought, failed crops and famine, notably in the North Shoa zone, where the rains failed to materialize in late 1996 and early 1997. [13] A high-altitude atmospheric haze layer existed over the Eritrean region at the start of the 1997 field work, with only a very diminished light blue coloration to open sky areas. This, in addition to a poorly-developed moisture layer, which prevented significant vertical development of clouds. News reports continued to emphasize the growing El Niño, with added predictions for a failed summer 1997 Indian Monsoon. [14]

The third year of Eritrean cloudbusting operations took place in the following two phases:

Phase I: 19 June to 7 July, 1997
Phase II: 15 August to 9 September, 1997

Using techniques similar to those applied in 1994 and 1995, the 1997 rains were characterized by several episodes of soaking Kiremti rains, as seen in Figure 6. Dates of cloudbuster operations are identified by the open boxes.

A buildup to an intensive peak in rainfall, of widespread distribution and excellent quantities, was observed during the Phase I experiments, but with a lesser

effect during Phase II. During the last half of 1997, an *extreme* El Niño finally developed in the Indian and Pacific Oceans, with surface water temperatures breaking all prior records, and as mentioned above, this event is correlated with a reduction of rains in East Africa as well. Nevertheless, cloudbusting operations produced good results for Eritrea, but not as dramatic as in prior years. Often, episodes of rainfall would develop and last for days after cloudbusting operations, only to be "blown down" with a resurgence of northerly Saharan hamsin winds, laden with dor-haze and dust. These dor-haze-dust storms usually start in September, but this year they appeared sporadically in late July and August as well, threatening to put a complete end to the rainy season. Nevertheless, several episodes of the characteristic widespread and saturating heavy rains, lasting late into the night, did occur, and these prevented Eritrea from slipping into a drought-agricultural crisis.

Specifically, during the cloudbusting operations of 26-28 August, in the Red Sea port city of Massawa, we observed a much greater quantity of atmospheric stagnation and dorish-haze pushing southward through the Red Sea basin than seen in either 1994 or 1995. The quantities were vast and appeared to be pushing up onto the escarpment, intensifying drought tendencies in the agricultural areas where rain was needed most. This atmospheric dor-haze, moving southward out the Red Sea into the Indian Ocean, and up across the African escarpment, may in fact be *the causal factor* which creates the El Niño phenomenon.

El Niño: A Secondary Consequence to Primary Saharasian Dor-Stagnation?

El Niño is poorly understood from the viewpoint of classical meteorology and climatology, but may find a solution from an orgonomic perspective, as *the consequence of an expanded Saharasian desert-dor atmosphere*. The phenomenon of *dor*, which is visible as atmospheric haze (marine-haze or desert-haze), tends to collect in the lower layers of the atmosphere. It is a rather stagnant phenomenon, but can be pushed along by winds, and robs clouds of both moisture-bearing and cohesive qualities, leading to their dissipation. All of this has been well-described by Reich as early as 1952, [14] but my own observations suggest the phenomenon of dor underlies major seasonal dry episodes, and the El Niño phenomenon, via the following mechanism:

In normal years, there appears to be a fairly large quantity of stagnating desert-dor being discharged from Saharasia at low altitudes, southeast from the Red Sea and Persian Gulf, directly into the Indian Ocean where it pools and accumulates. All these areas are seasonally characterized by a thick, obscuring haze layer. From there, this layer of dor-haze slowly is pushed eastward by larger circulation patterns, where it creates drought wherever it goes. Seasonally, it affects the Indian subcontinent and SE Asia, giving rise to their dry seasons, but it can also episodically affect SE Island Asia (Indonesia and the Philippines) on its way into the Western Pacific.

Clouds are diminished by the Saharasian dor-haze, and this allows intensive sunlight to warm the surface ocean waters. The large pooling of Saharasian dor-haze in the southern Red Sea, over Arabia and in the Indian Ocean may be the reason why the Tropical Easterly winds do not exist for some distance east of Eritrea, as the intensive quantities of dor tend to block out those winds, dissipating clouds as well. Stronger orgone streams from the south, however, seasonally push equator-ward through this layer, bringing seasonal Monsoon rains to India and SE Asia. If the dor-layer is too intensive, the monsoon rains may not push through to land, giving rise to the occasional massive drought catastrophes which afflict India and SE Asia, and the correlation of those droughts to similar droughts along the East Coast of Africa, and to Sahelian droughts. Saharasian dor-haze is the common denominator.

East of India from Indonesia and across the entire Pacific Ocean, the tropical easterlies are well-developed for most years — in "normal" years, the stagnant dor-haze layer does not generally move that far to the east, much less into the Western Pacific. However, in particularly hot and arid years, when dor-levels are extreme across Saharasia, the dor-haze accumulates to exceptional quantities, and spreads eastward from the Indian Ocean and Western Pacific into the Central and even Eastern Pacific. There, the dor-haze has a similar easterly-wind-reducing and cloud-dissipating influence. The *primary* effect of this arrival of significant dor-haze in the Central and Eastern Pacific is *a cessation of tropical easterly winds, cloud growth and rains*. The *secondary*

effect which occurs, is consequent to the absence of the tropical easterly winds at the ocean surface: a *slowing of the west-moving Pacific surface ocean currents*. This, in turn, creates a *tertiary* effect, of reducing the upwelling of cold nutrient-rich subsurface waters along the Peruvian-Chilean coast of South America, and increased sunlight warming of the surface ocean waters in the same regions.

From here, the environmental patterns follow the classically described pathways — dramatic convection storms along the desert coast of South America with big floods in some areas, massive droughts in other areas, out-migrations of fish populations towards cooler waters with die-offs of dependent populations of sea birds, massive forest fires in droughty areas, displaced storm tracks during winter months with consequent coastal damages, and so forth. *The abnormal intensification and eastward spreading of the "normal" stagnant dor-haze layer in the Indian Ocean and Western Pacific into the Central and Eastern Pacific is what we call "El Niño"*. These findings were the logical extension of materials I have previously published and presented to various international conferences on the relationships between deserts and drought.[15] More detailed discussion of these relationships must wait for another time.

Late in 1997, as a consequence of the particularly strong El Niño in that year, Southern Somalia, Kenya, Australia, California and Peru experienced incredible rains and flooding, while rains in the sub-Saharan region diminished. Other parts of SE Asia such as Indonesia and New Guinea also experienced droughts, with vast forest fires and a choking blanket of smoke-haze which received international alarm and attention. Brazil also suffered under drought, as did the central and western Sahel. Nevertheless, the positive Phase I

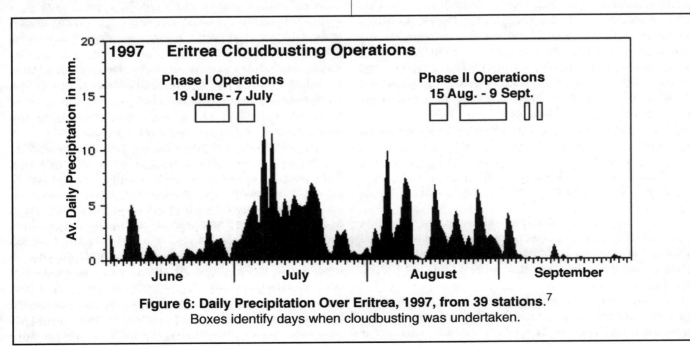

Figure 6: Daily Precipitation Over Eritrea, 1997, from 39 stations.[7]
Boxes identify days when cloudbusting was undertaken.

results in Eritrea, with the minimal but still positive results of Phase II, were against the general predictions being circulated by most climatological authorities, for an "El Niño drought" across the Eritrean region. NOAA-Climate Prediction Center forecasts for an eastern Sahel drought, and weak Indian Monsoon, proved wrong. In other world regions, their forecasts proved correct.

Without the cloudbusting work, the NOAA-CPC forecast probably would have proven correct in the eastern Sahel at least. This possibility became particularly apparent during the Phase II experiments, at which time hamsin dor-haze-dust storms appeared, and the Tropical Easterlies temporarily vanished. Very dry conditions followed, and these were only reversed — also temporarily — by the cloudbusting operations. Finally, the influences of a single cloudbuster were insufficient to keep the atmosphere alive and moving under these conditions, and so plans were made to construct additional cloudbusting devices for Eritrea.

Operations in 1998:

The fourth year of Eritrean cloudbusting operations took place in the following two phases:

Phase I: 15 July to 7 August, 1998
Phase II: 12 August to 31 August, 1998

Given the dramatic El Niño drought conditions observed in many parts of the Sahel in 1997, and the dramatic drought and forest fire situation observed in SE Asia during the winter of 1997-1998, three additional cloudbusting devices were constructed in Eritrea (starting in late 1997) for planned use in 1998. The new devices were similar in function to the larger trailer-mounted device, but more primitive with a simpler construction. During the Phase I 1998 operations, we arranged with the Ministry of Agriculture to have the three simple cloudbusters sited at different locations in Eritrea, with their operations directed by our team, and coordinated by radiotelephone. Two of the primitive devices were placed at new draw-sites, one in the far north at a small high-altitude reservoir near Keren (see Figure 1), and another in the far south of Eritrea, in a reservoir near Senafe. The third primitive device was placed in Mainifhi reservoir. The larger trailer-mounted cloudbuster continued to be operated as before, at the reservoirs of Mainifhi, MaiSheka and Massawa, based upon perceived need. This arrangement had both positive aspects as well as major drawbacks. The positive aspects were, that several cloudbusters could be operated at one time from different locations, assisted by local workers under the direction of our team, with the full backing and authority of the Ministry of Agriculture. We had previously driven to these locations, and found them to be well-suited for the cloudbusting work, but the long drive on difficult roads consumed a tremendous amount of time; establishing of permanent stations in those locations made good sense. The difficulties will be discussed below.

Figure 7 shows the daily precipitation over Eritrea for 1998. As before, large spikes are seen in the rainfall data during the cloudbusting operations, indicative of very good, widespread rains. The boxes identifying the days when work proceeded with the cloudbusters also identify whether one, two or three of the apparatus were being used at any given time.

Phase I operations, as seen in the graph, did not clearly produce the more widespread and abundant above-normal rainfall observed during prior Eritrean cloudbuster experiments. This may have been the consequence of having to learn new methods of operation using the multiple cloudbusting devices, and the delays which occurred as the new devices were driven by truck to the new locations, with time spent to educate new teams of Eritrean workers on how to set them into operations, and to terminate the operations when the orders arrived by radio-telephone, or in the event of severe weather. Safety precautions were given to the Eritrean helpers, including *full authority to terminate operations on their own judgements if rains or winds ever became too strong. Operations could never be initiated by the Eritreans without our direct orders*, but they could terminate operations independently.

We finally determined never to use more than two of the three devices at a single time, and also never to use any one of the devices at any single location for more than two days running. They were, in fact, alternated in their use according to a schedule that would see the most southerly apparatus set into operation first, followed the next day by the most centrally-located apparatus, and then finally the third most northerly apparatus would be used (while the first apparatus was shut down). The working hypothesis was to initiate a pulse of moisture from the south towards the north. The devices were set into operation *only at night, from sundown to sunrise*, to minimize adding to oranur over-excitation, which often could be considerable with even one cloudbuster in operation. By early August, at the start of Phase II operations, the new methodology was finally worked out and applied with good success.

Result of Phase II experiments were spectacular, to say the least. Three large spikes of rainfall occurred during those operations, with a fourth exceptionally good natural pulsation afterward. In fact, the rainfall spikes of the 1998 Phase II experiments, from 15-23 August specifically, were *the largest average daily rainfalls to be observed during the entire period of the cloudbusting operations*, with the possible exception of what might have occurred in 1994 when such rainfall data was not available. Reports from local people, farmers and government officials alike confirmed the beneficial nature of those rains. Farm fields were saturated and crops growing exceptionally well, reservoirs were full, and people were happy. Mainifhi reservoir was, in fact, at the highest level ever recorded by its caretakers, one of whom had lived and worked at that location for more than 30 years. Good to heavy rains were also reported during this period across Ethiopia, Yemen, and Saudi Arabia.[16] The following reports speak to the widespread and incredible changes observed following the abundant 1998 rains, which swept across most of Eritrea, Ethiopia and Sudan, and probably across much of the Sahel region as well:

9 September 1998: : "South Sudan Rains Turn Famine Zone Green. The rains have finally arrived in Bahr el Ghazal, the area of south Sudan worst affected by famine, transforming the region from an unforgiving dustbowl into what looks like an oasis." (Reuters, CNN Internet) Some flooding also reported along the Nile River in Sudan in the Khartoum lowlands. Lake Nasser, behind the Aswan Dam in Egypt, is also at very high levels due to the good rains, now flowing into Nile River tributaries.

2 Nov. 1998: News report of an excellent grain harvest in Eritrea. "... the best crop in 40 years..." ("Eritrea Has Unusual Farm Aid", Associated Press, AOL Internet)

16 Nov. 1998: The 1997 drought areas of southern Sudan receive good rains from mid-July through November of 1998. (Special Report, FAO Crop and Food Supply Assessment, Mission to Southern Sudan, United Nations Food and Agriculture Organization, Rome)

It does not seem coincidental, that this largest of all measured rainfalls to be seen in Eritrea in perhaps thirty years or more, which brought excellent moisture to a wide area of the Sahel, occurred just after the coordinated three-cloudbuster system was implemented.

Major Complications During 1998-1999

Two major unanticipated factors developed during 1998 which would eventually spell the end of our project.

Nuclear Bomb Tests in India and Pakistan:

Multiple nuclear bombs were tested in India and Pakistan in May of 1998, and these were quickly followed by heat waves and weather chaos around the region. It is known to workers in the field of experimental orgonomy (the science of orgone energy functions in nature) that underground nuclear bomb tests and nuclear power plant accidents can have a powerful detrimental influence upon weather.[17] The atmospheric orgone energy continuum is excitable by nuclear energy, which can disturb its natural properties. The orgone energy is also *mass-free*, and may penetrate deep into the Earth to some unknown distance, to be affected by underground nuclear explosions. *Such disturbances in the orgone continuum can thereby be transmitted across very large regions, similar to the effects of cloudbusting, but wholly life-negative and droughty in their characteristic effects.*

Underground nuclear bomb tests have been noted to cause geomagnetic, pressure and thermal atmospheric disturbances, though the evidence to support this claim constitutes a controversy in the atmospheric sciences at least as great as cloudbusting itself. Basically it is an issue which has not received sufficient study to resolve all the outstanding questions. Nevertheless, there are many published accounts of anomalous atmospheric and biological phenomenon associated with nuclear

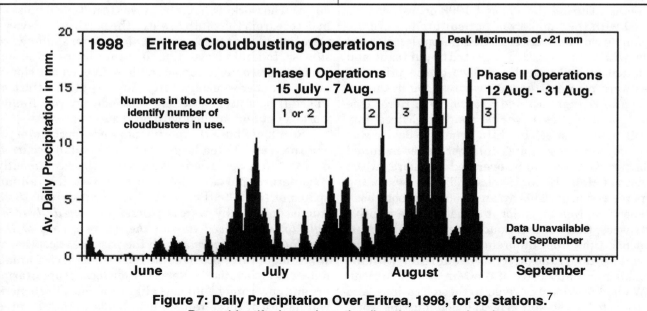

Figure 7: Daily Precipitation Over Eritrea, 1998, for 39 stations.[7]
Boxes identify days when cloudbusting was undertaken.

accidents (such as at Three Mile Island and Chernobyl).[18]

On May 11th and 13th of 1998, India tested five nuclear bombs at their test site in the western Rajasthan Desert. On May 28th, Pakistan responded by testing five nuclear bombs of its own, all at once, in their eastern desert regions. Based upon prior experiences of this kind, the cloudbusting research team predicted a massive desert-expansion in those regions, to be followed by heatwave conditions, and with complications for the field work in Eritrea. By late May, our predictions had unfortunately been fulfilled: a killer heat wave developed across India which ultimately claimed over 3,000 lives, the onset of which was so closely timed to the nuclear tests that ordinary people in India were asking if the two events were related — the Indian Meteorological Service in New Delhi also predictably issued a denial, that atmospheric effects from underground nuclear tests were "impossible". Subsequent drought across India, Pakistan, Afghanistan and surrounding regions over the next three years took an even greater toll upon human life and nature, an inestimable catastrophe lasting many years, all resulting from religious fanaticism and hatred between fundamentalistic Muslims and Hindus. The heat wave conditions spread across much of Central Asia, the Persian Gulf, NE Africa, Indian Ocean, SE Asia and Eastern Mediterranean, as detailed in the following sobering reports:[19]

* 21-31 May 1998: "The rainy season appears to have ended prematurely across eastern areas of East Africa...dry conditions prevailed... These areas began to experience steady decrease of rain at the beginning of the month."
(African Weather Summary, Africa Desk, Climate Prediction Center, US NOAA, Washington DC)

* 29 May 1998: Temperatures up to 122 °F in "one of the most devastating heat waves in years..." with tens to hundreds dying each day in India alone. "Hospitals have been flooded with victims of heat stroke, dehydration and other illnesses... in New Delhi...the temperature hasn't dropped below 112 °F in a week". (Medford Mail Tribune, 29 May wire report.)

* 9 June 1998: "Scorching temperatures have killed more than 2,500 during India's worst heat wave in 50 years" (Medford Mail Tribune, USA)

* 10 August 1998: Blistering Heat Roils Mideast "Sure, the Middle East is mostly desert, but 54° C with a dose of humidity? Day after day? A heat wave has swept the region..." 38 dead in Egypt, 35 in Cyprus. Similar superheated conditions across Israel, Jordan, Arabia, Persian Gulf region.

* 17 August 1998: Drought and Heat Wave continue across India/Pakistan and Middle East: In Bahrain (Persian Gulf) "...temperatures reached highs of 50°C (122°F)... the country experienced the hottest June and July since records began in 1902." (Arab News, p.3)

* Oct. 1998: Speaking about long term changes in Sudan, the Sudanese ministry of agriculture claims desertification is adversely affecting more than half the nation's territory where approximately 75% of the people live. Desertification has "caused poverty and displacement among 19.5 million people, three quarters of the population. The desert is reported to be creeping southward at a rate of about 10 kms (six miles) a year in Sudan, where reforestation has been largely abandoned for lack of money." (Reuters, CNN Internet, 27 Oct. 1998)

Monsoon rains in western India continued to be delayed after the multiple nuclear bomb tests, even after the cloudbusting work in nearby Eritrea. As observed from Eritrea during the Phase I operations, the upper-level easterly jet stream, which normally comes into Eritrea across northern India (close to the test sites), was poorly developed, and none of the rainstorms which developed during the Phase I cloudbusting operations spread dynamically to cover any significantly large area. The necessary ingredient of the easterly jet stream, in fact, could not be stimulated during our Phase I experiments, which were plagued by exceptionally dorish, hazy and immobilized atmospheric conditions. The lingering after-effects of this historically unprecedented series of nuclear tests may therefore be a contributing factor to the minimal, delayed results from the Phase I cloudbusting experiments. Only during the Phase II component of the 1998 work, which employed a radically different methodology with multiple cloudbusting devices stationed over a large area, were rains significantly better. As discussed above, the big rains of 15-23 August (shown in Figure 7) thankfully put an end to the drought danger in Eritrea, and much of the East African region.

Ethiopia-Eritrea Border Conflict:

In late May and early June of 1998, aggressive actions by the Ethiopian government led to a border conflict and eventual return to war conditions between Eritrea and Ethiopia. At the very time when we were trying to establish permanent bases of operation for separate cloudbusting devices at different ends of the country, the logistical and support capabilities of the Ministry of Agriculture were dealt a severe blow. Two of our team who intended to move to Eritrea from their homes in Italy and establish a clinic and orgonomic research facility in Eritrea, and to also take over the practical details of the work on a more permanent basis, Carlo and Aurelio Albini, decided not to move. Worse, the young people we had relied upon for help and assistance over the previous years, and whom we hoped to eventually train in basic operational methods, were called up for military service. Funding from the Ministry of Agriculture for expenses was also curtailed — we proceeded with the operations anyhow, as was the case for the 1999 operations which were totally funded by ourselves without contributions from the Eritrean government.

Ethiopian bombers also attacked the Asmara airport on 5 June 1998, shortly before our team was scheduled to depart the USA for Eritrea. All international flights were cancelled, forcing a temporary suspension of the planned cloudbusting work. By early July, flights resumed. Our analysis indicated the military conflict was confined to the Ethiopian-Eritrean border, which was at a good distance from where our cloudbusting work proceeded, and so the project resumed, though delayed and with a smaller work-crew. The fortuitous construction of the three primitive cloudbusting devices allowed our team to spend more of its time in Asmara, in relative safety, instructing the teams of helpers on use of the devices by radiotelephone. We could therefore reduce our long-distance travel on roads to a minimum, something which was absolutely necessary given the risk from Ethiopian military activity.

Operations in 1999:

The 1999 operations were greatly curtailed in scope, with only one worker travelling to Eritrea, with no financial and only limited logistical support from the Ministry of Agriculture. Only sporadic work was undertaken with the cloudbusters during only the planned Phase I period of operations, given the potential dangers involved. Ethiopian jets were flying overhead occasionally bombing the Asmara airport, and other "targets of opportunity" — the risks of driving across the countryside with a large trailered cloudbuster appeared all too apparent. Not only were our usual helpers off on the front lines of the growing conflict with Ethiopia, but we found — for the first time since our work began in 1994 — some of our equipment had been dismantled and stolen away, with increasing demands for "baksheesh" or money tips from the impoverished rural workers. Later in 1999, the military conflict widened even more so, dealing a devastating blow to the Eritreans and inflicting tremendous damage, deaths and misery. Our project was factually cancelled by that time. The operations in 1999 were of such a short time span, without the systematic applications of prior years, that no systematic analysis of their results has been undertaken here. A reliable data set, comparable to that available for prior years, also is not available for 1999. However, we did receive many reports by word-of-mouth, and from various news agencies, of good to moderate rains across most parts of Eritrea, Sudan, and surrounding regions, at least for the summertime rainy period on the highlands. These general reports were suggestive of at least some benefits from our limited 1999 operations, and also possibly of a carry-over *persistence effect*, or *continued atmospheric pulsation* from cloudbusting which can last at least one year in marginally harsh desert conditions. A similar phenomenon was seen in the years immediately following cloudbusting work in Israel in 1991-1992.[9] The excellent rains in Israel during that winter of 1991-1992, when cloudbusting was undertaken, were repeated in 1992-1993, before drought appeared once more. Eritrea seems also to have escaped the worst effects of drought in 2000 as well, though their food supplies were dramatically reduced due to the war with Ethiopia.

Combined analysis for 1995, 1997 and 1998:

As demonstrated above, our project had factually taken place during the summers of five years — 1994 through 1999 with a stoppage of work in 1996 — although the first and last years of operation, 1994 and 1999, could not be subject to systematic data analysis given the absence of a complete set of reliable data. However, systematically-collected weather data was available for 1995, 1997 and 1998 providing opportunity for an objective evaluation of the effects of cloudbusting in Eritrea for those three years. Daily precipitation data graphs for those years has already been presented, but we can make a further evaluation of the effects of cloudbusting on Eritrean weather by making an aggregate analysis of the same data.

If we use as a "starting point" the *first day of cloudbusting operations* for both Phase I and Phase II of each year, then under the assumption that cloudbusting stimulates an increase in rainfall, we should be able to show some kind of observable increase in the daily rainfall data starting approximately at or shortly after that starting date. In short, rains should demonstrably increase for some period "after the start of operations" as compared to "before operations".

Figure 8 presents the 1995, 1997 and 1998 daily rainfall data in such a manner, and clearly shows this observable increase in rains for the 15 days "after the start of operations" as compared to the 15 days "before". There was a marked increase in rains from the period "before" to "after", rising from an average of 38.1% of maximum values "before operations" to 57.5% of maximum "after operations", for the full 31 day period. *The percent-of-maximum rainfall during the "after" period constitutes just over 150% of the percent-of-maximum during the "before" period.* Specifically, *this constitutes an average 50% increase in overall rainfall for the whole of Eritrea* (further explanation of the analytical method is given below Figure 8, which employed rainfall data from all 39 Eritrean measuring stations). A simple t-test for probability of these rainfall amounts and distributions was also performed, showing a *very significant value* of $p < 0.0042$, meaning these "before" to "after" differences in rainfall data would occur by chance alone only a little more than 4 times out of a thousand.

While these data and graphs clearly demonstrate a positive result, we must acknowledge Eritrea anticipates some natural increase in rains during the Phase I period, *assuming the absence of drought*. Under *non-drought* conditions, a natural data bias towards increased rains exists during the same Phase I periods, raising the possibility our work "coincidentally" began just before natural rainfall peaks. However, *prior to our work, the drought existed, for 30 years in fact, with no long-term forecasts for its ending in 1994, or subsequent years of our work*. Also, we started each of the Phase I operations at variable dates ranging from 19 June to 15 July, with the actual starting dates fixed months in advance by purchase of our airline tickets and with other logistical difficulties beyond our control intruding into the process whereby the actual commencement of operations was finally set. Rainfall peaks could just as easily have appeared by nature alone *before* we started operating, and factually did so just before the 1998 Phase I operations. Our field operations team did not seek, and had no way to anticipate the onset of a natural rainy episode, and *given the drought conditions there*

was no certainty that any natural upward trend in rains would have existed during any of the Phase I periods.

For Phase II operations, the argument of a "chance-coincidental" timing of cloudbusting to a naturally-increasing rainfall cycle fails completely, as these operations took place during the *middle to the end of the normal rainy period*, and so the chance for a good rainfall "before" operations was by nature alone, equal to or greater than the chance "after" operations. The Phase II experimental period had a natural bias for *decreased rains*, as they took place as the rainy season was ending, *in most cases as an effort to maintain rainfalls against Saharan influences*. The data analysis for the Phase II trials also potentially suffers from the inclusion of carry-over "after" effects from the Phase I experiments into the Phase II "before" category. We could have reduced this carry-over effect by constraining the period of analysis to only 10-days before and after operations, for example, but this would also exclude some (though certainly not all) of the "after" effects from the Phase II operations as well, and so this constraint was not applied to the data analysis.

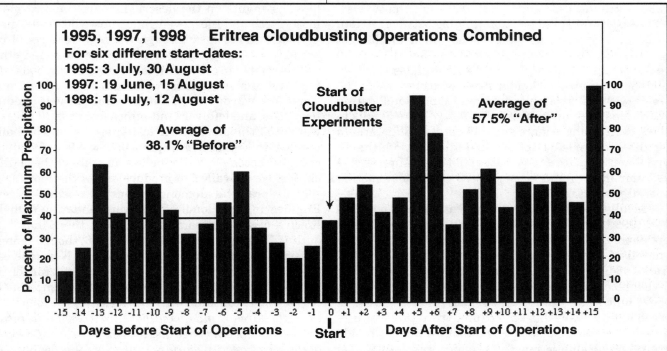

Figure 8: Daily Precipitation Percentages for 15 days before and after the start of six different Phases of cloudbusting operations in Eritrea. The graphed rainfall data were evaluated and organized as follows: Six "start dates" for the onset of six periods of cloudbusting operations (Phase I and II for each of three years) were identified. Average daily rainfall data was gathered for 15 days before and 15 days after each these six start dates (as well as for the dates themselves). Rainfall data was then converted to a percentage-of-maximum for each of the six 31-day periods, by identifying the greatest amount of rain for a given 31-day period, and dividing each of the daily values by that amount. Rainfall data in mm was thereby converted into percent-of-maximum values, allowing the six experimental periods to be aggregated in a way that no one experimental period with a large amount of rainfall would overshadow other periods of lesser rainfall. The percent-of-maximum data for the six 31-day periods were then overlapped and centered on day "zero" (start of operations) and then averaged together. The percent-of-maximum rainfall during the "after" period constitutes >150% of the percent-of-maximum during the "before" period, for a net increase of ~50%. Day zero (the start date of operations) was not used in the percentage or probability calculations.

If we examine rainfall data for 1995 and 1997 respectively, as given in Figures 4 and 5, for Phase I we see there was a dramatic increase in rains only after the start of cloudbusting operations. Rains in Eritrea *prior* to those operations were not very intense or widespread. *Early* rains in 1998, before cloudbusting, were reasonable, and the Phase I operations of 1998 did not appear to have significant widespread influence early on, possibly as a consequence of the nuclear bomb tests in India-Pakistan and the attendant drought which afflicted the entire region, as mentioned above. However, *the Phase II experiments for all three years were followed by an increase in rainfall, or a rekindling of rains after a short dry spell,* after the cloudbusting operations began.

A similar situation existed in 1994 and 1999, where there was a close correlation between the onset of cloudbusting operations and the development of significant regional rains — unfortunately, measured rainfall data is not available for these years to make an objective analysis, except indirectly, for 1994, in the Sahel Precipitation Index (Figures 2 and 3, and Table I).

As previously mentioned, the rainfall graphs for 1995, 1997 and 1998 additionally all show characteristic peaks of daily precipitation ranging between 10 mm to 20 mm (average for 39 stations), with the largest peaks since June 1995, and probably for at least 30 years, occurring shortly after the 1998 Phase II operations when multiple cloudbusters were employed. The single year of available data when no cloudbusting operations were undertaken, in 1996 (Figure 5) fails to show even a single large spike in rainfall data, and in fact has no single day of average rainfall more than 8 mm. The 1996 data appear rather flat and unimpressive as compared to the other years when cloudbusting operations occurred.

Ideally, we should have the weather data for 1994 and 1999 to include in this analysis, but as mentioned previously, that data is not available. An even better analytical tool would compare the full yearly rainfall from 1994, 1995, 1997, 1998 and 1999, against similar 5-year blocks of yearly rainfall data. Given the 30-years of drought which afflicted the region prior to 1994, it is reasonably certain this kind of analytical procedure — for which data are also not available — would provide even more dramatic proof of a major weather change from cloudbusting.

The available data, however, supported by observations by the field operations team and by local Eritreans, demonstrate a dramatic increase in rainfall over Eritrea, for the longer period of cloudbusting work. In fact, there was just over a 50% increase in the amounts of measured rainfall, for the aggregated 15-day period "after operations" as compared to the 15-day period "before" the commencement of cloudbusting operations.

Downstream Effects in Lake Nasser: An "Unbelievable Effect"

Following the final demise of our project in Eritrea, with the return of war conditions and the cancellation of ambitious developmental plans by the Albini brothers to move to Eritrea and establish a clinic and research center devoted to orgonomy and desert greening, everyone was struck with a depressive feeling. *While we had excellent data which proved the cloudbuster could work to end drought and green the land adjacent to one of the most harsh deserts on the planet, the social problems associated with armored humanity always seem to act as an effective barrier.* Over many years, our team of workers had overcome immense obstacles thrown in their path. By a small set of miracles we were able to obtain sufficient funding for the large expenses for this project. The logistical and technical details were then overcome, and we even weathered the attack upon our work, and our personal reputations, by the academic "skeptics". We had endured the hot days with hard blowing winds and lip-parching dryness, and the long freezing nights on the desert plateau, the swarms of mosquitoes and flies, even rancorous wild geese, making such a loud fuss through the night one could not possibly sleep. We endured the dor-sickness and other illness related to contaminated or unfamiliar foods, and made calculated risks to travel into areas where more timid folk warned us of dangers from armed bandits, terrorists, and leftover land-mines from the 30 years of war with Ethiopia. (Our African friends would probably laugh at this narrative, as proof of how soft we Westerners have become!) Nevertheless, in spite of these difficulties, we prevailed to produce one of the most spectacular practical demonstrations of Cosmic Orgone Engineering and cloudbusting ever, validating Wilhelm Reich's original dream of "greening the Sahara" as outlined in *Contact With Space* in 1956, though using a different set of operational parameters. Nevertheless, to see all the additional hard work, of organizing for the future, to develop a more permanent presence in the region and to continue with the work over the long haul, *to see that dream and incredible hard work for the future come crashing down against the stark reality of another outbreak of deadly warfare*, left everyone deeply saddened and depressed about the situation.

For nearly everyone in our group, however, this depression was immediately lifted when the following incredible news came to our attention. In December of 2000, international news reports were circulating on the development of *immense new lakes forming in the middle of the Sahara Desert*, some hundreds of kilometers to the north of Eritrea, as a consequence of exceptionally high water-flows in the Nile River. As shown in Figure 9, the two major tributaries of the Nile River, the White Nile and Blue Nile, drain the Sudanese lowlands and Ethiopian Highlands, respectively, and both of

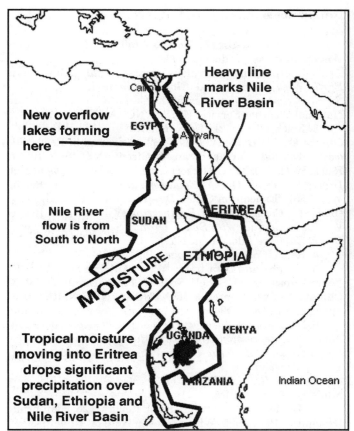

Figure 9. Map of the Nile River Basin, showing how moisture streamed towards Eritrea from the Southwest, creating good rains across both Sudan and Ethiopia before arriving in Eritrea. The exceptional rains across the larger region created some of the greatest downstream flows of the Nile River since the 1960s, when the Aswan High Dam was constructed.

these regions had always received excellent rains during the period of our Eritrean operations. The reports indicated, the water flowing into the Nile River during the late 1990s was so great, that Lake Nasser in Egypt, which was formed by the Aswan High Dam, had *for the first time since its completion in 1968, filled to capacity.* Furthermore, *excess water was being diverted from Lake Nasser out into the open desert, as it was too much water to be effectively used in the irrigation systems along the Nile River itself.* Figure 10 gives a photograph, taken from space, of these new Sahara Desert lakes.

The new lakes were immense, the largest of which was too large for people to see the shoreline on the other side. The government of Egypt was diverting these waters into an area which originally was termed the "New Valley Project" — to develop excessive Nile River waters for agriculture — which had never before been possible. Now, with the excellent water flows in the upstream tributaries, abundant water was available, to the point of excess. Excerpts from one newspaper-internet article are reproduced below.

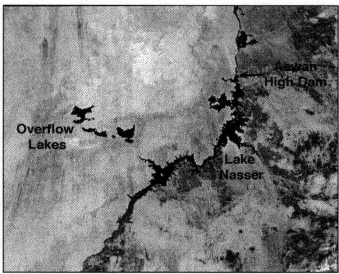

Figure 10. Satellite image of the Nile River around Lake Nasser and Aswan High Dam. The exceptional rainfalls in the Nile River Basin after c.1994 slowly filled Lake Nasser to capacity, for the first time in its 35-year history. The excess waters were diverted into the Toshka Depression, out in the open Sahara Desert, where four giant overflow lakes were created for the first time since the Sahara Wet Phase of c.5000 BCE. (From the MODIS imaging spectroradiometer, NASA, 10 October 2000.) http://visibleearth.nasa.gov/cgi-bin/viewrecord?6506

This "incredible result" constitutes a fitting conclusion to this Report on our 5-year project. Following other major international projects undertaken under the auspices of the Orgone Biophysical Research Lab, applying the cloudbuster to problems of drought and desertification in the deserts of Arizona,[20] Israel,[9] Namibia,[21] and now Eritrea, we have an excellent record of success, providing solid support for Reich's earlier work,[3] and the earlier supportive work of others,[22] on the cloudbuster and techniques of Cosmic Orgone Engineering. We are deeply gratified with these results, which hold forth a tremendous promise for the world.

Lakes Bring New Chance for Life in Sahara[23]
by Alexandra Witze
Dallas Morning News , 5 Dec. 2000
A change of biblical proportions is washing across the Sahara Desert. For the first time in 6,000 years, new lakes have risen from the sands of southern Egypt.

The Nile River, swollen by unusual rainfall, is spilling over a reservoir behind the Aswan High Dam. As expected, the water flows through an arroyo into an overflow lake. But the deluge has continued, and three more lakes now unexpectedly dot the desert.

In a land where water is scarce, this development could hold great promise, scientists say. The Egyp-

tian government has already begun an irrigation project around the first lake. The "New Valley" project aims to draw people from Egypt's crowded cities to a newly green landscape.

But project leaders hadn't planned on the bounty of three extra reservoirs. "The big question is whether they will make use of the rest of the lakes," said Mohamed Abdelsalam, a geologist at the University of Texas-Dallas.

Abdelsalam and other scientists have been monitoring the lakes' growth through satellite imagery. This month, the team brought the lakes to scientific attention by describing them at a meeting in Reno, Nev., of the Geological Society of America.

First spotted in 1998, the new lakes have fluctuated in size and shape through dry spells and monsoons. Together, the lakes hold about 700 billion cubic feet of water...

[The lakes] exist only because the Ethiopian highlands have received lots of rain in the last two years, Abdelsalam said. That water flows down the highlands and into the Nile, eventually coming to a halt behind the Aswan dam. Because of this rain, Lake Nasser, the giant reservoir at Aswan, is at its highest level ever.

But when the level reaches roughly 600 feet, excess water spills through a canal into a nearby dimple in the landscape, known as the Toshka depression. Here, the Egyptian government has built the New Valley project, a massive effort to irrigate the land and resettle people away from the Nile.

The first of the four new lakes -- the one for which engineers had planned -- is known as Toshka Lake.

The other three still go by the uninspiring names of lakes B, C and D, Thurmond said.

Astronauts aboard the space shuttle Discovery snapped the first pictures of Toshka Lake in October 1998.§ Lakes B and C appeared between February and March 1999. The final lake, D, formed sometime between August 1999 and last January, Thurmond said.

Lake D is the biggest, with a surface area of nearly 700 square kilometers.

The Texas scientists hope to get more lake pictures soon, from a radar system that flew aboard the space shuttle last year. Those radar pictures will map the landscape in unprecedented detail, Abdelsalam said. In a land with basically no topographic maps, the radar system has gathered information on the dips and ridges of the sand dunes. That information, in turn, could let scientists predict where water might spill in the future.

Monitoring the lakes from space is the fastest and easiest way to keep an eye on Egypt's changing water resources, said Bob Stern, a University of Texas geologist.

"One of the things I'm excited about is seeing if a fifth lake will form.." [23]

---

§ This was two months after the exceptional rains during Phase II of the 1998 cloudbuster operations, using three different cloudbusters.

References:

1. Trewartha, G.: *The Earth's Problem Climates*, Univ. Wisconsin Press, Madison, 1966.

2. Information from various sources, mainly published in *Earth Week Reports*, and *Global Climate Highlights* and *Special Climate Summaries*, of the Climate Analysis Center, National Weather Service, USDOC/NOAA, Washington DC.

3. Reich, W. (1952): "DOR Removal and Cloud-Busting", *Orgone Energy Bull.*, IV(4):171-182. (reprinted in Reich, *Selected Writings*, Farrar, Straus & Giroux, NY, 1960, 1973); Reich, W. (1954): "OROP Desert. Part 1: Spaceships, DOR and Drought", *Cosmic Orgone Engineering*, VI(1-4):1-140; Reich, W. (1955): "Expedition OROP Desert, Ea: DOR Clouds Over the USA", *Cosmic Orgone Engineering*, VII(1-2):4-19; Reich, W. (1957): *Contact With Space, Oranur Second Report: Orop Desert Ea*, Core Pilot Press, NY.

4. Reich, *Contact With Space*, ibid, p.258-259.

5. Graphs and data from: "Wettest Rainy Season in 30 Years Across African Sahel", *Special Climate Summary 94/2*, Climate Analysis Center, USDOC/NOAA, NWS/NMC, Camp Springs, MD, Oct. 1994.

6. DeMeo, J.: *Saharasia: The 4000 BCE Origins of Child-Abuse, Sex-Repression, Warfare and Social Violence, In the Deserts of the Old World*, Natural Energy, Ashland, Oregon, 1998, p.216-230.

7. *Daily Rainfall Record of Selected Stations*, Eritrean Ministry of Agriculture.

8. DeMeo, J.: "Core Progress Report #26: California Drought of 1990-1991, With a Special Note on Underground Nuclear Testing and the Oakland Wildfires", *Journal of Orgonomy*, 26(1):49-71, 1992.

9. DeMeo, J.: "Orop Israel 1991-1992: A Cloudbusting Experiment to Restore Wintertime Rains to Israel and the Eastern Mediterranean During an Extended Period of Drought", *Pulse of the Planet*, 4:92-98, 1993; DeMeo, J.: "CORE Report #30: The Desert Greening Project in Israel 1991-1992", *Journal of Orgonomy*, 26(2):248-265, 1992.

10. A listing of the published smear-attacks against Reich and orgonomy would take too much space to give here. The reader is referred to the "Emotional Plague Bibliography: American Period 1946 to Present", included within: DeMeo, J.: *Bibliography on Orgone Biophysics*, Natural Energy, 1986.

11. Personal communication, MOA official.

12. *Science News*, 24 May 1997.

13. *East African Standard*, Nairobi, 13 June 1997; *The Reporter*, Addis Ababa, 18 June and 25 June 1997; *The Monitor*, Addis Ababa, 24 June 1997.

14. *Science*, 27 June 1997.

15. DeMeo, J.: "Desert Expansion and Drought: Environmental Crisis, Part 1", *Journal of Orgonomy*, 23(1):15-26, 1989; DeMeo, J.: "Desert Expansion and Drought: Global Interconnections and the Desert/Drought Map", Presented to the Annual Meeting, *Association for Arid Lands Studies*, Portland, Oregon, April 1990, *Abstracts of Papers*, p.40; DeMeo, J.: "The Desert-Drought Map and its Implications", Presented to the 90th Annual Meeting, *Association of American Geographers*, San Francisco, California, 29 March - 2 April, 1994, *Abstracts of Papers*, p.81; DeMeo, J.: "Global Desert Haze/Dust Transport: An Interconnecting Common Denominator for Deserts, Droughts and El Niño?", Presented to the Annual Meeting of the *Association of Arid Lands Studies*, Western Social Science Association, Oakland, California, Session on "Climate, Climatic Change and Environmental Quality", April 1995, *Abstracts of Papers*, p.21.

16. *Arab News*, Saudi Arabia, 18-19-20 Aug. 1998.

17. DeMeo, J. (Ed.): *Unusual Long-Distance Atmospheric and Geophysical Effects from Underground Nuclear bomb Tests and Nuclear Power Plant Accidents: Suppressed Scientific Evidence*, Natural Energy 2000. A collection of papers on the subject by Katagiri, Whiteford, Kato, DeMeo and Nagy.

18. Katagiri, M.: "Tree Mile Island: The Language of Science Versus the People's Reality", *Pulse of the Planet* 3:26-38, 1991; Katagiri, M. & Smith, A.: "Three Mile Island Revisited", *Pulse of the Planet* 4:84-91, 1993.

19. For additional details on this catastrophe, see: http://www.orgonelab.org/oranur.htm

20. DeMeo, J.: "OROP Arizona 1989: A Cloudbusting Experiment to Bring Rains in the Desert Southwest", *Pulse of the Planet*, 3:82-92, 1991.

21. DeMeo, J.: "OROP Namibia 1992-1993", *Pulse of the Planet #4, On Wilhelm Reich and Orgonomy*, p.115.

22. Aside from Wilhelm Reich's publications on cloudbusting (about 10 in total) and James DeMeo's (about 25 in total) publications, only a few of which are cited above, the *Bibliography on Orgone Biophysics* (DeMeo, ibid) lists the following individuals, with the given number of paper citations by them, detailing successful cloudbusting operations, between the years of 1953 through 1986. Baker (2), Blasband (13), DeMeo & Morris (2), W. Hoppe (1), W. Moise (1), Reich & Moise (1), Kelley (1), Rosen (1), Constable (2), Eden (5), Fuckert (1). An additional number of published reports, roughly equal to these, has been published since 1996.

23. *Dallas Morning News* article posted to: http://www0.mercurycenter.com/premium/scitech/docs/newlakes05.htm

Appendix:
Extracts From Rebuttal Documents
(22 August 1994, 3 March 1995, & 25 August 1995)
Presented by James DeMeo, Ph.D.
to the Ministry of Agriculture
State of Eritrea, Asmara, Eritrea

On The Question of Atmospheric Haze:

One criticism of Prof. RVB and Mr. NM focused upon the issue of atmospheric haze. Dr. Wilhelm Reich characterized desert haze, and the haze present during drought conditions, as being partly composed of a stagnated energetic property capable of absorbing light, and that such haze was something more than only "dust particles". My own observations have extended this discussion to the issue of marine haze, as commonly found in the atmospheres of coastal deserts. From my own personal observations of both marine haze (so-called "dry fog") and desert haze in many different parts of the world (California, Arizona, Namibia, Israel, Eritrea), I have become convinced that Reich was correct. Prof. RVB and Mr. NM are critical of this viewpoint, but they fail to distinguish between "atmospheric haze" in general, and the specific drought-desert-marine haze which Reich and I are speaking about. A five minute conversation with me would have clarified this difference, but the questions were never asked. For the record, Reich was not the only scientist to come to the conclusion that desert and marine hazes are unusual and anomalous in character, and I have routinely presented the relevant citations on this issue in my own published papers.

For example, Dr. Reid Bryson of Wisconsin U. has for years maintained that desert haze has a precipitation-blocking influence, and his unorthodox theories have been widely debated. Bryson wrote the book, *Climates of Hunger* which had a profound impact, awakening many professionals (such as myself) to the dangers of desert spreading in Africa and elsewhere. His publications in *Science* and other scientific journals constantly raised a controversy regarding the role of desert haze in blocking cloud growth and precipitation. Glen Trewartha, whose world climate maps are found in nearly every English-language climatology and geography textbook, wrote a book titled *The Earth's Problem Climates*, in which he listed all those areas of the world where classical theory failed to provide adequate explanations as to how the weather functioned. Most of those climates, I observe, are characterized by significant seasonal components of desert haze or marine haze, and many were coastal fog deserts, such as the Namib, where high humidities prevailed but rain rarely fell, in spite of significant adiabatic lifting up adjacent mountain topography. The situation along the Red Sea coast appears somewhat similar in this respect, and Trewartha included a chapter on the Horn of Africa in his *Problem Climates*.

Prof. RVB and Mr. NM are not fully correct to say that this redefining of desert haze "contradicts the findings of meteorology", because there are *no* "findings" (experimental proofs) which demonstrate that 100% of what is called "desert haze" is composed of dust particles. This is only *an hypothesis* based upon the observation that desert haze does, indeed, *contain* dust particles. The question is, can desert and marine haze be accounted for 100% by the quantity of dust or salt particles suspended within it? To the best of my knowledge, this has never been demonstrated. I undertook a rather thorough literature search on the subject of desert haze some years ago, and discovered that this assumption, of desert haze being composed 100% of dust, is merely repeated by one meteorologist to another as "fact" without anybody providing evidence from laboratory experiments or field measurements. Perhaps the assumption is warranted from the *theory* of classical meteorology, and also because nobody before Reich ever thought to raise the question — but the fact remains, there is no objective measurements or other proof to show that haze can be *fully accounted for* by dust particles. In fact, classical meteorology breaks down into severe contradictions in attempts to explain this phenomenon as it relates to coastal deserts (such as the thick marine haze at the Red Sea). Meteorology then resorts to unproven and rather remarkable additional assumptions, such as the unproven "hygroscopic swelling of dust particles" in the presence of humidities well below saturation, or the existence of contradictory "dry fog", often observed in dry marine/coastal environments. Such "dry fog" may obscure visibility in a powerful way, but in fact remains invisible to the eye at the micro-level (there are no water *droplets* in "dry fog", only water in gaseous form). Such "dry fogs" may possess only a 60% to 70% relative humidity as measured in ocean breezes close to the open water surface. A few hundred meters from the ocean, and humidity may anomalously drop by 5% to 10%, and by the time you move inland a few miles, humidity might drop to 30% or less, whereupon you find yourself in the middle of a coastal desert environment — in such a case the "marine haze" literally becomes the "desert haze".

Such haze is entirely different from a true fog, which *is* composed of visibly observable tiny water droplets at saturation conditions of 100% relative humidity. While desert haze and dry fogs may remain contradictory and enigmatic from the viewpoint of classical meteorology, the contribution to their understanding from orgone physics provides some empirical clarification. For example, the cloudbuster will often reduce desert haze and/or marine haze in a rather quick manner, or alternatively change its character from greyish to milky-white coloration with increased opacity, in which case the haze appears to transmute towards true fog or cloud development. What determines this difference is the pre-existing meteorological conditions, and the type of operational technique employed — neither of these changes, which take place over very wide areas, would be possible if haze is composed 100% of hygroscopic dust or salt particles, or if the cloudbuster was inoperative.

Here is a practical example: During our 23-24 June 1994 operations in Massawa, such a transformation was observed: the marine-desert haze over the Red Sea and adjacent land did thicken and become more opaque and milky in coloration, to the point that visibility dramatically declined along the Red Sea coast of Eritrea, from Massawa to Asab, and possibly beyond. During that operation, we were attempting to confine the desert/marine haze layer to the Red Sea region, to prevent it from moving upslope into inland Eritrea. According to orgone theory, this "confining" of rain-blocking haze to the Massawa Red Sea area prevented its further movement westward, up onto the highlands; rains thereby increased in the interior, and haze thickened at the Red Sea coast. This *orgonomic* explanation, from Reich's findings, accounts for the observed changes; classical meteorology does not.

It is correct that Reich's explanation for certain kinds of atmospheric haze has no general acceptance. However, the contradictions pointed out by him in the classical theories, and which I have confirmed in my own field observations, appear not to be addressed by classical theory. Why should some kinds of "fog" be characterized by a very low humidity, when by definition it should be composed of tiny water droplets near saturation (100% relative humidity) conditions? The important discoveries of Aitken, Wilson, Langmuir, etc. on cloud-condensation processes, raised by the critics, do not directly address this controversy. The major classical research which does was undertaken by Reid Bryson (U. Wisconsin) who, like Reich, observed that "atmospheric haze" stood as a block to rainfall — his book *Climates of Hunger* should be read by all Eritrean scientists interested in drought-related processes. Likewise the writings of Glen Trewartha's *The World's Problem Climates*, gives open discussion to those places around the world where classical theory has a difficulty to explain how weather functions, and the issue of "fog-deserts" and coastal "dry-fog" or "marine haze". If our cloudbusting project ever becomes a reality, I would give lectures to bring these kinds of issues into open discussion, as I have done at American and European universities and conferences.

The fact that the World Meteorological Organization has not addressed this issue does not constitute a "rebuttal" or insurmountable challenge by classical theory. Regarding the WMO's opinion about cloudbusting, I seriously doubt if the issue has been raised in their organization. But even if so, their opinion would be scientifically worthless unless based upon some actual field experiments, or study of the issue which brought them into direct and open contact with natural scientists like myself who have studied the matter practically, with field testing. Theoretical arguments are only worth so much in resolving such a long-standing controversy. There is a very high probability that the WMO would simply interpret the cloudbuster theoretically or politically (eg., "at all costs, avoid controversy"). In this regard, I wish to emphasize that I am not the discoverer of cloudbusting, but rather an independent scientist with all the classical credentials one could want who seriously evaluated and confirmed the observations of the discoverer, Wilhelm Reich. While I am not the first person to confirm Reich on this issue, I was the first to undertake such a review of his atmospheric theories at a major US university, under the review and scrutiny of a panel of critical professors. Presentations of my work have been made to international scientific scholarly societies, and many publications have been prepared and circulated for open review and discussion. Normally, this is all that is necessary to open the doors of academic research institutes to serious funding and research assistance, especially for a discovery with so many beneficial possibilities.

Cloudbusting and Relativity Theory:

While peripheral to the issue of cloudbusting, I completely disagree with the assertion that Einstein's hypothesis is "now well verified", and suggest the growing controversy regarding the theory of relativity has nothing *directly* to do with cloudbusting or orgone energy. Indirectly, however, relativity makes the assumption that space is empty, and this is incompatible with the discovery of the atmospheric orgone energy, as well as with the plasma physics of Hannes Alfven, and the ether-drift experiments of Dayton Miller (which proved the existence of the ether, quite independent of anything discovered by Wilhelm Reich). Virtually every modern experimental "proof" offered up for relativity can be reinterpreted as the product of a light-affecting aether-like or plasma-like energy in space. Regarding the statement made by the meteorologists that "the acceptance" of the "scientific community" is the only thing that matters, I find ridiculous, and suggestive that these individuals have never studied the history of science which shows repeatedly how new discoveries which challenge older popular theories are squashed by political tactics, rarely supported in any meaningful way by academic establishments, and thereby not allowed to blossom in the light of day until years after the discoverer has died. Certainly, the case of Wilhelm Reich and his discoveries fits this general historical pattern, and the present situation of the attacks against this project are also a case in point.

Cloudbuster Operations:

To clarify, for drought-abatement work or desert-greening work, the cloudbuster is operated when natural rainfall potentials are most likely to occur. As a proof for effectiveness, we look for: a) Onset of rainy periods shortly after onset of cloudbusting, even though drought has been prevailing for years or months, b) Rains of quantities at the upper level of the general climate pattern, c) Persistence of rains for some weeks or months thereafter, d) generalized clearing of atmospheric haze for the period after onset of rains. Since there is no need to undertake cloudbusting in regions where drought or desertification is not already in progress, by definition we deal with an atmospheric condition where widespread and good rains are not generally expected.

My discussion on the actual operation of the cloudbuster could have been more clearly written, but for various reasons I don't write down the actual field operational techniques. It is correct that cloudbusting is not a "rain-making" technique, but is rather an *obstacle-removing* technique. The dry haze so thick along the Red Sea coast was observed to move west and upslope into the Eritrean highlands, and in my opinion constituted a major blocking obstacle to rains. By using the cloudbuster at Massawa, we hoped to soften this atmospheric haze, thereby reducing its blocking effects farther upslope. In this regard, the techniques applied appear to have been successful. Once clouds and rains begin to develop, the atmosphere then takes on a new dynamic all its own, and I have observed that this new dynamic often includes the ingress of moisture, clouds and even jet streams into the area. It would require some lengthy discussion to fully outline what I believe is working here, but one cannot understand the process if one assumes the atmosphere is a dead collection of chemicals working only from temperature and pressure. It is much more than this, and as argued by Reich and in later years by Lovelock, one can more readily understand these dynamic processes from the viewpoint of the life sciences.

Regarding the distribution of rains following cloudbusting in Eritrea, the moisture flow from the Gulf of Guinea in West Africa is the major source of moisture during the summertime Kiremti rains. The first appearance of heavier rains far to the west of our cloudbusting work, but closer to the source of moisture, is not a contradiction. Those rains eventually moved closer to the Asmara area as the nature of the block was understood and dealt with.

The meteorologists raise an important question, that the effects from cloudbusting might create dryness in some other place, that rains brought to Eritrea might be "taken" from some other place. This consideration appears to be true for certain kinds of *cloudseeding,* where downwind dryness has been observed — moisture is squeezed from the air and the downwind area dries out. In other cases, as documented by Irving Langmuir, cloudseeding can have downwind influences of increased rains, as increased instability which is created in one region propagates downwind. With cloudbusting, I have only observed the effect of increased downwind rains, and this also appears to have been the case with respect to our work in Eritrea — nations to the west of Eritrea also experienced a very good rainy season, and the intertropical convergence was well-developed with an unusually far northward transit following our operations. Such downwind influences should, however, be documented and studied more closely.

Given that cloudbusting was developed in the 1950s, it is asked why was it not attempted in Eritrea or other drought regions of Africa before the 1990s? The answer here should dispel the suspicions raised in this same question by the meteorologists. Firstly, Reich was thrown into jail in the 1950s, his books and research journals ordered "banned and burned" by the US Government during what is generally called our "McCarthy Period". He died in prison in 1957. Had Reich lived, he probably would have tried to undertake an expedition to Africa in the 1960s and 1970s, when severe droughts and famines occurred and were reported by the news media worldwide. At the time of those reports, I was a young student at the university, and had become rather frustrated at the conventional and generally ineffectual methods of "fighting desertification". Reich's approach was full of promise, but few professionals in the atmospheric sciences were willing to listen to it. I found a few interested professionals who had studied Reich's methods for years, and studied with them myself. Later, with help from professors at the University of Kansas, I undertook my own first experimental review of the question. Since that time, I have been constantly attacked and frustrated by groups of physicists and meteorologists in a manner similar to the current attempt to blockade this work in Eritrea. Few persons in an "official" position are willing to give it a try, or they are afraid of being ridiculed by the physicists, or they just are against it for other reasons. Slowly, and without any official support, I have built a track record and reputation for success with this new method. It has been tried in the USA, Germany, Greece, Cyprus, Israel, and Namibia, and reports on most of those experimental efforts have been delivered to the Ministry of Agriculture. But nothing is "advertised" and the knowledge is spread only slowly, mostly through research journals outside the mainstream, or by word of mouth. And so came the Eritrean liberation and the proposal for a cloudbusting project in Eritrea was made by the Albini brothers. Make no mistake about the following: *The reasons for the great delay in the practical application of Reich's works is due to the tendency of critics to attack rather than honestly and genuinely review the issue, and for theoretical arguments to take precedence over empirical data.* In this respect, if the meteorologists at Asmara Airport are successful in blocking the development of this project, then it may well be another 20 or 30 years before anybody decides to spend their time and money to come here and do it again.

The Mechanism of the Cloudbuster:

The mechanism of the cloudbuster has not been investigated to the same degree as the question of whether or not it has an influence upon the atmosphere. These are two separate questions. The simplicity of the cloudbuster's design, the absence of any chemical or electromagnetic inputs, suggests it must work by stimulation of some natural energetic principle. It is very similar in some respects to the lightning rod, but differs significantly in the use of water as a grounding element.

It is believed by Dr. DeMeo, and most other natural scientists who have experimentally investigated the findings of Dr. Reich, that Dr. Reich was essentially correct about the existence of the *orgone energy*. This energy satisfies many of the qualities of the older physics concept of *aether*, and has similarities also to the more modern concepts of *plasma energy*, or other concepts of *energy in space*; these latter concepts are openly and widely debated in science journals today, and constitute a genuine controversy within astrophysics. Dr. Reich's orgone energy should be similarly viewed.

There are several areas of the natural sciences where current research has hit upon fundamental phenomenon in nature which cannot easily be explained by classical mechanistic theory. Dr. DeMeo believes the cloudbuster functions in a manner very similar to these "areas of difficulty" within the sciences, and that Dr. Reich's orgone theory provides new ways of looking at these phenomena, which are:

A. *Water structuring or activation* (physical and organic chemistry)

B. *Air ionization* (meteorology)

C. *Electrical charge and surface tension parameters of cloud droplets* (meteorology)

D. *The energy of acupuncture* (Chinese medicine)

E. *The energy of homeopathic activation of water* (European holistic medicine)

F. *The elusive neutrino* (radiation physics)

G. *The biological effects of low-level electromagnetism and nuclear radiation.* (biophysics)

Of the above factors, the analogy of cloudbusting to medical acupuncture holds forth a promising model of reasonable accuracy. Considering the earth and atmosphere as a total system, charged with energetic forces which are not fully understood from the classical perspective, the cloudbuster antenna produces a set of influences which are as inexplicable to classical meteorology as the documented effects of Chinese acupuncture are to classical medicine. Chinese acupuncture, like cloudbusting, relies upon the existence of a special life-force (*Chi* energy) to explain the effects of the acupuncture needles, which restore flow and movement (firstly of energy, secondly of blood and lymph) within a situation of stagnated biological energy. The cloudbuster, similarly, restores flow and movement (firstly of energy, secondly of air and moisture) within a situation of stagnated atmospheric energy. If one accepts the existence of the energy, the observed effects of treatment (acupuncture or cloudbusting) are theoretically logical and consistent. There are additional experimental proofs, such as the use of orgone-type devices to produce bio-effects in human beings similar to acupuncture needles, and the arguments of Lovelock, et al., regarding the "Earth as organism" viewpoint which is very much in keeping with the findings of Reich — but space does not allow elaboration here.

It is an unavoidable, though regrettable historical fact, that Dr. Reich's work was unscientifically attacked and his books burned in the USA; for very political reasons there has been a reluctance among American scientists working within the official institutions to openly investigate this major scientific controversy. A great deal of disinformation now exists from official American sources on the matter of Reich's life and works, and caution is advised in the formation of opinions on the issue. As always, experimental evaluations of Reich's findings must be given greater weight than unfounded "opinions" of critics (scientists or non-scientists). There currently is a resurgence of interest in Reich's findings among younger students and scientists in the USA and Europe.

To conclude: *The mechanism of the cloudbuster is a question requiring additional experimental clarification, but this is, in my view, a completely separate question from the more immediate and practical concern as to whether it works or not to bring rains to drought or desert regions. I am committed to experimental investigation and clarification of both issues. But there are lines of argument, backed up by existing experimental evidence, suggesting the cloudbuster may directly influence the electrical charge and surface tension characteristics of cloud droplets, a factor which is central to the matter of growth and coalescence of cloud droplets, and therefore also central to the matter of cloud formation and growth. Other experiments suggest that air ionization and water structuring components may be involved in the mechanism. But presently more questions exist on these issues than answers. By analogy, we can also point to Chinese acupuncture, which similarly posits the existence of a unique biological life energy, existing in both organism and atmosphere, by which it functions to restore health to the organism. Cloudbusting is similar in its approach to "atmospheric health", or "atmospheric self-regulation", concepts more familiar to the biologist than the meteorologist. A major problem exists in the near total lack of research support whereby these questions might be fully clarified by experiment, though much has been accomplished in this regard over the years by dedicated researchers working in private laboratories (and within a few public institutions). I am personally dedicated to the eventual undertaking of such clarifying experiments. But, for the time being, there is good evidence the cloudbuster works, and I am satisfied*

to apply the theory of Dr. Reich as an effective working methodology (or working hypothesis, if you wish). Every question cannot be answered all at once, and I request the honest critic to be both open and patient in their search for clarifying answers. The published scientific literature on the question of orgone energy is vast, and includes the voluminous writings of Dr. Reich and his associates (1935 to 1956) plus those of other scientists since his death (1965 to the present). This literature should be the starting point for any genuinely honest critical review of the cloudbuster's mechanism, and I shall be happy to assist any open critic in obtaining the central documentation.

Appendix References:

Alfven, H.: *Cosmic Plasmas*, Kluwer Press, Boston, 1981.

Bryson, R. & T.J. Murray: *Climates of Hunger*, U. Wisconsin Press, Madison, 1977.

DeMeo, J.: "Cloudbusting: Growing Evidence for a New Method of Ending Drought and Greening Deserts", *Am. Institute of Biomedical Climatology Newsletter*, #20, Sept. 1996, p.1-4.

DeMeo, J.: "A Dynamic Biological-Atmospheric-Cosmic Energy Continuum: Some Old and New Evidence", *Geo-Cosmic Relations: The Earth and its Macro-Environment*, Proceedings, First International Congress on Geo-Cosmic Relations, 19-22 April 1989, Amsterdam, Netherlands, G.J.M. Tomassen, et al, Editors, PUDOC Science Publishers, Wageningen, 1989. Also: DeMeo, J.: "The Orgone Energy Continuum: Some Old and New Evidence", *Pulse of the Planet*, 1(2):3-8, 1989; German translation "Alte und neue Beweise fur das Orgon Energie Kontinuum", *Lebensenergie*, 2:13-20, 1991.

Langmuir, I.: "Analysis of the Effects of Periodic Seeding of the Atmosphere with Silver Iodide", in *The Collected Works of Irving Langmuir, Vol. 11: Cloud Nucleation*, G. Suits & H. Way, Eds., Pergamon Press, NY 1961. Esp. see Figs. 9-10, p.356; also see: *Vol. 10: Atmospheric Phenomena*, and chapters on "Widespread Control of Weather by Silver Iodide Seeding", "A Seven-Day Periodicity in Weather in the USA During April 1950", and "Introduction to Vol. 11" by H. Byers.

Lovelock, J.E.: *Gaia*, Oxford University Press 1979; Lovelock, J.E.: *The Ages of Gaia*, W.W. Norton, NY 1988.

Miller, D.: "The Ether-Drift Experiment and the Determination of the Absolute Motion of the Earth", *Reviews of Modern Physics*, 5:203-242, July, 1933.

Reich, W. (1952): "DOR Removal and Cloud-Busting", *Orgone Energy Bull.*, IV(4):171-182. (reprinted in Reich, *Selected Writings*, Farrar, Straus & Giroux, NY, 1960, 1973); Reich, W. (1954): "OROP Desert. Part 1: Spaceships, DOR and Drought", *Cosmic Orgone Engineering*, VI(1-4):1-140; Reich, W. (1955): "Expedition OROP Desert, Ea: DOR Clouds Over the USA", *Cosmic Orgone Engineering*, VII(1-2):4-19; Reich, W. (1957): *Contact With Space, Oranur Second Report: Orop Desert Ea*, Core Pilot Press, NY.

Senf, B.: "Wilhelm Reich: Discoverer of Acupuncture Energy?", Pulse of the Planet, 2:25-30, 1989; also in Am. J. Acupuncture 7(2):109-118, April-June 1979.

Trewartha, G.: *The Earth's Problem Climates*, Univ. Wisconsin Press, Madison, 1966.

Origins of the Tropical Easterlies: An Orgone-Energetic Perspective

by James DeMeo, Ph.D.*

Wilhelm Reich's discovery of the cosmic and atmospheric orgone energy has provided a functional — that is, *an energetic, non-mystical and non-mechanistic* — understanding of the universe, and an excellent working hypothesis for understanding specific planetary and atmospheric motions.[1] For the reader who is unfamiliar with Reich's ideas, or who strongly adheres to classical meteorological theorems for atmospheric motions, or to the diverse astronomical theorems founded upon the assumption of "empty space", this essay may be difficult to follow, given that it starts from *a completely different set of basic assumptions*. We assume space is energetically rich, without any "empty" parts, and that the energy filling space is motile, pulsatory, streaming and flowing, and *capable of putting matter into motion*. Indeed, we look upon this energy, given the name *orgone* by Reich, as akin to the older hypothesis of the *ether of space*. However, it is an "ether" with specific dynamical properties largely unconsidered by prior generations of ether-drift researchers, save for the notable exception of Dayton Miller.[2] As the energy filling space flows and moves, we argue here, so too do the planets and their atmospheres move, in a lawful manner.

Several of Reich's inventions, specifically the *orgone energy accumulator*[3] and *cloudbusting apparatus*,[4] provide much of the empirical foundations and proofs for his ideas, which otherwise would appear too fantastic for both the ordinary citizen and scientific specialist of the 20th, or even the 21st Century. However, taken by themselves, Reich's broad and interdisciplinary theory of orgone energy functions in nature — the *science of orgonomy* — provides a radical simplification over conventional scientific ideas, which often are exceedingly complex and theoretically top-heavy. Here, I wish to present the *orgonomic (life energetic) perspective* on the origins of a major planetary atmospheric phenomenon — the *Tropical Easterly wind belt* or *Inter-Tropical Discontinuity (ITD)* which girdles the Earth in the equatorial region — which heretofore has not been understood in the context of orgonomy and orgone biophysics.

Reich argued, the major winds are produced at their fundament by streaming motions of cosmic orgone energy, which in the process of converting from a mass-free

* Director, Orgone Biophysical Research Lab, Greensprings, PO Box 1148, Ashland, Oregon 97520 USA Tel-Fax: 541-552-0118 Email: demeo@mind.net

to a mass state, imparts momentum to both the mass of the planet and to the atmosphere. He postulated a rotating disk of cosmic orgone which produced the galaxies and the planetary ecliptical disk around the Sun. The basic pattern of unidirectional planetary revolutions around the Sun, of moons around the planets, as well as of the Earth's rotation on its axis, are fundamental expressions of this rotating disk of cosmic energy. Over eons of time, in its conversion from a mass-free to a mass state, the orgone formed the planetary bodies, and set them into motion.[5]

The streaming motions of cosmic orgone are also the source for *atmospheric motion*s, Reich argued, as well as for certain other changes in the physical properties of the air, though our discussion here will be limited only to atmospheric motions. He expressed it as follows:

"The west-east direction in the motion of the atmospheric orgone energy has great significance independent of the special variations that appear in the wave motion and in the pulses. The west-east direction is in agreement with the direction of rotation of the earth's sphere; thus, it is also in agreement with the general direction of rotation in the planetary system. A reversal of this generally valid direction on the Earth's surface takes place only before thunderstorms or heavy rain occurring to the west of the observer." [6]

"..the OR energy envelope of the globe... at bottom, is responsible for air movements and shifts of moisture, as it is responsible for the movement of the planet... the OR energy stream in the equatorial plane...makes both globe and atmosphere move from west to east." [7]

Reich's explanation fits very well with observations of the *Westerly winds* which exist in those mid-latitude regions of Maine and Arizona (46°N and 33°N latitudes, respectively) where he made his primary field observations. Winds in those regions are characterized by a basic west-to-east pattern, and, as we know today, by the *Polar Front Jet Stream*. This latter phenomenon, of a high-velocity west-to-east movement of air at high altitudes, was suggested to meteorologists as early as the 1930s, but only identified when jet aircraft began flying at very high altitudes, in the 1950s. The Polar Front Jet is known, today, to be the most permanent and

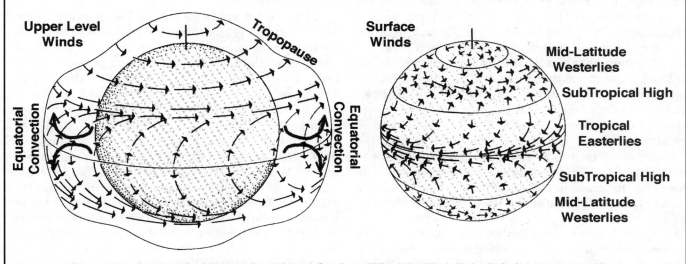

Figure 1. Contrast of Upper Level and Surface Winds. All global winds have a general west-to-east pattern, except for the dominant east-to-west flow in the Equatorial Tropics.[14]

intensive of all the jet streams on Earth. Reich, to my knowledge, never wrote about the atmospheric "jet streams" per se, as the upper atmospheric currents were not understood at that time sufficient to identify their specific streaming motions.[§]

Reich noted the generalized west-to-east *energetic streaming*, however, arguing that the atmospheric motions were the direct expression of a primary flowing movement of orgone energy, called the *Equatorial Orgone Stream*. This flowing energy could be accumulated to higher densities within the orgone energy accumulator, and stimulated by use of the cloudbuster in drought-abatement experiments, which he considered to be a validating proof of the essential correctness of his ideas.[1,2,4,5,6,7]

Starting in the early 1970s, and later when studying geography and meteorology at the University of Kansas, I reviewed Reich's discussions on the cloudbuster in detail, as well as the works of other scientists who had already replicated Reich's findings.[10] I also engaged in practical field tests with the cloudbuster in the USA,[11] firstly at the university, and later in states as far north as Washington (47°N), and as far south as southern Florida (26°N). Later, I directed desert-greening and drought abatement field operations with the cloud-

buster in regions close to the Equator and in the Southern Hemisphere,[12] specifically in Israel (34°N), Eritrea (15°N) and Namibia (22°S). My field observations basically *confirmed* Reich, suggesting the classically-described "jet streams" were, at their fundament, *streams or currents of orgone energy which moved at the higher altitudes, dragging the air along with them as they moved.* One primary empirical proof of this, is the fact that winds and jet streams could be "tapped" and stimulated to move and intensify according to skillful use of the cloudbuster — an extraordinary phenomenon to witness, and in total violation of classical theory. However, my field work in Eritrea and Namibia required practical work under weather systems dominated by the *Tropical Easterlies*, something quite different from anything I had previously experienced, or ever discussed by Reich.[‡] This required a critical examination of parts of Reich's theory.

Earth's Major Wind Belts and Jet Streams

Firstly, it must be stressed, *the majority of wind belts and jet stream motions within Earth's atmosphere do, in fact, flow from west-to-east, faster than the planetary rotation, and are in keeping with Reich's observations and theory.* The Tropical Easterlies are a major exception, however. There also exists a lesser easterly

---

[§] For example, Tannehill's 1945 book *Hurricanes*,[8] which Reich cited in his *Cosmic Superimposition*,[5] makes no mention of "jet streams" per se. Likewise for Petterssen's 1940s textbook *Weather Analysis and Forecasting*,[9] a meteorology classic, makes no mention of them. The great emphasis upon civil and military aviation weather forecasting since the 1950s led to a better understanding, and by the 1960s, every introductory meteorology textbook had a full discussion on jet-streams. Today, both TV weather forecasters and farmers routinely discuss them.

[‡] Charles Kelley, a former weather forecaster with the US Army who published in one of Reich's journals in 1955, made mention of the problem of the easterlies. This suggests Reich at least knew of the difficulty. Kelley stated: *"To be explained are the prevailing easterly surface winds in polar and tropical regions. These winds...unquestionably have a lawful relation to orgone energy flow, though the relation is not yet clear."*[13]

wind regime in the high polar regions, though this is seasonal or regional in most cases and not such a permanent widespread feature as is the case with the equatorial Easterlies. Both will be discussed here.

My attempts to resolve this apparent contradiction to Reich's theory led to the repeated viewing of moving satellite images, as well as to construction of three-dimensional models, and a detailed study of known atmospheric motions, including the classically-defined jet streams. For a long period, the findings from the classical researchers only seemed to add complication to the question, but finally a solution was uncovered which, once known, demonstrated itself to be quite simple, and "under the nose". First, let's review the basic phenomenon.

Figure 1 gives two diagrams of the Earth with generalized upper-level and surface winds drawn in. They are rough averages for winds around the Earth, but reflect very real conditions. The upper-air diagram identifies winds near the *tropopause*, which is roughly at the level of thunderstorm tops, at around 8000 to 18,000 m (~25,000-60,000 ft) elevation; it marks the upper surface of the *troposphere*, which is the lowest atmospheric layer around 10 km thick (~6 miles) where almost all of the Earth's clouds and weather systems develop and expend their life-cycles. Above the tropopause lies the stratosphere, which does have its own wind system, but that is subject for discussion at another time. The troposphere is thicker at the equator, and thinner in the mid-latitude and polar regions. As shown in Figure 1, *a west-to-east flow generally characterizes both upper and lower level atmospheric movements in the mid-latitudes*, and those winds are called the *Mid-Latitude Westerlies*. Both the Westerlies and the Easterlies are named according to the source-region from which they blow.

Surface winds in the polar regions are somewhat more chaotic, expressing components of both a westerly and easterly flow. The easterly component, sometimes called the *Polar Easterlies,* is mostly a seasonal feature and appears wholly connected with the regular passing of large cyclonic low-pressure cells in wintertime, which tends to create *temporary* east-to-west wind-reversals. One can clearly see this pattern in satellite image movies: *as strong wintertime low pressure cells move west-to-east in the sub-polar latitudes, the side closer to the poles experiences a strong but temporary east-to-west wind reversal.* Where a succession of lows passes along the same storm track, this wind regime can become more constant, and appear to be a specific "easterly" wind, but it is totally the product of circulation around the low pressure storm centers, which themselves are always moving on a general west-to-east track. The polar regions also experience west-to-east upper air currents, including a wintertime *Polar-Night Jet Stream* (occurring during the long period of extended nighttime), which moves west-to-east parallel to the Polar Front Jet Stream.

By contrast, *surface winds in the equatorial tropics are dominated by winds moving east-to-west as a fairly constant phenomenon circling nearly the entire globe*, which changes only in its seasonal amplitude and latitude. These winds are therefore called the *Tropical Easterlies*; they are also accompanied, at upper-levels, by the *Tropical Easterly Jet Stream*, which also moves from east-to-west, but only during summertime and over a limited geographical range — roughly from SE Asia, across India and Africa. It is not comparable to the major Polar Front Jet, in that it does not fully circle the Earth, is only seasonal, and does not have the same high velocities. This Easterly Jet vanishes during Northern Hemisphere wintertime, from around November through May, being replaced by general westerly flow at upper levels.

There are additionally the *Sub-Tropical Jet Streams*, which flow from southwest to northeast in the Northern Hemisphere, appearing to spiral around the Earth, from Equator to poles. Figure 2 maps the average frequency of winter surface frontal systems showing this general spiral-form path. The fronts are created by low-pressure storm centers which are guided along this path by the confluence of both the Polar Jet Stream, and the Sub-Tropical Jet Streams.[15] The predominant expression of this latter stream starts in the tropical Western Pacific, moves northeast from there to cross into North America, and from there into Europe, finally to expend itself into the high Arctic region. Additional Sub-Tropical Jets also emerge from the tropical eastern Pacific, Gulf of Mexico, and eastern Atlantic, near the Gulf of Guinea, to feed into this large spiraling storm track.

A similar poleward spiraling Sub-Tropical Jet Stream also exists in the Southern Hemisphere, though we have no map or figure to display its characteristics. It creates storm tracks which move from northwest to southeast, and feed into the Antarctic Polar Front Jet system, which circles Antarctica west-to-east. One such jet starts also in the tropical Western Pacific, moving southeast towards Antarctica, and is a formative agent for the *South Pacific Convergence,* a major seasonal rainy region. Another jet starts near the South American Amazonian tropics, also moving southeast, and helps to stimulate the *South Atlantic Convergence.*[§]

All of these subtropical jets are seasonal and episodic in nature (mostly late winter and early springtime), and undulatory, with only their average positions

---

[§] A SW to NE spiral-flow component to S. Hemisphere winds has also been suggested,[18] moving roughly from Australia (c.25˚S) ENE towards Southern Peru and Brazil (c.15˚S) and from there, having nearly circled the globe, to cross the Equator approximately in the Indian Ocean or SE Asia, whereupon it appears to join in with the N. Hemisphere spiral-flow as identified in Figure 2.

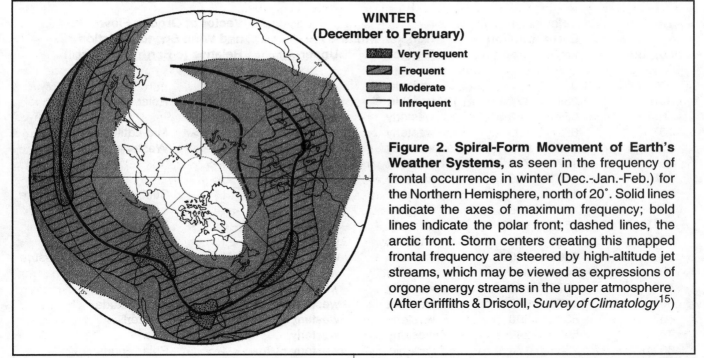

**WINTER
(December to February)**

- ▨ Very Frequent
- ▨ Frequent
- ▨ Moderate
- ☐ Infrequent

Figure 2. Spiral-Form Movement of Earth's Weather Systems, as seen in the frequency of frontal occurrence in winter (Dec.-Jan.-Feb.) for the Northern Hemisphere, north of 20°. Solid lines indicate the axes of maximum frequency; bold lines indicate the polar front; dashed lines, the arctic front. Storm centers creating this mapped frontal frequency are steered by high-altitude jet streams, which may be viewed as expressions of orgone energy streams in the upper atmosphere. (After Griffiths & Driscoll, *Survey of Climatology*[15])

being described on maps. As any good weather forecaster today will inform you, the locations of the major jet streams — *which we view as streams of primary water-attracting and negatively-entropic orgone energy* — have a high predictive value in terms of the locations of storms and rainfall.

The Westerlies and Easterlies also contain exceptionally cloudy and rainy weather systems; in fact, one of the more remarkable aspects of the Earth's climatic system is, that most rains occur in three major "rainy belts" which girdle the Earth. Two of the rainy belts are found within the mid-latitudes, roughly in bands between 30°–60° north and south latitudes, and move with the prevailing Westerly (west-to-east) winds in association with the Polar Front Jet. The third rainy belt is found in the region of the equatorial Tropical Easterlies. Large wintertime *long-wave cyclonic storms* and summertime thunderstorm complexes characterize the Mid-Latitude Westerlies, while *tropical waves* and also thunderstorm complexes characterize the Tropical Easterlies. Tropical hurricanes occasionally spawn from within the Easterlies, as tropical waves move over warm ocean waters.

Reich's Model, Revisited

The reversed flow of the Easterly winds at the Equator suggests there would be a slightly different flow pattern between the cosmic background of energy than was discussed by Reich, as otherwise the flow of winds should be west-to-east for the entire planet, even if possibly faster or slower at different latitudes. Such is not the case, however. The Tropical Easterly surface winds, marked by the Inter-Tropical Discontinuity, are well-developed and constitute a major belt of winds and rains at least as great as either of the two rainy belts of the Westerlies.

Consider the Earth, floating in the background sea of orgone energy, caught in a stream of this energy which moves it along on its path through the heavens, keeping it locked into a spiral-form movement with the Sun, as both are moved along through a space filled with streaming orgone energy. The energy imparts a patterned movement to all the planets, to all the various moons orbiting the planets, and to the rotational movements of the planets on their respective axes. There are some exceptions to the rule, but for the moment we will delay addressing this important issue. The almost uniform nature of this movement underlies the conventional theory of astronomy, that the Solar System developed as a whole from a swirling cloud of dust and gas which slowly, by gravitational forces, condensed into larger planetary masses. Reich's theory of *Cosmic Superimposition*[8] has similarities to this, except he argues the formative force and motional force are one and the same thing, and that the process is on-going, happening in the here-and-now, as well as in Earth's most ancient past. The swirling creative energy motion which formed the Solar System, now exists also as a swirling orgone-energetic movement girdling the Earth's equator as well, imparting a rotational force to both the planetary mass, and to the atmosphere as well, in a west-to-east direction.

This movement of cosmic energy is likely to be something much larger in size than the Earth, something not merely isolated to the equatorial region, but a fairly wide streaming phenomenon, as in Reich's conceptual model of a ball floating in a moving stream, or a

Table 1. Latitude	Velocity of Earth Rotation km/h	mph	General Winds Surface	Upper-Air	Vector of Orgone Flow and Wind Speed/Direction Relative to Earth's Surface	
90° N. Pole	0	0	variable	-??	W<-I->E	
80°	289	174	variable	westerly	<- I-->	Polar Winds
70°	569	342	westerly	westerly	<- I--->	
60°	832	500	westerly	westerly	I----->	Mid-Latitude
50°	1070	643	westerly	westerly	I---->	Westerlies
40°	1275	766	westerly	westerly	I-->	
30°	1441	866	westerly	westerly	I->	
20°	1564	940	variable	westerly	I	Subtropical High Pressure
10°	1639	985	easterly	westerly	<- I	
0° Equator	1670	1000	easterly	variable	<----I	Tropical Easterlies
10°	1639	985	easterly	westerly	<- I	
20°	1564	940	variable	westerly	I	Subtropical High Pressure
30°	1441	866	westerly	westerly	I->	
40°	1275	766	westerly	westerly	I-->	
50°	1070	643	westerly	westerly	I---->	Mid-Latitude
60°	832	500	westerly	westerly	I----->	Westerlies
70°	569	342	westerly	westerly	<- I--->	
80°	289	174	variable	westerly	<- I-->	Polar Winds
90° S. Pole	0	0	variable	-??	W<-I->E	

ball floating on the ocean waves, where the stream or wave are much larger than Earth. According to these conceptual models, Earth would be moved along, by a fairly large stream (or, large waves in the ocean of energy) which would affect all parts of the planet, and not merely the equator. The energy stream, or pulsatory waves, would push against the entire Earth and its atmosphere, moving in a west-to-east direction. However, whereas the Earth itself is a fairly solid object, the atmosphere is fluid, and so we would expect the atmosphere to be more easily moved by the streaming energy than is the Earth itself.

This line of reasoning, as well as direct observations of the movements of the Earth's orgone envelope, is what led Reich to assert the orgone energy streamed from west-to-east, faster than the rotational speed of the Earth, and that the Westerly winds originated from this movement. However, from here, important questions are raised: *Given enough time, would not the Earth's rotation and the atmospheric motions slowly accelerate until their motions matched, or averaged out the velocity of the energy stream?*

If the basic starting assumption is correct, that Earth is put into rotational motion by streams of orgone energy in space, which move it along in space as well, then it is logical to also assume the Earth is slowly accelerated to some *peak rotational speed which is close to the speed of motion of the energy itself.* After all, with eons of time as a background, and no frictional force to slow down the rotation of the Earth, we should expect the Earth's rotational speed to eventually *match the pace and speed of the moving orgone stream.* However,

while the orgone energy stream might have a relatively fixed or average velocity, *the Earth's "rotational speed" is a function of latitude, changing from around 1670 km/h (or 1000 mph) at the Equator, to zero at the poles.* For this reason, *there can only be one general latitude where the rotational speed of the Earth matches the "swirling speed" of the orgone stream.* This must be so, even though it appears probable, as Reich postulated, at very great altitudes the *mass-free* orgone energy streams uniformly west-to-east faster than the Earth.

In order to resolve this question, we firstly need to do some maths, to know the varying rotational speed of the Earth at different latitudes. We start with Earth's circumference of ~40,000 km, or ~24,000 miles. With one 360° rotation of Earth each 24 hours, this translates into a rotational speed of roughly 1670 km/h, or 1000 mph, at the Equator. The rotational velocity at the poles is basically zero, and rotational velocity is progressively increased as one moves from the Poles towards the Equator. Using the circumference figures above:

24,000 / 360° = 66.6 miles per degree of latitude, or
40,000 / 360° = 111 km per degree of latitude.

For each degree of latitude away from the Equator, the rotational velocity of Earth reduces according to the cosine of the latitude, by the following formula:

(Cosine x degree of latitude)
    x (distance per degree of latitude)
        x (360° rotation/24 hrs.)
or:

$$\cos(\text{deg.}) \times (111 \text{ km/deg}) \times (15°/\text{hr}) = \text{velocity, km/h}$$
$$\cos(\text{deg.}) \times (66.6 \text{ miles/deg}) \times (15°/\text{hr}) = \text{velocity, mph}$$

Table 1 gives the computed values for varying "speed of rotation" of the Earth at different latitudes. The latitudes of 60°, in fact, move at about *half* the rotational speed at the Equator.

Assuming the speed of the streaming orgone was *faster* than the maximum Equatorial rotation speed, as mentioned above, we might expect the Earth to slowly accelerate and, sooner or later, to match that faster speed. We have no evidence from astronomy, however, that the Earth is slowly accelerating in its rotational velocity. It is therefore reasonable to assume the speed of the streaming orgone — at least that state of the orgone where it is converting to mass and thereby imparting momentum to the atmosphere and to Earth itself — must be *no greater on average* than 1670 km/h (or 1000 mph).[§] If the *equatorial* rotational speed were *just equal* to the orgone flowing speed, however, then we would expect all of the planetary winds to blow from west-to-east, with only an area of "calm winds" existing near the Equator. This situation does not exist either, and so we may conclude that *the speed of the streaming orgone must be slower than 1670 km/h, the rotational speed of Earth at the Equator.*

The very existence of the Tropical Equatorial Easterlies forces us to consider the following: *The Earth is matching the rotational speed of the orgone streams, but only at latitudes somewhat removed from the Equatorial region,* AND, *the Earth's rotational speed at the Equator must be faster than the streaming motion of the orgone at the surface, giving rise to a "back-flowing" east-to-west motion in the tropical atmosphere.*

The Subtropical High Pressure regions lying approximately between 20° to 30° latitude appear to satisfy the general criterion, as the latitude band which rotates with a speed roughly equal to the rotational speed of the streaming orgone, as it moves down to Earth from space. On the poleward side of the subtropical high pressure regions, winds are driven west-to-east by streaming orgone moving at a speed *faster* than the rotational speed of the Earth. On the equator-side of the subtropical high pressure, the condition exists where *the rotational speed of the Earth, at the equator, is faster than the rotational speed of the larger orgone stream,* creating an east-to-west reversal of tropospheric winds. This *reversed-flow,* where the Earth is moving faster than the orgone, then, appears to be the source for the Easterly flow in the Equatorial regions.

[§] Jet stream velocities of up to 740 km/h in the upper troposphere, and up to 1800 km/h in the ionosphere have been observed.[16]

Discussion

From the above, it is possible to reconcile the broad regions of Mid-Latitude Westerly winds *and* the Tropical Easterlies, as well as the west-to-east rotation of the Earth, within the context of Reich's theory of a singular west-to-east motion of the cosmic Equatorial Orgone Stream. However, in doing so, the Earth is assumed now to be *moving with the orgone flow,* at approximately the same net speed. This is analogous to a ball floating in a stream, being carried along by the stream at the same speed of its current, and slowly being turned by slight variations or torques in the current. A better model here would be, of a ball submerged to a depth where it remained at a constant buoyancy, being moved along by a swirling deep ocean current

The observed reality does not appear to be completely analogous to the model of a ball floating on the ocean surface, with waves moving past the floating ball, moving faster than both the ball and the water itself. If this latter analogy were correct, then the *"orgone waves" would be faster than Earth's rotation at all latitudes, including at the Equator,* and the Earth's atmosphere would be moved in a uniformly west-to-east motion. We would also then be forced to postulate two differentiated expressions for the orgone energy medium: one for the wave-excitations which move the Earth, and another for the background medium of the orgone, which would move only slowly itself, and primarily act to convey the waves or pulses. This is, in fact, what we see with a ball floating on the ocean waves, with two different motional forces, one from the waves and another from the ocean medium itself, which restrains the ball against moving too easily with the waves.[‡] This latter model should not yet be completely or prematurely discarded, however, as the "ball in a moving stream" model emphasized in this paper, while solving the mystery of the Tropical Easterlies, raises other new and thorny questions.

For example, the predominant west-to-east flow of the orgone *appears* to contradict the flow of the ether-drift as demonstrated by the late Dayton Miller.[2] Miller's ether-drift measurements suggest the existence of a light-affecting energy flow moving at approximately 10 kilometers per second (36,000 km/h), approximately south to north along the axis of the Plane of the Ecliptic. This appears difficult to reconcile with a west-to-east flow of orgone which moves at less than half a kilometer per second (1670 km/h) at the Equator, or even slightly less than this at the subtropical latitudes. There are

---

[‡] Tropical waves, and frontal waves may be large expressions of "waves of excitation" within the Earth's atmosphere, but these would not be restricted only to the "ball on the ocean waves" model. The flowing motion of orgone energy through the atmosphere should, by itself, create wave-forms based upon its own discontinuities and tendencies to pulsate — that is, to contract and expand.

possible solutions to this problem, however.

Firstly, the streaming motions of *mass-free* orgone could well be at the 10 km/sec velocity recorded by Miller at Mt. Wilson observatory, affecting the speed of mass-free light waves. This velocity might be dramatically slowed down as the superimposition process occurs, where mass is being formed directly out of the orgone energy substrate. At such a point — being attracted to the Earth's surface, building in both charge and excitation, condensing into relatively slow-moving *orgone units*[5] which are mass-forming or mass-bound and capable of imparting a momentum to both atmosphere and planetary mass — the velocity of this more condensed orgone might be well under 1 km/sec, perhaps approximating the easterly velocity of Earth at the subtropical latitudes, of around 1500 km/h (or ~0.4 km/sec).

Secondly, the movements of Earth as detected in Miller's ether-drift experiments, and as postulated in Reich's Cosmic Superimposition theory, both suggest a significant spiral-form motion. The ether-drift does move *generally* south to north along the axis of the Ecliptical Plane, but as shown in Miller's own measured data, and as measured at the Earth's surface, *this motion displays an average 23.75° west-to-east displacement.*[17] In a similar manner, the orgone does *generally* flow from west-to-east, but also appears to *spiral around the Earth* with a general *southwest-to northeast displacement.*[17] Several lines of evidence suggesting a similar southwest-to-northeast component present in atmospheric weather systems were mentioned above,[18] and Reich also specifically discussed a separate southwest-to-northeast component to orgone energy dynamics, as an expression of the *Galactic Orgone Stream.*[19] This galactic stream, he argued, was a motion of cosmic energy derived from the spiraling plane of the Milky Way galaxy. As far-reaching as this may sound to the unfamiliar reader, it is important to note, that *Reich's ideas on the Equatorial and Galactic Orgone Streams appear to pre-date the explicit classical meteorological identifications of the Polar Front Jet and Subtropical Jet Streams.*

One may agree or disagree with Reich's theory of cosmic orgone, but his empirical observations on these and other matters have been corroborated by later findings in classical atmospheric science, and empirical validation is one of the more essential proofs for any theory.

References:

1. Reich, W.: *Ether, God and Devil* (1949), *Cosmic Superimposition* (1951), Farrar, Straus & Giroux, NY 1973.

2. Miller, D.: "The Ether-Drift Experiment and the Determination of the Absolute Motion of the Earth", *Reviews of Modern Physics*, Vol.5(2), p.203-242, July 1933; also see: DeMeo, J.: "Dayton Miller's Ether-Drift Experiments: A Fresh Look", *Pulse of the Planet*, 5:114-130, 2002; Allais, M.: "The Experiments of Dayton C. Miller (1925-1926) and the Theory of Relativity", *Pulse of the Planet* 5:131-136, 2002.

3. Reich, W.: *The Orgone Energy Accumulator: Its Scientific and Medical use*, Orgone Inst. Press, Maine, 1951; also see: DeMeo, J.: *The Orgone Accumulator Handbook*, Natural Energy, Oregon, 1989.

4. Reich, W. (1952): "DOR Removal and Cloud-Busting", *Orgone Energy Bull.*, IV(4):171-182. (reprinted in Reich, *Selected Writings*, Farrar, Straus & Giroux, NY, 1960, 1973); Reich, W. (1954): "OROP Desert. Part 1: Spaceships, DOR and Drought", *Cosmic Orgone Engineering*, VI(1-4):1-140; Reich, W. (1955): "Expedition OROP Desert, Ea: DOR Clouds Over the USA", *Cosmic Orgone Engineering*, VII(1-2):4-19; Reich, W. (1957): *Contact With Space, Oranur Second Report: Orop Desert Ea*, Core Pilot Press, NY.

5. Reich, *Cosmic Superimposition*, ibid.

6. Reich, *Ether, God & Devil*, ibid, p.150.

7. Reich, W.: "OROP Desert Project", *Cosmic Orgone Engineering* (CORE) VI(1-4):46-47, July 1954.

8. Tannahill, I.: *Hurricanes*, Princeton U. Press, 1945.

9. Petterssen, S.: *Weather Analysis and Forecasting*, McGraw-Hill, 1940.

10. Besides Reich, I would point to the various works of Richard Blasband and Jerome Eden, as listed in the *Bibliography on Orgone Biophysics*, Natural Energy, Oregon 1986.

11. DeMeo, J.: Preliminary Analysis of Changes in Kansas Weather Coincidental to Experimental Operations with a Reich Cloudbuster, Thesis, Geography-Meteorology Dept., Univ. of Kansas, Lawrence 1979; "Field Experiments With the Reich Cloudbuster: 1977-1983", *J. Orgonomy*, 19(1):57-79, 1985; DeMeo, J. & Morris, R.: "Preliminary Report on a Cloudbusting Experiment in the Southeastern Drought Region, August 1986", *Southeastern Drought Symposium Proceedings*, March 4-5, 1987, Columbia, SC., South Carolina State Climatology Office Publication G-30, pp.80-87, 198; "CORE Progress Report #20: Breaking the Drought Barriers in the Southwest and Northwest USA", *Journal of Orgonomy*, 23(1):97-125, 1989.

12. DeMeo, J.: "Orop Israel 1991-1992: A Cloudbusting Experiment to Restore Wintertime Rains to Israel and the Eastern Mediterranean During an Extended Period of Drought", *Pulse of the Planet*, 4:92-98, 1993; DeMeo, J.: "CORE Report #30: The Desert Greening Project in Israel 1991-1992", Journal of Orgonomy, 26(2):248-265, 1992; DeMeo, J.: "OROP Namibia 1992-1993", *Pulse of the Planet #4, On Wilhelm Reich and Orgonomy*, p.115; DeMeo, J.: "Green Sea Eritrea: A 5-Year Desert-Greening CORE Project in the SE African-Sahel", Pulse of the Planet 5:183-211, 2002.

13. Kelley, C.: "Orgone Energy and Weather", *Cosmic Orgone Engineering*, VII(1-2):54-67, March 1955.

14. Drawings adapted from Strahler, A.N. & Strahler A.H.: *Geography and Man's Environment*, John Wiley, NY, 1977, p.26.

15. Giffiths, J.F. & Driscoll, D.M.: *Survey of Climatology*, Charles E. Merrill, Columbus, 1982, p.82.

16. Reiter, E.R.: *Jet Stream Meteorology*, Univ. Chicago Press, Chicago, 1963, p.2.

17. DeMeo, J.: "Reconciling Miller's Ether-Drift With Reich's Dynamic Orgone", *Pulse of the Planet*, 5:137-146, 2002.

18. Nogues-Paegle, E. & Z. Zhen: "The Australian Subtropical Jet and the Second Observing Period of the Global Weather Experiment", *J. Atmospheric Sci.* 44:2277-2289, 15 Aug. 1987. See esp. Figure 6C on p.2282.

19. Reich, *Cosmic Superimposition*, ibid, p.225, 253; *OROP Desert*, ibid, p.91.

The Orgone Energy Motor*
by James DeMeo, Ph.D.**

In 1948 and 1949, Dr. Wilhelm Reich published several reports on a newly discovered motor force in the orgone energy continuum.[1,2] Reich had previously discovered the existence of a spontaneously pulsating, mass-free energy, which he called the orgone,[1,3] and published many papers on methods to objectify it and demonstrate its existence and properties.[4] His reports of 1948-49 were, however, the first indication that the orgone had the capability to be harnessed to run a motor. If proven correct, Reich's work here would constitute a major breakthrough in electrical energy production, wherein energy could be drawn directly from the cosmic energy substrate, anywhere, as if "from the air".

The orgone motor developed from previous experiments which Reich did on the nature of radioactivity, and its relationship to orgone energy.[5] Reich's experiments indicated that the pulses in the Geiger-Muller (GM) counter were not derived solely from nuclear disintegrations, but from an increased pulsatory activity created within the orgone energy continuum surrounding the radioactive materials. He made special glass and metal GM tubes — composed of parallel capacitor-type metal plates inside the glass tube, with an isolated wire stretched in between — and charged them up inside an orgone energy accumulator.

These special GM tubes, which he called *vacor tubes*, were evacuated to vacuum levels well below that at which ionization would occur (0.5 micron). Initially, the vacor tubes would not yield any pulses, nor would they respond to the influences of radioactive materials, as expected according to classical nuclear radiation theory. However, when the tubes had been sufficiently charged up inside a strong orgone energy accumulator, the vacor tubes would not only respond to background radiation, but would give substantially higher pulse rates than expected, on the order of hundreds to thousands of counts per second. Other inexplicable phenomenon were recorded with the vacor tubes. For example, small radioactive sources kept inside heavy lead containers would normally fail to register counts on a standard GM apparatus, but would register very high counts on the vacor tube/GM apparatus, even when the radioactive sources were kept behind the lead shield. Moreover, it was possible to maintain those very high count rates at very low exciting voltages, in defiance of conventional theory on the GM counter. Reich eventually replaced the pulse-counter circuit of the GM counter with a small motor, finding that its rotation would vary according to the strength or charge of the orgone energy.

Reich later determined that the motor, described as a Western Electric KS-9154, could be made to run more directly from the orgone, without the use of vacor tubes. It would run when hooked up to a special antenna, or to earth ground, or to an orgone energy accumulator; it would also turn when influenced by the energy field of a living creature. In this sense, the motor appears similar to another invention of Reich's, the orgone energy field meter.[1] The motor would also vary in its rate of rotation depending upon the weather; Reich had previously observed that the orgone energy charge inside his accumulators and vacor tubes would vary according to prevailing meteorology.

Reich's orgone motor exhibited other unusual properties. The motor could reverse its direction of motion quite spontaneously, and do so without significant slowing down or speeding back up in the reverse direction, as if defying the known laws of inertia. The full details of Reich's orgone motor were never published, although they may eventually surface when the Reich archives are opened after 2007 AD, as specified in his will. Reich never revealed one specific aspect of the invention, which he called the "Y-factor". However, operations of the motor were witnessed by a number of Reich's co-workers, some of whom have published their own eye-witness accounts, reproduced below.

"...it involved the use of an accumulator attached to a wheel [motor]; concentrated orgone energy was triggered by a small amount of electricity, an amount insufficient to rotate the wheel without the accumulator. I also recall that when the wheel was rotated entirely by electricity, it had a steady grinding motion. When powered by the combination of orgonotic and electrical energy, it ran smoothly and quietly; but its speed varied depending upon the weather — more rapidly on dry, clear days, more slowly when the humidity was high."

- Myron Sharaf [6]

"Reich first used vacor tubes in series attached to a small accumulator and connected to a transformer to build up an electrical charge to excite the orgone energy. He used four or five vacor tubes. All were

* Original monograph circulated since 1986.
** Director, Orgone Biophysical Research Lab, Greensprings, PO Box 1148, Ashland, Oregon 97520 USA. Tel-Fax: 541-552-0118 Email: demeo@mind.net

connected to a 25 volt electric motor.... Reich took away one vacor tube after another until all were taken away, and still the motor ran. The important ingredient was the so-called "Y factor" which Reich did not divulge. The motor ran on 1/2 volt of electricity and was noisy and wobbly. On orgone energy, it was practically noiseless and ran smoother and faster. At times, it would change direction. In damp weather, it would not run."

- Elsworth Baker [7]

"The one I saw was about the size of a large orange... It was hooked up to a special OR [orgone] accumulator with a "Y" factor that Reich did not divulge as he felt mankind was not ready to use such a potentially boundless power rationally. It was also connected to an electrical source with very low voltage because, as I remember it, the unexcited orgone energy by itself couldn't overcome the initial inertia. But it ran on atmospheric orgone energy fed to it through the accumulator and also from the human energy field... it ran erratically, as no motor with a mechanical energy source does: It slowed down and speeded up without any interference. Also, if one curved his hands over the motor, it picked up speed, and with one's hands over it, it also speeded up and slowed down,... the motor using orgone energy did something no motor using mechanical energy can do: It reversed itself every once in a while without slowing down, even without a jolt."(8:185)

- Lois Wyvell [8]

Other eyewitness reports were made of the motor in action, but these are lacking in detail.[9, 10, 11]

Reich made motion pictures of the motor in operation, and these have been preserved, transferred to videotape, and are now on display at the Wilhelm Reich Museum in Rangeley, Maine.[12] The Museum films, which I have seen, show the clock-type pulse counter of the GM apparatus spinning very rapidly when it is hooked up to a variety of orgone sources. The motor appears to have initially been connected to its high-voltage DC source, as a method for "priming the pump", but in all the sequences, Reich finally holds the unconnected end of the high voltage wire from the GM circuitry away from the motor, to show that it is not connected to the motor, which continues turning. In one sequence, the motor is hooked up to a "D" cell flashlight battery, but will not turn until Reich places his hand on the battery. The motor then starts turning, until his hand is withdrawn. The closer the hand to the battery, the faster the turning of the motor. Hence the confusions between his sometimes using a D-cell battery, which might also be removed while keeping the AC source, or vice-versa.

In another sequence in the Museum films, a series of capacitor-plate vacor tubes are hooked up to the motor, which continues to turn without use of the high voltage connection, or the battery, or the proximity of a hand. There does not appear to be an accumulator in the circuit, but it may simply be at another spot on the table, and therefore does not show up on the film. The same is true for antenna or Earth-ground attachments, which are discussed by Reich in other contexts. These films also show the motor spontaneously reversing its direction of spin.

In 1949, one of Reich's assistants, William Washington, who had worked on the motor with Reich for several prior summers, disappeared with one of the orgone motors.[6,9,14] Reich felt the man was being coerced or held against his will by the one of the US government agencies, or possibly by communist agents, as part of efforts, he felt, to obtain the secrets of his discovery. Reich contacted the FBI about the matter, and as revealed in recently-obtained internal FBI files, Washington was finally located; in a telephone interview he indicated he had left of his own free will, possibly only behaving irresponsibly rather than being coerced.[13] Mr. Washington recently surfaced during a visit to the Wilhelm Reich Museum, however, and more information about the episode may be forthcoming.

In the early 1970s, when I first heard of Reich's work with the orgone energy motor, I wrote the Western Electric company for specifications on the KS-9154 motor which Reich was able to set into motion with orgone energy. Copies of the specifications remaining in the Western Electric files on this motor were sent to me. These documents primarily contained information regarding quality control measures, casing specifications, and so forth, but did indicate that the motor possessed the following general characteristics.

Western Electric Motor #KS-9154
Spinner type
18 volts (for use with 12 volt system)
60 cycles
2 phase
Dimensions: 2-15/16" diameter, 4-1/16" long

There is a remote possibility the motor may have been rewired by Reich, and there also is no guarantee that he used the specified voltages given the unorthodox nature of his experimental work. The motor may be similar, or identical to that which powered the rotary pulse indicator of the original GM apparatus used in Reich's radiation experiments.

To the above, the following points can be added.

1. Folk wisdom holds that a dead flashlight battery will temporarily be brought back to life by placing it in a freezer for a day or two. I have found that this is so, but on several occasions, the same result has been achieved by placing the batteries inside a strong orgone accumulator for a week or two. Specifically, the small battery powered digital clocks respond quite well to this influ-

ence, and can sometimes be brought back to life after their batteries have gone totally dead. However, these small clocks (and similar ones run by "potato power", etc.) require extremely small amounts of current. Regardless, it does demonstrate the spontaneous development of electrical charge within the accumulator, a principle which is in agreement with another verified finding of Reich: an orgone energy accumulator can slow down the spontaneous discharge, or "natural leak" of a charged electroscope, and under special conditions may charge up to higher levels an electroscope which is only weakly charged.[15] In fact, there are an entire series of functioning electrostatic motors which use an antenna, earth-ground, and radiation sources for power, and nothing more (see the article to follow).

2. In the mid-1990s, a public debate occurred on internet between researchers Doug Marett and Paulo Correa suggesting that, besides the KS-9154 spinner motor, there were other variations such as the KS-8624 which were of similar construction. They additionally discussed the use of aluminum for construction of the rotor cup, confirming this author's belief that the device worked by virtue of eddy currents — which remain a mysterious force in nature, hardly understood in a deep manner though put to practical use by engineers.

3. Michael Rothenberg, an orgonomist who worked with Reich at Orgonon during the same summer when Myron Sharaf was there, informed me in 1999 of the following, which provides additional clues:

A) The motor itself was regularly soaked inside a strong orgone energy accumulator, and

B) A 110 volt AC current was "passed through some sort of converter before going into the motor; then the plug was pulled". Again, this suggests, the motor was firstly hooked up to run in exactly the manner as will be described shortly by Nick Reiter, but in at least one type of set-up, the AC source was removed.

4. During one of the Greensprings Independent Study Seminars, a team of students succeeded in getting a surplus KS-9154 motor to function, by feeding in a normal 60-cycle AC power source to one phase of the motor wiring, and by using capacitors to create an out-of-phase signal into the second phase. We could not, in the limited time available, get the motor to function in any unusual or extraordinary manner, but it was clear that the delicate construction of the motor would not require any significant quantity of energy to make it turn. Even a small quantity of electricity as generated from an orgone energy source, would be sufficient. A former Naval electronics engineer in attendance pointed out to the assembled group that the KS-9154 spinner motors were well-known in naval circles as "synchro motors", or more simply as *synchros*, and were widely used for radar targeting of large naval or anti-aircraft guns. One can, for example, find quite a lot of descriptive information on synchro motors in libraries and on internet.[16]

The above paragraphs summarize what is known about the orgone motor, the components of which include all or part of the following:

KS-9154, 8624 or similar synchro drag-cup motor
Vacor-type Vacuum Tube with Capacitor Plates
Earth-Field Antenna and Earth Ground
Orgone Accumulator
Temporary AC/DC "priming" sources
"Y-factor" circuitry

With focused work, and the above information, it should be possible to re-create Reich's orgone motor discovery.

References:

1. Reich, W.: *The Cancer Biopathy*, (Vol. 2, Discovery of the Orgone), Orgone Institute Press, 1948 (see section on "A motor force in orgone energy", p.127; also, p.125-126).

2. Reich, W.: "A Motor Force in the Orgone Energy. Preliminary Communications", *Orgone Energy Bulletin*, I(1):7-11, 1949.

3. Reich, W.: *Function of the Orgasm, Vol. 1, Discovery of the Orgone*, Orgone Institute Press, NY, 1942.

4. See the various listings in DeMeo, J.: *Bibliography on Orgone Biophysics*, Natural Energy Works, Ashland, 1986.

5. Reich, W.: *The Oranur Experiment, First Report (1947-1951)*, Wilhelm Reich Foundation, Orgone Institute Press, Rangeley, Maine, 1951.

6. Sharaf, M.: *Fury on Earth: A Biography of Wilhelm Reich*, St. Martin's/Marek, NY, 1983, p.354-355.

7. Baker, E.F.: "My Eleven Years With Reich (Part II)", *J. Orgonomy*, 11(1):15-34, 1977; see p.28.

8. Wyvell, L.: "An Appreciation of Reich", *J. Orgonomy*, 7(2):170-186, 1973; see p. 185.

9. Ollendorff-Reich, I.: *Wilhelm Reich, A Personal Biography*, St. Martin's, NY, 1969, p.86, 94.

10. Neill, A.S.: *Neill, Neill, Orange Peel! An Autobiography by A.S. Neill*, Hart Publishing, NY, 1970, p.192.

11. Neill, A.S.: "The Man Reich", in *Wilhelm Reich Memorial Volume*, Ritter Press, Nottingham, 1958, reprinted in Boadella, D.: *Wilhelm Reich, the Evolution of His Work*, Henry Regenery, Chicago, 1973, p.382.

12. The Wilhelm Reich Museum, Orgonon, Rangeley, Maine, 04970; open to the public during summer months.

13. Greenfield, J.: letter to the editor (point #2), *J. Orgonomy*, 16(2):285-288, 1982.

14. Reich, W.: *The Red Thread of a Conspiracy*, William Washington Supplement, Wilhelm Reich Biographical Material, History of the Discovery of the Life Energy, Documentary Supplement No.2, A-XII-EP, Orgone Inst. Press, Maine, 1955.

15. Reich, W.: "Thermal and Electroscopical Orgonometry", *Int. J. Sex-Economy & Orgone Research*, III:1-16, 1944; see other citations on the electroscope in reference #4, above.

16. For example, see: Brite, R.J. & C.H. Fioranelli: *Synchros and Servos*, Howard Sams, NY, 1967; also *Basic Synchros and Servos*, 1955. Old military electronic manuals dating to c.1950 also cover the subject quite well.

Examination of the Western Electric KS-9154 Motor

by Nicholas A. Reiter*

Background

In early December 1998, I received a copy of the surplus electronics catalog from Fair Radio in Lima, Ohio. For many years, Fair Radio has provided rare finds for electronics and Tesla coil hobbyists. Many of their parts are pulls from military surplus equipment, some going back decades.

In this particular issue, I was utterly surprised to find listed a WWII-era motor, which I had searched for in vain for nearly 10 years. This motor was the Western Electric KS-9154, the small two phase motor used by Dr. Wilhelm Reich in his orgone motor experiments of 1947-1949.

Many orgone energy experimenters and Reich historians have pursued the curious and enigmatic tale of the orgone motor. Most leads come to a halt, quite short of the full story and its outcome.

Dr. James DeMeo of the Orgone Biophysical Research Lab in Ashland, Oregon was key among individuals trying to piece together the orgone motor story. In the late 1980s, he put together a helpful dossier of all available information on the KS-9154 motor which came to his attention. Yet all combined, the amount of data on the motor was limited, and nobody, to my knowledge, had been able to procure one of the motors in the 5 decades since Dr. Reich caused one to rotate using pulsating orgone energy.

I ordered several of the KS-9154 motors from Fair Radio, and within a week had them sitting on my kitchen table. These were certainly the same unit as can be seen sitting on a workbench in an old photo of one of the lab rooms at Orgonon (Dr. Reich's lab), as well as seen in an archival film once shown at the Wilhelm Reich Museum. These were the same motors that Dr. Wilhelm Reich caused to spin with the energy of the orgone continuum; and though as non-scientific as it may sound, I regarded the little devices before me with a quiet and slightly reverent awe.

At this point, before moving on to the observations from my physical examination of one of the motors, I wish to add two historical footnotes with commentary.

The original orgone motor at Orgonon was, at one time, stolen in a 1970s theft at the Wilhelm Reich Museum. The thief, who was subsequently caught and incarcerated, confessed to have taken the unit to a motor shop for disassembly and examination. The mechanic on duty said, it is claimed, that he had never seen such a motor before. The small rotor appeared to be a hollow cylinder of metal, and ceramic or wooden chunks fell out of the stator upon disassembly. Four wires terminated from the stator. Supposedly, the motor did not turn when AC current was applied, nor with DC, but only slowly and jerkily when pulsed DC power was applied. It was not specified to which leads the mechanic had applied power.

Around the same time, in the late 1970s, I contacted Mr. Joe Daniels of Long Island, an electrical instrumentation engineer who claims to have acted as a consultant to Dr. Reich at the time of the orgone motor experiments. Daniels claimed to have been the one who procured the KS-9154 servo-motors for Reich, and that the units had come from off the shelf at a local surplus house.

Daniels was surprisingly skeptical about the supposedly enigmatic rotational actions of the orgone-con-

The KS-9154 Western Electric Spinner Motor, obtained from a surplus electronics shop.

* Photovoltaics Engineer, Gibsonburg, Ohio.
Email: <reit@ezworks.net>

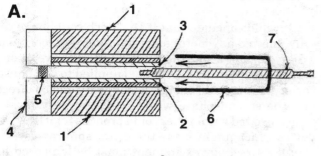

A.

B.

1. Stator
2. Cd Plated Steel Sleeve
3. Brass Sleeve
4. Brass End Bell (1 of 2)
5. Bearing (1 of 2)
6. Copper Rotor
7. Shaft (Steel)

nected motors. He felt that the effect was probably due to out-of-phase AC signals coming into the secondary winding of the motor by induction, or EMI (electromagnetic induction). However, Daniels recalled other experiments, and felt that the orgone was real, and that the To-T and vacor lumination experiments of Reich were genuine. To the best of Joe Daniel's recollection, the KS-9154 was typical of two-phase servo-motors used at the time for positioning or instrument driving. He claimed to not be aware of the later portion of the orgone motor story involving William Washington.

Physical Description:

The KS-9154 is, to the first glance, a beautiful and cunningly wrought device. It is about 3 inch diameter by about 4 inch long, with brass end bells. The central portion of the motor consists of the laminated steel stator, traversed by eight brass studs holding the end bells together. The shaft end is fitted with a small spring-loaded bakelite sprocket or gear. From the opposite end bell, four fiberglass jacketed wires with eyelets emerge.

One curious feature of the motor is that there does not seem to be any holes, lugs, pads or feet for mounting the motor to anything. It is unclear how the unit would have been secured. Most motors have end plate holes or feet with holes for horizontal mounting. Additionally, a colleague of mine commented that brass components were often the hallmark of naval use, however the known spec sheet for the motor lists it as a 60hz device as opposed to the 400hz often used for military applications, suggesting it was made for ordinary powerline voltages.

One of the motors was set aside for safekeeping, while the other was taken apart for examination.

Disassembly was not difficult but required a nut driver, as locknuts were used at either end of the shaft to draw up to small ball bearings sets.

Upon removal of the rotor and shaft, there is a very unusual geometry. The rotor proper consists of about a 1 inch diameter by about 2.5 inch long hollow cylinder of copper, open at one end, and affixed to the shaft at the other. The rotor cylinder has a wall thickness of about 1/16 inch.

When assembled, the rotor "cup" fits into a gap between the outer stator poles, and a central stator cylinder. The shaft passes through a hole in the central cylinder. This central cylinder consists of an inner brass sleeve, and an outer sleeve of a silvery metal. A small scraping was removed from this portion and analyzed. The silvery outer sleeve appears to be soft iron or steel which is cadmium plated to prevent rusting (see sketches A and B).

Electrical Description

The motor contains two phases, with six poles per phase (twelve stator poles all together). The windings are somewhat crude, and small wooden spacers are inserted into the stator slots to retain them, in agreement with the description heard years ago. The motor leads are connected such that the red and red-striped wires are one phase, while the green and green-striped wires are the other. Both phase windings are of the same resistance, about 7.5 ohms. All stator poles are equidistant.

Operational Description

When reassembled, we connected the motor up to a variable transformer, set at 12 volts AC output. The red phase leads were the ones connected to the AC. With no power applied to the second phase, no rotation occurs.

We then parallel the green phase with the red, thus applying in-phase power to both (at the same AC voltage). As expected from knowledge of two-phase servos, no rotation occurred. Next, a 1.0 microfarad capacitor was put in series with the green phase. This time, as per expectations, the phase shift caused the motor to spin at a modest clip.

So far, all actions resembled those of a standard servo-motor.

Next, we tried connecting the green phase wires to a small DC power supply, at about 3 volts. Surprisingly, the motor began turning slowly. A pair of D-cell batteries was substituted with the same result.

Next, we took a 9-volt battery and connected it to the green phase. No rotation occurred, only a jittering (from insufficient current?). However, when we taped one green wire to a battery terminal with the other firmly connected, at the moment of contact the motor spun rapidly for a few turns. Thus, it appears to respond to fast current spikes or pulses!

Operational Conclusions

The KS-9154 design is unique, however, not unheard of. It falls under the category of a drag cup or reluctance cup motor. The theory of operation is reasonably straightforward. A reference AC voltage is applied to one phase. The magnetic flux resulting from the current is coupled through the copper rotor and ferrous central stator, inducing eddy currents in the copper rotor. When a signal is applied to the second phase, there develops a reaction motor force which spins the rotor, as long as the flux is not in phase with the reference signal. The direction of rotation depends on the phase relationship, and can change very rapidly as the secondary signal changes.

Most two-phase servo-motors utilize a more standard rotor, with bars and laminations which provide phase shift rotation with reasonable torque. The KS-9154 motor by contrast was apparently meant for a very low-torque application, where precision of speed, direction, and immediate response (change of direction) was needed instead. Thus, almost any current applied to the second phase winding, except in-phase AC, will cause the motor to spin at least slightly.

It certainly gives cause to ponder that the mode which caused a vigorous rotation was the one with short impulses applied to the second phase from the 9 volt battery. The timing of these pulses is critical, and can cause the rotor to spin either way depending on where the AC flux is at, phase-wise. One of Dr. Reich's observations was that the orgone operated motor would change direction abruptly and randomly, which finds agreement with my observations.

Discussion

I would conclude that if Dr. Reich could have carefully selected any motor for orgone energy experiments, a drag cup motor like the KS-9154 would have been the best choice. With low AC signal applied to one phase, a variety of sources of energetic impulse could be directed into the second phase with interesting results. Certainly, excited vacor tubes could produce high frequency pulses which might make the motor spin rapidly.

Of course, our excitement must be tempered by a couple of factors. First of all, we still do not know the nature of the mysterious "Y function" which Dr. Reich apparently used to make his KS-9154 spin effectively. In a conversation about 1989, one of Dr. Reich's former assistants, Myron Sharaf, insisted that while he did not know what the "Y" was, he certainly felt that it was a physical component or "thing" rather than a wiring scheme or connection geometry.

Secondly, we do not know whether Dr. Reich ever succeeded in running a motor entirely from the orgone, without AC on one phase. If William Washington is still alive, he is probably the only person who might possibly know.

Nevertheless, a significant portion of the orgone motor mystery has now been brought out into the open light of day. By understanding the operation of the KS-9154, as well as the other components used by Dr. Reich in his study of orgone physics, we might very well be able to replicate those famous experimental results which have eluded so many for so long.

The Earth-Atmosphere Electrical Potential as a Possible Source of Energy*
by James DeMeo, Ph.D.

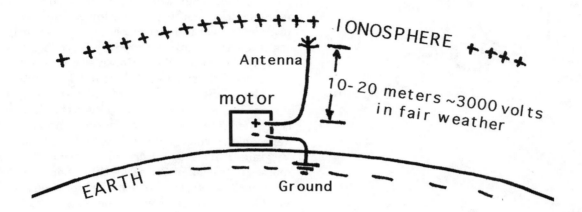

Editor's Note:
The following discussion addresses what is perhaps the only genuine and fully proven "free energy" type of motor, using electrostatic principles. It is included here, as the principles appear related to Reich's orgone motor. As recently as 1990, experimenters in San Francisco were using similar principles to power small digital clocks and charge batteries. The following discussion was penned around 1980, for a university seminar.

The Earth is negatively charged and is a reservoir for electrons. As one gains altitude the potential difference in electrical charge between the Earth's surface and that elevated point increases. In fair weather, this potential difference can rise to several hundred volts per meter height. The fair weather potential between the surface-ground and ionosphere may reach hundreds of thousands of volts. There are, however, problems to the simple tapping of this potential as a source of energy.

Firstly, while the voltages involved are high, the amount of current which is available to flow, the amperage, is extremely low. The electrical charges are also diffusely spread in the atmosphere and a large area of collectors would be needed to gather them. Such collectors may take the form of a wire mesh of high surface area, or metal antenna with many sharp points. While it is difficult to build a large area collector at a high altitude for connection into an earth-grounded circuit, a useful power of around 3000 volts may be available in clear weather from an antenna of only 10-20 meters in height. The current provided in such an hypothetical set-up would be high voltage, low amperage direct

current. Standard magnet-and-coil electrical motors would not function in such a circuit. Only *electrostatic* motors would function, as opposed to electromagnetic motors, when hooked to such an earth-field antenna.

Earth-field antennas can be made from almost any conductor topped with a point or many points. By one theory, the points collect static charges from the atmosphere, much like a lightning rod. Since the antenna wire conducts these charges towards the Earth more readily than the air, which is an insulator, a current is set up in the wire. A small radioactive alpha source, when placed near the antenna point, will increase ionization of the surrounding atmosphere, and facilitate further flow of current in the wire. Antennas can be constructed free-standing, or held aloft with a helium weather balloon.

The motors used with such a current are conceptually simple: An object is positively charged by contact with the Earth-field antenna. It is then automatically repelled by the antenna as it now has the same electrical polarity as the antenna. The charged object swings, in pendulum fashion, or rotates on a needle balance away from the antenna and is simultaneously attracted towards an earth-grounded electrode which holds a negative charge. Contact between the pendulating or revolving object and the Earth-ground is made, neutralizing the charge originally obtained from the antenna. The object then obtains the same negative electrical charge as the Earth ground, and is now repelled back towards the positive antenna, which begins to attract it also.

Thus, the static charge is converted into a pulsed bidirectional or rotary motion. Modern electrostatic motors spray charges from the Earth-field antenna onto a charge-adhering drum via knife-edge electrodes. The antenna-charged knife-edges induce or spray charges

* Original version presented c.1980, Seminar at the University of Kansas, Geography-Meteorology Dept.

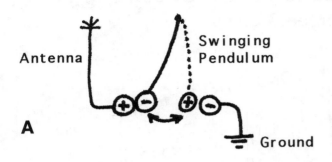

A

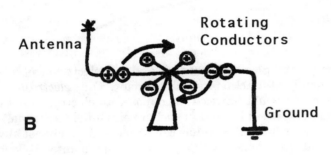

B

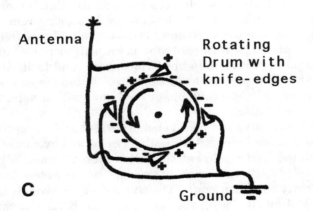

C

on the drum, which then rotates towards another set of knife-edges connected to Earth-ground where the accumulated charges are absorbed off the drum. Drum-type electrostatic motors can achieve very high speeds of revolution.

Such electrostatic motors have been built since the mid-1700s and were the first electrical motors ever to be constructed. They were largely constructed as amusement devices, or as toys for children, due to their lack of practical power production. Most of these early electrostatic devices were powered by Leyden jars or other early batteries or "piles". However, some were operated via Earth-field antennas of around 7-10 meters height.

The quality and power of these small electrostatic motors has steadily increased over the decades, given continued research and use of better materials. Dr. Oleg Jefimenko, formerly at the Physics Department of West Virginia University, described many novel electrostatic motors in a book of the same title. Some of the drum-type electrostatic motors achieved rotation speeds of up to 12,000 rpm, using conventional electrostatic generators providing 8-13 kilovolts. Jefimenko predicts it should be possible to make larger electrostatic motors of up to 1000 watt capacity, powered by Earth-field antennas, the science of which remains a largely unexplored territory.

References:
Jefimenko, O.: *Electrostatic Motors,* Electret Scientific Co., Star City, WV, 1973.
Chalmers, J.A.: *Atmospheric Electricity*, Pergamon Press, London, 1967.
Ford, R.A.: *Homemade Lightning*, Tab Books, NY 1996.
Moore, A.D.: *Electrostatics*, Doubleday, NY 1974.

Examples of Simple Electrostatic Devices, capable of being powered by either an electrostatic generator, or more simply by an Earth-atmosphere electrical potential.

A. Simple Pendulum, which transfers opposing charges by pushing the pendulum back and forth.

B. Rotating Conductors, which transfer opposing charges by rotating the conductor-wheel balanced on a point.

C. Rotating cylindrical drum, which obtains charges from knife-edges which "spray" charges onto the drum, which is then set into motion. All these devices have been operating for years, the simpler ones since the 1700s.

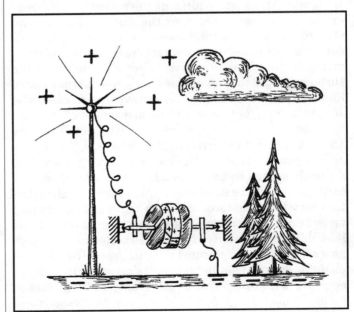

Diagram of a Working Electrostatic Motor, powered only by an Earth-field antenna and an Earth-ground, from Oleg Jefimenko's *Electrostatic Motors*, 1973, p.116.

Renewable, "Free" Energy from Nature:
Personal Experiences and Net-Energy Analysis*
by James DeMeo, Ph.D.**

Introduction

The following paper was written in 1979, following many years of research by the author into both conventional and renewable energy systems, including a short period of entrepreneurship, in selling and installing residential solar and renewable energy equipment in South Florida. Today, with a growing energy crisis developing once again, it seems pertinent to finally publish the materials. The concept of *net energy analysis* developed as an outgrowth of computer *systems analysis*, a form of dynamic modelling of the real world with revolutionary overtones. It can give us a vision into what the world would be like — and also what the world and society could best avoid — if the ordinary person, and their elected representatives, would embrace natural renewable energy sources, or if a genuinely "free" energy was to find its way into the marketplace. The net energy diagrams presented here are basically unchanged from the original 1979 research project, but the text of the paper was lost during many moves across the country since that time. This allowed a revisiting of the issue, with some added background information regarding my own path into this subject area.

I should also mention, while the concepts of net energy were firstly pioneered by Harold Odum and his students, their diagrams and models were exceedingly complex, and often were constructed partly as flowcharts for computer programmers. In attempts to teach these principles to university students who had no such specialized skills, I came up with my own diagrams which, I feel, are more easily grasped.

Early Work on Energy, in Florida and Kansas

The energy crisis following the Arab oil-boycott of the USA, in 1973, was filled with lessons for the Western industrialized nations. These lessons were quickly forgotten once the major oil-exporting nations lifted their boycott, and allowed the oil to flow again — albeit at a highly inflated price. The USA in particular forgot these lessons, and today, with around 6% of the world's population, we consume approximately 30% of the total yearly global oil production.

At the time when the 1973 oil embargo was creating long lines of cars at gasoline stations, and power outages here and there, I was teaching courses on solar and wind-power systems at the *Miami Museum of Science*, and at several adult education centers in South Florida. Before the crisis, the attendance was small, with maybe 10 students per class. During the energy crisis, the numbers ballooned to several hundred participants, all wanting to know what could be practically done to cut their energy bills, to make their cars run on less gasoline, and so forth. There were no easy solutions, I had to inform them, that the conversion from fossil fuels to renewables took time and investment, and required political action as well.

At this same time, I was a student in Environmental Science at Florida International University, and got a reputation as the "solar guy". I was asked to give lectures on such subjects, in the University and to private groups. I teamed up with a good friend, Donald Bill, who had a company building wind-electric generators, and we proposed that a new University Environmental Science Center then under design for Virginia Key (near Miami Beach), be made into a model for renewable energy systems. We outlined a plan for wind-electric generators, solar water heating, composting toilets and solar photovoltaics — the high-ups at the university were amused, but the proposal was never given serious interest. "Sow-Lar" energy, as I would learn, was considered something of a "hippie" endeavor, derisively contrasted to "saving the whales" or "tree hugging", and laughed at by all the "serious" people (ie., the emotionally rigid, heavily-armored high-ups in the social hierarchy).

In a private effort, I formed the *Natural Energy Company*, trying to sell solar water heaters, photovoltaic systems, wind-electric generators, composting toilets, solar ovens and so forth to the general public. I was able to reduce the electrical power bill at my small rented home to $3 per month, which was the minimum-charge of Florida Power and Light (FPL) company, and on several occasions during public lectures, I locked horns with FPL representatives over the nuclear power issue. I was written up in local newspapers (usually being misrepresented as a naive kid full of unrealistic dreams), interviewed by a disinterested Larry King (now of CNN fame) when he still had a radio talk show

* Earlier version presented to *Assoc. of American Geographers*, Annual Meeting, Los Angeles, 1981.
** Director, Orgone Biophysical Research Lab, Greensprings, PO Box 1148, Ashland, Oregon 97520 USA. Tel-Fax: 541-552-0118 Email: demeo@mind.net

on Miami Beach, and invited to lunch by visibly nervous and hostile executives of FPL (my friends advised, only half-joking, "don't eat the food").

FPL had invested millions in programs to build up nuclear power plants, and also to *willfully destroy solar energy in South Florida*. Their lobbyists in the capital city of Tallahassee used their influence to insure defeat of every single item of pro-solar legislation which was proposed, and their "Gold Medallion All Electric Home" program virtually destroyed the blossoming industry for solar water-heaters in the 1950s and 60s. That program gave various high-consumption electrical appliances — electric ovens and ranges, space heaters and water heaters — to local builders *free of charge*, who would then turn around and *sell* those same appliances to the home-buyers, who had no idea about the deal. No gas or solar appliances were allowed, or the hidden pay-off to the builders would be withdrawn. Wackenhut detectives (a private security firm) were also being employed by various nuclear-powered utility companies, secretly, to investigate and keep dossiers on local citizens who had joined environmental groups, or who even wrote a letter-to-the-editor in newspapers against nuclear power. The practice was finally exposed, but probably not ever changed. This was the time, in the early 1970s, of the Nixon "dirty tricks" campaign against his political enemies, the "plumbers" and other emotional plague groups within the White House that would eventually lead to Nixon's downfall. Young people today can scarcely appreciate the dark overtones of "National Security" which existed at that time at nearly every social level, but *without* any domestic terror threat as witnessed on 9-11.

Nuclear power was declared "essential to the national security", and so anyone who questioned the safety or efficiency of nuclear energy became a "threat to national security". My research at Florida International University had uncovered multiple violations of federal regulations on the operations of FPL's Turkey Point nuclear reactors, which were close to my home. Perimeter radiation alarms for warning local residents of accidental radiation releases were routinely shut off, as the creaking and leaking reactors there were so regularly burping up clouds of radioactive gas, that the alarms would otherwise go off on a regular basis. Temporary workers — mostly local plumbers given radiation-suits and told to go inside and fix pipes leaking radioactive water — were also overexposed to potentially lethal amounts of radiation. All of this was quite illegal, but the local representatives of the Atomic Energy Commission (later, the Nuclear Regulatory Commission) were apparently asleep at the switch, or willfully turning a blind eye. Together with an odd collection of environmentalists in the *South Florida CURE (Citizen's United against a Radioactive Environment)*, I submitted testimony to Intervenor Hearings, on the issue of low-level radiation, and SF CURE basically forced FPL to install special HEPA filters on their vent stacks for a few (but not all) of their nuclear plants, to remove at least *some* of the radioactive particles from their "routine" gaseous discharges.

In this effort, even the Florida Audobon Society — a major environmental group partly responsible for saving the Everglades swamp from drainage and destruction — was against us, as they considered nuclear energy the "only rational alternative" to coal-fired power. FPL officials had frightened nearly everyone into accepting nuclear power by posing the horrific scenario of regular five-mile-long freight trains, loaded with coal and limerock (for stack scrubbers), making their way down to South Florida every few days. Nobody wanted to talk about the solar-wind alternative. The woman then leading the Audobon Society came from a family owning a chain of stores selling microwave ovens, and was adamant that low-level radiation, of any sort, was harmless. Perhaps she suspected that criticism of nuclear power might spill over into criticism of microwave ovens. It was a tremendous learning experience, and a good fight, but I tired of only being *against* nuclear power. I wanted to be *for* renewable energy, *for* nature, and so focused more of my time into private efforts to sell and install renewable energy equipment, through my Natural Energy Company.

What I learned, unfortunately, was that older people who had accumulated expendable income sufficient to purchase the renewable energy devices were basically too fearful, or too full of hatred for living nature, to take such steps. One very wealthy man actually asked me *"If I buy your solar energy system, what happens to my stock in American Oil Company?"* I could only respond: *"What happens to the future of your grandchildren if everyone in your position takes that attitude? Are you willing to sacrifice your sons, to fight foreign wars for oil, instead of doing this?"* This kind of response was rarely effective in closing a sale, unfortunately. On the other side of the equation, I was contacted repeatedly by enthusiastic young people, and a few middle-aged working people with families, who needed no convincing and who wanted to purchase the equipment, but who could not afford it. Instead, they deluged me with questions on how the devices were constructed, how could they build it themselves — such information was always openly given. And so I found myself to be a much better educator than salesman. Natural Energy Company was eventually retired, I sold off my inventory at cost, and focused on educational efforts.

At this same time, I was deeply interested in the various discoveries on "Free Energy" as reflected in the works of individuals such as Townsend Brown, Henry Moray, and Wilhelm Reich. These were new areas, certainly "renewable" in the sense of harnessing a natural cosmic energy, but quite beyond the usual more mechanical considerations regarding solar energy or wind power. While I have yet to personally see a working "free energy" device that produces power beyond that necessary to run a small LCD clock, or a small motor which could be stopped by a tiny friction with your finger against the rotating element, these are at least *starting points*, and I continue to have much hope in this direction.

By the late 1970s, I had departed Florida for the University of Kansas, pursuing an advanced degree in a program where I had the golden opportunity to openly investigate Reich's life-energetic discoveries. However, I still maintained my interests in the broader issues of renewable versus non-renewable energy systems. At one point, with help from the KU faculty, I obtained a grant from the Solar Energy Research Institute (SERI) for *Development of a University-Level Undergraduate Curricula on Renewable Energy Systems,* teaching the revolutionary concepts to several hundred students.[§] Jimmy Carter was the President at that time, and the USA was being punished by the Arab/Muslim dictatorships for providing the Israelis with sufficient weaponry to defend themselves against the much larger Arab military machines, then armed to the teeth by the Soviets. The Iranian Revolution occurred on Carter's watch, as Iranians threw out the authoritarian Shah of Iran in favor of the totalitarian religious fanatic, and world class woman-hater, Ayatollah Khomeini.

While the Shah killed his political enemies, Khomeini's thugs killed not only their political enemies, but also various non-Islamic groups such as the Bahais, and any western-oriented women his "religious cops" could get their hands on. Iranian "students" kidnapped the US Embassy staff in Teheran, holding them hostage for over a year, and Carter instituted economic retaliations. OPEC (Organization of Petroleum Exporting Countries) thereafter dramatically jacked up the price for raw crude oil, creating big economic problems in the West. The right-wing blamed Carter for loss of Iran to Khomeini, and for the high gasoline prices and double-digit inflation, while the left blamed him for showing any backbone at all against the "spiritual" Khomeini. I can still remember various naive students proclaiming "a spiritual revolution is just what Iran needs", and then going silent as Khomeini began executing women, in the manner of the Saudis, for such "crimes" as driving a car, or going without a veil, speaking to an unrelated male, or for carrying birth-control pills. Similar airheads in the academic world, years later, could be heard talking about the "wonderful spirituality" of the Talibans, and how "a veil can be liberating". For myself, who grew up on the tropical beaches of Florida, where "liberating your spirit" meant to *take off as much clothing as you could legally get away with*, and go naked on the beach, it was not a good time. But the connections between oil supply, monetary inflation, domestic energy politics and sexual politics became increasingly clear. To get oil, the Western nations were quite willing to sell their principles on democracy, personal freedom and human rights, down the drain.

President Carter was a nuclear engineer by training, which may explain why he never strongly pushed the nuclear power "solution" for the USA. He staffed *SERI* with workers who were genuinely interested in energy conservation and renewable energy resources, such as solar energy, wind power and biomass. The soaring economic inflation created by the oil embargo led to his defeat in the presidential race against Ronald Reagan, but not before SERI produced a documentary blueprint showing how the USA could become energy independent by the year 2000. The blueprint — which Reagan unsuccessfully attempted to block from publication by firing SERI leaders and staff sympathetic to its solar-energy mission — called for a dramatic shift in the government's energy policy and spending priorities, away from the gargantuan tax breaks and give-away programs for coal, oil and nuclear power, and towards well-proven conservation efforts, and to solar and wind power systems. The SERI blueprint was published, but its recommendations were supported only by the environmental groups, and not a single Republican or Democratic leader in the USA has since taken up the issue with comparable vigor. The American public went back to sleep, content to pay triple at the gas pumps, and oblivious to the growing international environmental and social catastrophes which lay ahead: the meltdown of Three Mile Island and Chernobyl nuclear power plants, multiple oil spills at sea (the Exxon Valdez, etc.), widespread destruction and strip mining of pristine landscapes across the USA, the growing problems of water and air pollution, and their attendant climatic effects. Add to the list, the growing economic power of the fascist oil-exporting states of the Middle East and Persian Gulf (such as Iraq, Iran, Syria, and Saudi Arabia) whose undisguised contempt for human freedom and secular democratic traditions has led to numerous regional wars, along with the financing and global spread of fanatical Islamic misogyny and terrorism.

The Concept of Net Energy

At Kansas, a group of my students and fellow solar-enthusiasts later developed an Appropriate Technology Resource Center in Lawrence, Kansas, encouraging the state and local government, for awhile, to sponsor energy conservation and solar workshops for local citizens.

[§] This course was attacked, in a letter-writing campaign, by representatives of the American Nuclear Society. A similar course I proposed to teach at Illinois State University some years later was also attacked, and ended, by a conspiracy of various faculty who were then acquiring large grants from the nuclear industry and government, to basically white-wash problems at the Morris, Illinois nuclear waste facility. This kind of blockade against new ideas is unfortunately all-too common in the academic world.

I became familiar with the field of cybernetics, or systems analysis, and learned also to program computers and create dynamic models of complex natural and man-made systems. The writings of Howard Odum on the concept of net energy were most interesting on this point, as one could make a dynamic model of an entire ecosystem, and then predict what would happen if it was disturbed in some manner. An ecosystem could be modelled by a computer program, which would for example calculate how many rabbits would be eaten by the existing number of predatory birds each day, and how much grass was eaten by the rabbits, how much sunlight and water were available to grow the grass, and so on. Once the computer model was properly constructed, you could see what happened to the overall system when rainfall declined, or when the predatory birds were killed off by hunters or pesticides. In the former case, the grass would decline, followed by a decline in both rabbit and bird populations to low numbers, until such time that the rains returned. In the latter case, with predatory birds eliminated, rabbit populations would grow, leading to an increase in the number of coyotes, or if coyotes were not present, to over-browsing of available grass, followed by a collapse of the excessive rabbit population due to starvation and diseases.

The dynamic systems models were powerful stuff, being advocated by some as a new method to run entire governments and societies. Visionaries such as Buckminister Fuller created a special *World Game* wherein scholars from around the world were invited to create systems programs to identify human and social-environmental needs on the one side, and match them to resources on the other, without the usual political obstacles being thrown into the formulae. One such item that Bucky Fuller liked to point out, was that the total world consumption of elemental sulphur was approximately equal to the annual discharge of sulphate pollution from fossil fuel power plants, and that a problem in one place was invariably a solution in another place. One might think this kind of cybernetic planning would be immediately appreciated by governments with centrally-organized economies, but in fact, computer programmers in the Soviet Union who advocated cybernetic planning were actually sent to the Gulag, as they were seen as being "in competition" with the Communist Party bosses. In the USA, Buckminister Fuller, Howard Odum and others following this new method of analysis, made possible by computers, were never sent to prison, but neither were their efforts widely appreciated. Fuller was admired by many students, but basically dismissed as an eccentric by the larger scientific establishment, and certainly his World Game was never given the kind of support it deserved. Likewise, Odum and his students were never given much of a warm welcome by either industry or government, as his analytical methods could too easily show that plans for new factories or shopping centers would destroy this or that species in a given ecosystem. Even today, thirty years later, the inspired social and ecological approaches of those early cyberneticians and systems researchers have not been put into much practical use, except for the modelling of climate. Some aspects were seized upon and incorporated into "chaos theory" of the 1990s — but, it seems, often as a measure to water them down, and to eliminate their socially-controversial aspects.

The concepts of net energy were powerful material, nevertheless, as they allowed one to get a very clear idea about dynamic environmental and social processes involved with different energy systems. Aside from the very large and important issue of people's general emotional inertia — which renders them impotent and immobilized in times of crisis — net energy analysis allowed one to see the complex and powerful socioeconomic dynamics which supported the status quo, and which also stood in opposition to any new idea which would try and do things differently. However, one could also appreciate the immediate advantages of the new approach.

I was mostly interested in making comparisons between entire systems of energy use: contrasting coal versus nuclear versus solar energy, for example. One could immediately see, that energy derived from nature — as from the sun or wind — did not require mines or refineries, nor did the fuel itself require transportation to the place where it was used. Sun and wind was delivered free, by nature, to the location where it was to be used. One could make electricity from sun or wind, and then transport the electricity to distant locations, but this was accomplished by using the existing electrical grid. The transportation and refining of raw coal, oil and uranium each required massive amounts of energy all by themselves, and to make an honest comparison to solar or other renewable energy systems, one would have to subtract whatever energy was consumed in those early mining, refining and transportation steps from the final amount of energy being generated at the End Use. Net energy was, then, *the amount produced at the End Use, minus the energy consumed to mine, refine and deliver the energy in a usable form to that End-Use step*.

In a more generalized manner, we can contrast the heat-value of different sources of energy. To obtain 100,000 BTU, or 25,000 Kilocalories, requires any one of the following:

15 lbs or 7 kilograms of coal
1 gallon or 3.8 liters of oil
120 ft^3 or 3.4 m^3 of natural gas
30 KWH of electricity
Sunlight shining on an approx. 1m^2 (or ~10ft^2) surface for one day, Central USA (average day).

From the above, we can contrast different fuel systems with respect to their total net energy as delivered to the society at large. Energy systems with a *high positive net energy* are very efficient and wealth-producing, as for a given amount of fuel-work-value expended, a greater amount of fuel-work-value is obtained. However, as we will touch on briefly here, energy systems with a *low or negative net energy* consume as much fuel as they deliver, or more. Such fuels are inefficient and inflationary; they rob fuel-work-value and productivity from other sectors of the economy. One will note the assumption of a general equivalence between fuel (or energy value in a fuel) and work-value (or energy value of human labor).

In a sense, it is assumed that human labor of the ancient human was able to move into machine-use only via innovation which allowed *a more efficient use of human labor* , or via use of fuels which, when collected, provided *more work value than the amount of labor involved in collecting them*. The simplest comparison might be a group of cave-people that have to expend a certain amount of time every day to gather dry firewood. Then they discover an oil seep on a nearby pond, and spend only half as much time gathering the oil, for burning and cooking, as compared to what previously was devoted to firewood-gathering. By contrast, if a complex society turns from an easy-to-get high energy value fuel towards a hard-to-get low energy value fuel, it spends more and more of its time to obtain that fuel, and runs the risk that the low-energy fuel will ultimately deplete that society of wealth and work-value accumulated over prior years, and from other sources. Net energy is therefore more than merely an academic concept — it goes to the root of economics and focuses our attention on the actual nature of work in a given society.

Net energy equals the energy of work obtained from the use of a particular fuel, *minus* fuel costs and human labor expenditures for:

A. mining equipment and operations

B. refining equipment and operations

C. transportation equipment and operations

D. pollution control equipment and operations

E. construction and maintenance of the equipment needed for the above functions

F. borrowed money interest to finance the above

G. military hardware and fuel expenditures, to obtain and secure the fuel source from foreign lands.

H. human labor for all the above, with the personal energy expenditure of workers for their own food, transportation, etc.

Obviously, one could extend this list, and it would quickly integrate with virtually every aspect of society. Indeed, one complaint I have with some of the academic net energy studies is, they include so many peripheral factors that virtually every form of energy winds up with a negative net energy. For these and other reasons, my own study of the matter has been restricted only to those steps of the energy production cycle A through E above:

these are the steps which come into *direct physical contact with the fuel or energy in question*, or which are involved in manufacturing of equipment which comes into such contact, or which are involved in control of the pollution created by a given fuel. Steps F, G and H above, are not included in my analysis, as it is not altogether clear that any of these activities would be eliminated should a given energy resource cease to be exploited, with a shift to other resources. Coal miners will find other jobs and still drive to work, even if coal mines are put out of production. And a homeowner who gets all their energy from solar and wind power will surely have other work to take up their time, while the banks still will charge interest on other matters, and the military still be engaged in defense of the homeland, or in overseas adventures. Inclusion of these factors begins to blur the issues.

My analysis also is more qualitative than quantitative, though I believe the conclusions are sound, drawn partly from a good knowledge of what has been written and published on these subjects, as well as from personal study and a "hands-on" knowledge of the renewable energies. I have also been a consumer of fossil fuels and rate-payer of electrical energy in states with nuclear, hydro and natural gas systems, as well as a taxpayer in the USA, and so have some appreciation for the comparative economic aspects of the problem.

With these factors as a background, in 1979 I created a series of *simplified* net energy diagrams which make the analytical process, and the profound implications, quite clear.

Coal Power Systems

We start with coal, which fueled the industrial revolution. Figure 1 is a net energy diagram for coal, showing 11 basic energy-consuming activities (rectangles) required to bring combustible coal to the end use. Starting with the far left-hand part of the diagram, coal must be mined from the earth — but before even this is accomplished, machinery must be constructed for the mining operations: earth drilling, scooping and moving equipment, steamshovels, bulldozers, conveyer belts, and so forth, plus pumps and ventilation systems to keep the mines free of water and with breathable air; elevators and rail carts to move people and the coal itself into and out of the mine. All of that equipment must be constructed and assembled at the mine. Only then does the mine go into operation, and then, the mine operations start consuming additional power. The mines also create large pollution problems, which are represented by the letter "P" for pollution. Coal mines create enormous water-pollution problems, with acid-mine drainage, pollution of ground-waters, and strip-mines devastate entire landscapes over vast areas. The production of the mining equipment also produces pollution, at the factory where the bulldozers and drilling devices are

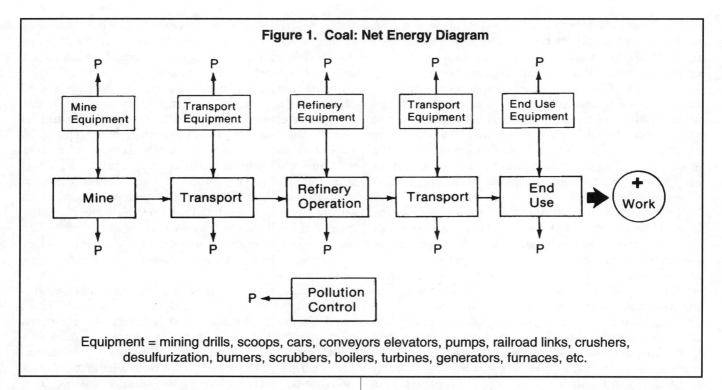

Figure 1. Coal: Net Energy Diagram

Equipment = mining drills, scoops, cars, conveyors elevators, pumps, railroad links, crushers, desulfurization, burners, scrubbers, boilers, turbines, generators, furnaces, etc.

manufactured. We could extend our diagram to include the iron mines and steel fabrication plants, where metal is produced which is then shipped to the factory which makes the mining equipment — but for practical reasons, we limit the net energy discussions only to those steps which come into intimate contact with the fuel resource itself, and the direct manufacture of the equipment which is used at such places of intimate contact.

After the coal is extracted from the ground, it must be transported to a refinery, where it is processed for end use. For coal, this transportation step is usually quite small, as the coal refining operations are often located at the same place where the coal is mined. Coal refining by itself can be a simple process of crushing the raw material into smaller bits which burn more readily, or the coal must be put through a process of desulfurization, depending upon its original quality, and the prevailing laws regarding air pollution.

The coal is then transported to the End Use location, the power plant or factories where it is burned. In many cases, coal-fired power plants are located close to the coal mine, and only conveyer belts are necessary to move it along, from the mine, through the refining steps, to the power plant. In other cases, the power plants or factories are located at a great distance, and the coal must be shipped via by railroad. Heavy rail cars must be made to carry the coal, and tracks laid. Historically, steel-making regions of the world were located in optimal proximity to both coal and iron deposits, so as to minimize transportation costs. However, as coal deposits were mined out, or restrictions placed upon low-grade coal containing high amounts of sulphur, factories and power plants burning coal had to look farther

and farther away to locate their supplies. New schemes were then created to lower transportation costs of coal, such as the use of coal-slurry pipelines — where the coal is crushed, mixed with water, and then pumped by pipeline over large distances. This latter scheme never was employed to any extent, given the intensive problems of highly acidified water at the point of delivery, and the depletion of water resources at the starting point. One can appreciate, however, that through all these discussions so far, we have not yet spoken about producing a single kilowatt of electrical energy, or a single calorie or BTU of heat being made available for an End-Use benefit. All of the efforts expended so far have only gone to bring the coal out of the ground, to the spot where, at some point, it will be burned to extract usable energy from it.

The End Use for coal is where it is burned, to produce heat. In power plants, water is boiled to create steam, which is used to turn a turbine to turn a generator, to make electricity. The coal burner and steam boilers must be constructed, as well as the steam turbine which converts the high-pressure steam into rotating movement. The electrical generator attached to the turbine converts this rotational energy into electricity. All of these large devices — burners, boilers, turbines and generators — must be constructed as well, and all of this consumes energy, and produces pollution. The pollution also consumes energy, in the construction and implementation of pollution control equipment. Scrubbers for coal-fired power plants using high-sulphur coal are very costly in terms of both energy and materials. Depending upon the sulphur content, each train-car load of coal can consume an additional train-car load of crushed limestone for use in the stack scrubbers, all of which must be mined and crushed and transported long distances. Complex electrostatic precipitators and filter bags are also used, which must be maintained, emptied, and replaced, with disposal problems for the filtered fly-ash. And still, with all of this activity, *we have not yet used the produced energy for any task outside that of trying to obtain energy.*

The specific thermodynamic laws governing all heat engines — including steam generators and known as the *Carnot cycle* — inform us that, *at theoretical maximum no more than about 35% of all the thermal energy contained in the raw coal can be captured and converted into rotary motion by the turbine.* The remaining 65% of the heat value of the coal, is simply discharged into the open atmosphere, or into cooling water. In real working conditions, however, most fuel-driven steam turbines operate at an efficiency much less than the theoretical maximum. Some cogeneration systems can reclaim perhaps an additional 10% of this lost energy from waste heat, but these are not always used. Frictional losses in the turbines and generators cause the loss of additional energy efficiency, and the electrical transmission lines themself also dissipate some of the energy into the atmosphere or into the Earth. Finally, at maximum, no more than around 20% of the original energy contained in the coal finally makes it to your house, where you can use it for life-essential purposes — such as illuminating light bulbs, running a refrigerator, or watching mindless television programs.

A similar calculation can be made where the coal is used in a factory, to produce heat for converting iron ore into steel, or for simple steam heating of an apartment building.

The energy produced at the End Use phase — for generating electricity, warming a building, or melting iron ore — shows up only at the far right-hand side of the net-energy diagram, and is given a positive value. All the energy *before* the End Use phase, required to extract, refine, and transport the fuel to the location of the power plant which converts the energy into electricity, is given a negative value, and at the end of our exercise will be subtracted from the End Use quantity, in order to make an honest comparison with renewable energy systems.

In spite of all its problems, and the large amounts of energy consumed in coal mining, refining and transportation, coal often has a positive net energy — but only in those regions where it is easy to obtain, as from deposits close to the surface and composed of high-grade ore, with a high energy value and low-sulphur content. Where this is not the case, where the coal is deep and low-grade, or where thick layers of earth must be strip-mined away, coal has a decisively negative net energy. This is particularly so if one includes the considerable costs for ecosystems restoration into the equation. In both deep shaft and strip-mine areas, ground and surface water is often too toxic to drink, or even to wash clothing. Ecosystems in such areas often wither away, become semi-dead zones, where most birds, fish, and other wildlife have vanished, along with other kinds of economic activity. Few of the modern residents in now mined-out coal regions of the American Midwest find cause to celebrate "King Coal", given the fact that the mining companies have generally behaved in an irresponsible manner, leaving the states or federal government, or local towns and homeowners, to pick up the pollution and land-rehabilitation costs. If the full costs for ecosystems restoration and water purification was included in the price of the coal, the price would skyrocket.

Oil-Petroleum Energy Systems

A net-energy diagram for oil or petroleum-based energy systems is given in Figure 2. Oil requires 13 basic steps to achieve a net energy. Oil is extracted from the ground by drilling deep holes, after which the oil either flows or is pumped to the surface. Pipes carry the liquid to storage tanks, after which it is diverted into pipelines, tanker ships or railroad tank cars, for shipping to refineries. As before with coal, the net energy analysis for oil requires an inclusion of the energy expended in construction of the oil drilling and pumping equipment. For land-based oil production, the expenditures of energy relative to the production which is obtained is relatively small, as oil has a relatively high thermal energy yield per unit of weight as compared to coal. Construction, maintenance and operation of pipelines and storage tanks do consume additional energy, but for oil this is still a relatively small amount as compared to the energy content of the fuel itself. Off-shore oil drilling rigs are much more complex undertakings to construct, as are the large ocean tankers that carry large quantities of unrefined oil from one location to another. Large cross-country pipelines are also very costly undertakings, in both economic and energy terms. Oil refineries require a major investment of energy and materials, for both initial construction and subsequent operations, and one must also consider the distribution network which carries the refined petroleum products out to the public. A large number of gasoline tanker trucks carry the refined gasoline to an even larger number of gas stations. The construction of this fleet of tanker trucks, their operation and maintenance, and also the construction and operation of the gas stations themself, all consume additional amounts of energy and material. None of this activity constitutes End Use; it is all energy expended with the goal of delivering energy. All the above activities also produce pollution. Oil spills at sea are major disasters, given the higher quantities of oil which spill. Refinery operation itself creates toxic fumes, and gasoline stations often contaminate the groundwater, all of which requires specialized clean-up equipment, and energy, to construct and maintain.

Finally, at the gas pump, the energy is available for End Use.

The End Use equipment in the case of petroleum products is generally your automobile. However, your car must be constructed at considerable cost in materials and energy. You fill it at the gas pump, and now it can deliver you from point A to point B at a speed faster than you could go by foot or bicycle — except for those big traffic jams, wherein you would wish you were on foot or bicycle!

End Use for oil systems also includes large buildings and individual homes employing steam or hot-air furnaces that use furnace oil, LP or natural gas. These actually are a more efficient use of the fuel than either steam-generated electricity or the internal combustion engine, which are subject to the severe limitations of the Carnot cycle, mentioned above. Or, it could include similar oil products used in electrical generators, by power companies, or in jet aircraft or light-rail mass transit systems which run from electricity generated by oil-fired turbine-generators. Pollution generated by both automobiles and jet aircraft is substantial, and the costs for maintenance is also high — the tires, engine repairs, insurance, and even the associated road network all consume vast quantities of energy and material to keep the vehicles running smoothly — we won't speak about the high energy and material costs of automobile crashes, or the possible costs should climate change melt the polar ice caps. Light rail mass transit is clearly the safest and most energy efficient of the transportation choices, with jet aircraft consuming the greatest quantity of fuel per passenger mile.

Nevertheless, in all these cases we are speaking about a device (furnace, generator, automobile, jet plane) which is the End Use consumer of the fuel, from which

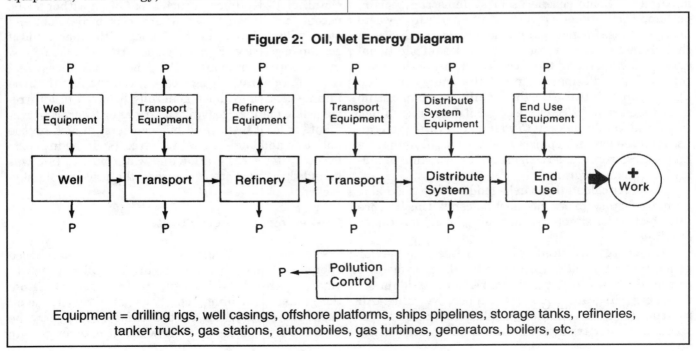

Figure 2: Oil, Net Energy Diagram

Equipment = drilling rigs, well casings, offshore platforms, ships pipelines, storage tanks, refineries, tanker trucks, gas stations, automobiles, gas turbines, generators, boilers, etc.

OIL: Steps to Net Energy
1. Manufacture of well equipment: casings rigs, offshore platforms, pumps, pipes.
2. Operation and maintenance of wells: drilling, pumping.
3. Manufacture of primary transportation equipment: tankers, pipelines.
4. Operation and maintenance of primary transportation equipment: tankers, pumps.
5. Construction of oil refineries and storage tanks.
6. Operation and maintenance of oil refineries
7. Manufacture of secondary transportation equipment for refined petroleum products: pipelines, tanker cars (railroads), tanker trucks (roads).
8. Operation and maintenance of secondary transportation equipment.
9. Manufacture of petroleum distribution systems: residential pipelines, gas stations, storage tanks, pumps.
10. Operation and maintenance of petroleum distribution systems.
11. Manufacture of end-use equipment: furnaces, generators, engines, automobiles, turbines, etc.
12 Operation and maintenance of end-use equipment.
13 Manufacture, operation and maintenance of pollution control equipment.

useful added work is obtained. The oil drilling, pumping, pipelines and storage, refining, distribution through tanker trucks to gas stations or other delivery sites, all constitutes pre-End Use activity, with a negative value that must be subtracted from the positive End Use where the fuel is finally burned and consumed.

By contrast to coal, oil and petroleum products are relatively easy to use and to transport from place to place, and this is reflected in the price. Oil from Alaska, or from Central Asian locations requiring long and expensive pipelines, and has a proportionately higher energy and economic cost, but not prohibitively so.

When all is said and done, oil based energy systems have a reasonably high net energy, with a high thermal energy content per unit of weight. However, this equation is quickly driven into a negative condition if the energy demands of various factors such as air pollution, the road network, automobile tires, insurance, repairs and crash injuries, and possible climate change, are included into the equation. There also is the factor, pointed out by Odum and others, that *we currently are using high net energy value petroleum energy from older shallow wells on land, to subsidize and extract lower or negative net energy petroleum from deeper reservoirs, or from offshore or very distant locations requiring vastly increased expenditures of materials and energy.* Older oil resources, tapped from easily accessible surface reservoirs, usually tends to be more fluid, easier to pump out of the ground, with a higher fraction of high-thermal energy content distillates. Newer oil resources are more often much deeper, or very thick and heavy, requiring much more energy to pump out of the ground, and contain a lower fraction of high-thermal energy distillates. The net energy of more recently-obtained petroleum resources is therefore more decisively negative as compared to those drilled and tapped in the first two-thirds of the 20th Century.

The older Persian Gulf oil resources, tapped and exploited in the mid-1900s, remains a very high quality petroleum resource. Even though it must be shipped by tanker across the oceans, it has a relatively high net energy value compared to the energy required to originally acquire it. However, not included in that calculation is the energy and materials cost when nations to go to war to obtain or defend petroleum resources, as in the oil fields of the Persian Gulf, or in Central Asia. Military campaigns also consume enormous amounts of energy, to manufacture all the sophisticated weapons systems — aircraft carriers, jet aircraft, tanks, bombs, bullets, missiles, etc. — and then to operate such a giant war-machine at long distance during either routine patrolling missions, or in active military campaigns. These energy costs are not computed or diagrammed in this discussion, but merely pointed out as an obvious fact and cost associated with petroleum resources. If they were included, oil might well reveal a negative net energy, across the board.

Nuclear Energy Systems

Nuclear power systems are the most complex of all currently in use, as seen from a net energy standpoint, and its inherently low net energy value is reflected in the high costs for constructing and operating nuclear power plants. Figure 3 gives the complex diagram of the nuclear fuel cycle, with *all transportation segments removed* to simplify things — otherwise, the diagram would be too complex to follow. Where transportation of fuel materials takes place, the letter "T" is placed on the arrow vector. Since nuclear fuel, in its refined state, has a very high thermal energy value per unit of weight, transportation is in many cases limited to single railcars or trucks, so compared to other steps in the nuclear net energy diagram, transportation of nuclear fuels is a relatively low cost. Pollution is also identified on the diagram, segregated into non-radioactive ("P") and radioactive ("RP") varieties, to acknowledge the fact that radioactive pollution is qualitatively different in its biological effects, and the greater period of time in which it retains its toxicity. Also, some key steps necessary for

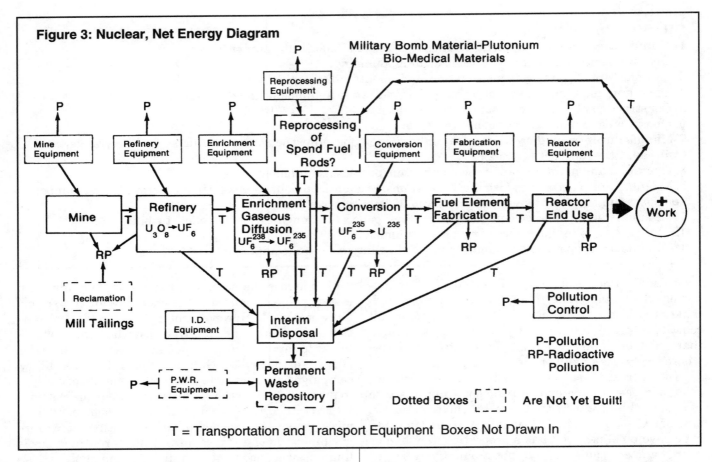

Figure 3: Nuclear, Net Energy Diagram

T = Transportation and Transport Equipment Boxes Not Drawn In

complete operation of the nuclear fuel cycle are identified in broken-line rectangles, denoting they presently do not exist, and have not yet been constructed.

There are 19 basic steps in the nuclear net energy diagram, not including transportation. Many of these steps are gigantic energy consumers, draining energy from hydroelectric sources or more generally from the larger public electrical grid system, long before any useful energy is ever generated by a nuclear power plant. Since nuclear power plants are basically water-boilers, similar to coal-fired electrical generators, they are also subject to the thermodynamic limitations of the Carnot cycle, meaning only about 20% of the thermal energy value of the nuclear fuel is converted into turbine rotation and electrical power. The rest of the waste heat is discharged into the air or cooling water. Worse, nuclear power plants themselves are notoriously inefficient, yielding only approximately 50% of their rated capacities (industry-wide average) — a figure known as the *capacity factor* — due to low-power operations, condenser inefficiencies, temporary shutdowns for fuel rod changes, or even permanent shutdowns due to accidents. They also, like coal and oil-fired generators, lose energy through the electrical transmission grid. Even before the nuclear fuel is burned in the reactor, however, there are tremendous energy costs involved.

The Oak Ridge, Tennessee gaseous diffusion enrichment facility, necessary for concentrating fissionable U^{235} in the uranium ore, consumes all by itself a whopping *5 billion watts* base load capacity, and is the nation's single largest consumer of electricity (as of c.1980).

Uranium mines are costly to run, and require special ventilation systems due to the unique character of the radioactive dusts created. They also create small mountains of radioactive radium sands as a waste product. Clean up of radioactive wastes at uranium mines — where this actually has occurred — has been a gigantic cost, but is never included in the price paid by the power company for the nuclear fuel, nor in the ratepayer costs for electricity. The staggering costs for cleaning up the big mess created by uranium mines, like the costs for the gaseous diffusion facilities at Oak Ridge, is covered by *taxpayer money*, collected by the federal government and by uranium-mining states. The health-care costs of uranium mining, with mine-tailings composed of radium sands contaminating air and water and land over large stretches of the western states, has never been fully computed to my knowledge, but it must be at least as staggering as the health-costs from cigarette smoking. Navaho Indians who worked in the early uranium mines died of lung cancer at rates of up to 60%, even greater than the deaths from black-lung disease among early coal miners. Soils and groundwater around nuclear waste dumps at Hanford, Washington, and Rocky Flats, Colorado, are contaminated with various

NUCLEAR: Steps to Net Energy (Transportation Steps Not Included):

1. Manufacture of uranium mining equipment: earth movers, augers, loaders, shovels, braces, power equipment.
2. Operation and maintenance of uranium mines
3. Manufacture of uranium refinery: ore crushers, grinders, acid washers
4. Operation and maintenance of uranium refineries (U_3O_8 conversion into UF_6)
5. Manufacture of uranium enrichment facilities: Oak Ridge gaseous diffusion facility
6. Operation and maintenance of enrichment facility: (UF_6^{235} enrichment over UF_6^{238})
7. Manufacture of fuel conversion facility: Precipitators
8. Operation and maintenance of fuel conversion facility (UF_6^{235} conversion into U^{235})
9. Manufacture of fuel fabrication facility and related components.
10. Operation and maintenance of fuel fabrication facility: fuel rod bundles for nuclear power plants
11. Manufacture of nuclear power plants
12. Operation and maintenance of nuclear power plants
13. Manufacture of fuel rod reprocessing facility
14 Operation and maintenance of fuel rod reprocessing facility
15. Manufacture of interim nuclear waste disposal facilities: storage tanks, pools, bunkers
16. Maintenance and operation of interim nuclear waste disposal facilities
17. Manufacture of permanent repository for nuclear wastes
18. Maintenance and operation of permanent repository for nuclear wastes
19. Manufacture, operation and maintenance of pollution control and radioactive pollution control equipment.

radionuclides (including plutonium), and the various cancer-clusters among the "downwinders" (people living downwind of the atomic facilities) are sufficiently extreme to prompt a public health crisis. Big lies and a cover-up by both industry and government on this matter, starting with the Cold War, have only recently been exposed. Lack of proper disposal and reprocessing facilities is currently causing a bottleneck of nuclear wastes at power reactor sites, in temporary storage facilities for radioactive wastes which will remain toxic for tens of thousands of years. All of these problems have very high energy and economic costs involved.

Originally promoted to the general public under the banner of "Atoms for Peace"§ and "power too cheap to meter", nuclear energy today is one of the most costly methods available, and public utilities which rely upon nuclear-generated electricity routinely charge their customers much more than non-nuclear utilities. For example, a charge of 6-8 cents per kilowatt-hour (KWH) is typical for Pacific Northwest utilities relying upon a

§ The phrase "Atoms for Peace" appears to have been originally coined by Wilhelm Reich in the early 1950s, though not in the context of conventional atomic power. In the early 1950s, he submitted documentation to the Atomic Energy Commission, claiming he had found a method for *detoxification of nuclear material*, with changes in its properties wherein very tiny amounts would yield powerful energetic effects of a life-positive character. Reich was an early critic of atomic bomb tests and radiological pollution. His work on these questions was ignored, unfortunately, but the catchy phrase used in his documents appears to have been copied verbatim as a government-industry propaganda slogan.

mixture of petroleum, hydroelectric and wind-power systems. Nuclear powered utilities may charge from 10-15 cents per KWH, or more, effectively doubling or tripling the bill of the customer. Nevertheless, this charge to customers of nuclear-generated electricity doesn't cover the full costs involved. Much of the true cost for nuclear energy, as with coal and oil, is subsidized by public taxes, through federal government programs intertwined with the military atomic bomb programs, and designed to help keep the bankrupt nuclear industry solvent. Nuclear power plants also enjoy federal protections against lawsuits in case of a major accident, thereby shielding the industry from liability and dramatically lowering insurance costs. Federal laws also exempted the owners of uranium mines from legal responsibility for the mine-tailings problem, allowing "cheap" uranium ore to be sold, while miners and townspeople near the mines suffer greatly. None of these costs, in terms of energy or money (much less, in terms of human misery) is reflected in the "standard economic model" used for assessing nuclear power. As both nature and people sicken and die, and nuclear reactors shut down due to accidents and inefficiencies, the balance sheets of the nuclear barons continue to show a handsome profit!

All of these facts work to lower the net energy of nuclear power plants into negative figures, even without inclusion of looming waste-storage, clean-up and worker health-care costs. The nuclear fuel cycle, in its full dimensions, consumes more energy than is produced by nuclear reactors.

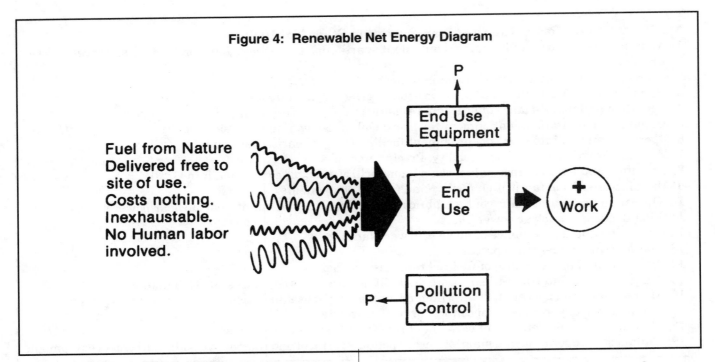

Figure 4: Renewable Net Energy Diagram

Fuel from Nature Delivered free to site of use. Costs nothing. Inexhaustable. No Human labor involved.

Solar, Wind, and "Cosmic/Free" Renewable Natural Energy Systems

In contrast to all the energy systems previously discussed, solar, wind and renewable or "free" energy systems require relatively few energy-consumptive steps. They are basically free fuels from nature, delivered without charge or energy cost to the site where they are used, in a form that does not need to be refined in the traditional sense. Not only are these fuels inexhaustible for all practical purposes, they are by comparison virtually pollution-free while being used. The only energy-consumptive and pollution-generating step is in the construction of the End-Use equipment itself.

For solar heaters, which are technically feasible for most areas of the USA today, construction consists of special collector panels composed of copper sheet, copper pipe, glass, wood, insulation, a storage tank, small heat-exchanger, small pump motor, and other fairly simple materials. In the southerly climates, one individual with ordinary plumbing skills, and proper knowledge, can construct and install a solar water or air heater in a day or two. In colder climates, a more elaborated panel with more insulation and an antifreeze coolant with heat exchanger must be used, but again, the skills to perform this task are present among home-builders and construction workers across the nation. The pay-back period, economically, is anywhere from 5 to 10 years, depending upon the amount of sunlight, cloud cover, wintertime air temperatures, and other factors. Since the renewable energy device will continue gathering and providing energy for 30 years or

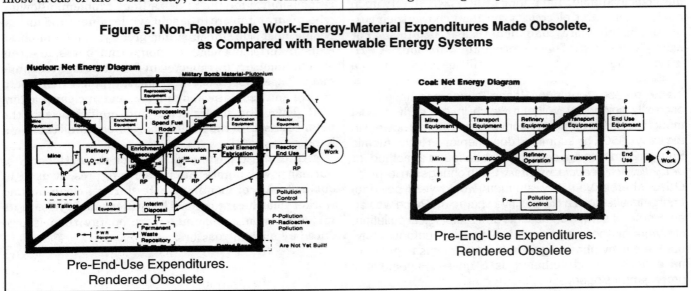

Figure 5: Non-Renewable Work-Energy-Material Expenditures Made Obsolete, as Compared with Renewable Energy Systems

Pre-End-Use Expenditures. Rendered Obsolete

Pre-End-Use Expenditures. Rendered Obsolete

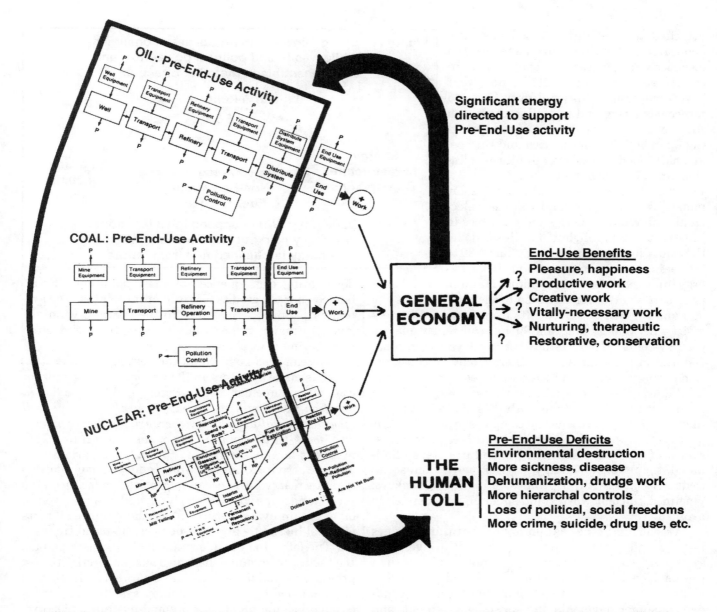

Figure 6. Total Social and Environmental Costs of the Pre-End-Use Portions of Non-Renewable Energy.

more, there is a considerable period of time when the home-owner pays little or nothing, save for maintenance costs.

Solar photovoltaic systems are also economically viable for much of the USA. They are composed of specially-grown silica crystals, set into a glass and metal frame, and mounted upon the roof, or on a separate stand. They can be used in large arrays, by the thousands, for power-generation by power companies, or in small numbers by individual homeowners. The *OBRL Greensprings Center*, where my home and laboratory is located, recently had an array of 16 solar photovoltaic panels installed, which produces about one-third of the electrical energy requirements. A special inverter ties the system into the existing electrical grid as a backup, so there are no batteries; excess energy generated when appliances are off, is automatically shunted into the electrical grid for other people to use, and is credited against the homeowner's monthly bill. Because this location has tall trees and an extended cloudy wintertime, the economic payback will be perhaps 15 years, with only a minimal subsidy from a state tax deduction. In other areas, such as the southern sun-belt states, the payback is faster. While the photovoltaic crystals and panels must be produced in a specialized factory, the installations are performed by individuals in a few days, requiring only basic home-building, carpentry and electrician's skills.

Wind electric systems can vary considerably in their construction, ranging from giant wind-turbines with blades of many meters length designed to add electricity directly into the grid system for large regions or for blocks of homes, or smaller wind-turbines made for single homes. They are basically large propeller blades attached to specially-designed electrical generators. The wind turns the blades and electricity is generated. They are sufficiently economically feasible today, that governments and utilities all over the world are constructing and installing them at a rapid pace. Large *wind-farms* are springing up in both North America and Europe, given the good economics, absence of pollution, and absence of fuel costs.

In each of these cases above, the solar panels, wind turbines, and accessory electronics all require energy and resources to construct and install, but once this is done, they work for extended long periods — 30 to 50 years or more, without additional energy input, save for some minimal maintenance. There is no cost whatsoever attached to the fuel itself, as the sun and the wind are free gifts from nature! Figure 4 gives a net energy diagram for natural renewable energy systems. There is no cost involved for mining, refining, or transportation of energy, only for construction of the collectors and wind-turbines.

Figures 5 and 6 contrast the simple energy diagram for natural energy systems with those for oil, coal and nuclear. We observe that, by comparison, *all the steps prior to "end use" are eliminated and become unnecessary and obsolete.* With the pre-end-use steps eliminated, the financial, energy, environmental and social costs associated with strip mines, refineries, oil tankers, pipelines, nuclear wastes and so forth, are completely avoided.

Cost of fuel at the gas pump or on the utility bill does not accurately reflect the whole cost of a given *fuel system* to society — the social cost is much different than the perceived individual cost. The social costs are a summation of the over-the-counter fuel prices plus hidden consumer payments and subsidies given out, and paid in higher taxes and as "externalities" — as the accountants call them — for the larger social and individual costs of pollution, to include sickness, ecosystems degradation, declining quality of life, and all the ramifications which flow from the slow toxification of nature. Natural energy systems completely skirt the entire gamut of pre-end-use activity, and consumption of energy to make energy, with all the attendant and hidden social costs.

Some have argued, that solar and wind power also today receive government subsidies and tax-breaks, and to a limited extent this is correct. It is not universally so, however, and these subsidies vary from state to state, and fail to have any substantial or long-term federal commitment. Oil, coal and nuclear, by contrast, have benefited from billions of dollars of subsidy, tax breaks and outright giveaways by the federal and state governments, decade after decade, with the major energy companies getting a free ride as regarding the

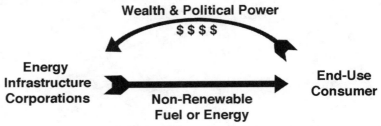

Figure 7. **Energy flows from producer to consumer, while wealth and political power flow and concentrate in the other direction.**

Wealth & Political Power

$ $ $ $

Energy Infrastructure Corporations

Non-Renewable Fuel or Energy

End-Use Consumer

Question: What happens to all the money normally paid out for fuel costs, when all energy is obtained free from Nature?

devastating consequences of their pollution. Small homeowner tax credits for residential solar energy systems are tiny, as compared to the gigantic windfalls given to major corporations by compliant and often profiteering politicians.

We can also point to an interesting consideration which is made apparent in the net energy diagrams for coal, oil and nuclear, and in Figure 7: *While the fuel in question flows with the arrows from the mine or well towards the end-use activity, there exists a flow of money, or of work-value, going in the opposite direction.* This money is largely distributed through the various pre-end-use activities, but much of it tends to accumulate as gigantic reservoirs or oceans of wealth, replacing on the social landscape what formerly existed as a reservoir of oil or coal in living Nature. From there comes all sorts of social hierarchy and anti-democratic social trends.

The following consideration is also thrust upon us: If a task once accomplished via a vast superstructure of pre-end-use activity (oil, coal, nuclear fuel cycles) is now accomplished by a natural energy system (sun, wind, cosmic) lacking all of that pre-end-use infrastructure, the backwards flow of money or work-value into that older infrastructure is dramatically ended. One does not pay for the sunlight, nor for the wind, but only for the equipment necessary to harness the sun or wind to transform its energy into a useful form — solar energy into thermal energy or electricity, or the mechanical force of the wind into electricity. Further, once the cost is paid for the apparatus to harness the sunlight or wind, the economic or work-value costs end, save for maintenance of the system. We may consequently ask: *What happens to all the money (work-value) paid for standard "fuel costs" (pre-end-use activity) when you obtain your energy free from nature?* The same end-use task is now accomplished with an enormous reduction in expenditure of human labor, non-renewable energy and materials, as exemplified by the elimination of entire aggregate blocks of pre-end-use activity. Work-value expended previously to make money to pay for fuel costs by the individual is now available for other tasks than purely "money-making" or "fuel acquiring" activity.

Assuming 100 years from now, society obtains most of its energy from natural systems, it suggests a vast reduction of human labor expenditure on activities which would degrade the quality of life or natural environment. Pollution problems would be reduced proportionately, and an economic revolution would spontaneously develop, as the vast reservoirs of wealth created and maintained by corporate fossil fuel concerns would slowly dwindle (as would their political power and influence), and money would be liberated to flow into new directions we can only imagine about today. Wars over oil would end, as would the disproportionate influence of small fascist nations of vast wealth based upon oil. It suggests a future filled with all the technological innovations we use and enjoy today — personal transportation vehicles, computers, television, radio, trains and possibly even air transport systems — but without the pollution and environmental problems of mines, refineries, oil spills, nuclear meltdowns, Middle-Eastern oil wars, and so forth. It is a future which all societies will inevitably, albeit slowly, stumble towards, with those addicted most to the heroin of cheap petroleum being dragged, by fate and necessity, kicking and screaming most of the way.

General References:

Anderson, B. & Riordan, M.: *The Solar Home Book*, Cheshire Books, Harrisville, NH 1976.

Cleveland, C.J., et al.: "Energy and the US Economy: A Biophysical Perspective", *Science*, 115:890-897, 31 Aug. 1984.

Bupp, I.C. & Derian, J-C.: *The Failed Promise of Nulcear Power*, Basic Books, NY 1978.

Clark, W.: *Energy For Survival: The Alternative to Extinction*, Anchor/Doubleday, NY 1975.

Center for Renwable Resources, K. Courrier (Ed.): *Renewable Energy in Cities*, Van Nostrand Reinhold, NY 1984.

Daniels, F.: *Direct Use of the Sun's Energy*, Yale Univ. Press, New Haven 1964.

DeMeo, J.: "Solar Energy", *Florida Urban and Environmental Issues*, 1:7-11, 1974.

DeMeo, J.: "Wind Power", *Florida Urban and Environmental Issues*, 2:8-10, 1975.

DeMeo, J.: "Legislation Needed to Promote Solar Energy Use", *Alternative Sources of Energy*, 25:32-33, 1977.

Eccli, E.: *Low-Cost Energy-Efficient Shelter*, Rodale Press, Emmaus, PA 1976.

Ford, D.F., et al.: *The Nuclear Fuel Cycle,* Union of Concerned Scientists, Cambridge, MA 1974.

Fuller, B.: *Critical Path*, St. Martin's Press, NY 1981.

Hackleman, M.: *Wind and Windspinners*, Earthmind Press, Mariposa, CA 1974.

Hanson, J.: "Energetic Limits to Growth", *Energy Magazine*, Spring, 1999 – www.dieoff.com.

Harding, J., et al.: *Tools for the Soft Path*, Friends of the Earth, San Francisco 1982.

Hayes, D.: *A New Prosperity: Building a Sustainable Energy Future*, Brickhouse Publishing, 1981.

Large, D.B.: *Hidden Waste: Potentials for Energy Conservation*, Conservation Foundation, Washington, DC., 1973.

Leckie, J., et al.: *More Other Homes and Garbage: Designs for Self-Sufficient Living*, Sierra Club Books, San Francisco, 1981.

Lincoln, J.W.: *Methanol and Other Ways Around the Gas Pump*, Garden Way Publishing, VT, 1976.

Lovins, A.B.: *World Energy Strategies*. Harper Colophon Books, 1975.

Lovins, A.B.: *Soft Energy Paths: Toward a Durable Peace*, Harper, Colophon Books, NY 1977.

Lovins, A.B., et al.: *The Energy Controversy: Soft Path Questions & Answers*, Friends of the Earth, San Francisco 1979.

Mazria, E.: *The Passive Solar Energy Book*, Rodale Press, Emmaus, PA 1979.

McGown, L.B. & Bockris, J.O.: *How to Obtain Abundant Clean Energy*, Plenum Press, NY 1980.

Mitsch, W.J., et al, Eds.: *Energy and Ecological Modelling*, Elsevier, NY 1981.

Odum, H.T.: "Energy, Ecology and Economics", *Ambio* 2(6):220-227, 1973.

Odum, H.T.: "Energy Analysis, Energy Quality and Environment", in *Energy Analysis: A New Public Policy Tool*, M. W. Gilliland, Ed., AAAS Select Symposia, Westview Press, 1978.

Odum, H.T.: *Environmental Accounting: Energy and Environmental Decision Making*, Wiley, 1996.

Odum, H.T., et al.: "Net Energy Analysis of Alternatives for the United States", *Congressional Record*, Hearings before the Subcommittee on Energy and Power, 94th Congress, 2nd Session, Serial #94-63, 25-26 March, 1976. Us Government Printing Office, 1976.

Odum, H.T. & Odum, E.C.: *Energy: Basis for Man and Nature*, McGraw Hill, 1976.

Platt, D.A.: "Energy Analysis of Electricity Supply and Energy Conservation Options", *Energy EGY* 2:1-7, 1977.

Pulfrey, D.L.: *Photovoltaic Power Generation*, Van Nostrand Reinhold, NY 1978.

Spreng, D. T.: *Net-Energy Analysis*. Praeger, 1988.

Singh, R.B.: *Bio-Gas Plant: Generating Methane from Organic Wastes*, Gobar Gas Research Station, India, 1975.

Stoner, C.H.: *Producing Your Own Power: How to Make Nature's Energy Sources Work for You*, Random House, NY 1974.

Strahler, A.N.: "Systems Theory in Physical Geography", *Physical Geography*, 1:1-27, 1980.

Strong, S.J. & Scheller, W.G.: *The Solar Electric House*, Sustainability Press, Still River, MA 1993.

Satellites or Silent Glowing Spacecraft?

Are Some Assumed "Satellites" Extraterrestrial?*

by James DeMeo, Ph.D.**

If one spends any amount of time observing the night sky, in the modern era one is accustomed to seeing the frequent passage overhead of star-like objects silently moving in straight lines high overhead. Common wisdom says these are satellites, reflecting sunlight from high altitudes. However, a careful consideration of this phenomenon suggests many of these objects cannot be satellites, nor anything which is visible due to reflected sunlight or moonlight. They must be self-illuminating and therefore outside the current technological capabilities of known Earthly craft.

Shortly following the 1957 launch of the first Russian Sputnik satellite, young people of my generation spent a lot of time looking up to the stars, straining to see the overhead passage of Sputnik, Vostok, Explorer, Mercury and other recently-launched satellites. One such satellite launched in 1960 was Echo, a huge balloon of 100 ft (~30 m) diameter composed of reflective aluminized mylar similar to a giant spherical mirror, with close to a 100% reflectivity. Echo was basically a communications satellite experiment, but its high light reflectivity allowed easy visibility, and local newspapers regularly printed a timetable predicting its passage. Entire neighborhoods often turned out at the posted time to wait and watch for the new and strange object, moving high overhead.

Today, of course, the overhead passage of a satellite is of no major consequence, in part because there are so many of them, but also because diminishing air quality in many areas of Earth have made nighttime observation of faint star-like objects impossible. Out in the countryside, particular at our high-altitude Greensprings laboratory (at 4200 ft or 1280 m elevation, with excellent air quality), even the Milky Way galaxy is directly observable with the naked eye, and the faintest of stars are readily observable with ordinary binoculars. Regular observations of satellites, or assumed "satellites" over the years have led to some startling, but rational conclusions. Some moving star-like objects exhibit characteristics suggesting they are not "satellites" at all. They move along curved lines, or in rare cases, make right angle turns or have a wobbling path. They fade in and out as they move, or only occasionally "blink", or

* Previously published in *Flatland Mag.*16:56-58, 1999.
** Director, Orgone Biophysical Research Lab Greensprings Center, PO Box 1148, Ashland, Oregon 97520 USA. Tel/Fax: 541-552-0118 demeo@mind.net

The Echo 1 Satellite, a 100 ft. diameter highly-reflective aluminized mylar balloon, and easily visible from Earth's surface during its orbit.

otherwise give off a light that suggests a rotating characteristic. While star-like objects making a shallow or radical turn in direction could not possibly be a satellite, neither could such silent objects be aircraft using known methods of propulsion. Even the highest-flying jet aircraft will create a sound that can be heard, though with a lag-time of some seconds. But even if we assume such silent, erratically-moving objects were Earth-based aircraft, why should we see them "glow" or self-illuminate? Forgetting for a moment the radical turning nature of a few of the star-like objects observed from the ground, or the absence of sound, the question of illumination becomes of central interest. It is, after all, through their illumination — their glowing nature — that we know of their existence.

Earthly craft propelled by propeller, jet engine or rocket are very noisy, and do not self-illuminate. For this reason, Earthy aircraft are identified in the night sky by their marker lights, on each wing-tip, and at the nose and tail of the craft, as well as by their sound. If an aircraft is high enough in the sky, around sunset or sunrise, it can catch the sunlight and glow brilliantly, but once night has fallen, such ordinary aircraft cannot get high enough in altitude to catch the sun's rays, and therefore become dark objects visible only by their marker lights. Satellites, however, orbit typically at altitudes where they often can catch the direct rays of the sun, late into the evening, and reflect them back to Earth. But this is not true for all latitudes, at all times of year, nor for all times of the night. When a satellite passes into the shadow of the Earth, it also becomes totally dark.

Add to this consideration the following facts: Very few satellites today approach the size or reflectivity of the old Echo satellite, previously described. Even the larger satellites launched by Russian A-2 or American Saturn rockets, and even those put into orbit by the Space Shuttle, do not have such large volumes or surface areas, and they are not coated with mirror surfaces. Generally, they are covered with dark-colored solar cells designed to absorb sunlight, not to reflect it. However, if we want to make an analysis of observed star-like objects moving overhead, since we don't know for sure what kind of satellites might be moving around, we can only point to this discrepancy, which remains a puzzlement. Even a 100% reflective satellite, similar to Echo, would become totally dark once it enters the shadow of the Earth. In fact, *there are certain times of the year, and of night, when virtually every object moving overhead should no longer be visible — save for those which are self-illuminating.* And this fact gives us an opportunity to test the hypothesis that at least some of the star-like objects moving overhead are not Earthly aircraft, Earthly spacecraft, or satellites. The test is made by ruling out possibilities known to yield reflected sunlight or moonlight from silently-moving high-altitude aerial objects.

Moving out into the night, in the countryside where the land is quiet and stars are easily visible, anything which is propelled by a combustion, rocket or jet engine can easily be identified by the sound, no matter what it looks like. Anything else, moving silently and appearing star-like, for the moment we may assume is a "satellite" reflecting sunlight or moonlight to us from high altitudes. However, if we observe such an object between approximately 10 PM and 2 AM, depending upon our latitude and the time of year, it will most likely be passing through the shadow of the Earth and therefore cannot be visible by reflected sunlight or moonlight — it therefore must be self-illuminating. We can narrow down the possibilities even more precisely.

Most satellites pass overhead at altitudes averaging no more than around 500 miles (800 km) maximum. Some geostationary satellites hover at higher altitudes, but these do not move — they are stationary in the heavens. Likewise, interplanetary or lunar spacecraft go to much higher altitudes, but they very quickly move far away from Earth and cannot be seen even if they were exactly like the old Echo, large with a 100% reflectivity. Since these interplanetary and lunar voyages are generally announced in advance, we can examine astronomy magazines to keep ourselves informed of their presence or absence. Also, we might rationally question if even a huge mirror of 100 ft (30 m) diameter (similar to Echo) reflecting sunlight would be visible at even 1000 miles distance — this question could be answered by computing light intensity as diminished by the inverse-square law — but to simplify matters, for our observational test we will assume even a smaller less-reflective satellite moving at 1000 miles would be visible from the Earth's surface. However, a satellite moving overhead at 500 or even 1000 miles would *not* be visible at all once it has entered the shadow of the Earth, and this can be determined by using a simple globe.

At the maximum Northern Hemisphere (NH) summer (June-July), the North Pole is pointing generally towards the Sun, and all latitudes above 23.5°N are in sunlight 24 hours a day, while polar latitudes in the

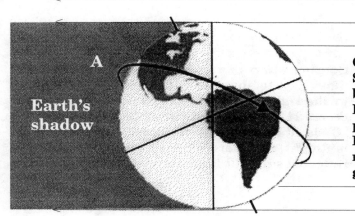

Sun ---->

Configuration of the Earth, Relative to the Sun's Rays for December-January. (Sun would be far off to the right side of the page.) North Pole receives 24 hours of darkness. Satellite path at point "A" is completely within the Earth's shadow for several hours around midnight, and therefore will not be visible unless generating its own light.

December-January Configuration

Southern Hemisphere (SH) experience a 24 hour night. In opposition, during NH winter months (Dec.-Jan.), the North Pole points generally away from the Sun, and all latitudes above 23.5°N experience 24 hours of night. For the NH, then, we can assure ourselves that latitudes lying between the Equator and 60°N would be fully into the Earth's shadow during the winter months from approximately 10 PM to 2 AM. Factually, this same latitudinal zone, Equator to about 60°N, is well into the Earth's shadow from the time of the Fall Equinox (Sept. 21st) to the Spring Equinox (March 21st). Any satellite passing overhead in this latitudinal zone between 10 PM and 2 AM, even at altitudes of 1000 miles, *cannot be visible from reflected sunlight.* But what about moonlight?

Moonlight constitutes a small fraction of the intensity of sunlight, but remains a remote possibility as a source of reflected light for satellites. Our observational test should therefore be constructed so as to rule out reflected Moonlight, to make our analysis 100% foolproof. To rule out moonlight as a source of illumination for aerial objects moving overhead, we must restrict our nighttime observations to times of the New Moon, when only the dark side of the moon is facing the Earth. Once this additional step is taken, if we are living in the Northern Hemisphere between Equator and 60°N, *any silent star-like object observed moving overhead at the time of the New Moon, between 10 PM and 2 AM and between the Fall and Spring Equinoxes, must be self-illuminating and therefore cannot be of known Earthly origins.*

For 2002, here are the dates for the darkest New Moon nights, when the overhead regions of space are deep within the Earth's shadow.

Optimal Viewing Nights for 2002
Northern Hemisphere

January 11 - 15
February 10 - 14
March 12 - 16

October 4 - 8
November 2 - 6
December 2 - 6

It is fairly simple to determine the optimal viewing nights for any other year, simply by obtaining a calendar which gives the day of the New Moon periods. Select approximately five days centered on the New Moon date, for the given six-month period October through March. For the Southern Hemisphere, a similar procedure is used, except the months between April through September are selected.

On these New Moon nights, the computed "hours of deep night" (when the Moon is not in the sky) range from approximately 6 to 12 hours per night, depending upon latitude. The above criterion therefore rule out any possibility of reflected sunlight or moonlight as a source of illumination for any moving star-like aerial object.

It is proposed that the interested reader who lives in the Northern Hemisphere between the Equator to 60°N Latitude consider to participate in the following observational test. Find a high-altitude countryside observation location with an unobstructed and clear view of the heavens, and dedicate the hours between 10 PM and 2 AM on the above-listed dates for observation of star-like objects. (Observers in the Southern Hemisphere could also participate, but would have to make their observations on New Moon nights between the Spring and Fall Equinoxes, from March through September, during their own wintertime months.)

Bring binoculars, compass, note pad and cameras

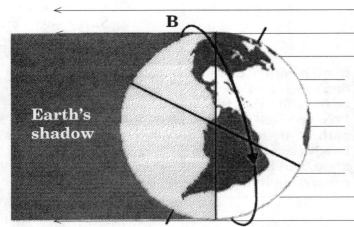

B　　　　　　　　　　　　　　　　　　　　　　　　*Sun ---->*

Earth's shadow

Configuration of the Earth, Relative to the Sun's Rays for June-July. (Sun would be far off to the right side of the page.) North Pole receives 24 hours of light. Satellite path at point "B" is illuminated by the Sun, even around midnight, and therefore may be visible due to reflected sunlight for most of the night.

June-July Configuration

with high-speed film. Separate tripods for the binoculars and camera would also be helpful. For those with the ambition to do so, a camera with wide-angle lens could be set up on a tripod to make constant-exposure time-recordings of star tracks during the approximately four hours of observation, when night sky exposures would be very dark and virtually no "satellites" should be observable. Analysis of star tracks might provide objective evidence for overhead passage of self-illuminating objects (similar to Wilhelm Reich's methodology as given in *Contact With Space*). Also bring lawn chairs, for easy reclined observation, and some serious helpers to assist with observations and to pass the time; four or eight eyes can cover much more of the sky than only two. Night-vision binoculars will also be helpful, if possible. Observations could proceed on any or all of the four nights given for each month, as above, or more conservatively only for the two darkest nights of each month (the two central-most dates of those given above). If weather is overcast, the four dates provide an opportunity for alternatives. Make note of any silent moving star-like objects observed: The time, direction of movement, and other characteristics should be recorded. At some point in the future, this kind of data could be organized from different viewing sites — although the large question of *what to do with such data* remains quite open. The main purpose of this exercise, is, assuming you have the patience to make extended observations, to *prove to yourself the reality of the phenomenon.*

It is to be expected the number of observable star-like moving objects will be dramatically reduced during these times, as all satellites visible by virtue of reflected light will become totally dark. Therefore, *any* silently-moving star-like object which is visible during the restricted times, dates and geographical coordinates given above *cannot be a satellite*. It must be self-illuminating, at light magnitudes far in excess of any known aircraft or space vehicle marker light. The observation of even a single star-like object meeting the above criteria would constitute a strong proof for the existence of self-illuminating objects flying in the upper atmosphere, or within the near-Earth space environment.

Anyone spotting a flaw with the logic or construction of the above observational test, please communicate this to me, as it is desired to make the test as strict and logical as possible, to rule out all known and explainable phenomenon.

As a species, we spend less and less time outdoors observing the sky, especially at night given the intrusion of city lights and air pollution, which obscure the heavens. Experience suggests there is a lot of readily observable unexplained aerial phenomenon occurring close to Earth. One does not have to wait for a chance encounter with ET to evaluate the possibility that Earth is being visited by space travelers. This simple observational test, performed simultaneously at different places around the globe, should be clarifying.

My UFO Observations*

by James DeMeo, Ph.D.
(Drafted June 1996)

Few aspects of Wilhelm Reich's research are so controversial as his discovery of the biological and atmospheric orgone energy (or "life energy"), and especially his later writings on *Contact With Space*. His development and applications of the *cloudbuster* apparatus to bring rains and green deserts in Arizona, was a prelude to subsequent, even more dramatic, indeed alarming events: UFO sightings and close-approaches by UFOs to Reich's research team in an isolated desert region. As a young student in the USA, I can still recall the intense feelings of amazement and disbelief, but also excited interest produced by Reich's writings. I had to investigate further, to convince myself in a clear way as to whether Reich had discovered profound secrets of nature, or was describing only a big fantasy.

After replicating some of his orgone accumulator experiments, and also personally experiencing the biophysical effects of his orgone therapy methods, I became fully convinced of the reality of Reich's central claims and devoted myself to his science of *orgonomy*, the study of orgone energy functions in nature. By the late 1970s, I was able to undertaken a systematic, scientific replication of parts of Reich's biophysical research at a mainstream university. My focus was upon the later and more controversial aspects of Reich's work, his atmospheric cloudbusting research. It was during this research program, undertaken in the American Midwest at the University of Kansas, that the profound factual reality of Reich's observations in the Tucson deserts became blatantly clear.

Orgone energy, Reich argued, is a ubiquitous sea of energy in which the Earth floats like a ball caught in a swirling ocean current. Orgone was a prime mover, filling all space of the universe, similar to the older theory of a streaming and convecting *cosmic ether*, but one with additional biological and meteorological properties; a water-attracting cosmic protoplasm, a creative force which builds up matter to more complex forms, in opposition to the "entropy" ideas of modern physics, which assumes "empty space" and a dead universe. Reich's universe is alive, streaming and pulsating, and we humans and other life forms are but smaller, more specialized expressions. Reich provided reasonable experimental evidence either demonstrating or strongly suggesting that the Earth, its near-space environment,

* Previously published as a Foreword to the book *Wilhelm Reich e il Segreto dei Dischi Volanti (Wilhelm Reich and the Secret of the UFOs)*, by Alessandro Zabini , 1996 Tre Editori, Via Principe Umberto, 35/1, 00185 Roma, Italy

and the atmosphere are both charged and animated by orgone energy.

My work at Kansas confirmed many of Reich's claims, that clouds could be gently stimulated to increase and grow by careful use the cloudbuster. Unexpectedly, on two occasions, when this work was underway at our rural field station, miles from any town, we were visited and apparently observed by Ea, or "Energy-alpha", Reich's term for the UFO — but these were not the first, nor the last of my observations. I have never before publicly presented these observations, which were a powerful personal confirmation of some of Reich's most controversial claims.

My first UFO sightings were in South Florida, around 1973, several years before I moved to Kansas. At the time, I was living about 8 miles north of the Homestead Air Force Base and Turkey Point nuclear reactors, and was deeply engaged in initial study of Reich's writings. Because my family lived so close to the nuclear reactors, his discoveries on *oranur* — the orgone anti-nuclear reaction — were of great interest. Even before developing the cloudbuster and writing about UFOs, Reich was experimentally investigating the relationship between orgone energy, or life energy, to nuclear energy. He observed that a small amount of nuclear energy could turn the normally soft and gently-moving atmospheric orgone energy into a highly irritated condition — much like the reaction of a wild tiger captured into a cage, throwing itself against the bars and angrily pacing back and forth. Exposure of natural orgone to refined nuclear materials irritated it into an enraged frenzy, the *oranur reaction*, which also caused Geiger-Muller (GM) counters to yield erratic readings. Following prolonged exposure to nuclear energy, the orgone then transmutes into a form of toxic energy called *dor* — short for *deadly orgone* — which saps the moisture and life from clouds, the landscape and exposed organisms. Freely moving energy, trapped and immobilized, firstly becomes highly irritated and agitated, but later on resigns, dies away and becomes highly poisonous; much like the caged tiger, several years after it is captured and has given up all hope of breaking free, and then only sits in a corner of the cage, immobilized.

Using a small GM counter in the area around the Turkey Point reactors, I was able to regularly detect anomalous increases in background radiation, and also the phenomena of "jamming" and "racing" of the counter, a clear expression of Reich's oranur effect. Such phenomena were never detectable with the same instrument when used 25 miles or more distant from the reactors. This phenomenon could also be felt, as a slight increased pressure in the head, along with light burning sensations (similar to light sunburn, but without the sun), and a metallic taste in the mouth. Only years later would these kinds of phenomenon be reported in a widespread manner, by people living near to the self-destructed Three Mile Island and Chernobyl nuclear power plants — though the physics community routinely dismisses such observations as "psychological reactions".

One summer evening, while riding a bicycle with my girlfriend in the rural farm area where we lived, we observed a strange glowing object the size of a large truck, appearing in an open field about 100 meters distant, and looking like a giant glowing pearl. Almost at the exact moment of being sighted, the object *leapt up into the sky at a fantastic speed*, passed behind a cloud, and then disappeared as quick as if a light-bulb had been shut off. I was shocked into animated excitement, while my girlfriend contracted into a depressed apathetic denial.

I quickly called the Homestead Air Force Base, excitedly reporting to them my observation, but was treated with laughing contempt by the soldier who answered the telephone. Undaunted, I began to make regular observations of the night sky, and read every available book on the subject of UFOs. I was astounded to observe very strange moving behavior of "star-like" objects, which are usually attributed to be "satellites" — in spite of their often anomalous movements, and statistically improbable clustering of two, three and four of such objects within a few degrees of each other, and all within a minute or two. On many nights during those subsequent weeks, it was possible to observe several of the silent "moving stars" at the same time, all within a small area of space, moving high overhead. At those times, within minutes I could hear the military jets scrambling to take off from Homestead Air Base. As I previously had been a student pilot, with much youthful dedication to identifying different types of civilian and military aircraft, and with strong interests in the space program and astronomy, I was well aware of the different types of jets and planes flying in the Florida skies, and also what was possible, and what not, regarding aeronautics and astronomical phenomena in general. The fast scrambling of military jets at Homestead was highly unusual, especially since to accomplish such a fast takeoff, they would use their afterburners, which was similar to a "sparkplug" in the tail pipe, by which exhaust gases were burned for extra thrust. This procedure also meant the jets were in "hot pursuit" of a target, something not normally done as the hot afterburner takeoffs created a very loud noise, and invariably broke a lot of windows of people living close to the Air Base. The broken windows would bring understandable complaints which subsequently appeared in the local newspapers, and so "hot pursuit" takeoffs were rare. Of course, nothing about the UFOs appeared in the newspapers. But night after night, the jets would roar up high into the sky towards the unusual "moving stars", which were always gone by the time the jets arrived.

It was exciting cosmic theater on a grand scale, and for several weeks that summer, each night I would spread out a blanket on the ground to observe the nighttime display of jets chasing "stars". Within a few months, through library research, I discovered the existence of the NICAP organization (National Investigations Committee for Aerial Phenomenon), headed by former Air Force officers and devoted to the open study of UFO phenomenon. I sent them $10 for membership, and shortly afterward got my first issue of their newsletter, *UFO Investigator*. The headline of that very first issue read: *"Jets Scrambled To Intercept UFO: Three Radars Confirm Unknown Object"*, detailing a series of events which I had personally witnessed. The article said radar sightings were made of at least one UFO over South Florida, with military jets being scrambled from Homestead Air Force Base to confront the intruder. NICAP was able to uncover at least some of the information, as its members maintained personal contacts with many ordinary Air Force officers, who were privately against the "official secrecy" on UFOs. The unofficial reality was quite opposite the "official" denials. The article provided a powerful confirmation, with many behind-the-scenes details of events to which I had been a personal witness. For me, from that time onward, I have never doubted the reality of UFOs, nor that they are flying craft, nuts-and-bolts vehicles capable of easily outmaneuvering our most sophisticated aircraft. It also gave me a greater sense that the claims made by Reich in *Contact with Space* required a careful and open-minded review before they could be judged. Within a few years after this episode, I began my program of study at the University of Kansas, with a research program focused directly upon Reich's cloudbuster apparatus.

As Reich described it, the cloudbuster was a passive device, appearing as an array of multiple "lightning rods", able to influence the weather over very large areas, and sometimes capable of doing so rather quickly, within minutes or hours. Properly used, and under the right conditions, the cloudbuster could trigger increases in clouds and rainfall, even during drought or desert conditions. He described many drought-breaking operations, including an expedition to the arid southwestern USA for an historical desert-greening expedition. As reported in his book, *Contact with Space*, Reich observed that careful application of the cloudbuster increased moisture across a broad area of the desert landscape, bringing increased humidities and rains to many dry areas, and causing many barren areas to green-up with the growth of new grasses — even in areas where local people had never seen grasses growing previously. As my special interest in the environmental sciences was focused upon desert spreading and drought, the possibilities were of great interest. From the classical scientific perspective, there are few, if any, realistic or effective measures which can be taken to assist people suffering in regions of drought-induced famine and starvation. Meteorologists may be highly skeptical of the cloudbuster, and often render unedu-

cated negative opinions about it, but have themselves nothing to offer to people living, and dying, in such regions of drought and famine. The 1970s was a time of widespread drought and starvation in African areas just south of the Sahara Desert. Reich offered the world a powerful new discovery and tool by which one could do something constructive. Fortunately, with considerable effort, I located an American university in Kansas where advanced study and research on the issue of cloudbusting would be openly permitted.

In 1976, after years of preliminary work and preparation, working and studying with Robert Morris and Richard Blasband (my mentors in the field of orgonomy, who followed Reich's approach in a close manner), I constructed a large cloudbuster, and transported it to Kansas. In the years 1977 through 1980, with assistance from Professors Robert Nunley, Joseph Eagleman, and John Augelli, I developed a series of systematic tests to evaluate the atmospheric effects of this amazing apparatus. My research Thesis was later presented to, reviewed and accepted by the faculty of the Geography-Meteorology Department at the University of Kansas: *"Preliminary Analysis of Changes in Kansas Weather Coincidental to Experimental Operations with a Reich Cloudbuster"* (1979). That study proved, through objective field trials conducted under methods generally accepted within the academic world, that the cloudbuster did in fact have an influence upon the weather over Kansas, verifying Reich's earlier claims. The cloudbuster was not a fantasy device, nor a hoax, but a *bona-fide and world-class discovery*. But not all of the observations made during the actual field trials were recorded in the official protocols.

In summer of 1980, there was a mild drought in Kansas, and I drove out to the isolated field operations site to use the cloudbuster, to try and bring rains into the area. It was noontime, without a cloud in the sky, and the operations had just been underway for about an hour, when I and my assistant spotted *two small white luminous dots suspended, unmoving and silent, high overhead in the bright blue sky*. Judging from the great distance, they must have been very large, perhaps as large as a commercial jet aircraft — except these made *no sound, and hardly moved*, only drifted ever so slightly.

I previously had read of Reich's reports in *Contact With Space*, that during his desert-greening operations with the cloudbuster, the UFOs had come down from the sky, apparently to observe the operations of his research team. He claimed the UFOs would harass his operations, that the UFOs consumed the healthy orgone energy, or life energy, of the atmosphere, and expelled an exhaust of decomposed *deadly orgone*, or *dor*, which evaporated the clouds and reinforced the desert conditions. Reich eventually was convinced the UFOs were not only hostile, but that they were reinforcing drought and desert tendencies, by virtue of their "exhaust". He found that the UFOs could be affected by the cloudbuster, that when pointed at them, they would begin to wobble, move away, and dim out. These latter reports of Reich were the most strange of all, as they did not have the kind of detailed supporting evidence and careful working-through which characterized his other scientific discoveries. *Contact With Space* was rich with many new and powerful insights and discoveries, about weather, droughts, deserts, and UFOs, though very unsettling in some of its conclusions.

That day in Kansas, we watched the UFOs hover and slowly drift from their high-altitude overhead position, over the course of around 20 minutes. One of the two objects then split into two, and within several minutes, the three objects slowly accelerated in separate directions, gradually shrinking and dimming, as if withdrawing to higher altitudes. I thought about pointing the cloudbuster at the objects, but deliberately chose *not to do so*, feeling it would have been a needless provocation. Finally, the objects could not be seen anymore, and never returned. Our cloudbusting operations ended also, as within a few days, the rains returned.

Some weeks later, drought conditions re-established, and another cloudbusting operation was undertaken. Now, whenever I went out to the rural field operations site, my eyes were constantly scanning the sky for unusual phenomenon. The cloudbuster was set up for operations in the early afternoon, during a completely clear sky. Operations continued into the evening and nighttime, and I stayed at a nearby home, periodically checking the equipment every half-hour or so. That night was very dark and clear with no moon, and in this rural area far away from city lights, the full panorama of stars, including the milky way, could be seen. I climbed to the top of a small hill near the cloudbuster, to get a better look at the stars. At that moment a completely dark object passed across my line of sight, very quickly. My mind conjured up the image of an owl or some other large dark bird flying across my sight, as the only thing I actually saw was something dark, blocking out the background of stars as it flew by. But what a shock, when I turned to look in the direction towards which the object had flown. *It was not a bird or owl, but rather, an apparently large, silent disk or oval-shaped flying vehicle which had swooped down to my location. Only at the moment when I turned my head to see what the dark object was, did that vehicle turn on its lights, and power-up its engines! The dark object immediately illuminated to the brightness of an automobile headlight, speeding away at what must have been several thousand miles per hour. In less than a second, the object approached some hills perhaps five or ten miles away, still glowing brightly, but now the size of a pinhead held at arm's length. Incredibly, the object then made a very rapid turn upward; much like a jet fighter would do, except in this case, the object accelerated as it soared upward, rather than slow down, as if gravity were*

something which did not affect it in the least. Within a second or two, the glowing object had flown so high, and so fast, it had dimmed to the status of only a "moving star", whereupon it vanished into the background of stars. Once more, I was left all alone on the hilltop, gasping for a breath, with the billions of stars and glowing galaxy spread across the sky, sole witness to a dramatic event hardly imaginable only a few seconds before.

In Florida, I had been a witness to UFOs which were, perhaps, making a survey of the Homestead Air Force Base and/or the nuclear power reactors in the area. In Kansas, for both the reported cases, the UFOs appear to have come down to "take a look" at the cloudbusting work which was being undertaken at our field station. Since then, there have been other sightings of unusual phenomenon in the sky, but nothing so dramatic or unusual as what is reported above. None of my own sightings constitute "proof" in any scientific sense, but for me at least, it was proof enough that Reich was on the right path in several of his basic conclusions about the UFO:

1. UFOs are spacecraft possibly powered by orgone energy.

2. The cloudbuster appears to perturb or otherwise affect the atmospheric and near-space orgone energy continuum in a manner which is detectable by such spacecraft moving in the near-Earth environment.

3. Such perturbations might affect the capacity of orgone-powered spacecraft for normal propulsion. If so, then surely the operators of the craft would be interested to closely investigate any such disturbances.

Other, more frightening aspects of Reich's observations and conclusions as given in *Contact With Space* have *not* been corroborated in my own research and observations. For example, I have *no personal observations or evidence* to support his claim that the UFOs are expelling dorish material as exhaust, nor that they play any role in the production or maintenance of desert atmospheric conditions, nor that they have a hostile character. Even with respect to my own cloudbusting work, which has taken place in many very isolated desert environments, I have observed no close approaches or threatening moves by UFOs beyond the reports given above. None of my desert or drought field work has brought forth observations suggesting the UFOs are either hostile or intensifying desert-formation through their "exhaust" or otherwise. However, this failure-to-confirm detracts nothing from Reich's earlier findings. Nor does *my* failure-to-confirm mean that Reich was wrong, only that I personally cannot provide any support for those specific questions. Even if these more alarming aspects of Reich's UFO work are never corroborated, it will not affect the validity of his earlier discoveries on the emotions, sexuality, the bions, cancer research, atmospheric orgone energy continuum, orgone energy accumulator, oranur effects, orgone-charged vacuum tubes, deadly orgone and the cloudbuster itself. These earlier findings have been confirmed in the independent and supporting research of many different natural scientists, among which I am only one individual.

Regarding the issue of the *spacegun* — where the cloudbuster is combined with a specialized form of orgone-charged and "denaturized" nuclear materials, which Reich claimed could be used to affect the flight of UFOs and cause them to withdraw — I confess to only a theoretical knowledge. I have never attempted to combine cloudbusting equipment with any radioactive materials, mainly because the toxic nature of even low-level radiation is so biologically noxious and repellent that I have been very cautious in taking such steps. Additionally, unlike Reich, I have never had my field operations harassed by a UFO, but suppose that if this were the case, I would investigate the spacegun in a prompt and serious manner.

In support of Reich I can make a strong argument that, even from the standpoint of classical physics, there are many gaps in our knowledge about the basic nature of inertia, gravitation, and radioactive materials. Dissenting scientists in the field of nuclear physics have documented anomalous variations in nuclear decay-rate "constants", and today propose new methods for "denaturizing" or "transmuting" nuclear wastes into less toxic forms. Even the older *ether theory* is now being seriously reconsidered by many classical physicists, as the metaphysical theories of "relativity" and "big-bang" cosmology are found to be seriously flawed. Reich's findings on a universal cosmic energy, filling all of space and fulfilling the role of cosmological *prime mover*, and his findings on *oranur* and the *denaturization of radio-isotopes* (as with his *orur* material) already have this kind of indirect and suggestive support from the classical sciences. His ideas, therefore, cannot simply be dismissed out-of-hand. And from such a standpoint, we are only a few steps away from the important question of *antigravity*, by which a spacecraft might be propelled through the heavens, or even the *spacegun*, by which an orgone-powered spacecraft might be disturbed or disabled in its flight. I, for one, am not willing to second-guess or dismiss even these more spectacular claims of Reich, even though my own research and observations have not provided any direct support. Even on these more spectacular claims, there is an important need for open-minded and serious investigation.

My own research with the cloudbuster has continued, and since completing the early studies in Kansas, I have been asked to bring equipment and use it to end droughts — often serious and long-term droughts — in places as diverse as Greece, Cyprus, Israel, Namibia, and Eritrea. Drought-abatement work has also proceeded in the USA. In 1989, a series of systematically-organized experiments were undertaken in the Arizona drylands, and these experiments fully confirmed the desert-greening capabilities of the cloudbuster, as first observed by Reich and reported in *Contact With Space*. Even the hard Sahara desert has yielded to the influence of carefully-conducted cloudbusting work, and field work in Eritrea (1994-1999), undertaken by an international team I was privileged to lead, ended a 30-year drought cycle in the region. The harvest from these research findings has been rich and abundant, with environmental and social benefits. Reich's ideas on atmospheric orgone and dor energy have also provided the necessary basic starting assumptions for developing a globally-integrated life-energetic understanding of deserts, drought, El Niño, and forest-death phenomenon. The concept of the Earth as a *living organism* gains significant support from Reich's concepts and discoveries, with practical approaches which just might, if we are fortunate, help to protect and maintain what remains of our blue-green living planet.

Negative Finding on T. Constable's "Bioforms"

In 1976, Mr. Trevor Constable published a book, *The Cosmic Pulse of Life* (Merlin Press, CA 1976; Borderland Sciences, CA 1986), which presented, among other things, various photographs of unusual atmospheric anomalies which he interpreted as being "invisible bioforms". He was able to make photographs of the unseen objects by using 35mm high-speed black and white infrared film and a special filter (Wratten or Tiffen #87) which blocked out all visible light frequencies, allowing only the near infrared frequencies into the camera. Infrared photos made in this manner show ordinary landscapes and people in a greyish surrealism. When such photos were taken under conditions of high energetic excitation (as during cloudbusting operations) Constable discovered darkish blobs scattered across the film, interpreting them as "bioforms" residing in an extra-dimensional reality. They appeared to be in rapid movement, quickly changing position and shape from one photo to the next. Using the "bioform" photos as a major evidence, Constable attempted to submerge Reich's experimentally-founded orgone energy discoveries into the pantheon of Rudolf Steiner's metaphysics. This subordination of Reich to Steiner was greeted with criticism by scientists familiar with Reich's biophysics (a scathing review was published, for example, by Jerome Eden, *J. Orgonomy* 11:121-131, May 1977) given Reich's own critical views about metaphysical mysticism, and also due to the many open questions which remained about the infrared photographic methods. For example: Are the blobs and forms on the film registering something in front of the camera at a distance (a "bioform"?), or some other unusual phenomenon *on the film emulsion*, as with film-development *halations*? The basic photographic anomaly was confirmed by James DeMeo at OBRL in the 1980s, by making the infrared photos in proximity to a working cloudbuster — something unusual did register on the film — but necessary follow-up tests were never undertaken, and so the matter remained a mystery.

Another book subsequently appeared, *Alien Energy* by Andrew Collins (ABC Books, Essex, England, 1994), which demonstrated the Constable "bioforms" were in fact *film artifacts* or reactions within the camera. In the early 1990s, Collins led a group in England attempting to photograph "bioforms" in a more systematic manner, also in proximity to either cloudbusters or groups of people engaged in outdoor meditation exercises. He resolved the open questions by making simultaneous stereo photos, in pairs, of identical scenes. These stereo photos also showed the unusual forms, but *they did not simultaneously register on both stereo pairs of images, only on one side or the other*. This result undermines the "bioform" hypothesis of Constable, demonstrating that something unusual occurs *on the film emulsion itself, inside the camera*. Aside from light-frequencies, film emulsions are known to be sensitive to phenomena such as solar flares, life-energy fields and, now, the excited field of a working cloudbuster. This would suggest an *orgone-energetic* origin for the Constable film anomalies, something which might eventually find a useful application in the documentation of orgone phenomena.

Stereo-Pair Infrared Photographs of the same landscape at the same instant in time, showing anomalous spots and forms (at arrows) but in different locations on the two halves of the film, suggesting *film artifacts* occurring inside the camera or during development. (Reproduced courtesy of Andrew Collins, from *Alien Energy*, p.197.)

Following are a series of short and preliminary reports, on various research and educational projects organized through the *Orgone Biophysical Research Lab (OBRL)* since publication of the last issue of *Pulse of the Planet* in 1993, beyond the research detailed in the previously-presented articles in this issue.

OBRL Greensprings Center

In 1995, OBRL was relocated to an energetically clean, high-altitude forested region of southern Oregon, with sufficient room for necessary expansion of facilities. A two-story, passive solar-heated laboratory structure designed by James DeMeo (Director of OBRL) was added and was in use by 1996 for seminars, research and office work. This new location for OBRL was given the name *Greensprings*, a name also used by local people due to the large number of springs in the area. The Greensprings facility is the home-base for Dr. DeMeo, with a working microscopy and analytical laboratory, seminar room, research library, and weather center for coordination of OBRL overseas desert-greening field operations. An orgone energy darkroom was constructed on site in 1997, with a CORE operations station in 2001.

New Solar-Photovoltaic System at OBRL

In Summer of 2001, with help from Bob Maynard of Energy Outfitters in Cave Junction, Oregon, a 1200 watt Siemens Solar Electric System composed of 16 solar panels and grid-intertie inverter (which requires no batteries, and puts excess power back into the utility

Orgone Biophysical Research Lab, Greensprings Center, in Summer and Winter scenes. Below, new solar electric system recently installed at the Center.

lines for our neighbors to use), was installed at the OBRL Greensprings Center. The system currently generates about one-third of the energy requirements of the Greensprings residence and laboratory buildings. After some initial period of evaluation, additional panels may be added (assuming the secrets of the orgone-motor power source are not solved beforehand). The decision to make this investment came shortly before the year 2001 California "energy crisis", and underscores the commitment of OBRL to "walk our talk" regarding social and environmental responsibility.

Educational Programs and Activities:

Ft. Mason Center Lectures: 1989-1994

During each year from 1989 through 1994, OBRL hosted a 16-week evening lecture series on *"The Life and Work of Wilhelm Reich"*, at the Fort Mason Conference Center in San Francisco. The lecture series was organized by James DeMeo and Theirrie Cook, with major lectures given by James DeMeo, and occasional guest lectures by Richard Blasband, Theirrie Cook, Lou Hochberg, Marilyn Milos and others, on relevant subjects. A similar series may be organized in Ashland, Oregon, during wintertime, assuming there is local interest to do so.

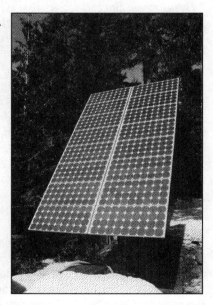

Greensprings Seminars: 1995-2001

Since the move to Greensprings in 1995, a more dedicated series of summertime weekend seminars have been presented at the OBRL Greensprings Center in Ashland, Oregon. These seminars — which have attracted a total of around 300 students from the USA, Canada, Mexico, Britain, Germany, Austria, Switzerland, Spain, Italy, Greece, Denmark, Czech Republic, France, Australia, Brazil, Japan and Indonesia — have included the following:

* Bions, Biogenesis, and the Reich Blood Test: Introductory Microscopy Seminar (presented yearly). Instructors: Richard Blasband, Stephen Nagy, Bernard Grad, James DeMeo.

* The Orgone Energy Accumulator: History, Construction, Experimental Use (presented yearly). Instructors: James DeMeo, Theirrie Cook.

* Today's Children and the Struggle for Tomorrow's Humanity (1996). Instructors: Michael Rothenberg, Daniel Schiff, Marilyn Milos, James Prescott, Tina Kimmel, Edward Applebaum, James DeMeo.

* Wilhelm Reich's Last Years: Oranur, CORE, Contact With Space, and the FDA "Investigations" (1997). Instructors: Jim Martin, Peter Robbins, James DeMeo.

* Orgonomic Medicine: Theory and Practical Experiences with the Orgone Accumulator (2000). Instructors: Jorgos Kavouras, Stefan Müschenich.

* Remembering Wilhelm Reich: The Man and his Work: 100th Birthdate Anniversary (1997). Instructors: Morton Herskowitz, Bernard Grad, Lou Hochberg, James DeMeo.

* On Drought, Desert-Spreading and Forest-Death: The Bioenergetic, Orgonomic Basis of Climate and Weather (1996, 1999). Instructor: James DeMeo

* Special Seminar with Morton Herskowitz and Michael Rothenberg (1999).

* Saharasia: Social, Historical and Environmental Aspects (1999, 2000, 2001). Instructor: James DeMeo

* Guided Independent Study Program (presented yearly). Instructor: James DeMeo.

Greensprings Seminars: Summer 2002

The 2002 Summer Seminars include the following:
* 27-28 July: Bions, Biogenesis & the Reich Blood Test Instructors: Bernard Grad, Richard Blasband, James DeMeo.

* 3-4 August: The Orgone Energy Accumulator. Instructor: James DeMeo.

* 10-11 August: The Rediscovery of Living Functions in Organism, Nature and Economy: Instructor: Bernd Senf.

* Guided Independent Study Program, 23 July through 8 August (each Tues., Wed. & Thurs.) for the more serious student. Instructor: James DeMeo.

Registration for Weekend Seminars is $180 per person, and limited to approximately 35 participants. The Guided Independent Study program is $500 per person (partial attendance for a reduced fee is possible), and limited to 8 participants. A half-price arrangement is possible for full-time students.

For more information on the continuing series of Greensprings Seminars, with a list of local restaurants, motels and tourist attractions, contact OBRL for a brochure and information package, or see the educational section of the OBRL internet web site:

http://www.orgonelab.org/events.htm

Top: Greensprings Seminar in progress
Bottom: Taking a break under the trees

Breaktime: James DeMeo, Lou Hochberg, Bernard Grad

Student Assistantships Available

OBRL routinely has openings for two student assistants during the four week period of our summer seminars. The assistants help prepare the lab facility for the seminars during the week before the events occur, and then assist with various experimental demonstrations, and with other tasks during the seminars. A full tuition waiver for the three summer weekend seminars and Independent Study, plus a place to stay in the student cabin, are offered. Students of any age interested in applying to the assistantship program should contact Dr. DeMeo early in the year to ascertain if the positions are open. Applicants should be prepared to submit a resume with statement of their interests and background in orgonomy, along with any recent university transcripts plus a letter of recommendation and a photo.

Field Research in Progress

Overseas Desert-Greening & Drought Abatement

Since the publication of reports on cloudbusting operations in back issues of *Pulse of the Planet, Journal of Orgonomy,* and as separate *Special Reports,* requests have come to OBRL Offices to undertake drought-abatement or desert-greening work around the world. These include inquiries from Algeria, Australia, Bolivia, Brazil, Canada, Cape Verde, China, Cyprus, Eritrea, Germany, Greece, India, Israel, Italy, Kenya, Morocco, Namibia, Nepal, New Zealand, Saudi Arabia, United Arab Emirates, and Zambia. We were able to positively respond to only a small percentage of these requests, usually due to extreme logistical difficulties and/or lack of financial resources. Nevertheless, operations were organized in Eritrea, Germany, Greece, Israel and Namibia, in addition to various regions of the USA. In each of these latter cases, we were able to find a combination of skilled teams of cloudbuster operators, local support from people familiar with Reich's discoveries, plus financial support and in most cases, permissions from local governments. The *obstacles in the way* which prevented operations in the other cases are illustrative: Absence of funding, no local support network, inability to obtain government permissions, terrorist groups creating havoc in the regions needing attention, and government fascism and/or corruption.

Unfortunately, the world regions suffering from the most intensive drought and desertification — within or adjacent to the large Saharasian desert belt — often suffer most from the various obstacles listed above, making cloudbusting field work a potentially hazardous enterprise. A general policy is, *we do not work in areas of terrorism, or where governments sponsor terrorism, or where governments are fascistic (right or left wing variants).* In fact, we have declined invitations to work, with extremely lucrative offers, in several of the Persian Gulf oil kingdoms. (In one case, when informed about how we would have to genuflect to the sponsoring King, on our

Weather Center at Greensprings (Top). Satellite imagery and weather maps are acquired here, and then transmitted to field operations teams. Bottom: Dr. DeMeo's research library and OBRL archive.

knees, we spontaneously broke out in laughter, which ended the negotiations.) This is not always the case, however, and many operations have taken place in very dry regions, bringing immense social and environmental benefits, with the restoration of widespread and oftentimes enduring rainfalls to parched landscapes.

CORE Network USA

Since the early 1990s, all cloudbusting field operations in the USA undertaken by OBRL staff have been coordinated with the USA CORE (Cosmic Orgone Engineering) Network, which currently has under 10 members. The CORE Network is dedicated to coordination of responsible cloudbusting work in the USA, for constructive critical review, oversight and evaluation of such operations, and training of responsible and serious individuals in the art of cloudbusting (as originally described by Wilhelm Reich). The Network has been most active on the West Coast during several years of drought in the late 1990s and in the 2000s. At some point in the future, information will be posted to a new internet site giving the CORE Network's policy statement, and an informal training and apprenticeship program. See: http://www.cloudbusting.org

On the Problem of Irrational Cloudbusting

In recent years, there has been an explosion of interest in "the cloudbuster", but mostly in an irrational and haphazard manner, with severe distortions of Reich's orgonomic discoveries and theory, and no concerns regarding atmospheric chaos. For this reason, Dr. DeMeo has posted his cautionary paper *"So You Want to Build a Cloudbuster"* to internet:

http://www.orgonelab.org/sobuildaclb.htm

Laboratory Research In Progress

Water Research

Some limited progress has been made into investigation of the question of orgone-charged water, as outlined previously in OBRL fund-raising letters. With assistance of students during the summertime Guided Independent Study Program, at the Greensprings Center, work with a duNouy-type Fisher surface tensiometer, orgone-charged water (kept in a strong accumulator for months) was shown to have a surface tension approximately 5%-10% *higher* than uncharged control water. The life-energy meter (detailed below) also showed a slightly higher reading with the orgone-charged water as compared to the control. Other evaluations were made of the solubility characteristics of orgone-charged versus control water, with indeterminate results. This work progresses slowly, but steadily.

Orgone Accumulator Temperature Differentials (To-T)

The To-T experiment of Wilhelm Reich has been undertaken at OBRL over the years, but nothing has yet been published, in part because many of its parameters required tighter experimental control procedures, to rule out classical thermodynamic expectations. Some of the problems encountered over the years are as follows:

1. Electronic thermometers involving thermistors or thermocouples always seemed to yield a different result from those obtained by mercury or alcohol thermometers. This anomalistic effect, which is quite interesting all by itself, was reproduced independently by both James DeMeo of the OBRL, and by Victor Milian, a Spanish physicist, who communicated their findings to each other (see p.182). Milian believes the effect is a direct orgonotic influence upon the current-carrying properties of the wire itself, though DeMeo suggests it may also be due to the production of a slight current within the wire by the higher orgone charge. The matter requires further study for clarification, but suggests use of electronic thermometers for the To-T would produce anomalies outside of the issue of any thermal effect.

2. Orgone accumulators exposed to radiating heat sources, such as direct sunlight, heat lamps or light bulbs, or even to the downward radiation of a heated roof surface, could develop slight warming effects on the exterior surfaces of the metal layer exposed to such an influence. This needs to be evaluated regarding Reich's early view of measuring thermal changes in a chamber above the accumulator.

3. The problems of heat capacity and thermal lag have not been sufficiently evaluated in the construction of orgone accumulators and control enclosures, in any of the studies published so far, though we do know that Dr. Richard Blasband of the Center for Functional Research (www.functionalresearch.org) did a lot of work on orgone accumulators thermally balanced against control enclosures, via empirical methods. Results of this work have not yet been published. Empirical evaluations of thermal lag, by direct evaluations of heat flow across wall surfaces (thereby matching a control against an accumulator, to external forcing thermal energy) appears to be the preferred approach to the matter.

A renewed effort to evaluate the To-T effect, taking into account all of the above classical thermodynamic problems, as well as the fundamentally-important prerequisites of orgone energy functions, is underway.

Photographing the Orgone Energy

Photographic documentation of orgone energy phenomena are of vital importance, and so a considerable effort has been undertaken over the years towards this goal. Various optical filters have been employed to make both energy fields and orgone energy units more appreciably visible to the eye, after which efforts were planned for enhanced photographic evaluations. However, this line of work led to the identification of a major problem: the possible confusion of *blood corpuscles in the eye* with spiral-form orgone energy units.

Optical filters allowing near ultra-violet frequencies of between 410-420 nanometers[§] to pass have proven very effective in making eye blood corpuscles readily visible — the filter is coupled with a microscope illuminator with diffusing screen, and readily shows blood cells which pulse along fairly constant pathways, surging with one's heartbeat. The phenomenon is somewhat similar to the orgone units visible in the atmosphere, and so the argument has been raised that what Reich and others have called *orgone units* might, in reality, be only *blood corpuscles*. However, there are powerful counter-arguments, suggesting the existence of *two separate phenomena*: blood corpuscles in the eye *and* orgone units.

For example, orgone units as visibly observed against the blue sky, or against a solid white screen or cloudy sky, tend to move in a manner *unconnected with one's heartbeat*. Trees, as observed against the blue sky as a background, often appear to be flaring orgone units off away from themselves, in a manner wholly disconnected from what one can see in the eye-corpuscle filter device. More telling, however, is the occasional observa-

---

[§] Such a filter is available from Coherent Optics, of Holliston Massachusetts, Item #35-3268.

tion of orgone units in the atmosphere *moving in a unidirectional manner*, or as Reich described, *in a spiralling manner*, and with velocities either slower or faster than is seen with blood corpuscles in the eye. Until the time that we can produce photographs of the orgone units, however, the critics of this particular orgonotic phenomenon may honestly point to the blood corpuscular explanation. The burden of proof rests with advocates of the orgone units.

Additional effort was made to objectify orgone units, using a variety of sensors, such as infrared and ultraviolet imaging devices and various image-enhancement and light-amplification sensors. Night vision equipment does yield what are called "random photons", and these may be visible expressions of orgone units impinging upon the front side of the detector in the dark. However, this is only speculation. Several new devices merging ultraviolet detectors with night-vision technology show better promise. There are new classes of *far ultraviolet* detectors, as currently used on the IMAGE satellite, using special cesium-compound phosphors, to produce photographs of the aurora and magnetosphere of the Earth from space. However, these have not been possible to study given their very expensive price and the limited financial resources of OBRL.

Several attempts have also been made to create orgonoscopes following Wilhelm Reich's methods, but exacting details were never published by Reich in this regard, and so these attempts have so far not been particularly revealing or validating. Naked eye observations, using simple hollow tubes or binoculars, have proven just as good in this regard (or just as poor, from the viewpoint of failing to allow objective photographs or video recordings of unusual phenomena).

Orgone energy phenomenon have been verified in the OBRL orgone accumulator darkroom, in the objective blue-grey glow within orgone-charged high-vacuum tubes (vacor tubes). This glowing has been produced by merely stroking the tubes with the bare hand, without electrical excitation, and has also been photographed. The phenomenon is most beautiful to see, and one

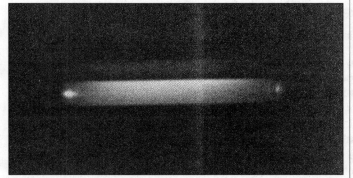

Glowing Vacor Tube, excited only by stroking with the hand, as photographed inside the orgone energy darkroom. 20-min. exposure with 3600 asa 35 mm color film.

physicist who observed it repeatedly declared "That can't happen!" Shorting out the electrodes at the ends of the tube by attaching a wire between them, or by grounding the electrodes to earth, or to the walls of the accumulator room, or to the person doing the stroking does not make a difference, as the glow regularly appears when the hand strokes the tube. However, not every person can produce the effect — some persons clearly can create the excitation, while others not, something which possibly reflects the orgone-charge of the hands of different people.

Another orgonotic light phenomenon visible in the orgone room is the distinct flimmering of light as seen against zinc sulfide screens. Long parallel strips of zinc sulfide material with spaces between, have shown the strongest effects. After about 20 minutes of visual dark-adaptation, the light along the strips dances or "flames" with a great activity. To date, we have not been able to record this particular phenomenon, which will require a special low-light videocamera not currently available. This effort continues.

Millivoltmeter Studies

Evaluations of the electrical potential of the Earth and atmosphere, following on the methods pioneered by the late Harold Saxton Burr, have been periodically undertaken at OBRL with interesting results. The methods are regularly demonstrated to students at the Independent Study Seminars, and will be published in a later edition of *Pulse of the Planet*.

New Life Energy Meter

OBRL is working to analyze and review a new life-energy field meter developed by Mr. Dave Marett, a Canadian scientist and engineer. The new meter is basically a solid state version of Wilhelm Reich's orgone energy field meter, and holds great promise for orgone biophysical research and therapeutic evaluations. An early version of the meter was distributed and sold for evaluations through Natural Energy Works company (www.natural-energy-works.com). The original design was limited given that the apparatus could detect and measure the strengths of life-energy fields at only a very short distance, of only a few centimeters. A new version is under preparation, however, to detect energy fields at from 30-60 centimeters distance, and should become available by Summer 2002.

Archaeological-Historical Research

Dr. DeMeo's interests in ancient history, and specifically on the question of early unarmored societies, have always been a part of the research and educational activity at OBRL. In 1980, he made an extended survey of the deserts of the American Southwest, from both an environment-ecological and human cultural viewpoint, visiting numerous sites of the old Anasazi peoples, and

Ice Age, Or Polar Axis Shift?

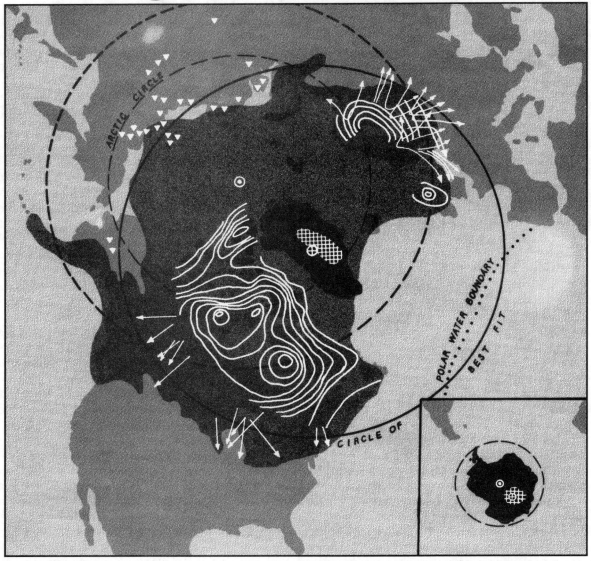

■ EXISTING POLAR ICE	↗ ERRATIC BOULDER PATHS (N. AMERICA) GLACIAL OUTFLOW (EUROPE)
▦ AREA OF MAXIMAL DEPTH IN EXISTING POLAR ICE	⊙ EXISTING POLAR LOCATIONS
▨ AREA OF PLEISTOCENE (WURM) GLACIAL MAXIMUM	⊕ OLD POLAR LOCATIONS ??
◉ ISOSTATIC REBOUND	▽ FROZEN MAMMOTH OR RHINO

Ice Age, or Polar Axis Shift? The maximum extent of the Pleistocene glacial maximum is identified, with a *circle of best fit* applied around it. The center of this circle is then plotted. It does not match with the existing North Pole, but instead is located over central Greenland, displaced 18° along latitude meridian 45°W, at the edge of the modern area of maximum ice thickness. An axis drawn through the center of the Earth from that point over Greenland matches a similar point over the maximum ice thickness in Antarctica, along latitude meridian 135°E. Isolines of isostatic rebound over de-glaciated areas of North America and Europe, and paths of major erratic boulders and glacial outflow, all align themselves around this center over Greenland, which also is the central mass of remaining polar ice in the Northern Hemisphere. Was this location formerly the North Pole, shifted to the modern location some 10,000 years ago? If so, it would also explain the plotted distribution of frozen Pleistocene mega-fauna, whose habitat would have been shifted into more frigid climates, killing most, but trapping some in ice environments, preserving them for the modern day. (Map prepared by James DeMeo, c.1983. Details and citations to be given in a larger article under preparation.)

other pre-Columbian sites, including all the significant museums in the areas to review their collections. Likewise in Europe, during many lecture trips, museum collections revealing the most ancient archaeological strata were a high priority. Later research took him to the old Minoan sites, on the islands of Crete and Santorini, and in Israel, Egypt, Eritrea and Namibia, Africa. Much was learned about the archaeology of these regions during those field expeditions, some of which was included for discussion in his major work, *Saharasia*, and also are discussed in this issue of *Pulse of the Planet*, in "Update on Saharasia", p.15.

However, there is an entirely different line of research being pursued, which covers some of the territory discussed in the works of Immanuel Velikovsky, and others of the catastrophist viewpoint. Some of Dr. DeMeo's work has suggested the presence of *a major polar axis shift in the period coincidental to the end of the Pleistocene Ice Age*. This new evidence is most exciting, as it may provide a clear connecting point between the Saharasian *origins of armoring* event, and the large-scale desert-forming process, with some elements of Velikovsky's catastrophic scenario, or something similar, at least. One of the maps developed from this line of research, titled *"Ice Age or Polar Axis Shift"* is presented here, as a *preliminary* indication of this work, and it should be self-explanatory for those with a background in the Earth Sciences.

There remain many large complications associated with making these connections, however, and consequently, full publication of these materials is being delayed until such time that additional necessary research can be undertaken, to either validate the connections, or refute them.

Lou Hochberg Awards

In 1993, shortly before his death, Mr. Lou Hochberg provided for the continuance of the cash prize award program which bears his name, with the purpose to stimulate university and high school students to engage in serious investigations of the *Social Aspects of Wilhelm Reich's Discoveries*. Advertisements were taken out in student newspapers in Columbia University (Mr. Hochberg's Alma Matter), and later in the *Chronicle of Higher Education*, announcing the Hochberg Awards, which fall into the following categories:
* *University Thesis and Dissertation Awards*
* *Thesis and Dissertation Improvement and Implementation Awards*
* *University/College and High School Essay Awards*
* *Outstanding Research and Journalism Award*
Several awards have been given out over the years, including individual cash prizes of up to $1000, and smaller gifts such as copies of Reich's books. The names of student winners are protected, given the ongoing attacks against students and faculty in American uni-

versities who openly express interests in Reich's work. However, we can announce one of our winners, Mr. Jim Martin, author of the book *Wilhelm Reich and the Cold War* (Flatland Publications, Ft. Bragg, 1999), winner of the *Outstanding Research and Journalism Award* category (see p.260). More information on the Hochberg Awards is available on request to OBRL, and also is posted to: http://www.orgonelab.org/hochberg.htm

The OBRL Internet Web Site

A great deal of information on the subject of orgonomy is now posted to OBRL's internet web site, specifically regarding the work of Dr. James DeMeo, and Dr. Wilhelm Reich. Many articles are posted, along with a bibliography and catalog of publications available for purchase, and information on forthcoming lectures and seminars hosted by OBRL. For those who have access to internet, this is a primary source for information. http://www.orgonelab.org

Fund-Raising Appeal

Many of the preceding articles, the works in progress as reported in this section, and even the typesetting and printing costs of this issue of *Pulse of the Planet*, were made possible in large measure by the generous donations of various individuals. Without those added financial resources, only a smaller portion of this work would have transpired. We therefore ask our readers to consider making a tax-deductible donation to the Orgone Biophysical Research Laboratory, or to include a bequest to OBRL in their will, to help us carry on with this work into the exciting, though already chaotic, New Millennium There are only a few places where the research tradition developed by Wilhelm Reich is openly worked with and carried forward in a serious and focused manner, and OBRL is one of the primary institutions on our small planet that is doing so. OBRL has been the organizational vehicle for James DeMeo's interdisciplinary work along this track, and in this effort he has been joined by others. With additional funding, even more could be done. We are now seeking donations for sponsoring student assistants during the OBRL Seminars, for a new astronomical telescope and telescope dome, for a DVD recording system to archive our many videotapes from lectures and field expeditions, and for continuance of basic laboratory experiments on water structure and the accumulator To-T and electroscopical discharge phenomena. A more formal and elaborated fund-raising letter is available on request, and is also posted to: http://www.orgonelab.org/funding.htm Send your tax-deductible donations or bequests to:

Orgone Biophysical Research Lab,
PO Box 1148, Ashland, Oregon 97520 USA.
Tel-Fax: 541-552-0118. Email: demeo@mind.net

SAHARASIA: The 4000 BCE Origins of Child Abuse, Sex-Repression, Warfare and Social Violence, In the Deserts of the Old World, by James DeMeo

1999, 454 pages. Softcover $34, Hardcover $90
ISBN: 0-9621855-5-8 Natural Energy Works,
PO Box 1148, Ashland, Oregon 97520 <demeo@mind.net>

Review by Peter Robbins*

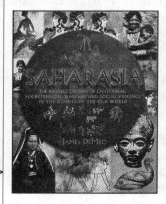

Occasionally a book is published which is so unique in its concept, and so remarkable in the originality of its research and findings, that I feel compelled to bring it to your attention. *Saharasia* is just such a book. Very few individuals that I am aware of have the abilities necessary to undertake such a challenging project, and fewer still possess the capacity to successfully complete same. This author, however, is in something of a class by himself.

Dr. James DeMeo did his undergraduate work in Environmental Science and holds a Ph.D. in Geography from the University of Kansas. His research in subjects ranging from early childhood development to UFO's is deeply rooted in his extensive knowledge and understanding of the life, work and discoveries of the late Dr. Wilhelm Reich, a scientific giant whose work and findings have probably been the subject of more distortion and vilification than those of any scientist of the last several hundred years. Dr. DeMeo has more than thirty years of experience investigating and extending Dr. Reich's original findings in both the social and natural sciences.

He is also the Director of the Orgone Biophysical Research Laboratory, located in the beautiful, vibrant and pristine mountain country outside of Ashland, Oregon. The Lab, also known as the Greensprings Center, was founded in 1978 and is a non-profit science research and educational foundation which over the years has supported various laboratory and field projects, educational lectures and seminars both here and abroad.

In *Saharasia*, Dr. DeMeo has done a quietly stunning job of overlaying original, painstakingly gathered research (and extremely well-documented research at that) across a field of established findings, and in the process has created an entirely new way of looking at the evolution of social and familial violence. Like a combination detective/explorer/scholar, the author lays out for us how 6,000 years of climactic changes centered in what is now the Sahara and Asian Deserts have paralleled crucial changes in human behavior. It may sound like a gross oversimplification, but the fact is that as this region evolved from a fertile, green center of emerging cultures into an arid, inhospitable desert, a similar phenomenon was occurring in the human psyche: the growth of violent, sexually repressive, male-dominated societies paralleled the growth of the region's deserts.

Rooted in the pioneering work of the late Dr. Wilhelm Reich, *Saharasia* is, in addition to the sum of its fascinating contents, one of the most beautifully designed and richly illustrated books on any subject that I have seen in a long time. Its large format, original, easy-to-read layout and print quality make it a pleasure for the eye as well as the intellect, and at $34.00, the privately published trade paper edition is a bargain. If you are a student of history, the Middle East, psychology, anthropology, archeology, climatology, child development, women's studies, pre-Biblical cultures, or just plain curious about how the world has gotten into the state it is currently in, do not hesitate to order your copy of *Saharasia*: you won't be disappointed. I wasn't.

SAHARASIA **Press Release** 11 September 1998

New Study On the Origins of Violence Proves: Ancient Humans Were Peaceful, Modern Violence is Avoidable.

A new geographical study on the ancient historical origins of human violence and warfare, drawing upon global archaeological and anthropological evidence, has just been published presenting substantial proof that our ancient ancestors were non-violent, and far more social and loving than are most humans today — moreover, the study points to a dramatic climate change in the Old World, the drying up of the vast Sahara and Asian Deserts, with attending famine, starvation and forced migrations which pushed the earliest humans into violent social patterns, a trauma from which we have not yet recovered in over 6000 years.

The study and book, titled ***SAHARASIA: The 4000 BCE Origins of Child Abuse, Sex-Repression, Warfare and Social Violence, In the Deserts of the Old***

* Peter Robbins is the Editor of *UFO City*, a major internet web magazine, with a long-time interest in the works of Wilhelm Reich. This Review originally appeared at the *UFO City* internet site, 24 June 1999.
<probbins@teamcpm.com>   http://www.ufocity.com

World, by retired professor James DeMeo, Ph.D., is the culmination of years of library and field research on the subject. Professor DeMeo undertook the original research as a 7-year dissertation project at the University of Kansas, which was concluded in 1986. He has since put an additional decade of research into the subject. His study is unusual in that it presents the first world maps of human behavior, as developed from large anthropological, historical and archaeological data bases. DeMeo's findings were also recently presented at a regional meeting of the AAAS, in Grand Junction, Colorado.

"There is very little evidence for warfare or social violence in the archaeological record prior to around 4,000 BC and the earliest evidence appears in specific locations, from which it firstly arose, and diffused outward over time to infect nearly every corner of the globe." says DeMeo, who today directs his own private institute in rural Oregon. *"A massive climate change shook the ancient world, when approximately 6000 years ago vast areas of lush grassland and forest in the Old World began to quickly dry out and convert into harsh desert. The vast Sahara Desert, Arabian Desert, and the giant deserts of the Middle East and Central Asia simply did not exist prior to c.4000 BC"* DeMeo asserts, pointing to numerous studies in paleoclimatology — the study of ancient climates. *"Something happened around 4000 BC which forced the drying-out of this vast desert region, which I call Saharasia, and the drier conditions created social and emotional havoc among developing human agricultural and hunter-gatherer societies in these same regions."*

DeMeo's maps show spreading centers for the origins of *patriarchal authoritarian cultures* within this same Saharasian global region — male-dominated, child-abusive, sex-repressive cultures with a great emphasis upon war-making and empire-building. DeMeo points to the work of the controversial natural scientist Wilhelm Reich to explain the patterns.

"Famine and starvation are a severe trauma from which survivors rarely escape unscathed. A lot of people die, families are split apart, and babies and children are often abandoned, and suffer enormously. Starvation affects surviving children in an emotionally severe manner. They shrink from the exhausting heat and thirst, emotionally withdraw from the painful world, and simultaneously suffer a severe stunting of the entire brain and nervous system due to protein-calorie malnutrition. Even if such starved children later get all the food and water they want, they are deeply scarred in an emotional-neurological manner which forever changes their behavior — specifically, there is an implanted inhibition of any impulse of a pleasure-seeking, outward-reaching nature, and a discomfort with deeper forms of body-pleasure, in both maternal-infant or male-female expressions. Additionally, the child's view of the mother, who could not protect or feed the child during the famine

period, is thereafter colored with suspicion and anger. These attitudes and behaviors are deeply protoplasmic in nature, and are passed on to ensuing generations no matter what the climate, by social institutions which reflect the character structure of the average individual at any given period of time."

As part of his project, DeMeo undertook a cross-cultural evaluation of Wilhelm Reich's original ideas on human behavior. *"Reich claimed humans became violent from two major causes: firstly from abusive and neglectful treatment of infants and children, and secondly from the repression of adolescent heterosexual feelings."* This latter consideration, DeMeo asserts, has gotten nearly no attention from specialists on child-abuse, given that our society still considers adolescent romance and premarital sex to be a bad thing. *"Premarital, adolescent sexual romance is normal among the most peaceful cultures, but is always repressed in violent warlike cultures. It is an even more precise predictor of social and individual violence than is child-abuse."* Ideas such as these got Reich into hot water in the 1950s, DeMeo says, and his own work has similarly stirred up controversy.

To test Reich's ideas, DeMeo reviewed social variables on childrearing, sexuality, the status of women, and violence, for over 1000 aboriginal cultures from around the world. *"The cross-cultural evidence is very clear about this: the most violent human societies are those which treat their children in a neglectful and punitive manner, <u>and</u> which also demand sexual abstinence from their young unmarried people. Such cultures also emphasize highly compulsive forms of marriage, with a reduced status for women, and a lot of strong-man political or religious bosses who order everyone around at the point of a knife, or gun."*

DeMeo does not pull punches about our own society. *"Americans are not as violent as the most extremely violent cultures around the world, but we certainly are not as peaceful as the most peaceful societies. Unfortunately, our culture appears to be going towards increased social violence."* He points to the general failure of parents and sex-education programs to say much of anything positive about sexual pleasure, with the great emphasis upon "abstinence education", as a major cause for the growing violence in our schools. *"Our young people should be warmly romancing each other, dancing and singing together, making love and enjoying what should be the happiest time of their lives. Instead, we start our children off with a lot of hidden cruelty in the hospital birth, with incubator-isolation, denial the mother's breast, timetable feedings, circumcision and so forth. Later, it is compulsory schooling, obedience-training and so-called 'tough love'. Then comes the biggest lie, the 'sex-can-kill' propaganda stemming from modern AIDS hysteria, a disease for which young adolescents and teens have virtually a zero risk."* DeMeo injects an additional controversy into his work, by siding with dissenting scientists who reject the "infectious-HIV" hypothesis of AIDS, and he points to various studies supporting this criticism (such as those by Prof. Peter Duesberg, the retrovirus specialist at the University of California at Berkeley, and by the larger *Group for the Scientific Reappraisal of the HIV Hypothesis of AIDS*).

"We give potent and dangerous psycho-drugs like Ritalin to perhaps 10% of the livelier kids, which is a major scandal in this country, to squash them into conformity with our obedience-demanding school system, or to the irrational demands of their families. Then we give them inaccurate and superstitious lies about the supposed dangerousness of lovemaking, and unrealistically expect them to behave in a loving and calm manner. We still define a 'good child' as the one who is quiet and obedient, who does not have any sexual expression — but our entire society is constructed like a social pressure cooker in which an enormous inner tension has built up. Social violence, suicide and drug abuse erupts from that high-pressure situation, in a very predictable manner."* The roots of modern violence are similar to the ancient roots of violence, DeMeo says: *"It is all in the treatment of our children, and in our sexual attitudes and behavior. If we would end institutional violence towards babies and children in the hospitals, making gentle home birth and midwifery more widely available, ending practices such as circumcision, allowing more freedom and even student-democracy in the schools, emphasizing 'hearts over heads', if we could be more tolerant of adolescent romance and premarital sex — giving kids a real education about contraceptives and love instead of a false education of AIDS hysteria — and also eliminate compulsiveness in our marriages, then social violence would gradually ebb away. Ending the better-known forms of child-abuse, such as beating of children, is very important but by itself is simply insufficient."*

DeMeo again points to the cross-cultural evidence to support his, and Reich's, controversial positions. *"If this theory was wrong, there would have been no positive support from the cross-cultural evidence, and no patterns on my world maps. Instead, the cross-cultural review demonstrated a 95% positive correlation between the many variables, at a high level of statistical significance."* DeMeo's *World Behavior Map* which was also prepared from cross-cultural data, appears strikingly similar to a world climate map, with the harshest desert areas of the Old World characterized by extreme patriarchal authoritarian culture. The geographical patterns, he asserts, are imbedded in the same data found in every university library. *"These data were gathered by hundreds of anthropologists who engaged in field work and published their studies over the last 100 years. The data was then coded by a team under the direction of George Peter Murdock at the University of Pittsburgh in the 1960s. I took the data and made maps from them, and the maps demonstrated the Saharasian patterns*

which can be clearly seen. This finding has therefore been subjected to a triple-blind control procedure, which virtually insures the pattern is real and not some methodological quirk or accident. My later review of archaeological and historical patterns demonstrated the same Saharasian pattern extended back in time to around 4000 BC, which was the starting point for both the vast Saharasian desert belt, and the very first child-abusive, sex-repressive, and violent patriarchal authoritarian societies. The drying up of the Saharasian desert belt was the cause of a vast epoch of generations-long famine, migration and land-abandonment, leading to the first-time appearance of warlike patriarchal authoritarian culture. The process started firstly in Arabia and Central Asia, spreading outwards over several thousand years to eventually encompass nearly the entire world."*

DeMeo believes his findings provide conclusive proof for other social theorists who have long argued for peaceful social conditions among the earliest humans. *"The 'Garden of Eden' myths, which exist in the historical literature of many Old World cultures, appear to be factually rooted in this early period of socially-cooperative and peaceful social conditions, when the Saharasia was green and fruitful. Then came the devastating climate change towards aridity, which formed the vast Saharasian desert belt, and humans were literally cast 'out of the garden'. The rest is history."*

Wilhelm Reich and the Cold War by Jim Martin

1999, 562 pages, Hardbound $150
ISBN: 1-878124-09-9 Flatland Books, PO Box 2420, Ft. Bragg, California 95437 <flatland@mcn.org>

Reviewed by

John Wilder* and Peter Robbins**

Wilhelm Reich and the Cold War is Jim Martin's documentation of conspiracy as a social force in its broadest sense. His 500+ page book is full of freshly-uncovered facts which speak for themselves, and these facts accurately capture the feel and smell of the subterranean cold wars which smoldered in Europe before World War II, and the post-1945 Cold War that also involved America until at least 1988.

In 1956, on the day he was sentenced to prison, Wilhelm Reich wrote to the trial judge, *"One day the*

*John Wilder is an educator in the Midwest with a long-time interest in the works of Wilhelm Reich. He can be reached at: <JohnW@mindspring.com>
** Peter Robbins is the Editor of *UFO City*, a major internet web magazine, with a long-time interest in the works of Wilhelm Reich. http://www.ufocity.com He can be reached at <probbins@teamcpm.com>

motives and legalistic maneuvers of the technical winner of today, the drug and cosmetic Hig [hoodlum in government], will emerge from archives and see the clean light of day."

Like all good histories *Wilhelm Reich and the Cold War* is based on numerous primary and secondary sources. Martin and his team of researchers "peeled back the onionskins in long-forgotten public archives." Original documents were secured from a variety of archival sources: the FBI, NARA, the Hoover Institute, the Leo Baeck Institute, the Consumers Research collection at Rutgers University, the Institute of Atmospheric Physics, Otto Fenichel's rundbriefes; and the Lewis W. Douglas papers, among others. Other primary sources included Martin's interviews with "people who were there" such as Michael Straight, Harvey Matusow, and Eva Reich. Also, his correspondences with Mildred Edie Brady's daughter, and with Lore Reich.

Other sources included numerous translations into English from German of materials presently available only in German: relevant histories, memoirs, and letters: many of these materials translated by Jim Martin's friend Peter Nasselstein. Also studied were: the materials selected to be published from Reich's closed archive at Harvard by Mary Higgins; new materials from the KGB and Comintern closed archives, selected for publishing by Russian and British intelligence; and unpublished Ph.D. theses. Other secondary sources included recent American histories and monographs, and, importantly, the re-readings and reinterpretations of these older materials in light of the new information and insights developed from all the above sources.

To conduct his research, Martin traveled to Central Europe, to the American Northeast, and, finally, to the American Southwest, paralleling Reich's own geographic moves. Martin's book has a similar structure: the eruption of sectional power struggles within the socialist, communist, and psychoanalytic movements of Central Europe; the secret underground continuation of these struggles in the U.S.A., following the immigration to America of more than 100,000 Central European intellectuals in the 1930s; and Reich's final years in the American Southwest where he was hunted down by

---

Wilhelm Reich and the Cold War

Winner of the Year 2000 Lou Hochberg Award for Outstanding Research and Journalism

---

agents of the Emotional Plague.

This book is full of evidence new to the public, more than enough to support Reich's statement that, ultimately, archives would reveal the hidden motives of his attackers; more than enough to support Reich's contention that Communists were behind the negative press and the FDA prosecution.

In fact, what this book does most of all, in my opinion, is to show that what we know now is but the tip of the iceberg, that there is much more evidence out there –waiting to be found, appreciated, and assembled logically. The new information in Martin's book has the power to make the reader question the logic of how the history of the last century has been written. It is clear to anyone reading his book that "there's golden truth in them there archival hills" and they'd better scramble if they want to find it first.

Martin's book reads well the first time. Indeed, I stayed up most of the night reading it through, and I hear that this is what other readers did, too. For me, the book read even better the second time through, a good sign of enduring quality. I have come to especially value the Introduction, the chapter on the Org (the Leninist Organization), and the chapter on the Bradys.

A. A. Milne's stories appeal, on different levels, to both children and adults, with irony a special pleasure to the latter. In *Wilhelm Reich and the Cold War* Jim Martin relates the possibility that the REAL "Christopher Robin," the boy whom Milne's fictive character was based on, finally grew up and went to Cambridge University. Graduating in the early 1930s, perhaps feeling a bit like Tigger, the young "Christopher" motorbiked around Europe, until he bounced into Austria, and into the loving arms of a pretty Communist Sex-Pol worker, Litzi Friedman. Over the next ten years, this young man, recruited to be a mole for Stalin's KGB by Reich's first Sex-Pol publisher, rose to the top level of British intelligence. One of the tasks given to an older "Christopher" by British intelligence in the latter 1940s was to train the newly-created CIA in counterintelligence. James Jesus Angleton, head of the CIA's counterintelligence, was "Christopher's" pupil and his close friend.

"Christopher" moved to the U.S.A. to be liaison with the young CIA during the years that the Stalinists began a public media campaign against Wilhelm Reich, a campaign developed and prosecuted by piglets and weasels. Martin tells us that he thinks in later years this same "Christopher Robin" (known to modern history as "Kim" H.A.R. Philby) fled to the protection of KGB headquarters in Moscow. From there he orchestrated the 1974 OPEC oil embargo which radically changed the world I grew up in. Although the child is the father of the man, did we see all this in Christopher Robin?

Most story plots follow one of two formulas: either a strange character comes to our familiar setting, or a familiar character goes to a strange setting. For most readers, Martin's history will twist, ironically, one plot formula into the other: at the beginning of the book American readers will have the mindset that strange European characters, including Wilhelm Reich, have immigrated into the familiar American setting; but, by the end of Martin's book, the familiar American setting will have become alien, and Reich becomes a spacegun-toting, All-American hero.

The sold-out first printing of Martin's first edition was distributed worldwide to interested parties. Martin says that this limited first edition will be revised into a second edition, probably paperback, that will include newly-discovered information; and that the second edition will clear up the many typographical errors inherent to first editions. Thus, this second edition should be even richer and more accessible than the first.

The sense and evidence of *Wilhelm Reich and the Cold War* is refreshing and the book, I believe, will induce the reader to rediscover Reich and to reevaluate his or her understanding of him, and of our world.

— John Wilder

"...One of the most eagerly awaited histories of one of the most significant figures of the twentieth century..."

Perhaps no social or political figure of the 20th century has had his work, reputation or particulars of his life more maligned or distorted than the late Dr. Wilhelm Reich. As a longtime student of the life and work of Reich, I say this based on years of real world experience. If only for this reason (and there others), Jim Martin should be applauded for his outstanding research, objectivity and perseverance in the publication his new book, *Wilhelm Reich and the Cold War*.

Let me make no secret of the fact that Jim Martin is a friend of mine, and a close one at that. But friend or not, I have never put myself in the position of recommending a book to anyone just because someone I know or like wrote it. On the contrary, friends who happen to be writers have to work harder for the approval or endorsement of their peers than that of the general readership at large.

Jim's abilities as a writer are well known to subscribers of his fine publication *Flatland*, as well as to visitors to his website <www.flatlandbooks.com>. More, his gift as a narrative writer, combined with his tenacity in tackling the life of such a complex individual during one of the most quietly frightening periods in American history combine to produce a scrupulously documented book which reads more like a page-turner of a novel than a biographical history.

But the real secret to this book's success lies in the author's formidable abilities as a researcher and to his long-term commitment to making real and sustained contact with every player in this drama still alive to talk with. And where this was not possible, Martin secured permission to review their private papers in detail, wherever they were housed.

I got to see this side of Jim Martin in action in late 1997. At the time I was on a kind of hiatus from Manhattan and living in (very) rural central New York State with my sister Helen (also a writer, and an outstanding singer/songwriter). Jim called from his home in Northern California to find out if he could stay with us for about a week while doing research at the Cornell University Library, only about 15 miles from where we lived.

Aside from the fact that he was great company and a superb house guest (he did a LOT of snow shoveling that week), Jim allowed me to accompany him on a number of his visits to the Cornell Library and gave me a window into how a first-class researcher is able to review the scope of an extensive personal archive, then drill down into it to extract the relevant information.

At sometime in the future, I hope to see *Wilhelm Reich and the Cold War* published in a mass market edition. For the present though, it is priced at $150.00 and available only in a clothbound special first edition, limited to 500 copies, numbered & signed by the author. This means that we, the purchasers of this edition, are actually taking up the role of patrons, after the fact, and helping the author to recoup some of the thousands of dollars this project has cost him to complete. Perhaps the idea of helping to support genuinely new research, and in the process acquire a rare and unique book appeals to you as it does me. Of course the fact is that $150.00 is real money to most of us, but over the course of this year, a few less movies, videos, CDs, DVDs or drinks could easily make up the difference.

Whether or not you decide to add this volume to your library, be aware that Jim Martin has accomplished something remarkable with the publication of Wilhelm *Reich and the Cold War* — a truly new and original work which helps to clarify some of the most convoluted aspects of post war history — and one hell of a great read as well.

— Peter Robbins

Additional Comments on WR and the Cold War:

"I thought your documentary proof of how the Stalin-headed conspiracy used character analysis negatively was a most important insight. Altogether excellent research. Congratulations." — Eva Reich, MD

"Jim Martin's thorough investigation into the mysterious life-and-times of Wilhelm Reich is a compelling and fascinating read, also bringing together many new elements about the secret history of the Cold War." — Dick Russell, best-selling author of *The Man Who Knew Too Much*

"One of the most eagerly awaited histories of one of the most significant figures of the twentieth century, Wilhelm Reich. Amassing a great deal of new information from previously untapped historical sources, Martin not only illuminates the life of Reich but puts the Cold War years into an entirely new perspective."
— Kenn Thomas, *Steamshovel Press* publisher

"Excellent job in digging up fascinating facts supporting the more remarkable claims of Wilhelm Reich as made during his last years, filling in details about his Tucson desert-greening experiments, his UFO observations, and so much more. Martin also sheds light on the dark side of Reich's detractors during that same period, exposing the people who publicly threw dirt and stimulated the FDA attack which led to the burning of his books and Reich's death in prison. They were, just as Reich claimed, deeply committed Communists (with a capital 'C'), possibly even paid Soviet agents as well. Some have chosen to view Reich's work and claims during his last years as evidence of delusion or paranoia — Martin provides additional proof that Reich was correct." — James DeMeo, Director of OBRL.

"Jim Martin's tenaciously thorough research and lucid engaging style combine to offer a fascinating insight into the latter years of Reich's life, a period sadly neglected by many other biographers. His meticulous digging into Reich's labyrinthine past has turned up some startling connections with other historical figures (eg Kim Philby) and offers a desperately needed fresh insight into the complex issue of Reich's downfall in the 1950s. Recommended." — Jon East, British film & television producer/director.

Left At East Gate:
A First-Hand Account of the Bentwaters-Woodbridge UFO Incident, its Cover-Up, and Investigation, by Peter Robbins
1997, 490 pages, Hardbound $24.95
ISBN: 1-56924-759-5 <probbins@teamcpm.com>
Reviewed by James DeMeo

Peter Robbins is a long-time researcher in the field of UFO studies, with a major contribution to the field of orgonomy with his excellent articles on "Wilhelm Reich and UFOs", appearing in the *Journal of Orgonomy* in 1994. This new book covers his several years of investigation of a notable UFO landing in southern England, at the Bentwaters-Woodbridge US Air Force Base. Eyewitnesses on and around the bases observed UFOs flying over the bases, landing with occupants who interacted with base personnel, and UFOs also shining beams down on bunkers which, later on, were found to

contain American nuclear warheads (in violation of Prime Minister Margaret Thatcher's declarations that no such American warheads existed on British soil). Of particular interest for this reviewer were the interviews he made with three different individuals, all military personnel stationed there, who observed a large cloudbuster at the bases. Robbins did not especially go "looking for" these reports, which fell into his lap by accident — which makes them all the more significant.

Moreover, he reports on an anomalous *dry hurricane* which hit southern England in October of 1987, flattening large parts of the nearby Rendelsham Forest. Hurricanes, according to classical theory, obtain their high winds by virtue of the tremendous precipitation which accompanies them, driving strong updrafts which "suck" the air inwards towards the core of the storm. Additionally, the high level of precipitation is the result of high levels of ocean-water evaporation and humidity, a factor which demands their natural point of origins to be over the tropical ocean areas, where sea-water is solar heated to a high evaporation. Hurricanes should not form over the cooler or cold waters of the northern Atlantic — but they did. And for such a storm to be "dry" makes it very anomalous indeed. A series of similar anomalous hurricane storms hit the same areas of England, Scandinavia, Denmark and northern Germany in 1990s also. I had been carefully observing weather changes in Europe at the time, and speculated there might be someone errantly working with a cloudbuster in southern England. Robbins' report appears to provide reasoned confirmation on this point.

His report strongly suggests the US military has been experimenting with Reich's discoveries, even as other US government agencies (FDA, NOAA, NWS, EPA) have turned a deaf ear, or even engaged in deliberate "dirty-tricks" and disinformation campaigns aimed at discrediting the few scientists who have openly investigated those same discoveries. This would be, by itself, a scandal of proportions similar to the original attacks against Reich himself.

Robbins' book also addresses some of the stranger aspects of ufology, such as underground facilities, unmarked helicopters, close encounters, etc., but as with his prior work investigating Reich's claims regarding UFOs, he cuts through illusions and mystical fogs, making it far more "down-to-Earth" than other investigators on similar subjects. It is all unsettling, nevertheless, documenting attempts by US officials to silence Larry Warren — a former Military Policeman at the US bases in England, who witnessed the landing of an alien spacecraft, and the subsequent "close encounter" between its occupants and top officers of the base — and similar efforts to impede Robbins' investigation.

From the account given in Peter's fascinating book, I would make the following admittedly highly speculative hypothesis: *The surprise visits by UFOs to the American bases in England were accompanied by terrible shock within the military hierarchy. Impotent in the face of such visits, with possible UFO targeting of atomic warheads stored in bunkers (neutralizing them?), it is possible the American military establishment scrambled for whatever scraps of ideas they could come up with as a countermeasure, leading to a rediscovery of Reich's findings, which had been carefully delivered to the US Air Force by Reich himself in the 1950s.* Reich had delivered such information to the Air Force in the hopes his work might be taken seriously by at least one US government agency. This is a terribly disturbing idea, however, as it would suggest the US military quickly built at least one giant cloudbuster, hoping to chase off the UFOs, but inadvertently created the disastrous dry hurricanes reported in Peter Robbins' book. I would rather wish my speculation is totally wrong, but... at present we have far more questions than answers.

For those who are searching for more details on the more extremely mysterious aspects of the UFO phenomenon, including those aspects discussed by Reich in his works *OROP Desert* and *Contact With Space*, Peter Robbins' *Left At East Gate* is highly recommended.

Other New Books of Interest, highly recommended on the subjects of Wilhelm Reich and Orgonomy

In the English Language:

* *Emotional Armoring: An Introduction to Psychiatric Orgone Therapy,* by Morton Herskowitz. Lit Verlag, Hamburg, Germany 1997. (English and German editions). One of the most clarifying and emotionally-touching publications ever to discuss Wilhelm Reich's method of orgone therapy. Herskowitz trained with Reich and retains a rare feeling for this difficult work. He writes from the heart, with chapters covering the theory and practical side of therapy, with case histories and personal anecdotes about both the author and Reich. An excellent book for anyone already in, or desiring to undertake Reich's emotionally-liberating orgone therapy. 171 pp. ISBN: 3-8258-3555-3

* *Gentle Bioenergetics: Tools for Everyone,* by Richard Overly. Gentle Bioenergetics Foundation, Asheville, NC, with a Foreword and Comments by Dr. Eva Reich, developer of Gentle Bio-Energetics. Discusses practical methods for restoring the natural flow of life energy, to enhance personal growth and healing. Specific methods are discussed and diagrams given to apply gentle massage-type bioenergetic methods for: mothers needing help in bonding with their babies; babies in distress from birth trauma; athletes recovering from injuries; abused individuals; recovering addicts; GI tract complications; and simple stress relief. 224 pp. Paper $25.00

* *Wilhelm Reich, Viva Little Man* (Video), a documentary by Digne Meller-Marcovicz. Natural Energy Works, Ashland, Oregon 2000. ISBN: 0-9621855-7-4

* *A Free Range Childhood; Self Regulation at Summerhill School*, by Matthew Appleton. Solomon Press, 2000. ISBN: 1-885580-02-9

* *Basic Orgonometry: Wilhelm Reich's Abstract Technique for Comprehensive Thinking* by Jacob Meyerowitz. rRp Publishers, Easton, PA. 32pp.

In the Italian Language:

* *Creazione e Castigo: La grande congiura contro Wilhelm Reich (Creation and Punishment: The great conspiracy against Wilhelm Reich),* by Carlo Albini, Tre Editori, Rome, 1997. ISBN: 88-86755-09-0

* *Wilhelm Reich e il Segreto dei Dischi Volanti (Wilhelm Reich and the Secret of the UFOs),* by Alessandro Zabini, with a Foreword by James DeMeo. Tre Editori, Via Principe Umberto, 35/1, 00185 Roma, Italy. Dr. DeMeo's Foreword is reprinted in this issue of *Pulse of the Planet*, on pages 245-249.

In the German Language:

* *Die Wiederentdeckung des Lebendigen (Rediscovery of the Living)* by Bernd Senf. Published by Zweitausendeins Verlag, Postfach, D-60381 Frankfurt am Main, Germany. ISBN: 3-86150-163-5

* *Der Gesundheitsbegriff im Werk des Arztes Wilhelm Reich (The Concept of Health in the Works of Dr. Wilhelm Reich),* by Stefan Müschenich, Doktorarbeit am Fachbereich Humanmedizin der Philipps-Universität Marburg, Verlag Görich & Weiershäuser, Marburg 1995, 425 pages. ISBN 3-922906-54-0.

* *Der Orgonakkumulator Nach Wilhelm Reich. Eine Experimentelle Untersuchung zur Spannungs-Ladungs-Formel,* by Günter Hebenstreit, Diplomarbeit zur Erlangung des Magistergrades der Philosophie an der Grung- und Integrativwissenschaftlichen Fakultät der Universität Wien, 1995.

* *Der Orgonakkumulator. Ein Handbuch (The Orgone Accumulator Handbook),* by James DeMeo, Zweitausendeins Verlag, Frankfurt, 1995. ISBN: 3-86150-067-1

* *Nach Reich: Neue Forschungen zur Orgonomie (After Reich: New Research in Orgonomy),* Edited by James DeMeo and Bernd Senf, Zweitausendeins Verlag, Frankfurt, 1998. ISBN: 3-86150-259-9

* *Lebensenergie durch Sanfte Bioenergetik,* by Eva Reich, Edited by Ester Zornanszky, 1997 Kosel Verlag GmbH, Munchen, Germany. ISBN 466-34372-0

In Memoriam
The Passing of So Many...

Following are personal recollections of a few of the quiet heroes of the chaotic 20th Century, who did more than their share to keep the torch of knowledge and the struggle for life and human freedom burning brightly. They shall not be forgotten.

Robert D. Morris
3 September 1914 - 25 November 1996

"Your father saved my life", "I don't know where I would be without Bob", "If it hadn't been for your Dad, I would probably be dead". These are the words we heard after our father, Robert Darrell Morris, died at age 82 on November 25, 1996, from the people who had worked with him. These testimonies were the greatest tribute to a man, who for 60 years as a therapist and self-described "life energy researcher", helped people lead healthier, freer lives. Robert Morris received his Bachelor of Arts degree in psychology and education on a full scholarship from Mount Union College in Ohio, in 1935. In 1938, he graduated from Boston University School of Theology where he began his helping profession under the auspices of organized religion. At Boston University, he received the prestigious Jacob Sleeper Fellowship for graduate study at Cambridge University. However, instead of following a traditional academic route, Dad chose to tour pre-World War II Europe and study the rise in National Socialism in Germany, first hand as a student at the University of Berlin. This was just the beginning of a life of "bucking the system" that often times led to ostracism by the medical and religious establishments. Dad returned to the United States as the Director of Clinical Training at Episcopal Hospital in Philadelphia, Pennsylvania, where he developed his passion for and commitment to the nurturing of children and families.

One of his greatest experiences was in 1948 as a clinical trainee at the Pioneer Health Centre in Peckham, London, England, where he witnessed and worked in an environment dedicated to growing healthy children and families.[§] He envisioned the development of a similar center in the United States, and returned to the U.S. in 1950. Although the dream of a Peckham-style center never came to fruition, Dad continued to incorporate the principles into his work with groups and individuals. In 1954, he went on to establish with Dr. Edward Carroll, the first private, non-profit, family

[§] See: Innes Pearse & Lucy Crocker: *The Peckham Experiment: A Study of the Living Structure of Society*, George, Allen & Unwin, London, 1943.

Photo courtesy of Susan Helmick

treatment center in Pittsburgh, PA. In the early 1960s, he helped start one of the very first *Mother's Day Out* programs at a church in Pittsburgh. He received his Masters Degree in Public Health from the University of Pittsburgh in 1960 and subsequently began his private practice of Clinical Orgonomy, which he continued until his death in 1996. His life and work were devoted to expansion and helping people remove the limitations of old trauma and pain. He rejected any philosophy that resigns human beings to discomfort, lack of pleasure, or painful aging. He remained a skeptic, a passionate student of life, always reading and learning about new worlds. His library held everything from art, architecture and classic literature to science, health, mythology, anthropology and the latest fiction. He had a marvelous, natural sense of aesthetics. The beauty of his environment was very important to him and wherever he lived, he made each home unique and a delight to the eye.

At age 79, he left Miami, Florida where he had lived for most of thirty years and moved to Arizona. There, he routinely drove a particularly steep and hair-raising stretch of road just to keep his reflexes honed. His pioneering and adventurous spirit was, at times, cause for consternation among his children. When his daughters would exhort him to *"Please let one of us know if you are heading off to explore places on your own"*, he generally scoffed saying that no harm would come to him. None ever did. His guardian angels may have been working overtime, but he also held a deep belief in his own invulnerability. He never retired and it would have been unimaginable to see him end his days in a nursing home or "senior citizen" community. He did not let go of life easily even as life wished to let him go. He saved the lives of many that worked with him and lived his own life entirely on his terms. For those of us who loved him, our lives have been made richer for knowing him.

— Heather and Tamara Morris

Added Recollections of Bob Morris:
by Jean Vondracek and James DeMeo

In 1938-39, Robert Morris, then 24 years old, bicycled through much of Europe, and studied German at the University of Berlin. One night in the stadium three blocks away, he heard thousands roaring "Heil Hitler!" He said that experience *"flooded my senses with chilling and foreboding."* It also fueled his natural curiosity: *"How could one man manipulate so vast a population? What was his reward? What was theirs?"* It also prompted him to hurriedly return to the USA.

At a weekend retreat in 1947, during a lunch break, Bob went outside to soak up some sunshine with others. His friend, Maury, said *"See them, Bob? See them moving, glinting?"* After awhile, Bob began to see the remarkable bits of energy that crowd the sky. Maury said *"I've been reading some books by Wilhelm Reich whose observations and ideas about energy are fascinating."* Soon, Bob was reading whatever he could find by Reich, and realized that he himself had noticed much that Reich had discovered. Finally, he began a soul-searching process that culminated in "the death of a clergyman". He would say: *"How can I, in clear conscience, observe the tenets of 'religion' and 'church' when so much of it is hypocrisy, mysticism, politics and the rewards for true living come only after death? How can I serve life and the church at the same time? Impossible!"*

In 1948, he went to London as a participant in a conference on family health. More than fifty of the speakers approached the subject by describing what was wrong in a family context. Only two speakers, Robert Morris and one Dr. Williamson, spoke about what was right with families. The two met. Williamson and his partner, Dr. Innes, a biologist, had set up a social experiment at the Pioneer Health Centre to include ordinary families whose membership in the neighborhood of Peckham (near London) gave each member the opportunity to enjoy socializing, through whatever the members wanted to participate in and suggest. There was swimming, piano lessons, musicals, sewing and knitting, a place to do homework in companionship with peers, a place for babies and toddlers, well taken care of, while mothers and fathers pursued their own interests. The people all lived in Peckham and upon joining the Center, each was given a thorough health checkup, and the results frankly discussed with each member and their family to emphasize what was healthy about the family and what might stand watching. Bob was invited to join the training course, a six-month opportunity to immerse himself and his wife and two little sons in the open and friendly atmosphere that was the Peckham Experiment.

Peckham had a profound effect on Bob. His aim was to establish a similar "going" concern in the USA. *"How to raise healthy, happy children in the family setting."* As he dug into the family life of people, he was staggered at the poverty-stricken emotional climate in so many homes. The need for pleasure in social situations was overwhelmingly obvious. *"Pleasure is not a luxury; it is an absolute necessity"* he would say.

From that unique training with families, Bob had it in his life and work to establish an American "Peckham". He traveled the country giving talks to Episcopal congregations about the need and satisfactions of families participating in such a project. He was a dynamic speaker and his audiences were enthusiastic. He happened to revisit a few cities a day or two after one of his talks and felt the despair of the people. He said it was *"like talking about dancing to people in wheelchairs."* He stopped his speaking tour.

About 1951, he became an early patient of Dr. Elsworth Baker, an orgonomist of prodigious energy and wisdom. The dream of establishing an American Peckham continued, although there were many projects and near-successes, his dream was never realized. It is not too far-fetched to say that his death in November 1996 was literally from a broken heart. As he would say, that's another way of saying "heart attack."

Around 1955, he moved to Pittsburgh, opened a private practice as a "worker for health", and joined the staff of the Craig House for Children. His work with troubled children always included work with their parents, to better understand the family dynamics, of what was bugging the child so much, and what created the action-reaction merry-go-round between parent and child. In addition, Bob took a course in playwriting and wrote several half-hour dramas, illustrating sources of friction, and suggestions on how to avoid it. They were produced by Pittsburgh's educational channel, WQED, with Bob as narrator.

Near the end of the 1950s, he enrolled in the University of Pittsburgh School of Public Health. With high marks, he earned his Master of Public Health in 1962.

Bob knew about Summerhill since 1949, and in the fall of 1963, his daughter went there with my 11-year old, Judy. Students ranged in age from 5 to 16 years. Around a third were from the States, a few from Canada and the rest from England. Bob had a silver pin made for his daughter, a four-leaf clover with each section having an imprinted word: *Love, Work, Learning, Play*. These words guided the life of Robert Morris.

In the early 1960s, the Unitarian Church had a large group of young mothers; a few had three children under five years old. Could there be a way to give these mothers a satisfying social activity which in turn would carry over to the children through a more contented mom? Bob inquired with the mothers, and quickly learned: *"We need to socialize with other adults; we need to practice our hobbies and use our academic training, to renew friendships, be stimulated physically and mentally while a competent child-care person and her assistant supervises the toddlers."* After informal discussions lasting about two months, with Bob's encouragement and guidance, the women most interested in forging a program for and by young mothers took the responsibility of planning the program, securing instructors, winning Board permission and encouragement, advertising, finding a loving nurse for the babies and planning the use of space in the Church. Thereafter, every Thursday from 9:30 AM to 2:30 PM, about thirty five women and forty toddlers and infants came to *Mother's Day Out*. The women praised Bob, and called him "The father of Mother's Day Out".

In this era of his life (1950s - 60s), his most productive, Bob gave a series of public lectures at the Pittsburgh Y.M.H.A. He was a master of language, to illuminate the need for life to move naturally and with pleasure. His talks were well received and touched upon parenting, ways of coping with "the problem no one mentions" — adolescent sexuality — and how to recognize the emotional plague. He emphasized the need for pleasure, and ways to foster good will and trust. On occasion, when invited, he would give talks elsewhere touching upon these same themes, and he also wrote thoughtful, graceful poetry.

In 1966, the opportunity came to study a whole neighborhood in Miami; so for the next three years, he divided his working week between his private practice and research in Pittsburgh, with a new group of patients and research in Miami. Robert Morris was never openly accepted as an orgonomist — and did not wish to be — but practiced his own emotionally-healing art, with skill and insight, uncompromising and with infinite patience.

— Jean Vondracek

My father firstly started orgone therapy with Robert Morris around 1970, which softened him considerably. With Bob's encouragement, he gave me, his 20-year old son, a copy of Reich's *Selected Writings* — totally amazed with Reich's findings, and desiring to learn more, first-hand, I soon entered therapy. Therapy with Bob was a life-changing experience, which rekindled my interest in the sciences which had been destroyed by the compulsive schools, bringing me back to core feelings I had as a young boy.

When I first met Bob, as a patient, I tried to engage him in conversation about Reich, to ask questions about orgone energy and accumulators. He listened patiently for awhile, and then simply said: *"Breathe"*. Bob would later more directly encourage my interests in Reich, but he maintained a focus upon my core, getting me to move and feel in a deep and more fluid manner. With increased energy and clarity from the therapy, I returned to the university, and excelled. Bob cautioned me about raising the issue of Reich with my professors in the university. *"Don't be throwing darts at bombs"* he would say, and I was encouraged to learn about character structure so as to avoid or deal with the political-types and emotional plague characters who often inhabit large institutions. On the other hand, he could see my deep engagement in the subject material, and so encouraged me to take some calculated risks, to pursue my heartfelt interests and not to compromise my passions. He often compared one's work with one's love-life, observing that too many people were willing to sacrifice deeper contact and engagement with their work, just as they did with their love-life. *"You don't compromise on essentials, only on smaller things,"* he would say.

He was an excellent therapist, and his methodology followed what I became familiar with in Reich's books, of a standard, no-nonsense orgone therapy — which is why it came as such a surprise when I learned he once was a "clergyman". Slowly, over the years, I learned more about his past. He told of an experience with one of the larger Episcopal churches in the Northeast, where he tried to get them to establish a birth-control clinic for the adolescents and young adults of the parish. *"The church must work to meet the real-world needs of people, and right now there are too many unplanned pregnancies and unwanted children"* he argued. That particular "social experiment", as he was inclined to call such efforts, was a total failure, and he was never asked back to that place again. In fact, one of the ministers at that church harassed and pursued Bob at other places where he would work, trying to get him fired. When years later he would read Reich's discussions on the emotional plague, he instantly understood it.

He told of another, more positive experience he had during his work at Pennsylvania Hospital, before he learned about Reich, of assisting a man with severe gallbladder problems who was scheduled for surgery the next day. After sitting and talking with the fellow, he told him *"My God, man, you look like your heart is about to break"*, whereupon the man broke down and cried and cried. Bob had to keep the nurses out of the room, to let the man cry, as he held his hand. After about an hour, the man's tears subsided, and he felt greatly relieved — in fact, by the next day, his gall bladder problem went away completely and the surgery was cancelled. The same thing happened with other patients, Bob said, and he got the reputation among the hospital staff of being a "miracle-worker", though the surgeons weren't too happy about seeing their business vanish.

Bob never spoke about "God" to me, except in cosmic, life-energetic of terms, and then only rarely. He had only sharp criticisms for the institution of the church. *"The world is filled with self-proclaimed 'saviors' who want to 'save the world', but who haven't saved their own families or children, or their neighbors or neighborhoods, much less themself"* he said. Over the years, as our relationship broadened beyond only therapist-patient, I would learn of his own accomplishments and struggles. He told me of *Mother's Day Out*, and of the Peckham Experiment, and his summer at Orgonon, a few years prior to Reich's trial. He expanded upon Reich's materials regarding the role of social institutions to sustain either life-positive or life-negative impulses within society. *"People are creatures of habit, and if social change becomes institutionalized, it tends to be more permanent, for better or worse. If you could put an end to circumcision in one hospital, for example, or get the insurances to stop paying for it, then the results will be a hundred times over what could be accomplished by a single individual."* He was a champion of mothers and babies, of midwives and Summerhill, working towards setting up clinics or free-schools at various times over the years.

At one point, Bob and my father teamed up to purchase 160 acres of land in Petaluma, north of San Francisco. It was to be the site of the new American "Peckham" institute. Unfortunately, the financial obstacles could not be overcome, and with great disappointment, the project was abandoned. He tried some years later to start a similar, more modest arrangement at different locations in Florida, but the money for land-purchase and building construction never materialized.

Dr. Baker and a few of the orgonomists in the Northeast referred patients to him regularly, as he did to them, based upon mutual respect for good work. As I would discover years later, however, they refused to publicly acknowledge him due to his not being a physician. About this, Bob would say (only half-joking) *"the best prerequisite for an orgonomist would be to live in the Trobriand Islands for a few years."* While Bob respected individual physicians, he was highly critical of the organized medical profession and the "medical model" of disease, which he called "sickness-care", rather than health-care. He was a wellspring of knowledge about alternative medicine, such as herbs, vitamins, new therapeutic methods and approaches, and always seemed to have the best books out on his table.

Bob's guidance was crucial in helping me to navigate many social mine-fields in the academic world, as he understood human character structure and social institutions better than anyone else I have known. Bob also undertook orgonomic research, long before I met him. He studied human energy fields with the millivolt-meter, and made personal tests and evaluations of the orgone blanket and accumulator. He knew about most

every kind of life-energy research from personal investigations, but always kept Reich squarely in the center. In this respect, I learned a lot from Bob, to keep open to new things, but not to lose focus upon the central ideas.

When Dr. Walter Hoppe, one of Reich's associates, was dying in Germany, he wrote to me asking for help. I was tied up with university studies, but I informed Bob about Hoppe's crisis, and he immediately responded. He flew on his own money to Germany, and tried to save Hoppe by introducing him to the Gerson detoxification method ... but it was too late. I mention this because it highlights his willingness to undertake great effort for important matters, without consideration of the personal costs. Decent to the core, and always looking for new ways to mobilize stagnant and deadly social situations which destroyed people. *"Social changes for the better can come about quickly, in unexpected ways"* he asserted on several occasions, to his skeptical student. Then I saw the Berlin Wall come down, and the Soviet Empire crumble, and understood what he meant.

While extremely patient, his anger could be dramatic if you did something dangerously stupid, and he did not tolerate fools or hucksters. He always said: *"The goal of every physician should be to work themselves out of a job. They'll never be able to do it, but that should be their goal"*, and was highly critical of the medical profession based upon what he saw with his own eyes — and from there, also critical of how orthodox medicine and the medical model was seducing so many of Reich's followers to focus solely upon therapy (after the damage was done), without active engagement upon preventative considerations, through the changing of social institutions. Some of this critique of medicine, I share today, having seen quite a lot of damage done by doctors, especially during my year of premedical studies.

Bob's therapeutic approach was exactly as described in Reich's *Function of the Orgasm* and Herskowitz' *Emotional Armoring*, orgone therapy without any compromises aimed to bring up buried feeling and to restore orgastic functioning, and included use of the light for eye mobilization, dor-buster on occasion, and teaching his open students about the orgone blanket and accumulator. He readily advised his more committed patients to read Reich, and the *Journal of Orgonomy*, though he also encouraged everyone not to fall into political traps common in orgonomic groups. He advised, for example, to read both E.F. Bakers *Man in the Trap*, but also Chester Raphael's *Wilhelm Reich: Misconstrued and Misesteemed*. He understood much of Reich from his core, intuitively, and his large library was a good indication of his breadth of knowledge and interest in the world. Bob and I later undertook cloudbusting experiments together, after my work was finished at the University of Kansas. Together, we directed the 1986 cloudbusting expedition which ended a drought of historical magnitude in the Southeast USA. He later built an elegant cloudbuster and used it in Florida also for some years, keeping things mobilized. He also pioneered new therapeutic innovations, but his clinical findings were never published.

He was a very sensitive, strong and emotionally deep person, who saved a lot of lives. Foremost, he was on the side of his patients, and of children and babies. Everything else was secondary. He disliked the identification of "therapist" even though he was one of the best, feeling instead that the real work needing to be done was in the way of social change, to prevent human armoring before it cemented into people's guts. Toward this end, he and several of his patients helped the Miami midwives who were then under attack by organized medicine and the prosecutor's office. At one point, he asked all his patients to read Jeffrey Masson's book *Against Therapy*, pointing out the pitfalls of therapeutic methods which refused to tolerate constructive criticism of their approaches, or which sprang from the "Doctors are Gods" ideology. When I was flirting with the idea to "become a therapist" early in my school studies, he warned me *"being a therapist can be a trap, as it keeps you sitting and isolated in the therapy room, convinces you the world is worse off than it actually is, and stands in the way of your actually doing something in the way of prevention."*

I should also affirm his artistic side, his home filled with paintings and sculptures of simple elegance and life-energetic expression. He particularly enjoyed Yul Brenner's portrayal in the musical, *The King and I,* with the lyrics: *"Sometimes I think that people going mad — Sometimes I think that people not so bad... Tis a Puzzlement!"* The lyrics seemed to catch his occasional mood, about crazy human society, and the better possibilities of the human animal.

His dream was to establish his own Center for helping to grow healthy families and children, modelled after Peckham but incorporating various self-regulatory models from Reich, Neill, and even the Trobriand Islands. Bob was never able to fully realize this dream, and it was a great disappointment in his life. Bob worked in Miami until 1992, thereafter moving to Arizona, where his days would end. His death from heart failure — exacerbated by undesired medical interventionism — was surely the result of this disappointment. I mourn his passing, but celebrate his life. Shortly after his death, I had the following dream: In his will, Bob had left me "his most valuable possession", his "dream house", which was in fact his concepts of a Center devoted to life-positive work, an oasis of sanity in the social desert. I cried that he was not here, to help with the work. He is deeply missed.   — James DeMeo

Michael B. Rothenberg
4 Jan. 1927 - 15 Jan 2000

It is with sadness that I write this memorial honoring the life of Michael B. Rothenberg. On Saturday, January 15, 2000, Michael died at his home in Clinton,

Photo courtesy of Jo Rothenberg

Washington on Whidbey Island of amyotrophic lateral sclerosis, just 5 months after his illness was diagnosed. He was 73 years young.

Michael was born in Boston, MA, on January 4, 1927. After graduating high school, he went into the army, but soon received a medical discharge for a chronically dislocating shoulder. He began college at Princeton, but after one term left to join the American Field Service, where he served as a combat ambulance driver in Burma during World War II. After the war, he continued his undergraduate work at Harvard, and was introduced to Reich's work by Myron Sharaf, his close high school friend who was also enrolled at Harvard at that time. During their years together at college, he and Myron read all the orgonomic literature they could get their hands on. After graduating college, Michael spent the summer of 1948 working as Ilse Ollendorff's lab assistant in Reich's laboratory at Orgonon. It was during this time that Reich was working with cancer mice, vacor tubes, and the orgone energy motor. At the end of the summer, Michael left Orgonon and began 2 years of graduate study in physiologic pharmacology at Tufts University. He returned to Orgonon in the summer of 1950 to help at the summer conference, and then began his medical training at Western Reserve University in Cleveland. During the next 6 years of medical school and pediatric residency, Michael kept in touch with Reich's work and the events at Orgonon through his readings, contact with Myron, and his daily use of the orgone accumulator. In 1956, he moved to New York to begin a psychiatric residency at the Albert Einstein College of Medicine. Desiring to be trained as an orgonomist, he began therapy with Dr. Elsworth Baker. In 1957, Dr. Baker started his technical seminars, with Michael as part of his first training group. By 1960, Michael had an orgone therapy practice, had begun to teach the technical seminar on working with children and adolescents from an orgonomic perspective, and had helped create a research lab for the study of orgone biophysics, in addition to a half-time faculty appointment at Einstein.

In 1964, Michael broke with Dr. Baker's organized group. In his opinion, the group was expanding orgonomy into a "way of life" with regulated modes of thought and behavior. Michael disagreed with this interpretation, and felt this was inconsistent with Reich's conceptualization of orgonomy as a *working body of knowledge*. He continued to practice orgone therapy in NY until he moved to Seattle in 1967 to join the faculty of the University of Washington School of Medicine. As a pediatrician and child psychiatrist, he trained medical students, residents and interdisciplinary staff, as well as provided direct service to children and their families. As a child advocate, he worked with legislators, parents, schools, hospitals and other health care providers. In 1987, Michael retired from the University of Washington, and shortly thereafter he and his beloved wife Jo moved to Whidbey Island. Though officially retired, Michael continued to actively donate his time and energy to child advocacy work, as well as generously share his wisdom and experience with his many friends and colleagues. He also began to impart his deep understanding and knowledge of orgonomy and his memories of Reich through symposia and training seminars offered by the Center for Orgonomic Studies, which he helped establish in 1977. In addition, he participated in seminars offered by OBRL's Greensprings Center and the Institute for the Study of the Work of Wilhelm Reich.

Michael's application of many of Reich's biopsychosocial and bioenergetic understandings was evident in the original contributions Michael made to the fields of pediatrics and psychiatry. He introduced to the practice of pediatrics the concept of *comprehensive care* as the systematic inclusion of psychosocial dynamics and personality development, in a family and community context. He was instrumental in the development of child psychiatry-pediatrics liaison work. He was the first physician to alert the medical community to the negative effects of television violence on children and youth. He was a pioneer in identifying the need for doctors and medical students to explore their own feelings and attitudes in order to improve the quality of patient care. And he was at the forefront of introducing the study of death, dying and bereavement into the medical school curriculum. He helped found the Washington chapter of Physicians for Social Responsibility, the Mental Health Professionals for Human Rights and

Responsibilities in Seattle, and the Puget Sound affiliates of Action for Children's Television and the Association for the Care of Children's Health. In addition, he published extensively in the medical literature and for parents, co-authored with Dr. Benjamin Spock the 1985 and 1992 editions of *Dr. Spock's Baby and Child Care,* and served as a consultant to the children's television program *Mister Rogers' Neighborhood.*

In the past 23 years, I had the opportunity to know Michael in a number of roles: as my therapist, supervisor and teacher, as my colleague and dear friend. To each of these roles, Michael brought his unique spontaneity and aliveness, his engaging warmth, his heartfelt compassion, and his ever-present humor. His gift as a therapist was his ability to bring himself fully to the therapeutic engagement. He did not rely on technique. He healed through his being. The same may be said for Michael as a teacher. In our teaching together, I often had the pleasure of watching the enraptured faces of students and symposia participants as Michael responded to their questions. Michael captured them, not with a polished speaking technique, nor only through his humorous stories and anecdotes, but mainly by the warm and respectful contact he made with the questioner and the audience as a whole. These same qualities made Michael the wonderful friend that he was.

In these years, I have also had the opportunity to witness the extraordinarily close and mutually supportive relationship between Michael and his wife Jo. From 1981 until the time of his death, Jo was at the center of his life, his loving and loved companion with whom he lived and worked side by side. The rewriting of the 1985 and 1992 editions of *Dr. Spock's Baby and Child Care* was a joint effort and accomplishment, as was much of his work of the past 19 years.

I deeply miss Michael, as I know so many others do. He profoundly enriched my life, and the lives of so many who knew him. — Daniel Schiff

Louis Hochberg
14 July 1918 - 28 April 1998

Lou Hochberg was a man whom I got to know well only after 1988, when I moved to the San Francisco Bay area. Lou became a regular attendee, and later all around helper and even guest lecturer at my evening course on "The Life and Works of Wilhelm Reich" at the Ft. Mason Conference Center. He was deeply committed to Reich's discoveries, his own life having been changed for the better from his orgone therapy and close friendship with Richard Blasband and others with the *American College of Orgonomy*. He was an Honorary Fellow of the College, and also received Honors from the Center for Functional Research, and Orgone Biophysical Research Lab.

Lou was trained as a Psychiatric Social Worker at the Columbia University School of Social Work, and was employed for many years with the California Depart-

ment of Health. His reading of Reich, and later orgone therapy, saved him from what he called the "conventional bureaucratic social work", and directed him instead towards the more central concerns of infants and children, and the prevention of armoring. He made an effort to introduce Reich's concepts into the social work profession, however, and his article "Wilhelm Reich in the Alternative Therapies and Clinical Social Work" was published in the *Clinical Social Work Journal* (V.5, No.2, p.99-107, 1977, also reprinted in *J. Orgonomy*, V.12, p.83-91, 1978), thereafter stimulating an additional article and discussions — to include the all-too-typical negative reactions against Reich — in the *National Association of Social Work Newsletter*.

Through many activities and friendships in the Bay area, he had the opportunity to show his generosity of character, in ways to numerous to give here, but it was his engagement in orgonomic work which I found to be most touching. After his retirement, he would collect used Reich books from local bookstores, and bring them to our class at Ft. Mason, selling them to raise money for one project or another, all associated with orgonomy. In particular, on one occasion he sent all the money from the books to Eva Reich, who was in a health and economic crisis at the time. He provided funds for different orgonomic groups in the USA, including a generous donation to OBRL for the initial financing of the *Greensprings Center*. Anonymously, as I would later discover, he provided funding for my 1989 Arizona cloudbusting experiments. And he later established, through OBRL, the *Lou Hochberg Awards* program,

designed to stimulate young students to investigate the social aspects of Reich's work.

The Hochberg Awards program was only the last of a long-time effort by Lou, to try and get Reich's work honestly discussed by social scientists, journalists and students. He always tried to get letters published in the *New York Times,* and *New Yorker* magazine (among others) correcting one or another historical error they might have made, especially as it related to Reich. And occasionally, his letters were published. Here is one of them, from *Mothering Magazine* (May/June 1998):

"History shows that the impetus for circumcision began in the US when a few hypocritical doctors of the Victorian era decided to punish boys for masturbation by circumcising to block pleasure. Circumcision not only disables the penis but initiates anxiety and hate. It is commonly known — and a great public secret — that masturbation is developmentally pleasurable enroute to mature sexuality.

Dr. Wilhelm Reich discovered that pleasure is the awareness and delight of the build-up and discharge of energy in the child and that the circulation of blood and oxygen facilitate the flow of life energy throughout the body. I emphasize here something of importance in child development which is rarely mentioned — the bioenergy flow to and from the genitals to the eyes. Interfere with and break the life-energy flow at one end, and you also impair the health at the other end, and in the middle, too. Interference causes the breathing to stop sharply as a natural defensive reaction to the peril felt to the overall life-pulsatory function. Someday, stopping this will be considered child abuse.

When we do not protect the healthy pleasure function in the child, we set the armored stage for the development of the mixed bag of anxiety, rage, longing, and sorrow in the adult, and the need for therapy. s / Lou Hochberg"

Lou's interest in children was not merely theoretical, and he actively helped with the care-taking and raising of children of his close friends.

After David Goldhagen's book *Hitler's Willing Executioners* was published, Lou (and a lot of other people) were dismayed at how Reich's earlier parallel findings in *Mass Psychology of Fascism*, which went much deeper into the matter, were not even cited by Goldhagen. So, Lou established a special award *"for the best essay by a college student worldwide on the book by David Goldhagen, applying the sociological discoveries of Wilhelm Reich"*. It was a provocative move, to try and force some open public discussion, though unfortunately not much came of it.

The year before his death, in addition to establishing the Hochberg Awards, he organized a *Celebration in Honor of Reich's 100th Birthdate* in Berkeley, California. I'll always remember our occasional dinnertime debates, as he was an advocate of the gold-standard economy, while I felt that "Caesar" would always find a way to exploit the value of currency bearing his image, no matter what. Reich was always the common element in our discussions, however, and on that, our agreements were firm and lasting.

Lou loved popular jazz music, and especially female jazz singers like Ertha Kitt. Once, attending one of her concerts where he applauded vigorously from a stage-side table, she came down and gave him a kiss — he was walking on clouds for a long time afterward.

In early 1998, at 80 years of age, Lou began having difficulties making his usual long walks from his home into downtown Berkeley. Always the risk-taker, he volunteered to undergo a triple-heart bypass, which promised to recover his energy and stamina — but he never recovered from the operation.

Lou was not a therapist, nor a well-known writer in the field of orgonomy, but working primarily behind the scenes he helped keep important work alive and moving. His assistance and friendship were critical, at critical times, and will not be forgotten. *Adieu, Lou, good friend!*   — James DeMeo

Myron Sharaf

7 July 1926 - 13 May 1997.

Myron (Mickey) Sharaf was endowed by nature and nurture with a sharp intelligence, playful humor and a conscience that directed him to examine issues from many sides. He was a warm, serious colleague; one always enjoyed his company.

He came to his intense appreciation of Reich in his adolescence. His mother had already been so impressed by her readings that she had arranged a meeting with Reich and conveyed her enthusiasm to her son. Myron was equally impressed after reading Reich's works and upon receiving his baccalaureate degree from Harvard College in 1949 he established a working relationship with Reich, serving as translator and editor, a relationship that lasted for many years. His formal education continued; he received a master's degree in education from Tufts in 1953 and a doctorate in education from Harvard in 1960.

Dr. Sharaf had a faculty appointment at Harvard where he introduced many classes of psychiatry residents to Reich's concepts. From report, he was one of the most highly regarded and beloved mentors at that institution.

He had a long established private psychotherapeutic practice which was deeply informed by his orgonomic studies. His candor, his wit and his contactful caring were the qualities which his patients valued. Myron did not suffer fools gladly. He had an especial distaste for Reichian cultists whom he referred to as "orgonomaniacs".

His magnum opus which involved from various reports, from 10-12 years of deliberate labor was his

Photo courtesy of Giselle Sharaf and Doug Levinson

biography of Reich, *Fury on Earth*. This, the most thoughtful and comprehensive review of Reich's life and work to this time, has been received with both acclaim and censure in the various orgonomic communities. One thing is sure: it is the product of sincere thought, respect and honesty.

Myron sought to speak of Reich and his work whenever the opportunity afforded. He traveled widely, and it was in the course of a speaking engagement in Vienna, at a conference commemorating Reich's 100th Birthday, with a subsequent working visit to Berlin, that he died in his sleep, as it were, with his boots on.

Those of us who knew him will miss his chain-smoking discussions delivered with his characteristic pacing mannerism. We will miss his dedication, his brightness and openness. Orgonomy has lost one of its most loyal, informed, intelligent, vital ambassadors.

                — Morton Herskowitz

Memorial Notes, Appearing in Other Publications:

Kari N. Berggrav 30 Nov. 1911 - 11 June 1996
Milton Daily Standard, Milton PA, June 13, 1996.

Robert Dew 30 May 1936 - 16 April 1997
Note of Remembrance published in *Annals, Inst. Orgonomic Research*, V.9. frontmatter, 1999

Chester Raphael 7 Oct. 1912 - 25 March 2001
Newsletter, Friends of the Wilhelm Reich Museum, #42, 2001.